*Organic Functional
Group Analysis*

by Micro and Semimicro Methods

Organic Functional

Group Analysis

by Micro and Semimicro Methods

NICHOLAS D. CHERONIS

Late Professor of Chemistry
Brooklyn College
City University of New York

T. S. MA

Professor of Chemistry
Brooklyn College
City University of New York

INTERSCIENCE PUBLISHERS

A DIVISION OF JOHN WILEY & SONS, INC.

NEW YORK · LONDON · SYDNEY

Preface

THIS BOOK has been written from the standpoint of microchemistry, which may be defined as a branch of chemistry dealing with the principles and techniques for using the minimum amount of working material to obtain the desired chemical information. At present, the minimum quantity for functional group determination in simple organic compounds (with molecular weight below 600) is a sample containing about 0.1 milliequivalent of the function. This is an arbitrary scale. The aim of the microchemist is to extend the lower limits of chemical experimentation. Furthermore, 0.1 milliequivalent may not be a suitable range for all kinds of working materials. For instance, such a quantity may entail a very large amount of the sample for end-group analysis in polymers or for the determination of the phenolic function in natural products. These subjects will be treated in another book which deals with organic functional group microanalysis in complex and complicated systems.

In preparing this book for publication, I have tried to give special consideration to the needs of organic research chemists as well as organic analysts. For clarity and coherence, the theoretical background of functional group analysis is presented in Part I; while a comprehensive and critical survey of the available micro methods is presented in Part II. The research chemist who does not intend to do the laboratory work can read about the principles, applicability, and limitations of the method which has been, or will be, employed to analyze his sample. It must be emphasized that no method or procedure can be expected to give unequivocal results for all compounds containing the same functional group. It is hoped that the research chemist will be in a better position to interpret the analytical data when he uses any of the methods described herein. Extensive references are cited in the survey section so that the reader can readily consult the original literature when the need arises.

Detailed and explicit laboratory instructions are presented in Part III, which consists of two chapters. Chapter 12 contains experimental procedures for which no special apparatus is required. By using such procedures, the operator can carry out the determination without delay. On the other

v

hand, procedures requiring special functional group apparatus are treated together in Chapter 13, so that the chemist knows what he should procure in advance. References are not cited in the experimental directions; the operator is referred to the particular section in the theoretical part if he wishes to fully understand the selected method and compare it with other methods.

I am convinced that a course of training in functional group analysis should be required of all advanced students majoring in organic chemistry. This book is also intended for such a course—as a text to teach chemical principles and manipulative techniques. I believe that quantitative organic functional group microanalysis can be advantageously handled by chemists who have had practice in measuring weights and volume. Usually some organic material can be recovered after the analysis. By performing his own determinations, the research chemist can immediately use the product for further investigation.

During the past twelve years Dr. Cheronis and I have been engaged in a research project on organic functional group microanalysis. The project included testing the available micro methods and developing new methods. Research students were given thesis topics in the area of quantitative analysis of functional groups. One or more of the organic functions was assigned to a student who was responsible for a critical study of the applicability and limitations of the various methods pertaining to the particular function. Modifications of the apparatus or procedure were tested. New principles of analysis were incorporated wherever they became feasible. Concurrently, a course was offered to graduate students in which these micro methods were evaluated. A large part of this book is based on the results and experiences of the project.

I am deeply indebted to Professor Nicholas D. Cheronis, who was instrumental in bringing this book to publication. He took an active part in planning the project, organizing the materials, and writing the book. It is most unfortunate that he did not see the completed work in print. I would like to think of this book as a testimonial to a revered friend and colleague with whom I shared the same philosophy of microchemistry and education.

I should also like to thank Mrs. Nicholas D. Cheronis, who prepared the author index and helped in reading proof.

I wish to give full credit to the two scores of research students whose painstaking efforts have produced most of the micro methods presented in the experimental part, and to some two hundred graduate students who helped test these methods. Thanks are due D. Shapiro, J. V. Earley, and M. Gutterson, who were laboratory instructors in the course and whose enthusiasm contributed much to the successful conclusion of the project; Mrs. Elizabeth G. Greenstein who prepared the drawings of the new apparatus; Mrs. Shirley LeVesconte who typed the manuscript; B. Burns who checked the references. Acknowledgment is gratefully made to *Analytical Chemistry, Microchemical Journal, Mikrochimica Acta,* and *Talanta,* for permission to reproduce the figures indicated in the text. Illustrations of equipment were generously furnished by the following firms: Wm. Ainsworth and Sons, Brinkmann Instruments, Greiner Scientific Corp., Fisher Scientific Co., Metro Scientific, Inc., Mettler Instrument Corp., Microchemical Specialties; Micro-Ware, Inc., E. H. Sargent Co., A. H. Thomas Co., and J. W. Towers & Co., Ltd.

T. S. Ma

New York, N. Y.
January, 1964

Contents

9. The Sulfur Functions   320

PART ONE

Principles and Techniques

1

Introduction

I. Organic Analysis

In chemical science *analysis* is an indispensable tool both in the area of research and in the field of applied chemistry. Organic analysis comprises the methods for the identification and estimation of organic substances. Qualitative organic analysis aims to identify one or more organic compounds present in an unknown. The term *identity* signifies the assigning to a pure substance a specific molecular or ionic structure so that it can be characterized as an isolated entity, always the same and different from other chemical substances.[1] Quantitative organic analysis aims to determine either the elemental composition of a pure organic compound or the extent to which a particular *reactive* or *functional group* is present in an organic substance or a mixture.

Elemental organic analysis involves the quantitative determination of carbon and hydrogen and less frequently of oxygen, nitrogen, sulfur, halogens, and other elements which qualitative tests indicate are present in an organic compound. In dealing with new compounds—that is, compounds that have not been previously described—elemental analysis is indispensable in the determination of an approximate empirical formula of the substance under investigation, and thus forms the first step in the systematic characterization of new organic substances. Prior to 1910 the methods of elemental organic analysis were laborious and time consuming. The introduction by Emich and Pregl[2] of elegant analytical procedures known as micro methods, which employed small samples of material, led both to the simplification of elemental analysis and to the attainment of precision and accuracy difficult to obtain by the older methods even by

[1] N. D. Cheronis, *Microchem. J.*, **2**, 43 (1958).

[2] N. D. Cheronis, *Microchem. J.*, **4**, 423 (1960); A. A. Benedetti-Pichler, *Ibid.*, **6**, 3 (1962).

experienced workers. A number of excellent texts dealing with elemental organic microanalysis are available[3-6].

The present work deals with analytical procedures based upon chemical reactions which are employed to estimate the quantity of functional groups present in an organic substance. Thus, the estimation of the per cent of the carboxyl group (—COOH) present in a new organic acid is of aid to the research worker in assigning a tentative structure to the new compound. Another and perhaps a wider application of the estimation of functional groups is in the analysis of compounds or mixtures whose structure is known to determine the percentage of each component.

Functional groups may be detected and many can be estimated by the use of physical methods, such as infrared, ultraviolet, visible, Raman, X-ray and mass spectra and by physical constants of pure substances. The exclusion of extensive discussion of these physical methods from the present treatise in no way indicates that chemical reactions are better adapted for the estimation of functional group. In fact, the practicing chemist must consider all available approaches and select the one that best fits the problem at hand. However, it was deemed desirable in a work of limited extent to concentrate on analytical procedures based on chemical reactions so as to provide the advanced student and practicing organic chemist with a critical review of the principal methods which have been proposed for the determination of each functional group and select those which are applicable to small samples commonly referred to as *micro* and *semimicro* methods.

II. The Functional Groups

A *function* or a *functional group* is defined as a reactive atom or group of atoms in an organic molecule. As used in this text it represents a reactive group in a molecule which, by means of a chemical reaction, can be determined quantitatively. Thus a nitro compound contains the nitro group [—NO_2] and an alkene, the *unsaturated* —CH=CH— grouping, both of which can be estimated quantitatively by appropriate chemical reactions. Table 1.1 lists close to 100 functions which are among the most important

[3] A. Steyermark, *Quantitative Organic Microanalysis*, 2nd ed., Academic Press, New York, 1961.

[4] G. Ingram, *Methods of Organic Elemental Microanalysis*, Reinhold, New York, 1961.

[5] H. Roth, *Pregl: Die Quantitative organische Microanalyse*, 7th ed., Springer, Wien, 1958.

[6] J. Grant, *Pregl: Quantitative Organic Microanalysis*, 5th ed., Blakiston, Philadelphia, 1951.

found in organic compounds. The functions are alphabetically arranged; column 2 gives the structure of the functional group and column 3 the classification used in this work: *oxygen, nitrogen, sulfur, unsaturated,* and *miscellaneous.* The latter category includes *active hydrogen, active methylene, methyl side chains, phenyl,* and the *phospho* and *phosphino* groups, etc. Table 1.2 arranges the functional groups based upon this classification. It will be noted that the second column of Table 1.2 gives a summary of the more important methods used for the estimation of each function, while the last column lists the page references in which the discussion of the various analytical procedures is given.

III. Problems Involved in Functional Group Analysis

A. Chemical Basis of Functional Group Analysis. The basis of all quantitative procedures for the estimation of functional groups is the *determination of substances formed or consumed by the reaction of the sample with the reagent:* the measurable substances are ACIDS, BASES, OXIDANTS, REDUCTANTS, WATER, GASES, COLOR COMPLEXES, and SPARINGLY SOLUBLE PRECIPITATES. The principles by which these measurable substances are determined are relatively simple and well known to the reader; hence, one would expect that the estimation of organic functions would be an arrangement of relatively simple procedures. In actual practice, however, the quantitative analytical procedures are beset with a number of formidable difficulties. The underlying reason for most of the obstacles is the fact that most organic reactions are slow and multidirectional; hence, it is usually not possible to choose experimental conditions under which all side reactions will be excluded. Moreover, even if all side reactions can be suppressed, the rate of reaction between the functional group —X in the compound R—X and the reagent Y depends to a large extent on the nature of the radical R, so that a general reaction may be applicable to a number of compounds in an homologous series, but not to others. This topic is discussed in detail in Chapter 4 dealing with the influence of molecular structure on the rates of reactions employed in analytical procedures.

B. Application of Functional Group Analysis to Compounds of Known Structure. Functional group analysis may be employed as an aid in the identification of pure organic compounds and particularly in the analysis of a mixture of compounds whose structures are known to determine the percentage of each component.

As an example of the use of functional group analysis in identification work, let us assume that preliminary tests indicate that the sample (which

TABLE 1.1

The Functions of Organic Compounds

Name of function	Structure	Classification	Ref. pages
Acetal (see ketal)	$=C(OR)_2$	oxygen	107
Acetyl (see acyl)	CH_3C—O, CH_3—C—N= (with $\parallel$ O under each C)	oxygen	114
Acetylene (see alkyne)	—C≡C—	unsaturated	382
Acid (see carboxyl, phenol, etc.)	HA	miscellaneous	396
Acid anhydride	$(R$—$CO)_2O$	oxygen	109
Acid halide	R—C—X (with $\parallel$ O)	oxygen	113
Active hydrogen (see hydrogen, active)	—A—H (A = O, N, S)	miscellaneous	409
Active methylene	$\diagdown$ CH_2 $\diagup$	miscellaneous	437
Acyl	R—C— (with $\parallel$ O) R—C—N= (with $\parallel$ O)	oxygen	114
Alcohol (see hydroxyl)	ROH	oxygen	183
Aldehyde (see carbonyl)	—CHO	oxygen	272
Aldose (see carbohydrate)	—CHOHCHO	oxygen	157
Alkaloid (see heterocyclic nitrogen)	$\diagdown$ $\diagup$ N	nitrogen	279
Alkene	$\diagdown$ $\diagup$ C=C $\diagup$ $\diagdown$	unsaturated	358
Alkimide	=N—R	nitrogen	222
Alkoxyl	—OR	oxygen	124
Alkyne	—C≡C—	unsaturated	382
Amide (see carbonamide)	R—C—NH_2 (with $\parallel$ O)	nitrogen	272
Amine, primary (amino)	—NH_2	nitrogen	229
Amine, secondary	=NH	nitrogen	229
Amine, tertiary	≡N	nitrogen	229
Amine salt	≡NHX	nitrogen	248
Amino acid	—$CHNH_2COOH$	nitrogen	242
Azide	—CN_3	nitrogen	254
Azo	—N=N—	nitrogen	262

TABLE 1.1 (Continued)

Name of function	Structure	Classification	Ref. pages
Azoxy	$-N{=}N-$ $\overset{\|}{O}$	nitrogen	262
Barbituric acid	$={=}C\begin{smallmatrix}CO-NH\\ \\CO-NH\end{smallmatrix}CO$	miscellaneous	279
Base (see amine, heterocyclic-N)	B:	miscellaneous	424
Benzylidene	$C_6H_5-CH{=}$	unsaturated	388
Carbonamide (carbamyl)	$-CONH_2$	nitrogen	272
Carbonimide	$-\overset{\|}{\underset{O}{C}}-NHR$	nitrogen	272
Carbohydrate	$-(CHOH)_nCHO$ $-(CHOH)_nCOCH_2OH$	oxygen	157
Carbonyl	$\diagdown CO \diagup$	oxygen	141
Carboxyl (carboxy)	$-COOH$	oxygen	165
Carboxylic ester (carboalkoxy)	$-COOR$	oxygen	174
Carboxylic salt	$-COO^-M^+$	oxygen	216
Cyano	$-CN$	nitrogen	254
Dialkoxy (see acetal)	$={=}C(OR)_2$	oxygen	107
Disulfide	$-S-S-$	sulfur	327
Diazo (see azo)	$-N{=}N-$	nitrogen	262
Diazo ester	$N_2CH-COOR$	nitrogen	266
Diazonium salt	$-N_2^+X^-$	nitrogen	265
Ene-diol	$-\underset{OH}{C}{=}\underset{OH}{C}-$	oxygen	198
Enol	$={=}CH-C(OH){=}$	oxygen	590
Epoxy (epoxide)	$={=}C\underset{O}{\diagdown\diagup}C{=}$	oxygen	169
Ester (see carboxylic ester, inorganic ester)	$G-\overset{\|}{\underset{O}{X}}-OR$	oxygen	174
Ether (see alkoxyl)	$R-O-R$	oxygen	124
Ethoxy (see alkoxyl)	$-OC_2H_5$	oxygen	124
Glyceryl (glyceride)	$-OCH_2(CHO-)CH_2O-$	oxygen	180

TABLE 1.1 (Continued)

Name of function	Structure	Classification	Ref. pages
Glycol	$\diagdown$C(OH)—C(OH)$\diagup$	oxygen	507
Hemiacetal	=C with OH and OR	oxygen	107
Heterocyclic-N	N	nitrogen	279
Hydrazide	—CONHNH₂	nitrogen	289
Hydrazino	—NHNH₂	nitrogen	289
Hydrazo	—NH—NH—	nitrogen	262
Hydrogen, active	—A—H (A = O, N, S)	miscellaneous	409
Hydroxamino (hydroxylamine)	—NHOH	nitrogen	—
Hydroxyl (hydroxy) (see alcohol, glycol, etc.)	—OH	oxygen	183
Imido (see carbonimide)	—C—NHR, ‖ O	nitrogen	272
Imino (see amine, secondary)	=N—R	nitrogen	229
Inorganic ester	ROA (OA = anion of inorganic acid)	oxygen	181
Isocyanate	—N=C=O	nitrogen	297
Isocyano	--NC	nitrogen	254
Isonitroso (oximino)	=N—OH	nitrogen	—
Isopropylidene	(CH₃)₂C=	unsaturated	388
Isothiocyanate	—NCS	nitrogen	297
Ketal	$\diagdown$C(OR)₂$\diagup$	oxygen	107
Ketene	=C=C=O	oxygen	388
Ketene acetal	RCH=C(OR)₂	oxygen	107
Keto	$\diagdown$CO$\diagup$	oxygen	141
Ketose	—COCH₂OH	oxygen	157
Lactone	$\diagdown$C—(CH₂)ₙ—C=O$\diagup$ └—O—┘	oxygen	180

TABLE 1.1 (Continued)

Name of function	Structure	Classification	Ref. pages
Mercapto (sulfhydryl, thiol)	—SH	sulfur	320
Methoxy (see alkoxy)	—OCH$_3$	oxygen	124
Methyl (side chain) (see terminal methyl)	—CH$_3$	miscellaneous	438
Methylene ether (methylene dioxy)	—OCH$_2$O—	oxygen	201
Methylal (see acetal)	CH$_2$(OCH$_3$)$_2$	oxygen	107
Methylol (see hydroxyl)	HOCH$_2$—	oxygen	183
Nitrile (cyano)	—CN	nitrogen	254
Nitro	—NO$_2$	nitrogen	301
Nitroso	—NO	nitrogen	301
Olefin (see alkene)	$\diagdown$C=C$\diagup$	unsaturated	358
Ortho ester	—C(OR)$_3$	oxygen	—
Oximino (see isonitroso)	=NOH	nitrogen	—
Oxymethylene (see enol)	—C=CH— $\overset{|}{O}$H	oxygen	361
Peroxy (peroxide)	—O:O—	oxygen	204
Phenol	Ar—OH	miscellaneous	445
Phenyl	C$_6$H$_5$—	miscellaneous	443
Phosphino (phosphinic)	—POOH	miscellaneous	466
Phospho (phosphonic)	—PO$_2$OH	miscellaneous	464
Quaternary ammonium salt	≡NR$^+$—X$^-$	nitrogen	248
Quinone	O=C(Ar)C=O	oxygen	212
Reactive hydrogen (see active hydrogen)	—A—H (A = O, N, S)	miscellaneous	409
Semicarbazido	—NHNHCONH$_2$	nitrogen	290
Sulfonamide (sulfamyl)	—SO$_2$NH$_2$	sulfur	339
Sulfonamido	—SO$_2$NH—	sulfur	—
Sulfhydryl (see mercapto)	—SH	sulfur	320
Sulfide (thio)	—S—	sulfur	327
Sulfinic (sulfino)	—S—OH $\overset{||}{O}$	sulfur	334
Sulfone (sulfonyl)	$\diagdown$SO$_2$ $\diagup$	sulfur	343

TABLE 1.1 (Continued)

Name of function	Structure	Classification	Ref. pages
Sulfonic (sulfono)	—SO_2OH	sulfur	334
Sulfonoxy	$-\overset{\overset{O}{\|\|}}{\underset{\underset{O}{\|\|}}{S}}-O-$	sulfur	—
Sulfoxide (sulfinyl)	$\diagdown SO \diagup$	sulfur	343
Terminal methyl (see methyl side chain)	—CH_3	miscellaneous	437
Terminal methylene	=CH_2	unsaturated	388
Thiocarbonyl	=C=S	sulfur	355
Thiocyanate	—CNS	sulfur	348
Thioisocyanato (see isothiocyanate)	—NCS	nitrogen	297
Thiol (see mercapto)	—SH	sulfur	320
Thiosemicarbazido	H_2N—CS—NHNH—	sulfur	289
Thiourea	$RHN-\overset{}{\underset{\underset{S}{\|\|}}{C}}NHR$	sulfur	348
Unsaturation (see alkene, alkyne)	$\diagup\diagdown C=C \diagdown\diagup$, —C≡C—	unsaturated	358
Urea	—NHCONH—	nitrogen	315
Vinyl	CH_2=CH—	unsaturated	358
Vinyl ether	CH_2=CHOR	unsaturated	392

TABLE 1.2

Classification of Organic Functional Groups and Summary
of the More Important Methods for Their Estimation

Name of function	Summary of the more important methods used for estimation[a]	Page refs.
	Class I. Oxygen Functions	
Acetal	(a) Alkoxyl groups	107
	(b) Hydrolysis and detn. of =CO and —OH	
	(c) Aquametry	
Acetyl	See Acyl	
Acid anhydride	(a) Hydrolysis followed by aquametry	109
	(b) Aqueous and nonaqueous titrimetry	

[a] For abbreviations see end of Table 1.2.

TABLE 1.2 (Continued)

Name of function	Summary of the more important methods used for estimation[a]	Page refs.
	(c) Anilide formation with acidimetry or iodometry	
	(d) Gasometric	
	(e) Colorimetry of hydroxamate complexes	
	(f) Infrared spectra	
Acid halide	(a) Argentimetry	113
	(b) Aqueous and nonaqueous acidimetry	
	(c) Colorimetry of hydroxamate complexes	
Acyl	(a) Hydrolysis followed by titrimetry	114
	(b) Colorimetry of hydroxamate complexes	
Alcohol	(a) Low mol. wt. compounds by colorimetry with ceric ions	199
	(b) High mol. wt. compounds by reaction with $ClSO_3H$ followed by titrimetry. See also Hydroxyl	200
Aldehyde	See Carbonyl	
Aldose	See Carbohydrate	
Alkoxyl	(a) Cleavage with HI and formation of alkyl iodide, detd. by gravimetric, or titrimetric or gasometric methods	124
	(b) Gas chromatography	
Carbohydrate	(a) Oxidimetry by periodate, cerate, hypobromite, ferrocyanide, or cupric ions	157
	(b) Colorimetry by reduction of Cu^{+2}, phosphotungstate, phosphomolybdate compounds	
	(c) Reduction by $NaBH_4$	
	(d) Enzymatic methods	
Carbonyl	(a) Oximation followed by titrimetry	141
	(b) Hydrazone form. followed by gravimetry or titrimetry or gasometry	
	(c) Gravimetry of 2,4-DNPH's, thiosemicarbazones, methone, or Schiff's base derivs.	
	(d) Addition of $NaHSO_3$ followed by titrimetry	
	(e) Addition of Grignard reagent followed by gasometry	
	(f) Reduction by $LiAlH_4$, $NaBH_4$, or polarography	
	(g) Oxidation by Ag_2O, Tollens', or Nessler's reagent, and peroxytrifluoroacetic acid	
	(h) Infrared or ultraviolet spectra	
	(i) Colorimetry of 2,4-DNPH's or products with other reagents	

TABLE 1.2 (Continued)

Name of function	Summary of the more important methods used for estimation[a]	Page refs.
Carboxyl	(a) Alkalimetry	165
	(b) Decarboxylation followed by titrimetry or gasometry	
	(c) Esterification and aquametry	
	(d) Oxidimetry of readily oxidz. acids	
	(e) Gravimetry of sparingly soluble salts	
	(f) Action of Grignard reagents and use of gasometry	
	(g) Colorimetry after conversion to acid chlorides → hydroxamate complexes	
Carboxylic ester	See Ester	
Carboxylic salt	(a) Ashing followed by gravimetry	216
	(b) Liberation of the free acid followed by fractionation and titrimetry	
	(c) Direct acidimetry	
Dialkoxy	See Acetal	
Ene-diol	Iodine or N-bromosuccinimide oxidation	198
Enol	See Hydroxyl	
Epoxy	(a) Reaction with HX in nonaqueous media followed by titrimetry	169
	(b) Iodometry	
	(c) Oxidation to aldehyde by $HClO_4$ or catalytic isomerization	
	(d) Infrared spectra	
Ester	(a) Hydrolysis followed by titrimetry or chelometry	174
	(b) Grignard reagent followed by gasometry	
	(c) $LiAlH_4$ followed by potentiometry	
	(d) Colorimetry of hydroxamate complexes	
Ether	See Alkoxyl	
Ethoxy	See Alkoxyl	
Glyceryl	Periodate oxidation	193
	See also Ester	
Glycol	(a) Periodate oxidation	193
	(b) Oxidation by various reagents	
	(c) Colorimetry of complexes	
Hemiacetal	See Acetal	
Hydroxyl	(a) Titrimetry after acylation	184
	(b) Aquametry after acylation	
	(c) Colorimetry of hydroxamate complexes	
	(d) Gasometry after reaction with CH_2N_2 or Grignard reagent	
	(e) Infrared spectra	
	(f) Indirect polarography	

TABLE 1.2 (Continued)

Name of function	Summary of the more important methods used for estimation[a]	Page refs.
Inorganic Ester	(a) Hydrolysis followed by titrimetry or gasometry	181
	(b) Colorimetry of complexes	
	(c) Polarography	
Ketal	See Acetal	
Ketene	(a) Hydrolysis to carboxylic acid followed by titrimetry	391
Ketene acetal	See Acetal	
Keto	See Carbonyl	
Ketose	See Carbohydrate	
Lactone	See Ester	
Methoxy	See Alkoxy	
Methylene ether	(a) Hydrolysis to yield CH_2O followed by gravimetry or colorimetry	201
	(b) Infrared Spectra	
Methylal	See Acetal	
Methylol	(a) Periodic oxidation followed by colorimetry with chromotropic acid	197
	(b) Condensation with phenol followed by aquametry	
Ortho ester	See Ester	
Peroxy	(a) Reduction with one of the following: $MnCl_2$, Fe^{++}, I^-, As_2O_3, $TiCl_3$, $SnCl_2$ followed by titrimetry	204
	(b) Hydrolysis and detn. of H_2O_2	
	(c) Colorimetry with various reagents	
	(d) Polarographic reduction	
	(e) Infrared spectra	
Quinone	(a) Reduction with $TiCl_3$ followed by titrimetry	212
	(b) Reduction with HI followed by iodometry	
	(c) Reduction with $SnCl_2$ followed by titrimetry	
	(d) Reduction by $C_6H_5NHNH_2$ followed by gasometry	
	(e) Colorimetry with various reagents	
Salts	See Carboxylic salt or Amine salt	

Class II. Nitrogen Functions

Acid amide	(a) Reduction by $LiAlH_4$ to amine followed by titrimetry or gasometry	272
	(b) Hydrolysis followed by titrimetry	
	(c) Reaction with Grignard reagent followed by gasometry	

TABLE 1.2 (Continued)

Name of function	Summary of the more important methods used for estimation[a]	Page refs.
	(d) Dehydration to nitrile followed by non-aqueous titrimetry	
Alkaloid	See Heterocyclic nitrogen	
Alkimino	(a) Treatment with HI → quaternary ammonium salt which is pyrolyzed to alkyl iodide detd. by gravimetric, titrimetric, or gas chromatographic procedures	222
Amine, primary	(a) Acidimetry	229
	(b) Acetylation followed by acidimetry	
	(c) Aquametry after acetylation	
	(d) Nitrosation followed by gasometry or titrimetry	
	(e) Condensation with carbonyl compounds	
	(f) Colorimetry of products with various reagents	
Amine, secondary	(a) Acidimetry	229
	(b) Nitrosation followed by titrimetry or gasometry	
	(c) Formation of sparingly soluble salts	
	(d) Colorimetry of products with various reagents	
Amine, tertiary	(a) Formation of sparingly soluble salts	229
	(b) Colorimetry of products with chloranil or aconitic anhydride	
Amine salt	(a) Titrimetry in aqueous and nonaqueous media	248
	(b) Sparingly soluble salts with tetraphenyl boron	
	(c) Colorimetry of products with various reagents	
Amino acid	(a) Nitrosation with gasometry or titrimetry	242
	(b) Colorimetry with use of ninhydrin	
	(c) Enzymatic methods	
	(d) Nonaqueous titrimetry	
Azide	(a) Reduction by AsO_3^{-3} followed by iodimetry	254
	(b) Rearrangement to RNCO followed by gasometry	
Azo	(a) Reduction by Ti^{+3} or Cr^{+2} followed by titrimetry	262
	(b) Heating or action of $C_6H_5NHNH_2$ followed by gasometry	
	(c) Polarographic reduction	
Azoxy	(a) Reduction by Ti^{+3} followed by titrimetry	262

TABLE 1.2 (Continued)

Name of function	Summary of the more important methods used for estimation[a]	Page refs.
Carbonamide	See Amide	
Carbonimide (imide)	(a) Reduction by LiAlH$_4$	276
	(b) Reaction with Grignard reagent followed by gasometry	
Cyano	(a) Hydrolysis followed by titrimetry or aquametry	256
	(b) Reaction with Grignard reagent followed by gasometry	
Diazo	(a) Heating in presence of catalyst followed by gasometry	265
	(b) Reduction with Ti^{+3} followed by titrimetry	
	(c) Colorimetry after coupling with arylamines	
Diazo ester	See Diazo	
Diazonium salt	See Diazo	
Heterocyclic nitrogen	(a) Nonaqueous titrimetry	279
	(b) Argentrimetric titrimetry	
	(c) Precipitation of (C$_6$H$_5$)$_4$B salts followed by titrimetry	
	(d) Iodimetric titration	
	(e) Gravimetry by means of halides, perchlorates, oxalates, picrates, picrolonates	
	(f) Colorimetry with various reagents	
	(g) Ultraviolet spectra	
	(h) fluorometric methods	
Hydrazide	(a) Oxidation followed by gasometry	289
	(b) Oxidation by IO$_3^-$, I$_2$, Br$_2$, ICl, BrCl, VO$_3^-$ followed by titrimetry	
Hydrazino	(a) Oxidation followed by gasometry	289
	(b) Oxidation by IO$_3^-$, Br$_2$, ICl, BrCl, VO$_3^-$ and other oxidants followed by titrimetry	
	(c) Reduction followed by titrimetry	
	(d) Colorimetry	
Hydrazo	(a) Reduction with Ti^{+3} followed by titrimetry	269
	(b) Oxidation with MnO$_4^-$	
	(c) Polarographic reduction	
Imido	See Carbonimide	
Imino	See Amine, secondary	
Isocyano	(a) Hydrolysis followed by titrimetry	258
	(b) Reaction with oxalic acid or hypobromite followed by gasometry	
	(c) Reaction with Grignard reagent followed by gasometry	

TABLE 1.2 (Continued)

Name of function	Summary of the more important methods used for estimation[a]	Page refs.
Isocyanate	(a) Addition of amines followed by titrimetry	297
	(b) Colorimetry of hydroxamates	
Isonitroso	See Nitroso	
Isothiocyanate	(a) Addition of ammonia and amines followed by titrimetry	297
	(b) Hydrolysis followed by titrimetry	
Nitrile	See Cyano	
Nitro	(a) Reduction by Ti^{+3}, Cr^{+2}, Sn^{+2}, V^{+2}, Fe^{+2}, $Zn(Hg)_x$, Cd followed by titrimetry	301
	(b) Coulometric reduction	
	(c) Acidimetry of primary and secondary	
	(d) N—Nitro + Hg followed by gasometry	
	(e) Hydrogenation	
	(f) Colorimetry	
Nitroso	(a) Reduction by Ti^{+3}, Cr^{+2}, Sn^{+2}, Fe^{+2} followed by titrimetry	301
	(b) Iodometric titration	
	(c) Reduction followed by gasometry	
	(d) Hydrogenation	
	(e) Colorimetry	
Oximino	See Isonitroso	
Quaternary ammonium salt	(a) Titrimetry in aqueous and nonaqueous media	248
	(b) Sparingly soluble salts with $(C_6H_5)_4B^-$	
	(c) Colorimetry of complexes	
Semicarbazido	(a) Oxidation by halogens followed by gasometry	290
	(b) Oxidation by IO_3^-, I_2, Br_2, ICl, BrCl, followed by titrimetry	
Urea	(a) Nonaqueous titrimetry	315
	(b) Enzymatic hydrolysis	
	(c) Oxidation by BrO^- followed by titrimetry or gasometry	
	(d) Colorimetry	

Class III. Sulfur Functions

Disulfide	(a) Precipitation followed by titrimetry	330
	(b) Reduction to RSH followed by titrimetry	
	(c) Colorimetry	
Dithiocarbamate	(a) Hydrolysis to CS_2	357
	(b) Colorimetry	
Sulfhydryl	See Mercapto	
Sulfide	(a) Acidimetric titration	327

TABLE 1.2 (Continued)

Name of function	Summary of the more important methods used for estimation[a]	Page refs.
	(b) Oxidation followed by titrimetry or gasometry	
Sulfone	(a) Conversion to sulfate	343
Sulfonic	(a) Acidimetric titration	334
	(b) Formation of amine salts followed by titrimetry	
	(c) Precipitation of metal salts	
Sulfonoxy	See Sulfonic	
Sulfoxide	(a) Reduction to sulfide	344
	(b) Oxidation to sulfone	
	(c) Nonaqueous titration	
Thiocarbonyl	See Thiourea	
Thiocyanate	(a) Conversion to NaCNS followed by titrimetry	349
Thioisocyanate	(a) Reaction with amine followed by titrimetry	297
Thiol	See Mercapto	
Thiosemicarbazido	(a) Nitrosation	295
Thiourea	(a) Nonaqueous titration	350
	(b) Formation of metal salts followed by titrimetry	
	(c) Oxidation by OI^-, ICl, Br_2, H_2O_2, SeO_2, followed by titrimetry	
	(d) Colorimetry	
	Class IV. Unsaturated Functions	
Acetylene	See Alkyne	
Alkene	(a) Addition of Cl_2, Br_2, ICl, IBr, BrCl, followed by titrimetry	359
	(b) Catalytic hydrogenation	
	(c) Addition of mercuric acetate and other reagents followed by titrimetry	
	(d) Oxidation by O_3, MnO_4^- and IO_4^-	
	(e) Addition of RSH or Na_2SO_3 or R_2NH on alkenes which do not readily halogenate	
	(f) Colorimetry	
Alkyne	(a) Nonaqueous titration with $AgClO_4$	382
	(b) Catalytic hydrogenation	
	(c) Catalytic hydration to ketones	
	(d) Formation of Hg- and Cu-acetylides followed by titrimetry	
Benzylidene	(a) Hydrolysis and detn. of benzaldehyde with 2,4-dinitrophenylhydrazine	390

TABLE 1.2 (Continued)

Name of function	Summary of the more important methods used for estimation[a]	Page refs.
Isopropylidene	(a) Oxidative cleavage followed by haloform reaction or colorimetry	388
Olefin	See Alkene	
Terminal methylene	(a) Oxidative cleavage to formaldehyde followed by colorimetry	392
Vinyl	See Alkene	
Vinyl ether	(a) Oxidative cleavage to acetaldehyde	392
	(b) Methoxymercuration	

Class V. Miscellaneous Functions

Acidic	(a) Aqueous and nonaqueous titrimetry	396
	(b) Reaction with Grignard reagent or LiAlH$_4$ followed by gasometry	
Active hydrogen	(a) Reaction with Grignard reagent and measurement of CH$_4$	409
	(b) Reaction with LiAlH$_4$, measurement of H$_2$	
Active methylene	(a) Reaction with carbonyl compounds	437
Barbituric acid	(a) Nonaqueous titration	409
Basic	(a) Aqueous and nonaqueous titrimetry followed by colorimetry	424
Hydrogen, active	See Active hydrogen	
Methyl side chain	(a) Oxidation to acetic acid followed by titrimetry	438
Phenol	(a) Halogenation, oxidation, nitrosation, and esterification followed by titrimetry	445
	(b) Nonaqueous titration	
	(c) Reaction with Grignard or LiAlH$_4$ followed by gasometry	
Phenyl	(a) Bromination followed by titrimetry	443
	(b) Reaction with tetracyanoethylene	
	(c) Reaction with carbonyl compounds followed by colorimetry	
	(d) Formation of 2,4-dinitrophenyl ethers followed by gravimetry	
	(e) Colorimetry	
	(f) Fluorometry and spectrophotometry	
Phosphino	(a) Iodimetry	465
Phospho	(a) Colorimetry	467
Reactive hydrogen	See Active hydrogen	
Terminal methyl	See Methyl side chain	

Abbreviations: mol., molecular; wt., weight; DNPH, dinitrophenylhydrazone; derivs., derivatives; oxidz., oxidizable; detn., determination; detd., determined.

contains a small amount of water) is either 1,2-propanediol (1,2-propylene glycol) or 1,3-propanediol (trimethylene glycol). The preparation of derivatives does not give an easy differentiation between the two isomers. However, determination of the vicinal glycol group by the periodate oxidation method provides a more conclusive answer. Further, if we assume that the sample is a mixture of the two isomers and it is desired to estimate the percentage of each component, it is apparent that elemental analysis (for C, H, and O) serves no purpose since the two compounds, being isomers, have identical elemental percentage composition. But periodate oxidation will give the ratio of one component and the other is obtained by difference. Even in mixtures containing compounds of different molecular structure (such as nitrobenzene and aniline or aniline, methylaniline and dimethylaniline) it is very difficult to estimate the composition of the mixture by means of elemental analysis. For this reason functional group analysis is generally applicable to the analysis of mixtures of organic compounds, particularly in routine control work encountered in the production of organic chemicals.

C. Application of Functional Group Analysis to Compounds of Unknown Structure. Functional group analysis is very useful in the determination of compounds of unknown structure. For example, when a new substance is isolated from a natural product it is subjected to elemental analysis and molecular weight determination in order to establish the atomic ratios of the elements in the molecule and the molecular formula. In contrast to the investigation of inorganic compounds, where elemental analysis, molecular weight determination, and chemical reactions usually suffice to establish the structure of a new substance, the organic research worker invariably requires the determination of functional groups before he can assign a proposed structure to the new compound. The results of functional group determination serve as quantitative confirmation of the presence of such an atomic grouping which may be detected either by chemical reactions or by absorption spectra, and as a means to check the accuracy of the elemental analysis and molecular weight determination.

When a new compound is obtained by chemical synthesis through a known reaction, the present-day practice is to submit a sample for elemental analysis, usually carbon and hydrogen. The success of the synthesis is often claimed when the elemental analysis gives results within the range of the expected formula. However, this is not always an unambiguous proof. For example, when the compound $C_{14}H_{11}O_5(OH)$ is acetylated, the acetyl derivative will have the formula $C_{14}H_{11}O_5(OCOCH_3)$ or $C_{16}H_{14}O_7$. Calculation of the carbon and hydrogen percentages in the two compounds (original and its acetyl derivative) shows that the starting material has the values of $C = 60.88\%$, $H = 4.35\%$, and the acetylated product, $C = 60.38\%$ and $H = 4.43\%$. These two sets of values are too close to permit critical differentiation. On the other hand, clear-cut decision can be made if the product is analyzed for the acetyl group since the starting material does not contain such a functional group.

While an analytical method for the estimation of purity of a sample should have high precision and accuracy, the requirement is not so critical in the proof of the structure of a new organic compound. Since the functional group in question can be present in the molecule only as an integral number, a result accurate to $\pm 5\%$ relative is usually sufficient to determine this number.

2

Classification and Limitations
of Analytical Methods

I. Basis of Classification

Analytical methods are classified in many ways. Thus volumetric and gravimetric methods are considered the two main divisions in a course in elementary quantitative analysis. A detailed classification based on the techniques of analytical operation has been proposed by Strong.[1] In this chapter a discussion will be given of the classification of analytical methods for quantitative organic analysis *based on the size of the sample used for a determination.*

A. Basis of the Analytical Procedure on the Weight of the Sample. The methods for functional group analysis may be classified according to the weight of the sample used for the determination. Thus there are methods which demand a few grams of the sample, and others which employ decigram quantities of the material to be analyzed; still other methods employ milligrams or smaller quantities of the compound under investigation. When the sample is a liquid or in solution form, and the amount used is more than one gram, measurement of the sample by volume and density is sometimes more expedient than actually weighing the material to be analyzed.

B. Basis of the Analytical Procedure on Equivalency of the Sample. While the classification methods by sample weight may appear to be a simple and convenient way in the first step of functional group analysis, complication often arises during the determination when it occurs that the amount of material present is not within the desired range of volume of the titrant or precipitant employed. For example, when a 10-ml. buret is used for titration, the volume consumed should be within 3–9 ml.

[1] F. C. Strong III, *Anal. Chem.*, **29**, No. 3, p. 19A (March 1957).

When a semimicro balance is used for weighing the precipitate, the product should be approximately 15–75 mg. The reagents used in functional group analysis are dependent on stoichiometric or molar relationship of the reactants. Because of the great difference in molecular weights and structure among organic compounds, it is impossible to select a quantity of sample by weight which will fit in all types of compounds. Thus in the determination of carboxyl group, 3.0 mg. of acetic acid (m.w. 60.05) requires 5 ml. of 0.01N base for neutralization, and the corresponding amount of sample for stearic acid (m.w. 284.47) is 14.2 mg. In the determination of hydroxyl group, 9.3 mg. of dodecanol (m.w. 186.33) consumes 5 ml. of standard acetic anhydride solution; equal weight of sorbitol (m.w. 182.17) will require 30 ml. of the same solution. Therefore, the rational way to judge the sample size is by equivalency and not by absolute weights. Because a gram equivalent of an organic compound is much too large for chemical analysis, the milliequivalent (abbreviated as *meq.*) was adopted by the authors[2] as the analytical unit.

II. Nomenclature of Methods

Since the introduction of the term "quantitative organic microanalysis" by Pregl in 1911,[3] various names have been given to analytical methods based on the quantity of material taken for analysis. Thus one finds such distinctions as *macromethods, semimicromethods, micromethods, submicromethods,* and *ultramicromethods.* Recently the determination of trace constituents in a mixture, known as trace analysis, has also become important. The material present in trace analysis is in the order of parts per million; hence the amount of the compound taken for analysis is extremely small.

In the following sections the *macro, semimicro,* and *micro methods* are discussed in connection with functional group analysis.

A. Macro Methods. More than 2 milliequivalents of the material are required in the macro method, and the corresponding weight taken is usually 0.5 g. or more. Relatively crude weighing and measuring devices may be used, and 0.1N or more concentrated standard solutions are employed. Methods of this scale are common in the industrial laboratory and are performed by technicians for routine control work.

[2] See N. D. Cheronis, *Micro and Semimicro Methods,* Interscience, New York, 1954, p. 573.

[3] F. Pregl, *Quantitative Organic Microanalysis,* trans. by E. Fyleman, Blakiston, Philadelphia, 1924.

B. Semimicro Methods.   Semimicro methods use about 1 milliequivalent of the compound to be determined, or approximately 50–200 mg. sample. A semimicrobalance will give the precision of weighing required. The standard solutions used are from $0.05N$ to $0.1N$, being measured in an ordinary 50 ml. buret.

C. Micro Methods.   When Pregl developed quantitative organic microanalysis,[3] his attention was on elemental analysis and he made a big stride in reducing the sample size 100-fold from the 0.2–0.5 g. macro scale to the 2–5 mg. micro scale. After his success with the microdetermination of the elements present in organic compounds, attempts were made to analyze organic functional groups in the same scale by weight, with the sample size kept below 10 mg. This necessitated the use of elegant micro apparatus and delicate analytical techniques. A few methods were worked out, such as the methoxyl and carboxyl groups. However, the "Pregl micro methods" for functional group determination usually do not give the same precision and accuracy as is obtained in elemental analysis, because the reaction used in the functional group determination is relatively mild and subjected to the influence of the structure of the compound analyzed and other factors described in Chapter 4.

In order to render the functional group determination more readily adaptable to general use, the Pregl approach of limiting the micro method to sample size below 10 mg. has been discarded. Unlike elemental analysis, where the organic compound is totally destroyed to form inorganic products, it will be shown that in most methods for functional group determination the organic compound may be recovered or converted into another organic compound which may serve as a step for further investigation. Thus the material is not entirely wasted after the analysis, and hence, the use of slightly larger amounts of sample can be tolerated. Further, this approach permits the use of these methods for instruction without the use of elaborate equipment or exact manipulative procedures.

Therefore, the range of about 0.1 milliequivalent of the compound to be determined has been designated as the *micro scale*.[4] In terms of weight, the sample required is approximately 5–20 mg. The choice of 0.1 milliequivalent is based on several considerations.

(1) When the compound has an equivalent weight of 50 or more, the weighing device need not have a precision better than 0.005 mg.

(2) If the gravimetric method is used, a conversion factor leading to

[4] T. S. Ma, in *Proceedings of the International Symposium on Microchemistry*, Pergamon, London, 1959, p. 151.

100 mg. or more per milliequivalent can easily be found, and the precipitate will weigh more than 10 mg.

(3) If the gasometric method is used, 0.1 millimole of gas will occupy approximately 2.5 ml. under ordinary conditions.

(4) If the titrimetric method is used, 0.1 milliequivalent of material will consume 10 ml. of $0.01N$ solution.

III. Microchemical Units

Table 2.1 gives the microchemical units employed at present. It should be noted that the quantities of materials employed in the procedures

TABLE 2.1

Microchemical Units of Mass and Volume

Name	Definition	Symbol
Gram[a]	10^{-3} kg.	g.
Milligram	10^{-3} g.	mg.
Microgram	10^{-6} g.	μg.
Nanogram	10^{-3} μg. or 10^{-9} g.	ng.
Picogram	10^{-6} μg. or 10^{-12} g.	pg.
Microliter	10^{-6} l. or 10^{-3} ml.	μl.

[a] Reference unit.

described in this work are in the range of a few milligrams. However, the frontiers of the qualitative organic analysis are already in the nanogram and picogram range; already some methods of quantitative organic analysis have been elaborated below the milligram range or in the microgram range. The authors prefer to designate the range rather than to employ such ambiguous terms as *"ultramicrochemistry"* for the microgram procedures. It has been pointed out[5] that if we designate by ultramicrochemistry the microgram procedures, we will be obliged to use ultra-ultramicrochemistry or some such ambiguous term for the picogram procedures.

IV. Advantages of Micro Methods

The chief advantages of micro methods are the saving of time, labor, and materials. The savings of time and of labor are important considerations in

[5] See N. D. Cheronis, ed., *Symposium on Experimentation below the Microgram Range, 1960*, Wiley, New York, 1961.

any institution and do not need any elaboration. However, the saving of materials and apparatus does not usually refer to the reagents, though in many cases over a period of a year even here it can be shown to be considerable. The saving of material more often refers to the sample which is to be analyzed. Much of the work on vitamins, hormones, and in general, compounds isolated from biological systems, *would not have been possible* had more than fractions of a gram been required for analysis and the elucidation of structure of these compounds. Historically, Pregl's development of micro methods for quantitative elementary analysis and a few functional groups and their immediate wide acceptance was impelled by such a necessity and illustrates the advantages of work on a small scale. In 1909–1910 Pregl isolated from gallstones an extremely small quantity of an apparently new organic compound and it was important to determine the carbon and hydrogen content quantitatively. "Thus a decision had to be arrived at either to continue the investigation with exceptionally large quantities of the original material or so to modify the quantitative analysis of organic substances that it should be possible to obtain correct analytical figures with quantities of material hitherto unheard of, so that a formula could be determined with certainty."[6]

The economy of sample material is also of importance in many phases of control work, as for example in costly pharmaceutical preparations. Finally, for teaching purposes the use of small-scale experimentation offers a number of decided advantages over the macro procedures. According to teachers who have worked with these methods, none of the objectives of chemistry instruction are sacrificed. In addition to savings in time, labor, and materials, the student acquires superior habits of care, cleanliness, and manipulative skill from his experience with microtechniques. The present trend toward the use of analytical micro methods in research, particularly in biochemical and structural investigations, is shown by the several hundreds of papers reviewed in the annual progress issues of the *Microchemical Journal*.[7]

V. Guiding Principles in Microanalytical Procedures

A. Factors Which Introduce Errors. The main difference between a macro method and a micro method of chemical experimentation for a

---

[6] F. Pregl, *Quantitative Organic Microanalysis*, Blakiston, Philadelphia, 1924, p. 1; A. A. Benedetti-Pichler, "Fritz Pregl—The Work and Personality of a Nobel Laureate," *Microchem. J.*, **6**, 3 (1962).

[7] "Progress in Microchemistry," *Microchem. J.*, **3**, 275–475 (1959); **4**, 271–396 (1960); **5**, 293–549 (1961); **6**, 315–517 (1962).

particular function or element X is the quantity of sample used for the estimation. If the micro method is to be used it is expected that the results should not be significantly different between the two methods. A micro-analytical procedure is of value only when it gives approximately the same degree of precision and accuracy which are obtained by a macro method employing many times larger quantity of the sample.

It is well known that every quantitative estimation is subject to a number of errors. These may be due to (a) the nature of the chemical reaction employed in the estimation; (b) the environment, such as presence of impurities and interfering substances; and (c) the inaccuracy of the measuring device. If the analytical results are expressed in percentages, it may be given by the general formula:

$$\text{Per cent} = \frac{(P - B)F}{S} \times 100$$

where P is the exact amount of the product formed from S quantity of the pure material investigated; B is the algebraic sum of all errors which are produced by other substances and the measuring device. This is known as the "blank" error because it occurs irrespective of the presence or absence of the pure material investigated; and F is the conversion factor between the product and the pure material investigated.

Expansion of the above equation gives:

$$\text{Per cent} = \left[\frac{P}{S} - \frac{B}{S}\right] \times F \times 100$$

The factor P/S is governed by the nature of the chemical reaction and is rarely affected by the change of the quantity S from several milliequivalents to 0.1 milliequivalent, since the latter still holds a tremendously large number (6.06×10^{19}) of molecules. Thus in the determination of acetyl group by hydrolysis followed by distillation and titration of the acetic acid, if the hydrolytic reaction is 98% complete when 10 milli-equivalents of the acetyl compound are used, it can be assumed that the same degree of completion is attained in the 0.1 milliequivalent scale. On the other hand, the factor B/S, which is dependent on the environment, may be greatly affected when the macro procedure is reduced to the micro scale. In order to attain the same precision and accuracy when the sample size is reduced, the error B has to be reduced in the same proportion. The microanalytical result may be disappointing if the following factors are not taken into consideration.

1. *Effect of Contamination.* If contamination is inadvertently introduced while handling the sample, reagent, and product during the determination,

the effect may be negligible in a macro method, but may become highly significant in the micro procedure. For example, when acetic acid is steam distilled from a sulfuric acid solution in the acetyl group determination, if 0.01 milliequivalent of sulfuric acid passes into the condenser, the relative error in the final result due to this factor is 0.2% when 5 milliequivalents of the compound are used, but becomes 10% when the procedure is on the 0.1 milliequivalent scale. Similarly, if 0.2 mg. of inert material is introduced while weighing the sample, the relative error will be 0.04% for a sample of 500 mg. and 2% for a sample of 10 mg. Hence, care and exact procedures must be observed in small-scale experimentation.

2. *The Use of Clean Apparatus.*   In order to reduce to the minimum the error due to contamination, the microanalytical laboratory and the apparatus used should be kept meticulously clean. Glassware which has been washed with cleaning solution, detergent, or an organic solvent should be thoroughly rinsed, first several times with tap water and finally with distilled water. The inner walls should not be wiped, but air or oven dried. Small apparatus like *microboats, crucibles, filter tubes,* and *charging tubes* may be conveniently gathered together under a large bell jar or hard plastic cover to protect them from dust. A microspatula with flat ends is preferable to one with fine grooves because the latter type is difficult to clean. In general, meticulous cleanliness is absolutely essential.

3. *Effect of Contact Area of Apparatus.*   It will be noted that while the sample size is reduced approximately 100-fold from the macro method to the micro method, the containers such as reaction vessels, titration flasks, and filtration tubes are not reduced as according to scale models. Thus the macro crucible has a capacity of 10 ml. and the microcrucible, 1.5 ml. Macro titration procedure calls for 250-ml. Erlenmeyer flasks; micro method uses 50-ml. flasks. Therefore, the contact area between the sample solution and the container is 10 to 20 times larger in the micro procedure than in the macro procedure. This should be borne in mind when one considers the error due to contamination or due to the loss of the sample by adherence to the walls of the vessel. For instance, in the determination of hydroxyl group by acetylation in a sealed tube, the error due to the reaction between acetic anhydride and the glass wall is significant if soft glass tubing is used. Hence, acid-resistant material like borosilicate glass or quartz tubing should be employed. In all micro work the vessel should be as small as possible for the size of the sample, and the procedure should involve as few transfers as possible.

4. *Effect of Interfering Substances.*   Many analytical procedures are affected by the gases and vapors in the atmosphere. Thus ammonia in the laboratory atmosphere will vitiate the micro-Kjeldahl results of amino

nitrogen, and hydrogen sulfide will cause difficulty in the determination of the methoxyl group by precipitation of silver sulfide besides silver iodide. While a good analytical laboratory probably is free from such contaminating gases, the sample will of necessity come into contact with oxygen, carbon dioxide, and moisture. Oxygen interferes with the determination of nitro group by titanous chloride; carbon dioxide interferes with the nonaqueous titration of weak acids; moisture interferes with the determination of carboxyl group by the Karl Fischer reagent. Since the contact area is relatively large in the micro procedure, provisions have to be made to eliminate these interferences. In general, a closed vessel is desirable so that the analytical reaction may be carried out in the absence of the interfering vapors. In special cases a controlled atmosphere cabinet is constructed and all operations are performed inside the cabinet.

B. Problems Involved in Titrimetric Micro Procedures. There are two approaches to employ micro procedures of titrimetric analysis when the same chemical reaction is used as in the macro method with the sample size being reduced 100-fold. One approach is to retain the concentration of the reagent solutions and use suitable devices to conduct the reduced scale operations. The other approach is to retain the macro analytical apparatus and reduce the concentration of solutions proportionally.

1. Reduction of Volume of Sample and Reagent Solutions. When the concentration of the sample and reagent solutions is kept unchanged from the macro to the micro method, the volume will be proportionally reduced. Thus when the macro procedure requires 25.0 ml. of the titrant, the micro procedure will consume 0.250 ml. This necessitates the use of precision buret accurate to ± 0.001 ml. and other micro reaction vessels. It also entails special titration techniques. Microtechniques for titration under such conditions have been developed by Benedetti-Pichler[8] and serve admirably well in the inorganic field. This approach has been advocated by Siggia for organic analysis.[9] However, it should be mentioned that quantitative inorganic analysis employs only aqueous media and chemical reactions which go to completion instantaneously. On the other hand, determination of organic functional groups often requires heating (such as in acetylation process), volatile solvents (such as methanol, benzene in nonaqueous titrations), and as a rule reactions with slow rates (such as hydrazone formation for carbonyl compounds). Manipulation of this kind with volumes of solution below 1 ml. becomes a difficult problem when one

[8] A. A. Benedetti-Pichler, *Introduction to Microtechniques of Inorganic Analysis*, Wiley, New York, 1942.

[9] S. Siggia, *Quantitative Organic Analysis via Functional Groups*, 2nd ed., Wiley, New York, 1954, p. 2.

wishes to attain the same degree of accuracy and precision as in the macro procedure.

2. Use of Very Dilute Solutions. Another approach towards micro-titrimetry is to use the same equipment as in the macro method and dilute the sample solution and reagents 100-fold so that the volume of titrant consumed will remain the same. Since the concentration of standard solutions used in the macro methods is usually $0.1N$, micro methods will require solutions of $0.001N$. The preparation and use of solutions of such dilution present certain difficulties.

A. INSTABILITY OF VERY DILUTE SOLUTIONS. As the standard solution is made more and more dilute, it becomes increasingly difficult to maintain a constant normality due to the effect of the atmosphere and the contact surface of the container. Thus it is extremely difficult to perform an accurate titration of an acid with a $0.001N$ sodium hydroxide solution because of the interference of carbon dioxide in the air. When the redox reaction is used in the titrimetric micro method, the problem of the constancy of the normality of the titrant is even more serious. It is practically impossible to keep a solution of titanous chloride beyond $0.01N$.

B. TITRATION ENDPOINT AND DILUTION. Dilution of the solution invariably affects the sensitivity of the titration endpoint. Thus in the case of acid-base titrations, the inflection on the neutralization curve progressively shortens as the concentration of the acid and alkali solutions is reduced. If a visual endpoint is detected by means of an indicator, the inflection range should be greater than two pH units.[10] Hence, there is a limit to the dilution where a color change of the indicator can be observed. The intensity of the color of a solution is also inversely proportional to the concentration. If the solution is too dilute, a color endpoint may be too faint to be discernible.

3. Optimum Conditions in Organic Microanalysis. It is evident from the above considerations that neither extreme reduction of the working volume nor extreme dilution of the titrant is suitable for organic microanalysis. The present work is based to a large extent on the use of standard solutions which are 5 to 10 times more dilute than those used in the macro procedures, and burets of 5- to 10-ml capacity. Reagents of $0.01N$ are generally employed in works on quantitative organic microanalysis.[11−13]

[10] T. B. Smith, *Analytical Processes*, 2nd ed., Arnold, London, 1952, p. 228.

[11] J. B. Niederl and V. Niederl, *Micromethods of Quantitative Organic Analysis*, 2nd ed., Wiley, New York, 1942.

[12] A. Steyermark, *Quantitative Organic Microanalysis*, 2nd ed., Academic Press, New York, 1961.

[13] J. Grant, *Quantitative Organic Microanalysis Based on the Methods of Fritz Pregl*, 5th English ed., Blakiston, Philadelphia, 1951.

Even for solutions of such concentration, the selection of a reagent which is least susceptible to atmospheric interference is indicated. Thus it is easier to keep $0.01N$ standard acid than $0.01N$ alkali solution, and methyl isobutyl ketone is a more convenient solvent than ethylenediamine for nonaqueous titration of organic bases.

C. Problems in Sampling

1. Analysis of Pure Compounds. The problem of sampling in quantitative organic microanalysis depends on the purpose of the determination. If the sample is a single entity, the determination is primarily for identification purpose. The material should be systematically purified and the best sample is then submitted for analysis. Foreign matters which may be brought along, such as filter paper fibers and the solvent used in the purification process, should be thoroughly removed before the determination. It is assumed that the sample is uniform throughout. In case a certain peculiarity is observed in a part of the sample, this part should be discarded or analyzed separately. Here the micro method offers some advantages over the macro method. When milligram quantities of the sample are taken for analysis it is relatively easy to detect difference in color and crystal forms.

2. Analysis of Mixtures. The purpose of the quantitative analysis of a mixture is either (a) to determine the percentage composition of each constituent in the specimen, or (b) to estimate the purity of the main component. Since the whole specimen submitted to the laboratory is not taken for analysis, the aim is to select a representative sample. This can easily be done in the case of liquid mixtures (solutions). The specimen should be thoroughly agitated before a sample is taken for analysis, lest the heavier component settle at the bottom. In the case of solid mixtures, an attempt should be made to see if the specimen can be brought to a molten state without decomposition or loss by volatility of its constituents. Another approach to obtain a homogeneous specimen is to dissolve the mixture in a suitable solvent and then an aliquot is taken for the determination. Failing this, the solid mixture should be finely ground and thoroughly mixed. The conventional sampling technique may be applied.[14] A series of determinations may be made of the mixture and the results subjected to statistical interpretation. Since micro methods in general require less time for each determination, it is more economical to perform multiple analyses in the micro scale than in the macro scale.

[14] A. A. Benedetti-Pichler, in W. G. Berl, ed., *Physical Methods in Chemical Analysis*, Vol. 3, Academic Press, New York, 1957, p. 183.

3

Chemical Basis of Functional Group Determinations

I. Introduction

As stated in Section III of Chapter 1, the estimation of functional groups by chemical reactions involves the determination of substances *formed* or *consumed* by the reaction of the sample with the reagent. Further, the measurable substances are *acids, bases, oxidants, reductants, water, gases, sparingly soluble precipitates,* or *colored* species. Though it is assumed that the reader is familiar with the general principles of these reactions, a brief survey will be given of each type of measurement as it is related to its application to organic analysis.

There are, however, a few reactions used in the quantitative estimation of organic functions which at first sight do not appear to fit in any of the above categories. For example, the determination of alkene linkages by means of halogens or hydrogen appear at first sight as addition reactions:

$$\begin{array}{c}\diagdown \\ \diagup \end{array} C{=}C \begin{array}{c}\diagup \\ \diagdown \end{array} + Br_2 \rightarrow \begin{array}{c}\diagdown \quad \overset{\textstyle Br}{\underset{\textstyle Br}{\mid}} \diagup \\ \diagup \quad \mid \quad \diagdown \end{array} C{-}C \qquad (1)$$

$$\begin{array}{c}\diagdown \\ \diagup \end{array} C{=}C \begin{array}{c}\diagup \\ \diagdown \end{array} + H_2 \rightarrow \begin{array}{c}\diagdown \\ \diagup \end{array} CH{-}CH \begin{array}{c}\diagup \\ \diagdown \end{array} \qquad (2)$$

However, if these reactions are examined in the light of the prevalent theories as to the mechanism involved in such additions, it will be evident that the process entails electron shifts and hence they can be classified as oxidation-reduction reactions:

$$: \ddot{Br} : \ddot{Br} : \rightleftarrows [: \ddot{Br} :]^- + [\ddot{Br} :]^+ \qquad (3)$$

$$\begin{array}{c}\diagdown \\ \diagup \end{array} C : : C \begin{array}{c}\diagup \\ \diagdown \end{array} \leftrightarrow \begin{array}{c}\diagdown \\ \diagup \end{array} C : \underset{+}{C} \begin{array}{c}\diagup \\ \underset{-}{\diagdown} \end{array} \qquad (4)$$

31

$$\underset{/+ \quad -\diagdown}{\overset{\diagdown}{\text{C}} : \overset{\diagdown}{\underset{\diagdown}{\text{C}}}} + \left[: \overset{\cdots}{\underset{\cdots}{\text{Br}}} \right]^+ \rightarrow \underset{/ \quad :\overset{\cdots}{\underset{\cdots}{\text{Br}}}: \diagdown}{\overset{\diagdown}{\overset{+}{\text{C}}} : \text{C}\diagup} \tag{5}$$

$$\underset{/ \quad :\overset{\cdots}{\underset{\cdots}{\text{Br}}}: \diagdown}{\overset{\diagdown}{\overset{+}{\text{C}}} : \text{C}\diagup} + \left[: \overset{\cdots}{\underset{\cdots}{\text{Br}}} : \right]^- \rightarrow \underset{/ \quad \underset{\text{Br}}{|} \diagdown}{\overset{\diagdown}{\text{C}} - \overset{\overset{\text{Br}}{|}}{\text{C}}\diagup} \tag{6}$$

The formation of the bromonium and bromide ions (eq. 3), the polarization of the double bond (eq. 4) and the reaction of the polarized molecule first with the bromonium ion then transwise with the bromide ion (eqs. 5 and 6) all involve electron shifts. Further, the determination of the quantity of halogen consumed employs mostly redox titrimetric methods (see pages 519–525).

II. Acid–Base Reactions

A. Acid–Base Concepts. Historically, the earliest chemical definition of acids was made by Boyle (1663) as having the following properties: "They dissolve many substances, they precipitate sulfur from its solution in alkalies, they change blue plant dyes to red, they lose all these properties in contact with alkalies."[1-3] However, the existence and properties of acids and alkalies (bases) had been known from antiquity and through the Middle Ages, and we may regard Boyle's definition as a statement of the prevailing concepts. It should be noted that the use of indicator dyes and the reaction of acids and bases is clearly stated. By 1840 the concept of acids had been expressed by Davy (1811) and Liebig (1838) as "compounds containing hydrogen, in which the hydrogen can be replaced by metals." By 1890 this concept was altered by the advent of the dissociation theory of Arrhenius. An acid was a compound that ionized in water to form hydrogen ions and a base one which gave hydroxyl ions. The acid-base neutralization involved the formation of a salt and water:

$$H^+Cl^- + Na^+OH^- \rightarrow H_2O + Na^+Cl^- \tag{7a}$$

The driving force of the acid-base reaction (eq. 7a) was considered to be the extremely weak ionization of water.

The success of these concepts in explaining and broadening chemical

[1] W. F. Luder, *Chem. Rev.*, **27**, 547 (1940).

[2] W. F. Luder, and S. Zuffanti, *The Electronic Theory of Acids and Bases*, Wiley, New York, 1946.

[3] R. P. Bell, *Acids and Bases*, Methuen, London, 1952.

equilibria in aqueous systems overshadowed a number of inadequacies. For example, the reaction of gaseous hydrogen chloride with ammonia to form NH_4Cl could not be adequately explained while ammonia (and amines) in water were assumed to form hydroxyl ions through the formation of hypothetical hydroxides:

$$NH_3 + H_2O \rightleftarrows NH_4OH \rightleftarrows NH_4^+ + OH^- \tag{7b}$$

Aside from the fact that there is no evidence for the existence of molecular NH_4OH, this concept meets great difficulties in attempting to explain the behavior of sodium hydroxide dissolved in methanol and a solution of sodium methoxide, $CH_3O^-Na^+$, formed by the reaction of sodium metal in anhydrous methanol. While it could be argued that a solution of sodium hydroxide in methanol contained hydroxyl ions (hence a base) no such ions could be postulated in a solution of sodium methoxide. The same and greater complication arose in attempting to account for the behavior of other nonaqueous systems. For example, the basic ion in the liquid-ammonia system is the amido ion, NH_2^-, which cannot be adequately explained by a concept that all bases form hydroxyl, OH^-, ions.

A different concept was proposed by Franklin (1905) which takes into account the role of the solvent.[4] According to the solvent theory, an acidic solution is one which contains as one of the predominant species a solvo-positive ion and a basic solution, one which contains as one of the predominant species a solvo-negative ion. Hence, acidity and basicity are properties of certain solutions and neutralization is the union of solvo-positive ions with solvo-negative ions to give molecules of the solvent.[5]

The behavior of water, ammonia, and methanol was postulated as shown in equations 8–10

$$H_2O + H_2O \rightleftarrows H_3O^+ + OH^- \tag{8}$$
$$NH_3 + NH_3 \rightleftarrows NH_4^+ + NH_2^- \tag{9}$$
$$CH_3OH + CH_3OH \rightleftarrows CH_3OH_2^+ + CH_3O^- \tag{10}$$

The solvent theory did not gain many adherents due to lack of modifications of the main concepts to account for acid-base reactions in aprotic solvents, and to the rapid acceptance and development of the new concept of acids and bases proposed by Brönsted[6] and about the same time (1923) by Lowry[7] which is independent of the solvent. An acid is a substance that can donate protons and a base a substance that can combine with protons.

[4] E. C. Franklin, *J. Am. Chem. Soc.*, **27**, 820 (1905); *The Nitrogen System of Compounds*, Reinhold, New York, 1935.

[5] R. Ginell, *J. Chem. Educ.*, **20**, 250 (1943).

[6] J. N. Brönsted, *Rec. trav. chim.*, **42**, 718 (1923); *J. Phys. Chem.*, **30**, 777 (1926); *Chem. Rev.*, **5**, 231 (1928).

[7] M. T. Lowry, *Trans. Faraday Soc.*, **20**, 13 (1924).

Thus, an acid HB dissociates to give a proton and the conjugate base B^-:

$$HB \rightleftarrows H^+ + B^- \tag{11}$$

The acid HB can be a neutral molecule, such as hydrogen chloride, HCl, a cation such as hydronium ion H_3O^+, or an anion such as the hydrosulfate ion, HSO_4^- as shown in equations 12–15:

$$HCl + H_2O \rightleftarrows H_3O^+ + Cl^- \tag{12}$$
$$acid_1 + base_2 \rightleftarrows acid_2 + base_1 \tag{13}$$
$$H_2SO_4 + H_2O \rightleftarrows H_3O^+ + HSO_4^- \tag{14}$$
$$HSO_4^- + H_2O \rightleftarrows H_3O^+ + SO_4^= \tag{15}$$

Thus all acid-base reactions are represented by the general equation 13 and the general formula of an acid HB is called a conjugate acid-base system. It will also be noted that the water molecules act as proton acceptors or bases, forming the solvated hydronium ion which is represented for simplicity as H_3O^+, though the actual structure is $H_3O^+ \cdot nH_2O$. However, water in reacting with ammonia and amines donates protons acting as an acid:

$$H_2O + \ddot{N}H_3 \rightleftarrows NH_4^+ + OH^- \tag{16}$$
$$acid_1 + base_2 \rightleftarrows acid_2 + base_1$$
$$H_2O + CH_3\ddot{N}H_2 \rightleftarrows CH_3NH_3^+ + OH^- \tag{17}$$

Bases considered as proton acceptors may be neutral molecules such as NH_3 and CH_3NH_2, anions such as HSO_4^-, HCO_3^-, $CO_3^=$, $PO_4^\equiv$, CH_3O^-, or cations such as $Al(OH)_2^+$. It should be noted, however, that such anion bases as HSO_4^-, HCO_3^-, $H_2PO_4^-$, $HPO_4^=$ may act as ampholytes; that is, either as acids or bases:

$$HPO_4^= + H_2O \rightleftarrows H_3O^+ + PO_4^\equiv \tag{18}$$
$$H_2O + HPO_4^= \rightleftarrows H_2PO_4^- + OH^- \tag{19}$$

According to these concepts the neutralization of a strong acid by a strong base is a quantitative transfer of protons from a strong acid to a strong base to form a feeble acid and base, or simply a protolysis reaction:

$$H_3O^+ + OH^- \rightleftarrows H_2O + H_2O \tag{20}$$
$$\text{strong} \quad \text{strong} \quad \text{feeble} \quad \text{feeble}$$

Generally, $HA + B \rightleftarrows BH^+ + A^-$. When either the acid HA or the base B is weak or intermediate, the transfer of protons is not quantitative since in the reaction, bases and acids of equal or lesser strength are formed:

$$CH_3COOH + OH^- \rightleftarrows H_2O + CH_3COO^- \tag{21}$$
$$\text{intermediate} \quad \text{strong} \quad \text{feeble} \quad \text{intermediate}$$

$$H_3O^+ + NH_3 \rightleftarrows NH_4^+ + H_2O \tag{22}$$
$$\text{strong} \quad \text{intermediate} \quad \text{weak} \quad \text{feeble}$$

The pH at the equivalence point in the protolytic reaction shown in equation 21 can be calculated by considering that the acetate anion is a base:

$$CH_3COO^- + H_2O \rightleftarrows CH_3COOH + OH^- \qquad (23)$$

and generally:

$$HA + H_2O \rightleftarrows H_3O^+ + A^- \qquad (24)$$
$$A^- + H_2O \rightleftarrows HA + OH^- \qquad (25)$$

The pH at the equivalence point may be calculated by the equation:

$$H_3O^+ = \sqrt{\frac{K_w K_a}{C_{A^-}}} \quad \text{and pH} = \frac{1}{2}pK_w + \frac{1}{2}pK_a + \frac{1}{2}\log C_{A^-} \qquad (26)$$

where K_w = the autoprotolysis constant for water, K_a is the protolysis constant for the acid HA and C_{A^-} the concentration of the anion A^-.

In concluding the discussion on acid-base concepts, mention should be made of the proposal by G. N. Lewis.[8] According to Lewis, acids are electron pair acceptors, and bases electron donors, and neutralization the formation of a coordinate covalent bond. On the basis of this theory, the bases are similar to those of the Brönsted-Lowry concept but not all the acids since substances like boron chloride, boron fluoride, aluminum chloride, stannic chloride, would be considered as acids.

$$F_3B + : NH_3 \rightarrow F_3B : NH_3$$

acid   base   neutralization
product

In order to distinguish such substances from the generally accepted (Brönsted-Lowry) acids, they are often referred to as Lewis acids.

B. Acid-Base Titrimetry.   Only a brief summary of the quantitative aspects of the acid-base reactions in aqueous and nonaqueous solutions will be given in this section. The reader is referred for a more extensive discussion of the theoretical background to advanced treatises.[9,10] The chief objective in the present discussion is the application of acid-base titrimetry and its limitations to the determination of organic functions.

Table 3.1 gives a summary of the more important functions which are determined by acid-base titrimetry in aqueous and nonaqueous solutions. An inspection of the second column discloses that the basis for the determination of more than half of the functions listed is titrimetry in nonaqueous solvents.

[8] G. N. Lewis, *Valence and the Structure of Atoms and Molecules*, Chemical Catalogue Co., New York, 1923.

[9] I. M. Kolthoff and P. J. Elving, *Treatise on Analytical Chemistry*, Part I, Vol. 1, Interscience, New York, 1959, pp. 405–542.

[10] L. Meites and H. C. Thomas, *Advanced Analytical Chemistry*, McGraw-Hill, New York, 1958, pp. 70–105.

TABLE 3.1

Summary of Determination of Organic Functions Based on Acid-Base Reactions

Function	Method of Determination
Acid anhydride	Nonaqueous titration with $CH_3O^-Na^+$
	Titrimetry in aqueous solutions after hydrolysis
Acid halide	Nonaqueous titration with $CH_3O^-Na^+$
	Titrimetry in aqueous solutions after hydrolysis
Acyl	Aqueous titration after hydrolysis
Alkimide	Titrimetry after hydrolysis
Alkyne	Nonaqueous titration after addition of $AgClO_4$
Amide	Alkalimetry after hydrolysis
	Nonaqueous titration
Amine (1°, 2°, 3°)	Direct acidimetry; titrimetry after acetylation; nonaqueous titration with $HClO_4$
Amino acid	Titrimetry in nonaqueous solvents
Carbonyl	Titrimetry after oximation or after reaction with bisulfite or hydrazine sulfate
Carboxyl	Titrimetry in aqueous solvents
Carboxylates (alkali)	Titrimetry in nonaqueous solvents
Epoxy	Nonaqueous titration with HBr
Ester	Titrimetry after hydrolysis
Heterocyclic N-base	Titrimetry in nonaqueous solvents
Hydrazino	Nonaqueous titration with $HClO_4$
α-Hydroxycarbonyl and carbohydrate	Periodate oxidation followed by titrimetry of formic acid
Sulfonic acid	Titrimetry in aqueous solvents
Sulfonamide	Nonaqueous titration with $HClO_4$
Sulfoxide	Titrimetry in nonaqueous solvents
Thiol	Titrimetry in nonaqueous solvents
Thiourea	Titrimetry in nonaqueous solvents
Urea	Titrimetry in nonaqueous solvents

In all acid-base titrimetry, a measurable volume of titrant is gradually added to the solution of the sample until either a change in the color of the indicator dye or a rapid change in pH measured by a pH meter shows that the endpoint has been reached. At the endpoint, it is assumed that just a sufficient volume of the titrant has been added to react completely with the sample or that the equivalence point has been reached. However, as is well known, the endpoint of the titration does not always coincide with the equivalence point. For example, in the titration of $0.1N$ acetic acid ($K_a = 1.8 \times 10^{-5}$) with $0.1N$ sodium hydroxide, the pH of the solution at the equivalence point calculated by means of equation 26 is 8.7. Hence, the use of such indicators as methyl orange or methyl red which change color between pH 3.0 and 5.0 is not suitable, while phenolphthalein with a color change between pH 8.3 and 9.8 is within the range of the pH of the solution at the equivalence point. Generally the indicator should be so selected that the midpoint of its color change is as near as possible to the calculated pH at the equivalence point. Table 3.2 gives a list of indicators

TABLE 3.2

Color Change Intervals of Some Acid-Base Indicators

Common name	Chemical name	Useful pH interval	Color change
Crystal violet	Hexamethyl-p-rosaniline chloride	0.0–1.8	Blue to purple
Cresol red	o-Cresolphthalein	0.2–1.8	Red to yellow
Malachite green	Tetramethyldiaminotriphènylcarbinol	0.1–2.0	Yellow to green
Thymol blue	Thymolsulfonphthalein	1.2–2.8	Red to yellow
Methyl violet	Pentamethylbenzyl-p-rosaniline hydrochloride	0.2–1.8	Blue to violet
Tropeoline 00	Diphenylamino-p-benzene sodium sulfonate	1.3–3.0	Red to yellow
Eosin Y	Tetrabromofluorescein	2.0–3.5	Colorless to yellow
Methyl yellow	Dimethylamino-azobenzene	2.8–4.0	Red to yellow
Bromophenol blue	Tetrabromophenolsulfonphthalein	3.0–4.6	Yellow to purple
Methyl orange	Dimethylamino-azobenzene sodium sulfonate	3.1–4.4	Red to yellow
α-Naphthyl red		3.7–5.0	Yellow to red
Bromocresol green	Tetrabromo-m-cresolsulfonphthalein	3.8–5.4	Yellow to green, blue
Methyl red	Dimethylazobenzene sodium sulfonate	4.2–6.2	Red to yellow
Chlorophenol red	Dichlorophenolsulfonphthalein	4.8–6.4	Yellow to red
Bromocresol purple	Dibromo-o-cresolsulfonphthalein	5.2–6.8	Yellow to purple
Bromothymol blue	Dibromothymolsulfonphthalein	6.0–7.6	Yellow to blue
Phenol red	Phenolsulfonphthalein	6.4–8.0	Yellow to red
Neutral red	Dimethyldiaminophenazine chloride	6.8–8.0	Red to yellow, brown
Cresol red	o-Cresolsulfonphthalein	7.2–8.8	Yellow to red
m-Cresol purple	m-Cresolsulfonphthalein	7.4–9.0	Yellow to purple
Thymol blue	Thymolsulfonphthalein	8.0–9.6	Yellow to blue
Phenolphthalein	Phenolphthalein	8.0–9.8	Colorless to pink
α-Naphtholbenzein		8.2–10.0	Green to yellow
Thymolphthalein	Thymolphthalein	9.3–10.5	Colorless to blue
Alizarine yellow G	p-Nitrobenzene-azosalicylic acid	10.1–12.1	Yellow to violet

with the pH range and the color changes. Tables 11-2 (page 404) and 11-7 (page 432) list those indicators found most useful for acidimetric and alkalimetric titration, respectively.

The chief problems of acid-base titrations are to choose the proper conditions so as to obtain an observable endpoint which is as near the equivalence point as possible. This involves consideration of the K_a of the acid or the K_b of the base and selection of the proper titrant and solvent system. Inspection of Table 3.3 which lists the K_a's of a number of monocarboxylic and dicarboxylic acids shows that most are of intermediate or weak strength with K_a's, mostly in the range of 10^{-5}. Similarly inspection of Table 3.4 shows that most of the amines listed are of intermediate or feeble strength. The alkylamines have K_b's in the range 10^{-5}, the arylamines in the range of 10^{-10}–10^{-12}. Hence, the choice of the solvent and titrant are of importance. Furthermore, in using samples of 0.1 meq. and titrant of

TABLE 3.3

K_a's of Some Carboxylic Acids

Monocarboxylic	$K_a \times 10^5$	Dicarboxylic	K_{a_1}	K_{a_2}
Formic	1.8	Oxalic	1×10^{-1}	4.9×10^{-5}
Acetic	1.8	Malonic	1.6×10^{-3}	2.0×10^{-6}
Propionic	1.4	Succinic	6.5×10^{-5}	2.9×10^{-6}
Butyric	1.5	Glutaric	5×10^{-5}	2.9×10^{-6}
Pentanoic	1.6	Adipic	3.6×10^{-5}	2.4×10^{-6}
Hexanoic	1.4	Pimelic	3.2×10^{-5}	2.6×10^{-6}
Heptanoic	1.4	Sebacic	2.3×10^{-5}	2.5×10^{-6}
Acrylic	5.6	Maleic	1.5×10^{-2}	5.7×10^{-7}
Crotonic	2.0	Fumaric	9×10^{-4}	3.4×70^{-5}
Chloroacetic	155	Phthalic	1.2×10^{-3}	3×10^{-6}
α-Chlorobutyric	139	Isophthalic	2.9×10^{-4}	2×10^{-5}
Dichloroacetic	3320	Terephthalic	1.5×10^{-4}	—
Trichloroacetic	20000			
Benzoic	6.6	Carbonic acid	4.3×10^{-7}	4.7×10^{-11}
Phenylacetic	4.9	(for comparison)		
o-Chlorobenzoic	132			
p-Chlorobenzoic	9.3			
o-Nitrobenzoic	656			
p-Nitrobenzoic	40			
o-Hydroxybenzoic	105			
p-Hydroxybenzoic	2.9			
o-Aminobenzoic	1.0			
p-Aminobenzoic	1.2			

TABLE 3.4

K_b's of Some Amines

Base	K_b
Methylamine	42×10^{-5}
Dimethylamine	62×10^{-5}
Triethylamine	61×10^{-5}
Ethylamine	56×10^{-5}
Diethylamine	126×10^{-5}
Triethylamine	56×10^{-5}
Aniline	4.2×10^{-10}
o-Chloroaniline	5×10^{-12}
p-Chloroaniline	1.5×10^{-10}
o-Aminoaniline	3.2×10^{-10}
p-Aminoaniline	110×10^{-10}
o-Nitroaniline	3.5×10^{-14}
p-Nitroaniline	1×10^{-13}
o-Methylaniline (o-toluidine)	2.5×10^{-10}
p-Methylaniline (p-toluidine)	12×10^{-10}
N-Methylaniline	2.6×10^{-10}
N-Dimethylaniline	2.4×10^{-10}
Benzylamine	2.4×10^{-5}
Ammonia	1.8×10^{-5}

$0.01N$ strength, consideration must be given to the effect of the carbon dioxide in the atmosphere since the K_a of carbonic acid is 4×10^{-7}.

C. Titrimetry in Nonaqueous Solvents. The strength of an acid-base system and its titration characteristics are affected by the acid-base properties of the solvents and their dielectric constants. If we wish to titrate any of the feeble bases listed in Table 3.4 with K_b's 10^{-10}–10^{-12} in water with a strong acid:

$$B + H_3O^+ \rightleftarrows BH^+ + H_2O \tag{27}$$

the molecules of water will compete with the base for protons:

$$H_2O + H_3O^+ \rightleftarrows 2H_2O \tag{28}$$

Therefore, the titration shown in equation 27 is not quantitative at the equivalence point due to the reaction shown in equation 28, that is, reaction of the hydronium ions with the solvent. In order to titrate such feeble bases it is necessary to choose a solvent with weaker basic properties than water. In order to discuss the application of nonaqueous titrimetry, it is necessary to consider the classification of solvents.

1. *Aprotic or Neutral Solvents.* These solvents include *benzene, chloroform, acetonitrile, acetone,* and other *ketones.* They have relatively low dielectric constants and do not donate or accept protons readily; that is, they do not react with acid-base systems though they may form hydrogen bonds with the solute. Addition of aprotic solvents to solvents with high dielectric constants which favor acid-base reaction depresses the solvolysis of the neutralization product and hence, sharpens the endpoint.

2. *Amphiprotic Solvents.* These solvents include *water, methanol, ethanol,* and other *alcohols.* They have relatively high dielectric constants, exhibit acid-base properties and ionization properties similar to those of water:

$$H_2O + H_2O \rightleftarrows H_3O^+ + OH^- \tag{29}$$

3. *Protogenic Solvents.* *Acetic acid* and *sulfuric acid* are examples of this class and are stronger acids but weaker bases than water. For example, acetic acid may react as an acid as shown in equation 30 and as a base as shown in equation 31:

$$CH_3COOH \rightleftarrows H^+ + CH_3COO^- \tag{30}$$
$$2CH_3COOH \rightleftarrows CH_3COOH_2^+ + CH_3COO^- \tag{31}$$

The extent of the reaction in equation 31 is less than the one shown in equation 30. Since acetic acid is a stronger acid and a weaker base than water it can be employed either alone or mixed with an aprotic solvent to titrate a feeble base. For example, perchloric acid may be dissolved in acetic acid giving the equilibria shown in equations 32 and 33:

$$HClO_4 \rightleftarrows H^+ + ClO_4^- \tag{32}$$
$$CH_3COOH + H^+ \rightleftarrows CH_3COOH_2^+ \tag{33}$$

The titration of the feeble base then can be formulated in such a solution:

$$B + CH_3COOH \rightleftarrows BH^+ + CH_3COO^- \tag{34}$$
$$CH_3COOH_2^+ + CH_3COO^- \rightleftarrows 2CH_3COOH \tag{35}$$

It will be noted that equation 35 is identical with the autoprotolysis of acetic acid shown in equation 31. The over-all reaction of the titration by perchloric acid may be written:

$$HClO_4 + B \rightleftarrows BH^+ + ClO_4^- \tag{36}$$

In order that the reaction 36 be quantitative at the equivalence point the base B must be a stronger proton acceptor than the other bases present in solution which are the solvent and the perchlorate ions (that is, the conjugate base of $HClO_4$).

4. *Protophilic Solvents.* These include *dimethylformamide, pyridine, n-butylamine,* and *ethylenediamine* which are stronger bases but weaker

acids than water. A solvent of this type may react with an acid HB to yield a solvated proton and the conjugate anion base B⁻. For example, the solution of benzoic acid in dimethylformamide may be represented thus:

$$C_6H_5COOH + HCO\underset{\cdot\cdot}{N}(CH_3)_2 \rightleftarrows HCO\overset{+}{N}(CH_3)_2 + C_6H_5COO^- \tag{37}$$
$$\underset{H}{}$$

The solution now can be titrated by sodium methoxide:

$$CH_3ONa \rightleftarrows CH_3O^- + Na^+ \tag{38}$$

$$HCO\overset{+}{N}(CH_3)_2 + CH_3O^- \rightleftarrows HCO\underset{\cdot\cdot}{N}(CH_3)_2 + CH_3OH \tag{39}$$
$$\underset{H}{}$$

and the over-all reaction in the titration may be written:

$$C_6H_5COOH + CH_3O^-Na^+ \rightarrow CH_3OH + C_6H_5COO^-Na^+ \tag{40}$$

In order that the reaction be quantitative at the equivalence point, the methoxide ion CH_3O^- must be a stronger base than either the solvent or the benzoate ion. In general, as the strength of the acid function being titrated decreases, the solvent selected for its titration should be more strongly basic (see page 399); conversely, as the strength of the basic function decreases the solvent selected for its titration should be strongly acidic. Further discussion on procedures for both aqueous and nonaqueous titrimetry, particularly with their application to the determination of acidic and basic functions, is given in Chapter 11. A summary of indirect acid-base methods for the determination of functional groups has been presented by Critchfield and co-workers[10a].

III. Redox Reactions

A. Concept of Redox Reactions.   As indicated in the introduction to this chapter, the term redox reaction is employed in a broad sense. Generally increase in the electron density of an atom is regarded as reduction and decrease as oxidation, and such electronic shifts occur together so that a reductant cannot react unless an oxidant is present. Thus in the series of changes given in the following formulas, there is a stepwise decrease of the electron density

$$R{-}\overset{*}{C}H_3 \underset{[H]}{\overset{[O]}{\rightleftarrows}} R{-}\overset{*}{C}H_2OH \underset{[H]}{\overset{[O]}{\rightleftarrows}} R\overset{*}{C}HO \underset{[H]}{\overset{[O]}{\rightleftarrows}} R\overset{*}{C}OOH \tag{41}$$

of the starred carbon atom from left to right and an increase from right to

[10a] F. E. Critchfield et al., *Symposium on Organic Functional Group Analysis*, American Chemical Society, Spring Meeting, 1961, St. Louis, Missouri.

left. Halogenation of the starred carbon atom is likewise considered as involving oxidation. Since RCH_2Cl hydrolyses to RCH_2OH, $RCHCl_2$ to RCHO, and $RCCl_3$ to RCOOH it can be assumed that the replacement of one more hydrogen atom by halogens has been accompanied by a decrease in the electron density of the carbon atom.

Although it is rather easy to apply the above concept to the C—O and C-halogen linkages, the C—N linkages present difficulties which, however, are not insurmountable. In the $R\overset{\text{H}}{\underset{\text{H}}{-\text{C}-}}NH_2$ the electron density of the carbon atom may be regarded as being of the same order as in the alcohol $R\overset{\text{H}}{\underset{\text{H}}{-\text{C}-}}OH$ and that of nitrogen of the same order as in ammonia $\overset{..}{N}H_3$. However, the R—C≡N linkage presents difficulties which can be resolved by considering the following relations:

$$R\overset{\text{H}}{\underset{\text{H}}{-\text{C}-}}NH_2 \xleftarrow{\text{[H]}} R-C{\equiv}N \xrightarrow{\text{[H_2O]}} R-CONH_2 \xrightarrow{\text{[H_2O]}} RCOOH + NH_3 \quad (42)$$

Since the nitrile can be catalytically reduced to the amine, and hydrolyzed to the carboxylic acid (with the amide as a demonstrable intermediate) it can be assumed that the hydrolysis of the —C≡N linkage involves a redox reaction in which the electron density of the carbon atom is decreased and that of the nitrogen atom increased.

B. Measurement of Redox Reactions.   Redox reactions do not take place at the same rapid rate as acid-base reactions which are considered instantaneous. Further, they are mostly irreversible. The number of reversible organic redox systems is small and among the best known is the hydroquinone $\rightleftarrows$ quinone system:

$$HO-C_6H_4-OH \rightleftarrows O{=}C_6H_4{=}O + 2H^+ + 2e \quad (43)$$

The majority of redox reactions involved in the determination of functional groups is summarized in Table 3.5. A few of the reactions summarized in the second column will be discussed in detail in order to illustrate the type of redox reactions involved in such determinations.

As the first example, the estimation of the anhydride function by reaction with a substituted aniline will be considered. The basis of the determination is to react the sample with a substituted aniline such as 2,4-dichloroaniline as shown in equation 44:

$$(RCO)_2O + C_6H_3Cl_2NH_2 \rightleftarrows RCONH-C_6H_3Cl_2 + RCOOH \quad (44)$$

TABLE 3.5

Summary of Determination of Organic Functions Based on Redox Reactions

Function	Redox reaction(s) involved in determinations
Acid anhydride	Reaction with 2,4-dichloroaniline and determination of un-reacted amine with KBr—KBrO$_3$ and iodometry; reaction with oxalic acid
Acyl	Reaction with KI—KIO$_3$ followed by iodometry
Alkene	Epoxidation; ozonolysis; periodate oxidation
Alkimide	Formation of alkyl iodide, reaction with Br$_2$ followed by iodometry
Alkoxyl	Formation of alkyl iodide, reaction with Br$_2$ followed by iodometry
Alkylidene	Oxidative cleavage followed by iodometry
Amide and imide	Reduction by LiAlH$_4$ followed by titrimetry
Azo	Reduction by Ti^{+3} or Cr^{+2}
Carbonyl	(a) Reduction by LiAlH$_4$ or NaBH$_4$; (b) oxidation by Ag$_2$O, or Tollens' reagent or peroxytrifluoracetic acid; (c) reaction with 2,4-DNPH or NaHSO$_3$ and measurement of excess by iodometry; (d) for methylcarbonyl: haloform oxidation
Carboxyl	Permanganate oxidation of readily oxidizable acids
Disulfide	Reduction to RSH followed by titrimetry
Epoxy	(a) Oxidation by HClO$_4$; (b) reaction by HI followed by iodometry
Hydrazine, hydrazide, and semicarbazide	Oxidation by IO$_3^-$, Br$_2$, I$_2$, ICl, BrCl, or VO$_3^-$ followed by titrimetry
Hydrazo	(a) Reduction by Ti^{+3}; (b) oxidation by MnO$_4^-$
α-Hydroxycarbonyl, carbohydrate, and 1,2-diketone	(a) Oxidation by periodate, cerate, hypobromite, ferricyanide, or cupric ions; (b) reduction by NaBH$_4$
Mercapto (thiol)	Oxidation by I$_2$, IO$_3^-$, BrO$_3^-$, or Cu^{+2} followed by titrimetry
Methyl (terminal)	Oxidative cleavage to CH$_3$COOH followed by titrimetry
Methylene (terminal)	Oxidative cleavage to formaldehyde
Nitro and nitroso	Reduction by Ti^{+3}, Cr^{+2}, Sn^{+2}, V^{+2}, Fe^{+2}, Zn(Hg)$_x$, or Cd
Peroxy	Reduction by I$^-$, Fe^{+2}, Ti^{+3}, Sn^{+2}, Mn^{+2}, or As$_2$O$_3$ followed by titrimetry
Quinone	Reduction with I$^-$, Ti^{+3}, or Sn^{+2} followed by titrimetry
Sulfide	Oxidation by Br$_2$ or ClO$^-$
Sulfinic	Oxidation by ClO$^-$ to RSO$_3^-$
Sulfonamide	Oxidation by HNO$_3$ to N$_2$O
Sulfoxide	(a) Reduction to sulfide; (b) oxidation to sulfone
Thiourea	Oxidation by IO$^-$, H$_2$O$_2$, Br$_2$, or SeO$_2$
Urea	Oxidation by BrO$^-$

In order to obtain a quantitative reaction, excess of the substituted amine is used and the unreacted excess is determined by a series of redox reactions shown in equations 45–48:

$$BrO_3^- + 5Br^- + 6H^+ \rightarrow 3Br_2 + 3H_2O \tag{45}$$
$$\text{excess } C_6H_3Cl_2NH_2 + Br_2 \rightarrow NH_2C_6H_2Cl_2Br + HBr \tag{46}$$
$$\text{excess } Br_2 + 2I^- \rightarrow 2Br^- + I_2 \tag{47}$$
$$I_2 + 2Na_2S_2O_3 \rightarrow 2NaI + Na_2S_4O_6 \tag{48}$$

It will be noted that the reactions represented by equations 45, 47, and 48 are well-known inorganic redox reactions while equation 46 represents the basis of the determination, namely, addition of an excess of bromine followed by measurement of the amount consumed. An over-all inspection of all the reactions involved indicates that conditions must be chosen so as to obtain (a) complete reaction of the sample with the amine; (b) no side reactions in the monobromination of the excess of the amine; (c) the usual precautions to avoid loss of bromine and iodine and other errors in the iodometric titration.

The second example to be discussed is the determination of the alkoxyl function. The first and basic reaction is the formation of an equivalent quantity of an alkyl iodide which does not involve any redox reaction:

$$-OR + HI \rightarrow -OH + RI \tag{49}$$

However, the basis of the determination is to measure by an appropriate method the iodine content of the alkyl iodide formed by the sample (eq. 49). This can be done by a gravimetric procedure of converting the alkyl iodide to silver iodide. However, the method commonly used involves redox titrimetry. The alkyl iodide is absorbed in a buffered solution of glacial acetic acid and sodium acetate. Then the iodide is oxidized to iodic acid by bromine; the excess of bromine is eliminated by reaction with formic acid, and finally the iodic acid is converted to iodine which is determined by titrimetry. The reactions are shown in equations 50–53.

$$RI + 3Br_2 + 3H_2O \rightarrow HIO_3 + RBr + 5HBr \tag{50}$$
$$Br_2 + HCOOH \rightarrow 2HBr + CO_2 \tag{51}$$
$$HIO_3 + 5KI + 5H_2SO_4 \rightarrow 3I_2 + 3H_2O + 5KHSO_4 \tag{52}$$
$$I_2 + 2Na_2S_2O_3 \rightarrow 2NaI + Na_2S_4O_6 \tag{53}$$

An over-all inspection of the reactions involved and reference to the more detailed discussion on pages 125–129 indicates that conditions must be chosen to achieve (a) quantitative cleavage of the alkoxyl function and conversion to alkyl iodide; (b) suppression as far as may be of the possible reaction between the alkyl iodide and hydriodic acid:

$$RI + HI \rightarrow RH + I_2 \tag{54}$$

(c) complete separation of the alkyl iodide from the reaction mixture, particularly from HI and I_2; (d) quantitative oxidation of the alkyl iodide to iodic acid (eq. 50); (e) care not to use great excess of formic acid (eq. 51) since some of iodic acid may be reduced; (f) finally the usual precautions of iodometric titrations (eqs. 52 and 53).

As a third example of the application of redox reactions to the determination of organic functions the various methods for the determination of the carbonyl function will be considered. An inspection of the methods listed in the second column of Table 3.5 for the determination of the carbonyl function discloses that they are based on one of the following reactions of the carbonyl group: (a) reduction to the alcohol function; (b) oxidation to carboxyl; (c) addition of various reagents with or without elimination. In the reductive procedures an excess of lithium aluminum hydride or sodium borohydride is employed to obtain quantitative reduction of the sample:

$$4R_2C{=}O + NaBH_4 \rightarrow R_2CHONa + (R_2CHO)_3B \tag{55}$$

The excess of the hydride may be determined either by potassium bromate-potassium iodide mixture to generate iodine which is titrated with standard thiosulfate, or by converting the excess of hydride to hydrogen which is measured gasometrically:

$$NaBH_4 + HCl + 3H_2O \rightarrow 4H_2 + NaCl + H_3BO_3 \tag{56}$$

The oxidative procedures are based upon the use of silver oxide, Nessler's reagent, Tollens' reagent, peroxytrifluoroacetic acid, hypoiodide, or hypochlorite (see pages 153–155) and then measurement of the oxidant consumed. Most of these procedures, however, entail difficulties due to incomplete oxidations and side reactions, which give rise to several products simultaneously rendering the method unsuitable for quantitative measurements.

The initial step in addition reactions of the carbonyl group may be represented by the general equation 57:

$$\diagup\!\!\!\diagdown C{=}O \leftrightarrow \diagup\!\!\!\diagdown \overset{+}{C}{-}\overset{-}{O} + H\overset{+}{B}\overset{-}{} \rightleftarrows \diagup\!\!\!\diagdown \underset{B}{\overset{|}{C}}{-}OH \tag{57}$$

The addition reaction is reversible and not all carbonyl compounds form addition products with the same rates or completion. In the oximation procedures the measurement of the reagent consumed is based on the

$$\diagup\!\!\!\diagdown C{=}O + H_2NOH \cdot HCl \rightarrow \diagup\!\!\!\diagdown C{=}NOH + H_2O + HCl \tag{58}$$

determination by alkalimetry of the liberated acid; however, in the hydrazone or bisulfite addition, redox reactions are employed in a number of procedures to measure the quantity of reagent consumed. For example, the sample may be reacted with excess of a substituted hydrazine and the excess determined by titration with sodium nitrite or sodium stannite or titanous chloride or by iodometry. Similarly the excess of bisulfite may be determined iodometrically.

As a final example, the application of periodate oxidation to organic analysis will be considered. A more detailed discussion of the application of this redox reaction to estimation of adjacent hydroxy functions in glycols and carbohydrates is given on pages 193–196 and 157–160. A more comprehensive review has been given by Kolthoff and Belcher.[11] Periodate oxidizes adjacent hydroxyl groups, but it has no effect on monohydroxy groups or polyhydroxy compounds in which the hydroxyl groups are separated by one or more carbon atoms. In such oxidations every "adjacency" (not every pair of hydroxyl groups) consumes one mole of periodate, the stoichiometry being shown in equation 59:

$$CH_2OH(CHOH)_n\text{—}CH_2OH + (n + 1)HIO_4 \rightarrow$$
$$(n + 1)HIO_3 + 2HCHO + nHCOOH + H_2O \quad (59)$$

Formic acid is produced only when there are more than two adjacent hydroxyl groups.

$$CH_2OHCHOHCH_2OH + 2HIO_4 \rightarrow 2HIO_3 + 2HCHO + HCOOH + H_2O \quad (60)$$
$$CH_2OHCH_2OH + HIO_4 \rightarrow HIO_3 + 2HCHO + H_2O \quad (61)$$

The measurable substance in such oxidations may be the periodate consumed or the iodate, aldehyde, or formic acid produced. However, there is no accurate method to determine the quantity of iodate in presence of periodate. Therefore, for glycols, the excess of periodate is measured by adding an excess of sodium arsenite and followed by back titration with standard iodine solution:

$$HIO_4 + Na_3AsO_3 \rightarrow Na_3AsO_4 + HIO_3 \quad (62)$$

In carbohydrates, besides measurement of the periodate consumed, several procedures have been proposed for the measurement of the quantity of formic acid produced. However, periodate oxidation of a mole of an aldohexose and one mole of a ketohexose does not produce the same number of moles of formic acid. For example, glucose gives 5 and fructose 3 moles (see page 160). Finally, as indicated in Table 3.5, carbohydrates may be

[11] I. M. Kolthoff and R. Belcher, *Volumetric Analysis*, Vol. 3, Interscience, New York, 1957, p. 475.

determined by oxidimetric procedures such as cerate, hypobromite, ferricyanide, and cupric ion oxidation.

In concluding this brief discussion on the application of redox reactions to organic analysis it should be emphasized that the conditions must be chosen carefully so as to insure a quantitative reaction of the sample with the oxidant or reductant with as few side reactions as possible; also, that although often it is more accurate to measure one of the reaction products formed, this is not always feasible and many of the determinations are based on the measurement of the excess of oxidant or reductant remaining in the reaction mixture.

IV. Measurement of Water Formed or Consumed

A. General.   Table 3.6 gives a summary of the determination of several

TABLE 3.6

Summary of Determination of Organic Functions Based on Aquametry

Function	Reaction for formation of measurable H_2O
Acetal or ketal	Heating with CH_3COOH and BF_3
Acid anhydride	Hydrolysis and measurement of unreacted H_2O
Amino	Acetylation or reaction with carbonyl compound $\rightarrow$ Schiff's base $+ H_2O$
Carbonyl	Oximation
Carboxyl	Esterification
Hydroxyl	Esterification

eral organic functions by measurements of the quantity of water formed[12] or consumed[13] as illustrated in equations 63 and 64:

$$RCOOH + R'OH \rightleftharpoons RCOOR' + H_2O \qquad (63)$$
$$(RCOO)_2O + H_2O \rightarrow 2RCOOH \qquad (64)$$

The esterification reaction shown in equation 63 may be employed to determine either hydroxyl or carboxyl functions. Since esterification is a reversible reaction, the conditions specified in the procedure insure completion of the reaction between the carboxyl and hydroxyl groups. For the determination of the hydroxyl group a large excess of acetic acid is used

[12] W. M. Bryant, J. Mitchell, Jr., and D. M. Smith, *J. Am. Chem. Soc.*, **62**, 1 (1940).
[13] D. M. Smith, W. M. Bryant, and J. Mitchell, Jr., *J. Am. Chem. Soc.*, **62**, 608 (1940); **63**, 1700 (1941).

with dioxane as solvent and boron trifluoride as catalyst. The reaction is completed in 2 hours at 67°C. In the carboxyl determination excess of methanol is used and boron trifluoride as catalyst. After completion of the reaction, pyridine is added and the water in the reaction mixture is measured by titration with the Karl Fischer reagent. Only the general aspect of this titration will be discussed in this section. For details the reader is referred to the work on aquametry by Mitchell and Smith.[15]

B. Karl Fischer Reagent. The Karl Fischer reagent is composed of iodine, sulfur dioxide, pyridine, and usually methanol. The over-all reaction with water is given by equation 65. However, equations 65 and 66 show that the reaction involves two steps:

$$H_2O + SO_2 + I_2 + 3C_5H_5N \rightarrow 2C_5H_5N \cdot HI + C_5H_5N \cdot SO_3 \tag{65}$$
$$C_5H_5N \cdot SO_3 + CH_3OH \rightarrow C_5H_5N(H)SO_4CH_3 \tag{66}$$

The reaction represented by equation 66 involves the pyridine-sulfur trioxide complex. The strength of the reagent is established by determination of its iodine content. For macro titration, a concentration equivalent to 3 mg. of water per milliliter of reagent is used. For micro or semimicro samples a concentration equivalent to 1-2 mg. of water per milliliter of titrant is employed. The reagent is standardized by using methanol containing a definite amount of water or finely divided sodium tartrate dihydrate.

Visual titration may be used for macro titration; the change of the reagent from canary yellow to chromate yellow and finally to brown serves as the endpoint. For micro procedures, however, potentiometric titration is employed. In all procedures the sample and reagent must be protected from atmospheric moisture. The assembly used for the determination of the carboxyl function by this procedure is shown in Figure 7.1. Organic compounds which interfere with the application of the Karl Fischer reagent are carbonyl quinones, peroxides, and a few others.[15,16]

V. Measurement of Gases

A. General. The measurement of the quantity of gas evolved or consumed during a reaction provides the basis for the determination of several organic functions. The best known procedure based on gas evolution is the Van Slyke method for the determination of the amino group in α-amino carboxylic acid, while the procedure of measuring unsaturation by catalytic hydrogenation is the best example of the procedures based on the measure-

[15] J. Mitchell, Jr. and D. M. Smith, *Aquametry*, Interscience, New York, 1948.

[16] J. Mitchell, Jr., in *Treatise of Analytical Chemistry*, ed. by I. M. Kolthoff and P. J. Elving, Part II, Vol. 1, Interscience, New York, 1961, pp. 82–93.

ment of the quantity of gas consumed. These methods are designated as gasometric procedures. The quantity of the gas evolved is determined by placing the sample in an appropriate apparatus and treating it with excess of reagent then measuring either the *volume* of the gas while the pressure is kept constant or the *pressure* of the gas while the *volume* is kept constant. The latter method is usually called a manometric procedure. The quantity of the gas (usually hydrogen) consumed is similarly measured in an appropriate apparatus by starting with a known volume of gas in a buret at a known pressure and then adding the sample and measuring the volume or pressure after the reaction. Hence, all gasometric procedures are based on the change of either the volume or the pressure of a gas in a closed system as a result of the reaction of the sample in such a manner as to produce or consume a measurable gaseous substance.

Various gasometric assemblies are discussed on pages 232 and 368. The techniques and procedures are illustrated in detail in experiments 33 and 39, on the determination of the carbonyl and hydrazino groups and experiments 45 and 46 on the determination of unsaturated linkages.

B. Reactions Which Yield Measurable Quantities of Gaseous Products. Table 3.7 gives a summary of the various organic functions which are determined by gasometric procedures. Inspection of the second column of Table 3.7 discloses that of the 23 procedures listed, 9 are based on evolution of nitrogen, 5 on methane, 3 on oxides of nitrogen, 3 on evolution or absorption of hydrogen and 1 of each on evolution of carbon dioxide together with carbon monoxide, and of oxygen.

1. Evolution of Nitrogen. Many if not all of the nitrogen functions in which the nitrogen atom is in a relatively *negative* stage of oxidation (high electron density) may be made to yield *molecular nitrogen* by reaction with a reagent containing nitrogen atoms in a positive state of oxidation (low electron density). For example, in the well-known determination of the amino group by nitrosation, the essential reaction may be represented thus:

$$R—NH_2 + HNO_2 \rightarrow N_2 + ROH + H_2O \tag{67}$$
$$N^{-3} + N^{+3} \rightarrow N_2^0 \tag{68}$$

The oxidant in this case is nitrous acid. In the diazo and azo groups (page 264) the two N—N nitrogen atoms are in different states of oxidation and the reagent is in general an acid or a catalyst used to bring about the cleavage and reaction to yield molecular nitrogen. In the determination of hydrazines, hydrazides, and semicarbazides, various oxidants have been used, such as cupric ions, halogens, and halogen oxyacids (page 290).

There are three formidable difficulties encountered in all the determinations based on evolution of nitrogen. The first is due to the fact that the

TABLE 3.7

Summary of Determination of Organic Functions Based on Gasometry

Function	Reaction for gas production or absorption
Alkene	Catalytic hydrogenation and measurement of hydrogen absorbed
Alkoxyl	Formation of alkyl iodide $\rightarrow$ iodic acid with $NH_2NH_2 \rightarrow N_2$
Alkyl nitrate	Reduction to NO
Amide and imide	Reaction with Grignard reagent $\rightarrow CH_4$
Amino	Nitrosation $\rightarrow N_2$
Anhydride	Reaction with oxalic acid $\rightarrow CO + CO_2$
Azo	Heating with $C_6H_5NHNH_2 \rightarrow N_2$
Carbonyl	Reaction with Grignard reagent $\rightarrow CH_4$; reduction with $NaBH_4$ and detn. of excess $\rightarrow H_2$ Reaction with $C_6H_5NHNH_2 \rightarrow N_2$
Carboxyl	Decarboxylation $\rightarrow CO_2$; reaction with Grignard reagent $\rightarrow CH_4$
Diazo	Heating with catalyst $\rightarrow N_2$
Ester	Reaction with Grignard reagent, measure CH_4 from excess reagent Reduction with $LiAlH_4$ and use of alcohol to measure $\rightarrow H_2$
Hydrazine and hydrazides	Oxidation $\rightarrow N_2$
Hydroxyl	Reaction with $LiAlH_4 \rightarrow H_2$; reaction with Grignard reagent $\rightarrow CH_4$
N-Nitro	Reaction with $H_2SO_4 + Hg \rightarrow NO$; hydrogenation
N-Nitroso	Reduction $\rightarrow N_2$; reaction with $Hg + H_2SO_4 \rightarrow NO$
Phenol	Reaction with $LiAlH_4 \rightarrow H_2$; reaction with Grignard reagent $\rightarrow CH_4$ coupling with ArN_2X then decompose $\rightarrow N_2$
Quinone	Reaction with $C_6H_5NHNH_2 \rightarrow N_2$
Semicarbazide	Oxidation $\rightarrow N_2$
Sulfinic acid	Oxidation (IO_3^- followed by H_2O_2) $\rightarrow O_2$
Sulfonamide	Oxidation (HNO_3) $\rightarrow N_2O$

redox reaction is not as unidirectional as shown in equation 67. As previously noted, in any particular organic reaction, there is more than one equilibrium involved and those which are not desirable are called side reactions. Hence, there are other products formed and the reaction is not as stoichiometric as shown in equation 67. Even with compounds such as amino acids which react readily at room temperature, the evolution of nitrogen does not always yield the stoichiometric quantity of nitrogen. For example, glycine yields a variable error of 3–9%, depending on the condition of the reaction.

The second difficulty arises from the fact that not all amino functions react at the same rates because the radical attached to the amino group has a profound effect on the redox reaction. For example, many amino acids react completely within five minutes at room temperature; alkylamines require from 0.5 to 1 hour; some arylamines react at elevated temperatures while others do not react completely. Finally, a variety of organic compounds such as oximes, phenols, and compounds containing an active methylene group interfere due to the formation of oxides of nitrogen and/or molecular nitrogen. In general, however, conditions can be chosen so that satisfactory results are obtained with many determinations which are based on evolution of nitrogen. The oxides of nitrogen which are usually evolved in the nitrosation reactions are removed by scrubbing the gas with a solution of alkaline permanganate or potassium bromate. The side reactions during nitrosation are suppressed either by the addition of catalysts or by using nitrosation in nonaqueous systems. Finally, the apparatus and type of determination may be standardized by the use of a known quantity of pure sample of the compound determined or closely related.

2. *Evolution of Methane.* Hydrogen atoms attached to oxygen as in —OH, and —COOH or to nitrogen as in —NH_2, R—NHR′ are called *active* hydrogens and react readily with methyl Grignard reagents to yield methane:

$$CH_3MgX + ROH \rightarrow CH_4 + ROMgX \tag{69}$$

Therefore alcohols, phenols, carboxylic acids, amines, amides, and imides may be determined under certain conditions by reacting the anhydrous sample with the Grignard reagent and measuring the volume of methane produced. Other compounds such as esters and carbonyl compounds which readily react with Grignard reagents can be determined by the indirect procedure of measuring the excess of reagent. For example, a sample of an ester is reacted with a known amount of methyl magnesium iodide and then the excess of the Grignard reagent is determined by adding aniline to generate methane:

$$R—COOR′ + 2CH_3MgI \rightarrow R(CH_3)_2C—OMgI + R′OMgI \tag{70}$$
$$\text{excess } CH_3MgI + C_6H_5NH_2 \rightarrow C_6H_5NHMgI + CH_4 \tag{71}$$

The chief difficulties encountered in the procedures based on evolution of methane are the varying rates of reaction between the compounds containing active hydrogen and the interferences due to the presence of compounds in the sample which react with the Grignard reagent. For example, in the reaction shown in equations 70 and 71, the presence of water, alcohols, carboxylic acids, amides, alkyl halides, and other compounds which react with the Grignard reagent will cause errors. The methods are discussed on pages 411 and 178.

3. *Evolution of Oxides of Nitrogen.* Alkyl nitrates, N-nitro, and N-nitroso compounds liberate nitric oxide upon reduction when treated with acids in the presence of mercury:

$$2NO_3^- + 8H^+ + 3Hg \rightarrow 2NO + 3Hg^{+2} + 4H_2O \qquad (72)$$

$$2R_2N\text{---}NO_2 + 6H^+ + 3Hg \rightarrow 2NO + 2R_2NH + 3Hg^{+2} + 2H_2O \qquad (73)$$

$$2R_2N\text{---}NO + 2H^+ + Hg \rightarrow 2NO + 2R_2NH + Hg^{+2} \qquad (74)$$

The volume of nitric oxide formed is measured in an assembly known as an azotometer or nitrometer. Although these procedures give fairly good results with explosive organic nitrates (nitroglycerin and nitrocellulose), difficulties have been reported with the N-nitroso and N-nitro compounds since these rearrange to C—NO$_2$ and C—NO groups which do not yield nitric oxide on reduction (see page 312).

4. Evolution and Absorption of Hydrogen. Compounds which were described in the preceding section as having reactive hydrogen and which yield methane with Grignard reagents also react in the same manner with lithium aluminum hydride to produce hydrogen:

$$4R\text{---}OH + LiAlH_4 \rightarrow 4H_2 + LiOR + Al(OR)_3 \qquad (75)$$

The hydrogen gas evolved is measured in an assembly described in experiment 40. Esters can be determined by first reducing them with excess of the hydride:

$$4R\text{---}COOR' + 2LiAlH_4 \rightarrow LiAl(OCH_2R)_4 + LiAl(OR')_4 \qquad (76)$$

Then alcohol is added to react with the excess of the reagent and the volume of hydrogen produced is measured. Since the carbonyl group in esters is reduced to the alcohol, the method can be applied to other carbonyl compounds. For this purpose, sodium borohydride has been found more suitable than lithium aluminum hydride which is very sensitive to moisture, oxygen, and carbon dioxide (see page 151).

Compounds which have unsaturated linkages are catalytically hydrogenated and the quantity of hydrogen required for saturation is measured either volumetrically or manometrically (see pages 368 and 372):

$$\begin{array}{c} \diagdown \\ \diagup \end{array}\!\!C\!\!=\!\!C\!\!\begin{array}{c} \diagdown \\ \diagup \end{array} + H_2 \xrightarrow{\text{catalyst}} \begin{array}{c} \diagdown \\ \diagup \end{array}\!\!CH\!\!-\!\!CH\!\!\begin{array}{c} \diagdown \\ \diagup \end{array} \qquad (77)$$

The choice of the catalyst is of importance since the hydrogenation is usually performed only slightly above the atmospheric pressure and complete reaction is required within a short period. Detailed directions for the preparation of palladium and nickel catalysts for microhydrogenation at atmospheric pressure have been published by one of the authors.[17] (see also pages 604–606).

As discussed in greater detail on page 367, catalytic hydrogenation is

[17] N. D. Cheronis, *Micro and Semimicro Methods*, Interscience, New York, 1954, pp. 239–241.

performed for analytical purposes more often on complex compounds containing unsaturated linkages than on unsaturated hydrocarbons. However, olefins, conjugated dienes, and polyenes are more readily hydrogenated than conjugated unsaturated acids and their derivatives.

Nitro compounds may be determined by catalytic hydrogenation (page 313):

$$R-NO_2 + 3H_2 \rightarrow RNH_2 + 2H_2O$$

Either palladium carbon or palladium in barium sulfate[18] may be used as a catalyst.

5. *Evolution of CO, CO₂, or O₂.* Acid anhydrides react with anhydrous oxalic acid in dry pyridine to produce carbon dioxide, carbon monoxide and a carboxylic acid:

$$(RCO)_2O + (COOH)_2 \xrightarrow{C_5H_5N} 2RCOOH + CO_2 + CO \tag{78}$$

The determination of the anhydride can be made either on the oxalic acid consumed[19] or on the gasometric measurement of the carbon dioxide and carbon monoxide produced.[20] For further discussion of this method, the reader is referred to page 112.

The decarboxylation of malonic acids, β-keto acids and related compounds at relatively low temperatures is well known. Further, many carboxylic acids are catalytically decarboxylated when heated in presence of quinoline and cupric carbonate.[21,22]

$$HO \cdot C_6H_4COOH \xrightarrow[\text{catalyst}]{\text{heat}} HOC_6H_5 + CO_2$$

The carbon dioxide liberated can be measured either through a gasometric apparatus or a gas chromatograph as described in experiment 44.

The determination of the sulfinic group by evolution and measurement of oxygen[23] is attended by many interferences. This reaction is cited as an example of the use of hydrogen peroxide as a reductant to produce oxygen:

$$3RSO_2H + KIO_3 + 2KI \rightarrow 3RSO_2I + 3KOH \tag{79}$$
$$RSO_2I + H_2O_2 + 2KOH \rightarrow O_2 + RSO_2K + KI + 2H_2O \tag{80}$$

This method is not applicable to micro quantities.

[18] H. Hörmann, J. Lamberts, and G. Fries, *Z. Physiol. Chem.*, **306**, 42 (1956).
[19] C. K. Rosenbaum and J. H. Walton, *J. Am. Chem. Soc.*, **52**, 3366 (1930).
[20] E. S. Whitford, *J. Am. Chem. Soc.*, **47**, 2939 (1925).
[21] M. H. Hubacher, *Anal. Chem.*, **21**, 945 (1949).
[22] T. S. Ma and C. T. Shang, unpublished data; see C. T. Shang, *Master's Thesis, Brooklyn College*, 1961.
[23] S. Krishna and A. B. Das, *J. Indian Chem. Soc.*, **4**, 367 (1927).

VI. Formation of Precipitates

Table 3.8 gives a summary of the organic functions which may be estimated by means of gravimetric methods. Inspection of column 2 of Table

TABLE 3.8

Summary of Determination of Organic Functions Based on Precipitation Reactions

Function	Reaction for separation of solid phase
Acid halide	Formation of silver halide
Alkimino	Formation of alkyl iodide followed by determ. of AgI
Alkoxyl	Formation of alkyl iodide followed by determ. of AgI
Alkene	Formation of complex with $OsO_4 + C_5H_5N$
Amine and amine salt	Formation of tetraphenylborates
Carbonyl	Formation of derivatives with: (a) 2,4-DNPH[a]; (b) methone; (c) bisulfite; (d) amines → Schiff's bases
Carboxyl	Sparingly soluble salts
Heterocyclic N-base	Formation of halides, perchlorates, oxalates, picrolonates, tetraphenylborates, tungstosilicates
Methylene ether	Formation of precipitate as formaldehyde + phloroglucinol
Phenol	Formation of 2,4-dinitrophenyl ethers
Sulfonic acid	Formation of salts with Ag^+, Ba^{+2}, and Hg^{+2}
Sulfonamide	Formation of salts with Ag^+

[a] 2,4-Dinitrophenylhydrazine.

3.8 discloses that the precipitates may be classified under the following categories: (a) inorganic precipitates, most of which are silver halides; (b) metal salts of carboxylic and sulfonic acids; (c) well-defined salts of amines such as tetraphenylborates and of heterocyclic bases such as the halides, perchlorates, and the like; (d) sparingly soluble derivatives such as the 2,4-dinitrophenylhydrazones and methone derivatives formed by carbonyl compounds; (e) complexes and chelates.

In general, for micro and semimicro quantities, gravimetric procedures are not recommended unless other alternative methods have poor precision and accuracy. The chief difficulty of gravimetric procedures as applied to micro and semimicro quantities of sample is the losses involved by adsorption on the walls of the vessels and in transfer. Although most of these can be overcome by proper techniques which minimize the losses as illustrated in experiments 7, 25, and 26, such techniques entail care and manipulation which are acquired only by considerable practice.

A. Inorganic Precipitates. The formation of inorganic precipitates in the determination of organic functions differs in some respects from the well-known heterogeneous ionic equilibria when only inorganic ions are present. There are two important factors that must be considered: one is that the functional group X which is attached to the organic radical R— by a partially ionic covalent bond must be completely cleaved. The second factor is that the conditions of formation of the precipitate should be controlled so that no adsorption of organic substances on the precipitate takes place. Two examples will illustrate that often when both gravimetric and volumetric procedures are available for the determination of the same function, the latter is usually preferred.

The halogen content of an acid halide RCOX may be determined argentimetrically either by a gravimetric or a volumetric procedure:

$$RCOX + Ag^+ \rightarrow AgX + RCO^+ \tag{81}$$

However, acid halides can also be titrated either in a nonaqueous or aqueous medium:

$$RCOX + NaOCH_3 \rightarrow RCOOCH_3 + NaX \tag{82}$$
$$RCOX + 2NaOH \rightarrow RCOONa + NaX + H_2O \tag{83}$$

Considering the methods shown in equations 81–83, it is obvious that in all three methods the presence of halogen acid in the acid halide sample will constitute an interference; however, the presence of free carboxylic acid will be titrated in equations 82 and 83, but most likely will not be an interference in equation 81 unless the carboxylic acid forms a sparingly soluble silver salt. But when consideration is given to the time required for the determination by each procedure and the operational losses with samples of a few milligrams, one of the titrimetric procedures will most likely be chosen.

In the determination of the alkoxyl groups an alkyl iodide is formed by the cleavage with hydriodic acid which after separation from the reaction mixture is analyzed for iodine either by gravimetric or titrimetric procedure. Pregl devised the elegant gravimetric procedure[24] by absorbing the alkyl iodide in alcoholic silver nitrate solution to form silver iodide, then filtering, drying, and weighing the precipitate. However, it was observed by Friedrich[25] that the precipitation of silver iodide from alcoholic silver nitrate solution is incomplete and proposed a correction factor of 0.06–0.07 mg. for each milliliter of silver nitrate solution placed in the receiver. This correction factor was accepted by Pregl and his followers. However, the application of the correction, irrespective of the weight of the silver iodide obtained, affects the precision and accuracy of the alkoxyl determination.

[24] F. Pregl, *Die Quantitative organische Mikroanalyse*, 3rd ed., Springer, Berlin, 1930, p. 201.
[25] H. Friedrich, *Z. Physiol. Chem.*, **163**, 141 (1927).

The titrimetric procedure based on the oxidation of the alkyl iodide by bromine to yield iodic acid (see page 137) is usually preferred. The main reason for the application of the correction factor is not loss in manipulation and transfer of the silver iodide formed but incomplete cleavage of the alkyl halide and formation of silver iodide since this involves the following steps:

$$RI + 2AgNO_3 \xrightarrow{C_2H_5OH} AgI \cdot AgNO_3 + RNO_3 \qquad (84)$$

$$AgI \cdot AgNO_3 \xrightarrow[H_2O + HNO_3]{\text{digestion}} AgI + AgNO_3 \qquad (85)$$

The double salt which is first formed is decomposed by digestion with water and nitric acid.

B. Metal Salts of Carboxylic and Sulfonic Acids.   Many carboxylic acids, particularly those of high molecular weight, form sparingly soluble salts with Pb^{+2}, Mg^{+2}, Ca^{+2}, Ba^{+2}, and Ag^+ ions. Similarly many sulfonic acids form sparingly soluble salts with Ba^{+2}, Hg^{+2}, and Ag^+ ions. There are three factors which should be taken into consideration for a successful gravimetric determination. The first is that the solubility of the sparingly soluble salt should be known fairly accurately; the second is that the sample should not contain interfering anions; the third that the metal salt should be stable at the temperature of drying (usually 105–110°C). The last condition excludes many silver salts which decompose with explosive violence when heated. Finally, care must be exercised in the formation and coagulation of a precipitate that is readily filtered.

C. Salts of Amines and Heterocyclic Bases.   Of the sparingly soluble salts formed by amines and N-heterocyclic bases the tetraphenylborates have recently been extensively used for the gravimetric determination; a review of this application has been published by Flaschka and Barnard[26] who list about 35 references on the gravimetric determination of amines and N-heterocyclic bases as tetraphenylborates. The formation of these sparingly soluble salts takes place upon addition of sodium or lithium tetraphenylboron to an acid solution of the amine:

$$RNH_3^+ + B(C_6H_5)_4^- \rightarrow RNH_3 \cdot B(C_6H_5)_4 \qquad (86)$$

Similar equations may be written for secondary and tertiary amines and quaternary ammonium compounds. The solubility of a number of

[26] H. Flaschka and A. J. Barnard, Jr., Tetraphenylboron as an Analytical Reagent in *Advances in Analytical Chemistry and Instrumentation*, Vol. 1, C. N. Reilly, ed., Interscience, New York, 1960, pp. 87–98.

organic tetraphenylborates has been determined. The solubility of the salts of C_1 to C_4 alkylamines is in the range of 36×10^{-4} mg./l., for methylamine, to 11×10^{-4} mg./l. The optimum pH's for precipitation are 2–6 from warm buffered solutions and conditions must be chosen to coagulate the voluminous precipitates before filtration. A drying temperature below 100°C is recommended where no reliable information exists as to the thermal stability of the salts because generally the thermal stability is low. Interfering inorganic ions are NH_4^+ and K^+ and interfering organic ions are the tetraryl onium compounds of P, As, Sb, Bi and in general most onium organic ions including diazonium.

D. Sparingly Soluble Derivatives. From the large number of derivatives formed by organic functions only a few can be selected for their quantitative determination by gravimetric procedures. This is due to the fact that most derivatives have appreciable solubilities in the solvent systems employed for their formation and also because the conversion of a particular organic compound to a well-defined derivative is seldom quantitative. Among the few that have been found suitable are the 2,4-dinitrophenyl ethers formed by reaction of phenols with 2,4-dinitrochlorobenzene or 2,4-dinitrofluorobenzene:

$$ArONa + FC_6H_3(NO_2)_2 \rightarrow ArOC_6H_3(NO_2)_2 + NaF \tag{87}$$

and the 2,4-dinitrophenylhydrazones and methone derivatives formed by carbonyl compounds:

$$R_2C{=}O + H_2NNHC_6H_3(NO_2)_2 \rightarrow R_2C{=}NNHC_6H_3(NO_2)_2 + H_2O \tag{88}$$

Methone (dimethylcyclohexadione) reacts only with aldehydes. Of lesser importance as derivatives suitable for gravimetric estimation of aldehydes are the bisulfite addition products and the formation of a Schiff's base by reaction with an amine.

The formation of 2,4-dinitrophenyl ethers is quantitative with 2,4-dinitrofluorobenzene in presence of sodium bicarbonate without heating while reaction with 2,4-dinitrochlorobenzene requires heating. The interferences are amines and amino acids and amides.

The determination of carbonyl groups by reaction with 2,4-dinitrophenylhydrazine has been extensively investigated and is discussed in detail on pages 144–146. The determination involves either the gravimetric procedure of filtering and weighing the derivative or determining the unreacted hydrazine titrimetrically. In this case the microgravimetric procedure is superior to titrimetric method because the substituted hydrazine reagent is unstable and requires frequent standardization. The gravimetric procedure is described in experiment 7. The interfering organic compounds are those which oxidize the reagent (forming tarry products) and those which yield carbonyl functions on hydrolysis (acetals and ketals).

E. Complexes and Chelates. As shown in Table 3.8 the number of organic functions which are determined by the formation of complexes or chelates with metallic ions gravimetrically is rather small. Alkene linkages may be determined gravimetrically by the formation of a complex with osmium tetroxide and pyridine. Also alkynes can be determined by the formation of the silver acetylide complex (page 385):

$$RC{\equiv}CH + Ag^+ \rightarrow RC{\equiv}CAg + H^+ \tag{89}$$

Due to the instability of this complex the preferred method is to react the alkyne with silver perchlorate to form a silver acetylide-silver perchlorate complex and determine the perchloric acid liberated by nonaqueous titration (see page 527):

$$RC{\equiv}CH + 2AgClO_4 \rightarrow RC{\equiv}CAg{\cdot}AgClO_4 + HClO_4 \tag{90}$$

Though gravimetric determinations of organic functions based on formation of complexes and chelates are limited, the general application of metal ion complexes and chelates is of importance to colorimetric determinations which are discussed in the following section and also on the qualitative detection and quantitative estimation of a large number of inorganic cations.[27-30a] Therefore, a brief discussion will be given on their general nature and conditions of formation and stability.

When a metallic cation, Me^{++} combines with molecules that can donate electrons, the resulting ion is called a complex ion (eq. 91):

$$Cu^{++} + 4R{-}NH_2 \rightarrow R{-}N : Cu^{++} : N{-}R \qquad {\cdot}(91)$$

When the organic molecule has two or more electron donor groups, the resulting complex is called a *chelate*. One of the best known examples of chelate formation is the reaction of Ni^{+2} ions with dimethylglyoxime:

[27] F. J. Welcher, *Organic Analytical Reagents*, Van Nostrand, New York, 1947.
[28] F. Feigl, *Spot Tests in Inorganic Analysis*, 5th ed., Elsevier, Amsterdam, 1958.
[29] G. Schwarzenbach, *Compleximetric Titrations*, Interscience, New York, 1957.
[30] H. A. Flaschka, *EDTA Titrations*, Pergamon, London, 1959.
[30a] R. Pribil, *Komplexometrie*, Verlag f. Grundstoffindustrie, Leipzig, 1960.

Generally organic compounds which form complexes or chelates have at least one of each of the following two types of functions: (a) proton accepting functions: $-NH_2$, $-RNH$, $-R_2N$, $=N-$, $-N=O$, $C=O$, and $C=S$; (b) proton donating functions: $-COOH$, $-OH$, $=NOH$, $=NH$, and $-SH$. Other requirements for stable ring formation are the proper bulk of the organic groups and the proper radius of the metallic ion. For example, five- or six-membered rings have the greatest ease of formation which indicates that the functions enumerated above if they are in ortho positions in aromatic compounds have a greater possibility to form metal chelates than if they are in meta or para positions.

A general idea of the stability and optimum conditions of formation of complexes and chelates is obtained by consideration of the lower limits of detection of inorganic cations by means of organic reagents. In most cases these are in the range of a few micrograms per milliliter and in some cases in the range of 0.1 $\mu g./ml$. Also it is well known that pH has an important effect on the formation of the colored complexes and chelates used in the detection and estimation of inorganic cations. The reverse procedure of using metallic ions to form complexes and chelates in order to estimate organic functions is governed by the same principles. Although an excess of the metallic ion may be used, the pH must be controlled within certain limits; otherwise the reaction is not quantitative or does not take place. This is illustrated in the following section of the discussion of the ferric hydroxamate complex.

VII. Formation of Colored Products

Table 3.9 gives a partial summary of organic functions which are determined by formation of a colored product which may be either a relatively simple substance (as in the case of nitration of phenols), a colored complex or chelate, or in some instances, a colored product of unknown composition. Although procedures based on the formation of colored products of unknown composition are not desirable, still they are useful in the absence of other methods, particularly when the precision and accuracy of the method

TABLE 3.9

Summary of Determination of Organic Function by Colorimetry

Function	Reaction for formation of colored product
Acid anhydride	(a) Formation of hydroxamate complex; (b) reaction with diazotized amines
Acid halide	Formation of hydroxamate complex
Aldehyde	(a) Reaction with Schiff's reagent; (b) specific for formaldehyde: reaction with chromotropic acid
Alkyl nitrate	Reaction with phenols → nitrophenols
Amine (1°, 2°)	(a) Reaction with diazonium salts
	(b) Reaction with carbonyl compounds → Schiff's bases
α-Amino acid	Reaction with ninhydrin
Carbonyl	Reaction with (a) 2,4-DNPH; (b) amines → Schiff's bases; (c) phloroglucinol and other compounds
Carboxyl	Conversion to acid chloride followed by formation of hydroxamate complex
Diazonium salt	Coupling with arylamines
Ester	Formation of ferric hydroxamate complex
Heterocyclic-N bases	Colored complexes with various reagents
α-Hydroxycarbonyl and carbohydrate	(a) Colored complexes with copper ions and phosphotungstic or phosphomolybdic acid; (b) formation of colored formazans with tetrazolium salts
Isocyanates	Reaction with hydroxylamine → hydroxamate complex
Mercapto (thiol)	Reaction with phosphotungstic acid or nitrous acid, or sodium nitroprusside and other reagents
Methylene ether	Hydrolysis followed by colorimetry of formaldehyde with chromotropic acid
Methylol	Periodic oxidation followed by colorimetry of formaldehyde with chromotropic acid
Peroxy	Reaction with pertitanate, or with leuco methylene blue
Quinone	Formation of colored compounds with amines and other reagents
Phenol	Reaction with diazonium salts or phosphomolybdic acid or xanthydrol and other reagents (see Table 11-9)
Sulfonamide	Diazotization followed by coupling
Thiocyanates	Hydrolysis → cyanide followed by picric acid
Thiourea	Reaction with sodium nitroprusside, Nessler's and other reagents

has been thoroughly tested and found satisfactory. For example, the exact nature of the reaction between formaldehyde and chromotropic acid (1,8-dihydroxynaphthalene–3,6-disulfonic acid) is not known although it is assumed to be analogous to phenol-formaldehyde condensation followed by oxidation of the condensation product to a quinoid compound. However, the color intensity of the reaction mixture measured photometrically can be shown to be proportional to the concentration of formaldehyde under specified conditions, and in addition, the color is not formed by other carbonyl compounds. The detailed procedure is described on pages 506–507.

Inspection of Table 3.9 shows that the estimation of a number of functions is based directly or indirectly on the formation of the ferric hydroxamate complex. Among these are esters, carboxylic acids, acid halides and anhydrides, alcohols, and isocyanates. In addition, the ferric hydroxamate reaction has been reported[31-35] to be given directly or indirectly by amides, aldehydes, ethers, imides, ketenes, lactams, nitriles, nitro and nitroso compounds, oximes, sulfonic acids, and some trihalomethyl compounds. Some of these groups can be distinguished from one another by using an appropriate modification. For example, only esters and acid anhydrides and halides react at alkaline pH, but only the latter two groups react at neutral pH. Therefore, the formation of this colored complex has been selected for detailed discussion.

The general steps of the reaction leading to the formation of the ferric hydroxamate complex are shown in equations 92–96:

$$[NH_2OH_2]^+Cl^- + OH^- \rightarrow NH_2OH + H_2O + Cl^- \tag{92}$$
$$NH_2OH + OH^- \rightarrow NH_2O^- + H_2O \tag{93}$$
$$NH_2O^- + RCOOR' \rightarrow RCONHO^- + R'OH \tag{94}$$
$$RCONHO^- + H_3O^+ \rightarrow RCONHOH + H_2O \tag{95}$$
$$3RCONHOH + 3H_2O + Fe^{+3} \rightleftarrows Fe(RCONHO)_3 + 3H_3O^+ \tag{96}$$
$$\text{red to violet}$$

The mechanism of the reaction can be assumed to be analogous to the well-known, base-catalyzed hydrolysis of esters and such nucleophilic displacement can explain a number of facts about the rates of formate esters as compared to the acetates.

The most probable structure of the ferric hydroxamate complex is the metal ion chelate shown in the following formula proposed by Werner:

Ferric hydroxamate complex

[31] F. Feigl and V. Anger, *Mikrochemie*, **15**, 9 (1934).
[32] D. J. Davidson, *J. Chem. Educ.*, **17**, 81 (1940).
[33] H. L. Yale, *Chem. Revs.*, **33**, 209 (1943).
[34] R. E. Buckles and C. J. Thelen, *Anal. Chem.*, **22**, 676 (1950).
[35] S. Soloway and A. Lipschitz, *Anal. Chem.*, **24**, 898 (1952).

The influence of such factors as pH, concentration of the reactants, temperature, and the effect of substituents on esters have been studied by Goddu et al.,[36] Hestrin,[37] Bergmann,[38] Wollish and Schmall,[39] and Goldenberg and Spoerri.[40] A large molar excess of hydroxylamine is required for a rapid and complete reaction. In aqueous solutions a maximum color yield is obtained at 8°C but for best reproducible result room temperature is used. In nonaqueous solvents the reaction is slow and higher temperatures must be used for a short period, since prolonged heating causes decomposition of the hydroxamate. The two most important factors for the formation and stability of the complex are pH and the excess of ferric ion used.

In the initial stages of the reaction leading to the formation of hydroxamic acid an optimum pH between 9 and 13 is required. Above pH 13 the alkaline hydrolysis of the ester proceeds at an appreciable rate. After the formation of the hydroxamate ions (eq. 94) the solution is acidified and ferric ions are added in excess to produce the colored complex. A considerable molar excess of ferric ion concentration is required for attainment of maximum color yield, but the blank values also increase, limiting the accuracy of determination of small quantities. The pH of the final solution has a profound effect; it has been shown[41,42] that there are three possible colored complexes depending on the pH of the final solution as shown in equation 97.

$$\text{Fe(RCONHO)}_3 \underset{I}{\overset{H_3O^+}{\rightleftarrows}} \text{Fe(RCONHO)}_2{}^+ \underset{II}{\overset{H_3O^+}{\rightleftarrows}} \text{Fe(RCONHO)}^{+2} \underset{III}{\overset{H_3O^+}{\rightleftarrows}} \text{RCONHOH} \quad (97)$$

$$\underset{\text{RCONHOH}}{+} \qquad \underset{\text{RCONHOH}}{+} \qquad \underset{\text{Fe}^{+3}}{+}$$

As shown by equation 97, a very high acidity will inhibit the formation of the complex and favor the existence of free hydroxamic acid, IV. Structure I is reddish brown and is formed at weakly alkaline solutions; structure II is cherry red and is formed at weakly acidic solutions while structure III is red-violet with an absorption maximum at 520–540 mμ., is formed at relatively strongly acidic solutions (pH 1–3), has the greatest stability of the three, and is the preferred complex. These relationships explain the discrepancies in the literature with respect to the maximum absorptivity of the hydroxamate complex produced by the same ester or carboxylic acid.

[36] R. F. Goddu, N. F. Le Blanc, and C. M. Wright, *Anal. Chem.*, **27**, 1251 (1955).
[37] S. J. Hestrin, *J. Biol. Chem.*, **180**, 249 (1949).
[38] F. Bergmann, *Anal. Chem.*, **24**, 1367 (1952).
[39] E. G. Wollish and M. S. Schmall, *Anal. Chem.*, **22**, 1033 (1950).
[40] V. Goldenberg and P. E. Spoerri, *Anal. Chem.*, **30**, 1327 (1958).
[41] E. Bayer and K. H. Reuther, *Berichte*, **89**, 2541 (1956).
[42] G. Atsnes, *Acta Chem. Scand.*, **11**, 710 (1957).

The lower limits of detection and estimation of esters were investigated by Fleisher and Cheronis,[43] using spectrophotometric measurements at 540 mμ. For the range of 90 μg. to about 10 μg. or 10^{-1} to 10^{-3} M, Beer's law relationships were found to hold. Below this range (10^{-3} M), large positive and negative fluctuations in optical density were observed and at 10^{-5} M no evidence of complex formation was found.

The preceding discussion indicates that metal cation complexes or chelates are produced in steps and that the formation, composition, and stability varies with the pH of the reaction mixture. In general, all colorimetric determinations should be studied with samples of the pure compound being sought in order to determine the optimum conditions unless extensive information is available in the literature.

[43] D. Fleisher and N. D. Cheronis, unpublished data.

4

Influence of Molecular Structure
on the Reactions Employed
for the Analysis
of Organic Compounds

I. General

The determination of a functional group X in an organic compound RX by means of a reaction with a reagent AY will be discussed in great detail in order to point out first the ideal conditions from the point of view of the analyst and then to discuss the limitations imposed by the molecular structure of organic compounds and the nature of organic reactions.

The reaction of the pure compound RX and the reagent AY may be written as:

$$RX + AY \rightleftarrows RY + AX \tag{1}$$

However, aside from this desired equilibrium, there are in practically all organic reactions several possible equilibria, which are usually designated as "side reactions." Thus, AY or RX may react with one of the products or RX may undergo decomposition, condensation, and polymerization or both products may undergo further reactions.

For example, let us assume that it is desired to estimate the epoxy function by the addition of a halogen acid:

$$\tag{2}$$

The hydroxyl group of the halohydrin formed has feebly acidic properties and the halogen atom of the halohydrin is also relatively unreactive; hence, the reaction can be followed by measuring either the decrease in acidity or the decrease in the concentration of the halide ions. Consideration of the reaction shown in equation 2 indicates at least two possible side reactions. The acid HX may react further with the halohydrin formed as shown in equation 3:

$$
\underset{\underset{\text{OH}}{|}}{\overset{\diagdown}{\text{C}}}\!\!-\!\!\underset{\underset{\text{X}}{|}}{\overset{\diagup}{\text{C}}} + \text{HX} \rightarrow \underset{\underset{\text{X}}{|}}{\overset{\diagdown}{\text{C}}}\!\!-\!\!\underset{\underset{\text{X}}{|}}{\overset{\diagup}{\text{C}}} + \text{H}_2\text{O} \tag{3}
$$

and the epoxide molecules may polymerize as shown in equation 4:

$$
x \,\, \overset{\diagdown}{\text{C}}\!\!-\!\!\overset{\diagup}{\underset{\diagdown_{\text{O}}\diagup}{\text{C}}} \rightarrow \left[-\overset{|}{\underset{|}{\text{C}}}\!-\!\overset{|}{\underset{|}{\text{C}}}\!-\!\text{O} \right]_x \tag{4}
$$

Indeed both of these side reactions do take place and the successful analysis of the epoxy compound by a procedure which employs the reaction shown in equation 2 depends on the choice of conditions under which the rate of the addition of the halogen acid is extremely rapid, while the rates of the reactions shown in equations 3 and 4 are very slow. Thus, the use of this method with styrene oxide gives quantitative yield of the chlorohydrin with $0.1N$ hydrochloric acid but incomplete reaction with $0.05N$ and $0.01N$ acid. Generally, *if the reaction of $RX + AY$ is thermodynamically feasible the direction is decided primarily by the laws of kinetics.*

Returning to equation 1 we can express the equilibrium of the desired direction as:

$$RX + AY \rightleftarrows RY + AX$$

and at equilibrium,

$$\frac{[RY][AX]}{[RX][AY]} = K_{eq.} \tag{5}$$

The ideal conditions from the analytical objective are that: (a) one or both of the products, RY and AX, should be measurable by means of titrimetry, gravimetry, gasometry, colorimetry, potentiometry, or physical methods (if this is not feasible then it should be possible to use an excess of reagent AY and measure the unconsumed quantity); (b) the rate at which equilibrium is reached in equation 5 is rapid and, if possible, instantaneous; (c) if the rate is slow then heat or catalysts or both should accelerate it so that the reaction attains equilibrium in less than one half hour; (d) the reaction has proceeded to completion when it reaches equilibrium or the equilibrium constant (which expresses the ratio of the product to the reactant) should be as large as possible (100 or larger); (e) if the condition set forth in (d) is not realized, then it should be possible to alter the conditions so as to displace the equilibrium rightwards; and finally (f) the reaction expressed in equation 5 should not have other competing equilibria or, in other words, be free from "side reactions."

In practice not all of the ideal conditions can be realized due to the nature of organic molecules and their reactions. It is possible by judicious selection of the reagent AY to satisfy condition (a) and to a certain extent (b). Most organic reactions proceed at slow rates and heat and catalysts are often employed to accelerate the reaction rates. Moreover, although there are only scant data on equilibrium constants of organic reactions, a vast knowledge of preparative data indicates that the equilibrium yield of the desired product in most organic reactions seldom approaches 100%, even when changes in concentration and choice of conditions are made to shift the equilibrium in equation 5 as far to the right as possible. Finally, as previously stated, in most organic reactions there are several competing equilibria and in order to obtain stoichiometry in equation 5 all side reactions must be suppressed as far as possible. Therefore, the selection of the reagent and the conditions requires consideration of the rates, equilibria, and other factors for attaining the desirable yield. Finally, attention should be given to interfering substances, that is, the presence of other organic compounds which may react with the reagent or the products.

II. Selection of the Analytical Reagents

As an example for the discussion of the problems involved in the selection of analytical reagents, the determination of the carbonyl group, $=CO$, in aldehydes and ketones will be considered.

Examination of the reactions of the carbonyl group indicates that they fall into three categories:

(1) addition reactions with or without elimination;

(2) reduction of the carbonyl to an alcohol or oxidation to a carboxyl group;

(3) condensation reactions.

Of these, the first two appear suitable at first glance to organic analysis. A detailed survey of the analytical procedures employed in the determination of aldehydes and ketones has been published by Mitchell[1] and covers the voluminous literature that has been published up to 1951. An extensive discussion is given in Section VII of Chapter 6.

The oxidation procedure is beset with difficulties since more than one product is formed and this renders the reaction unsuitable for quantitative estimation (see page 153). Reductive procedures are useful with some compounds, but not with others (see page 151). By far, the methods which are applicable to a large number of carbonyl compounds are those that

---

[1] J. Mitchell, Jr., in *Organic Analysis*, Vol. 1, Interscience, New York, 1953, p. 243.

depend on addition of a basic reagent, H_2B, to the carbonyl group, $=CO$, without or with elimination:

$$\begin{array}{l} R \\ \diagdown \\ CO + H_2B \rightleftarrows \\ \diagup \\ R' \end{array} \qquad \begin{array}{l} R \\ \diagdown \\ C\!\!-\!\!OH \\ \diagup\;| \\ R'\;BH \end{array} \qquad (6)$$

$$\begin{array}{cc} R \quad OH \\ \diagdown\;\diagup \\ C \\ \diagup\;\diagdown \\ R'\quad BH \end{array} \rightleftarrows \begin{array}{l} R \\ \diagdown \\ C\!\!=\!\!B + H_2O \\ \diagup \\ R' \end{array} \qquad (7)$$

The use of bisulfite and Grignard reagents is similiar to reactions shown by equation 6, and the use of hydroxylamine, hydrazine, and substituted hydrazines are examples of reactions shown by equation 7. The methods are summarized more specifically in equations 8–13[2]:

$$RCHO + NaHSO_3 + H_2O \rightleftarrows R\!\!-\!\!\underset{\underset{OH}{|}}{C}HSO_3Na \qquad (8)$$

$$RCHO + Na_2SO_3 + H_2SO_4 \rightleftarrows R\underset{\underset{OH}{|}}{C}HSO_3Na + NaHSO_4 \qquad (9)$$

$$R_2C\!\!=\!\!O + CH_3MgI \rightleftarrows R_2\underset{\underset{CH_3}{|}}{C}\!\!-\!\!OMgI \qquad (10)$$

$$R_2C\!\!=\!\!O + H_2NNHC_6H_3(NO_2)_2 \rightleftarrows R_2C\!\!=\!\!NNHC_6H_3(NO_2)_2 + H_2O \qquad (11)$$

$$R_2C\!\!=\!\!O + H_2NOH\!\!-\!\!HCl \rightleftarrows R_2C\!\!=\!\!NOH + H_2O + HCl \qquad (12)$$

$$RCHO + R'NH_2 \rightleftarrows RCH\!\!=\!\!NHR' + H_2O \qquad (13)$$

Equations 8 and 9 represent the addition of bisulfite; in reaction 8, the measurable product (hydroxyl ion) is estimated by titration with $0.5N$ acid; in reaction 9, the residual acid is measured after formation of the addition product. Also a variation of this reaction is to carry the addition of bisulfite at pH 7.0 and measure the unreacted reagent iodometrically. In reaction 10, the excess of a Grignard reagent is measured gasometrically by its conversion to methane; in reaction 11, the hydrazone produced or the amount of reagent consumed by the sample may be measured in several ways (gravimetric, titrimetric, gasometric); in reaction 12, the usual procedure is to measure the free acid formed. Reaction 13 represents the formation of a Schiff's base by aldehydes, the unreacted amine being determined by nonaqueous titration.

The selection of the most suitable reagent (eqs. 8–13) for the determina-

---

[2] For bibliographical references to these reactions see pages 142–149.

tion of a particular carbonyl compound is made after a literature search of the methods which have been used either for the carbonyl compound under consideration or closely related carbonyl compounds. Attention should be given to the reaction rate data and equilibrium constants, particularly as it is related to the concentration of the compound sought in the sample. For example, if the compound to be determined is formaldehyde and the sample is an aqueous solution of 5–10 ml. containing approximately 0.1–0.01 mg. of the aldehyde, none of the reagents shown in equations 8–13 will be found suitable since formaldehyde at this concentration fails to give a stoichiometric relation with any of the reagents listed in equations 8–13. However, examination of the literature (see page 157) will indicate that the colorimetric procedure based on the reaction of formaldehyde with 1,8-dihydroxynaphthalene-3,6-disulfonic acid gives good precision and accuracy.

When no information is found in the literature the best procedure is to use a pure sample of the compound sought (or a closely related homolog) and try several reagents and select the one that *reacts most rapidly and completely and gives a stoichiometric relation.* In such a selection the influence of the radical R attached to the functional group is of considerable importance because in most cases it determines the rate at which the functional group reacts, and also the value of the equilibrium constant.

III. Effect of the Radical on the Reactivity of the Functional Group

The influence of the radical R on the reactivity of the functional group —X is such that no single analytical procedure can be applied for its quantitative estimation in all members of the homologous series in which —X occurs. As shown in equations 1 and 5 the basis of all chemical quantitative estimations is the cleavage of the R—X bond by means of an appropriate reagent. However, the strength of the bond depends not only on the nature of X, but also on the radical R. Rate studies and equilibrium constants of the reaction RX + AY (or of closely related reactions) are very useful in providing information as to whether such a reaction is useful for analytical purposes. For example, the data of Conant and Bartlett[3] on semicarbazone formation may be used to estimate the formation constants for analogous reactions such as hydrazones (eq. 11) and oximes (eq. 12). However, such data should be used with extreme caution since equilibrium constant obtained in an aqueous system with reagent AY may not hold in a different

[3] J. B. Conant and P. D. Bartlett, *J. Am. Chem. Soc.*, **54**, 2881 (1932).

solvent system with a reagent BY. For example, the formation constant of acetaldehyde semicarbazone in water solutions at 25°C is approximately 100 times larger than that of acetone and cyclohexanone. Contrastingly, Cheronis and Levey[4] in studying the formation of 2,4-dinitrophenylhydrazones in methanol at 55°C found the reverse to be true. Further, it has been shown by Veibel and Andersen[5] that stoichiometric relations are not possible in the formation of the 2,4-dinitrophenylcarbazones of many carbonyl compounds as, for example, salicylaldehyde and formaldehyde. The latter also failed to yield a semicarbazone, and attempts to catalyze the reaction by changing the pH resulted in a polycondensation product.[6]

The influence of the radical on the reactivity of the functional group will be illustrated by consideration of the problems involved in the estimation of acyl and amino groups.

The general method for the estimation of the acyl function, R—CO—, when it is joined to an alkoxyl (as in esters, RCOOR′) or to an alkimino (as in amides and substituted amides, R—CONR₂′, R′ = H, alkyl, or aryl) is hydrolysis:

$$RCOOR' + H_2O \rightleftarrows R\text{—}COOH + R'OH \tag{14}$$
$$RCONR_2' + H_2O \rightleftarrows R\text{—}COOH + R_2'NH \tag{15}$$

The carboxylic acid R—COOH resulting from the hydrolytic cleavage may be determined by several methods. However, the precision and accuracy of any procedure depends primarily on the hydrolysis rates and the equilibrium constants under the conditions of the analytical procedure.

If we consider the acyl chlorides R—COCl, esters R—COOR′, the amides R—CONH₂ and substituted amides R—CONHR′, we know from the general behavior of these four related groups of compounds that most acyl halides hydrolyze rapidly at room temperature and the reaction proceeds to completion and that esters react at slow rates but at appreciable rates in the presence of catalysts. There is a fair amount of information on equilibrium constants for the hydrolysis of esters which indicate that the reaction at equilibrium does not proceed to completion and hence, basic catalysis is often employed which, besides increasing the rate, also increases the value of K_{eq}. The small amount of information available on amides indicates that their rates of hydrolysis are very slow as compared with those of esters and that the rates diminish as the complexity of R in RCONH₂ increases.

From the available information it can be predicted that if the acyl

[4] N. D. Cheronis and V. Levey, *Microchem. J.*, **1**, 230 (1957).

[5] S. Veibel and I. G. K. Andersen, *Anal. Chim. Acta*, **14**, 320 (1956).

[6] N. D. Cheronis and J. B. Entrikin, *Semimicro Qualitative Organic Analysis*, 2nd ed., Interscience, New York, 1957, p. 393.

function is acetyl, $CH_3CO—$, the O-acetyl compounds will hydrolyze readily at appreciable rates and that it is possible to develop an analytical procedure at room temperature while the N-acetyl compounds will hydrolyze at slow rates even with acid or base catalysis and heating.

An analytical procedure of O-acetyl compounds based on shaking the sample with $0.01N$ sodium hydroxide solution has been published.[7] The hydrolysis of relatively simple and substituted amides requires heating in presence of acidic or basic substances for at least one hour or more. Fatty acid amides (R=10–18 carbon atoms) are not quantitatively hydrolyzed by refluxing with alcoholic solutions of sodium hydroxide but require heating at the boiling point of ethylene glycol.[8] Although most N-acetyl linkages are hydrolyzed by heating at 80–100°C for 3 hours with acidic and basic catalysts, wide variations occur depending on the nature of the radical. For example, if a procedure is standardized with acetanilide to 0.4–0.5% accuracy, an error of about 3–5% or more is introduced when the identical procedure is used with p-hydroxyacetanilide,[9] and the error is nearly 10% if p-aminophenyl acetate is used. Hence, the application of a general analytical procedure for the estimation of acetyl function requires consideration of the radical attached to the acetyl group. This is further discussed in Section V of Chapter 6.

The estimation of the amino group, $—NH_2$, offers another example of the differences in its reactivity as a result of the radical attached to it. The differences in strength of alkylamines and arylamines (Table 3.4) indicate that any general acidimetric method must take the K_b's into consideration in order to determine whether to apply either aqueous or nonaqueous titration. The same reservation applies to the older gravimetric procedures based on the precipitation of chloroplatinates and perchlorates or mercury salts of the bases. Similarly the evolution of nitrogen on treatment with nitrous acid (Van Slyke method) can be applied to some amines, but not to others. Acetylation with acetic anhydride and measurement of the acetic acid formed or of the unchanged anhydride gives an accuracy of 0.5–1% for many amines, but errors of 10–20% for others.

The same variation in reaction rates due to the radical attached to the amino group is shown in the formation of azomethines (Schiff's bases):

$$—NH_2 + O{=}CR_2 \rightarrow —N{=}CR_2 + H_2O \tag{16}$$

Studies with chloro- or bromosalicylaldehyde[10] gave quantitative results

---

[7] J. F. Alicino, *Anal. Chem.*, **20**, 590 (1948).

[8] S. Olsen, *Die Chemie*, **56**, 202 (1943).

[9] N. D. Cheronis, *Micro and semimicro methods*, Interscience, New York, 1954, p. 547.

[10] T. Tsukamoto and K. Yuhi, *J. Pharm. Soc. Japan*, **78**, 706 (1958).

with arylamines using 10–30 minutes of heating and incomplete reaction with alkylamines after heating for 2–3 hours.

A large number of examples of the influence of the organic radicals on the reactivity of the functional groups attached to them will be found in Chapters 7–11 which deal with a critical discussion of the analytical methods that have been published for the determination of the various organic functions. Of interest in the present discussion is the well-known influence of neighboring groups. For example, proximity of the hydroxyl (OH) to the carbonyl ($=CO$) does not interfere with the determination of the former by the procedure outlined in Section IV of Chapter 7; however, the estimation of the carbonyl function is profoundly affected by the proximity of hydroxyl groups since it cannot be determined by oximation, hydrazone formation, or addition of bisulfite. Another illustration of the effect of neighboring groups as it applies to analytical procedures is the action of some of these upon the rate of decarboxylation of carboxylic acids:

$$RCOOH \rightarrow RH + CO_2 \qquad (17)$$

Most carboxylic acids are very stable and the decarboxylation shown in equation 17 takes place only at relatively high temperatures (350°C) and in presence of catalysts. When hydroxyl, carboxyl, or nitro groups are introduced in the radical R of R—COOH and such groups are close to the carboxyl, decarboxylation takes place on heating at temperatures below 200°C and often in absence of catalysts. The ease of decarboxylation on heating of oxalic, malonic, and nitroacetic acids is well known.

Since no single method is applicable to the determination of a functional group, all the methods that have been developed should be considered and the one is selected which gives the best accuracy for compounds whose structure is related to the sample. In addition, consideration should be given to modifications of the method depending on the nature of the sample. The main objectives of the modifications are: (a) to increase the reaction rate; (b) to obtain a large value for the $K_{eq.}$ or completeness of the reaction; (c) to avoid interferences.

IV. Acceleration of Reaction Rates

The well-known methods for the acceleration of reaction rates by increasing the temperature of the reaction mixture by catalysis and change in the concentration of the reactants need no elaborate discussion except to point out the limitations imposed by the analytical objectives.

Since most organic reactions are slow, it is common practice to heat the mixture of sample and reagent in order to accelerate the reaction rate.

However, in dealing with micro quantities, heating in an open vessel should be avoided or if the time required for equilibrium at room temperature is inordinately long, the heating should be done in a closed tube. For example, in the determination of a primary alcohol, several procedures prescribe heating of the sample with acetic anhydride in pyridine at 60°C for 2–2.5 hours (Section IV, Chapter 7). If the sample is only a few milligrams, heating for such a length of time will cause serious errors due to unavoidable losses. Hence, the heating is accomplished in a closed tube (experiment 5). When the sample is less than a milligram, it is preferable to avoid transfers and allow the reaction to reach equilibrium at room temperature.[11] In considering prolonged heating for an analytical procedure, attention should be given to the possibility that heating may have an adverse effect on the over-all accuracy because the rates of the side reactions are also increased.

[11] J. J. Quattrone and T. Choy, *Microchem. J.*, **6**, 259 (1962).

5

General Analytical Techniques

I. General

After selection of the proper analytical procedure to be employed in the analysis, the operational steps comprise: (1) measurement of the sample to be used in the determination; (2) mixing of the sample and reagent under conditions which insure as far as possible stoichiometric relation between reactants and products formed; (3) determination of the *measurable* substances consumed or formed by the reaction; and (4) calculation of the percentage of the functional group, or the compound, present in the sample from the data obtained.

These operational steps involve the use of a number of techniques: *weighing, measurement of volumes, heating, stirring, grinding, pulverizing, filtration, drying, and preparation of the sample before weighing.* It is assumed that the reader is generally familiar with all of these operations; however, it was deemed important to include a detailed discussion of each of these techniques particularly as they are employed with relatively small quantities of samples. The discussion of weighing is very extensive because it is one of the operations which most commonly cause introduction of errors.

II. Weighing

A. Use of Ordinary Analytical Balance and Semimicro Balance for Micro Work. The first step in quantitative analysis is the measurement of the amount of material used in the determination. With the exception of a few cases (e.g., determination of amino groups in a solution of protein hydrolyzate), the sample is measured by weighing. Therefore, an accurate weighing device is essential.

A good ordinary analytical balance may serve very well for the micro-determination of functional groups using 0.1 milliequivalent of the sample.

Benedetti-Pichler[1] has long advocated the use of ordinary sensitive analytical balances for quantitative microanalysis. The method of weighing is identical to that for the microbalance (see below). For those who are used to the conventional method of weighing in macro quantitative analysis, it may be pointed out that microweighing technique has several distinct features:

(a) The rider is placed only on a whole number of milligrams on the balance beam. The fractional divisions of the beam are never used.

(b) The scale divisions on the pointer scale are designated as 10, 20, 30, . . . up to 100 units instead of 1, 2, 3, . . . 10, so that each division is divided into 10 parts by estimation. Decimal points are not used to record pointer readings.

(c) The inflection points (or the equilibrium position for a damped balance) are never divided by two.

(d) The sensitivity of the balance is determined by the displacement of the pointer (in number of scale units) when the rider is moved from zero to the 1-mg. mark on the beam. The exact weight of the object is calculated from the sensitivity and the inflection point of the pointer.

Various types of semimicro balances are available commercially. These balances have been adjusted by the manufacturer to give a sensitivity of 100 scale units per 1 mg. An ordinary analytical balance has sensitivity between 40 and 60 scale units. The sensitivity may be increased by raising the screw on the pointer which controls its center of gravity. For most balances, the sensitivity remains constant after readjustment, though it is advisable to check the sensitivity from time to time.

B. Microbalances. The first microbalances were constructed by Bunge and also by Kuhlmann and were used by Emich and his co-workers between 1906 and 1909 in developing the basis of inorganic microanalysis.[2] Pregl saw these balances when he visited Emich's laboratory (1909–1910) and later he suggested to Kuhlmann the construction of the microanalytical balance[2a] which he used in the development of the elegant methods for the determination of carbon and hydrogen in organic compounds. The Kuhlmann microbalance has a sensitivity of 100 scale units per 0.1 mg. and can take a maximum load of 20 g. on each pan. This microbalance is distinguished by its relatively small size as well as simple and rugged construction. It usually retains excellent sensitivity even after 10–20 years of constant use. No Kuhlmann microbalance has been produced since World

[1] A. A. Benedetti-Pichler, *Ind. Eng. Chem., Anal. Ed.*, **8**, 373 (1936); **11**, 226 (1939).

[2] F. Emich's historical memorandum, *Microchem. J.*, **5**, 442 (1960).

[2a] F. Pregl, *Quantitative Organic Microanalysis*, transl. by F. Fyleman, Blakiston, Philadelphia, 1924, p. 7.

TABLE 5.1

Microbalances Commercially Available (1963)

Manufacturer	Model	Type	Approx. price, $
Ainsworth	FH (Fig 5.1a)	Double pan	870.00
Ainsworth	FHM	Double pan	1,090.00
Becker	EM-1 (Fig. 5.1b)	Double pan	875.00
Bunge	25 DKN	Double pan	800.00
Bunge	25 DKOS	Double pan	1,100.00
Oertling	141	Double pan	1,080.00
Oertling	147 (Fig. 5.2a)	Double pan, damped	1,270.00
Sartorius	1801 (Fig. 5 2b)	Double pan, damped	1,385.00
Mettler	M-5 (Fig. 5.3)	Single pan	1,450.00

War II. Table 5.1 shows the microbalances available at present. If a microbalance is available in the laboratory it will be advantageous to use it for the microdetermination of functional groups instead of the ordinary analytical balance.

C. Weighing Techniques with a Microbalance. All weighings in microanalysis are obtained by difference—the sample (or the product) being placed in a container and the change in weight determined. Therefore, it is not necessary to know the exact weight of the container. On the other hand, it is important to measure the increase or decrease of the weight when the sample (or product) is introduced or removed from the container with a precision commensurate with the other measurements (e.g., the volume of titrant, the color intensity of the solution, etc.). Microweighing techniques vary with the type of balance. Three different types of balance are discussed below.

1. Free-Swing Balance. It is assumed that the operator is familiar with the use and care of an ordinary balance. The microbalance requires a little more gentle handling because it is more susceptible to thermal and vibrational disturbances.

The balance beam should be *released* and *set in motion* smoothly *without jerking or pushing.* The operation of the free-swing microbalance may be illustrated by the determination of its "zero point" (the rest point when there are no loads on either pan) in the following manner.

A. DETERMINATION OF THE "ZERO POINT" OF A FREE-SWING BALANCE. With both pans empty and the rider placed at the position marked 0.0 mg., set the beam in motion gently. Draw a vertical line on a piece of paper and mark *Left* and *Right* (or − and +) as shown in the example which follows. Record all inflection points as the pointer swings back and forth. If the

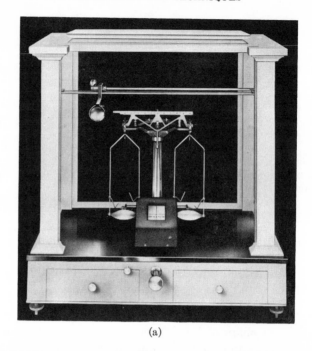

(a)

(b)

Fig. 5.1. Microbalance, free-swing type. (a) Courtesy of Wm. Ainsworth & Sons, Inc. (b) Courtesy of Christian Becker Division of The Torsion Balance Co.

(a) (b)

Fig. 5.2. Air-damped microbalance. (a) Courtesy of L. Oertling Co. (b) Sartorius, courtesy of Brinkmann Instruments, Inc.

pointer travels through both the right and left halves of the pointer scale, it is not necessary to write a + or − sign before each reading. However, if the pointer does not reach the left half of the pointer scale on its swing to the left, add a + sign to indicate that the reading is on the right half. Similarly, use a − sign to indicate a swing to the right which does not reach the right half.

Example. Both pans empty, rider at 0.0 mg. Pointer readings:

Left (−)	Right (+)
	31
02	
	30
01	
	29
00	
	29
+01	
	27
+01	
	26

Now calculate the rest point of the balance beam using the above set of pointer readings by either of the following two methods. Because the pointer

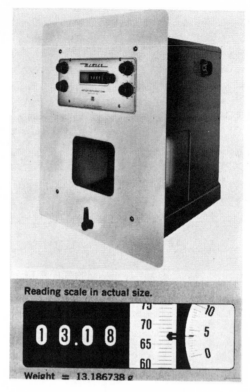

Fig. 5.3. Single-pan microbalance, courtesy of Mettler Instrument Corporation.

readings were taken with no loads on the pans and the rider at zero, this rest point is known as the "zero point."

B. CALCULATION OF THE REST POINT BY THE CONVENTIONAL METHOD. Average the readings at the right and at the left, and calculate the algebraic sum, thus,

Left (−)	Right (+)
−02	+31
−01	+30
00	+29
+01	+29
+01	+27
5/−01	+26
Av. = −00	6/+172
	Av. = +29

Therefore, the rest point is $(-00 + 29) = +29$, or 29 deflection units to the right of the center line on the pointer scale.

c. CALCULATION OF THE REST POINT BY THE PAIRING METHOD. This rest point is obtained by calculating the algebraic sum of each pair of right and left swings, thus,

	Left swing	Right swing	Rest point
1st pair	-02	$+31$	$+29$
2nd pair	-01	$+30$	$+29$
3rd pair	00	$+29$	$+29$
4th pair	$+01$	$+29$	$+30$
5th pair	$+01$	$+27$	$+28$

Therefore, the average rest point is 29 units to the right.

d. COMPARISON OF METHODS B AND C. The conventional method is given in most laboratory manuals on quantitative analysis, since it is assumed to be more exact. There is practically no difference in accuracy between the two methods for microweighing. On the other hand, the pairing method has several advantages:

(1) It can detect the improper release of the beam or the disturbance of the balance during the weighing. In both cases, successive pairs of swings will be erratic and the weighing should be repeated.

(2) A little practice will enable the experienced worker to carry out mental calculation of the successive pairs of swings, thus eliminating the tedium of writing down the pointer readings. However, the beginner should write the readings and make the calculations until experience in mental calculation has been acquired.

(3) Two or three pairs of swings are sufficient in getting the rest point. In order to prolong the life of the knife edge, the balance beam should not be allowed to swing for a considerable length of time during each weighing. Furthermore, it will be noted that, as the period of the swings becomes smaller, the accuracy of the weighing decreases.

2. *Damped Balance.* While magnetic or air-damped semimicro balances are in common use, the microbalance is seldom provided with a damping device. When the damped balance is employed, the pointer indicates the rest point directly. This saves the work of computation, but it does not provide a means of checking if the balance is not operating properly.

3. *Single-Pan Balance.* The single-pan balance is a recent development in weighing. Operation of this type of balance is simple and rapid. The object to be weighed is placed on the only pan provided in the balance cage, which is balanced by a spring at the other end. Weights are then

removed from the top of the pan (usually concealed) by a suitable mechanism until the amount removed is compensated by the weight of the object. This amount is read on a dial, to the *microgram* on a microbalance, or to the *hundredth* of a milligram on a semimicro balance.

It should be noted that the single-pan balance is operated on a constant maximum load and is not expected to last as long as the other types of balance. The accuracy of the dial readings should be checked occasionally by weighing a reference standard weight on the pan.

D. Determination of Sensitivity.   When a microbalance is installed, its sensitivity is usually adjusted to 100 (that is, 100 deflection units per 0.1 mg.) in order to simplify calculation (thus, one deflection unit is exactly equal to 1 μg.). The sensitivity gradually drops on long use, but the change should not be appreciable for a period of 3–6 months unless the balance has been mishandled or improperly installed. The sensitivity of the balance at zero load may be checked in the following manner:

1. For Single-Pan Balance.   Take the rest point of the balance when the pan is empty. Place a calibrated 1-mg. weight on the pan and take the rest point. Replace this weight with a calibrated 10-mg. weight and take the rest point. Calculate the weights from the dial and vernier readings. The errors should not be greater than 3 μg. for a microbalance. Because the single-pan balance has unequal arms, its sensitivity is easily affected by temperature variations. Hence, the maintenance of a constant temperature in the balance room is essential.

2. For Two-Pan Balance.   Take the rest point of the balance when both pans are empty and the rider sits at the 0.0 mg. notch. Now place the rider at 0.1 mg. and again determine the rest point. The displacement between these two rest points is the sensitivity of the balance. The difference between repeated determinations should not be more than 3 inflection units.

III. Care of the Microbalance[3]

The microbalance should be placed on a solid bench free from vibrations, air currents, and uneven heating at the two sides. The following rules should be observed in using the balance:

(1) The object to be weighed should be brought to the temperature of the balance before being placed on the balance pan.

(2) The weight of the container should be less than two-thirds the maximum permissible load for the microbalance.

[3] A. A. Benedetti-Pichler, *Waagen und Wägung*, in *Handbuch der mikrochemischen Methoden*, Vol. 1, Part II, Springer, Vienna, 1959.

(3) No sample or chemicals may be placed directly on the balance pan. If paper is used as the container the paper should be placed on a watch glass or an aluminum dish.

(4) The balance beam should be arrested as soon as the reading is completed. For the free-swing type microbalance, the arrestment should be made when the pointer is at the center line.

IV. Weights and Tares

Since the quantity of sample or product employed in microdeterminations of functional groups rarely exceeds the magnitude of 100 mg., it is not necessary to calibrate the weights beyond the 100-mg. piece. Fractional weights of spiral type (see Fig. 5.4d) covering the range of 10-, 20-, 30-, 50-, 100-, 200-, 300-, and 500-mg. are convenient to handle.

It is often advantageous to tare the containers used for weighing the sample or product. Three types of tares are shown in Figure 5.4. A small and

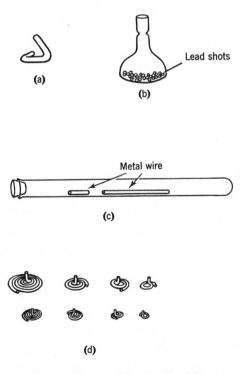

Fig. 5.4. Tares and fractional weights.

light container may be tared with a piece of thick copper wire bent into a triangular shape (Fig. 5.4a). A heavy but small object may be tared with a small flask into which lead shot is placed (Fig. 5.4b), and a reaction tube or flask should be tared with an object of similar size and shape (Fig. 5.4c) in order to correct for buoyancy. Of course, it is understood that weights and tares are not needed for weighing on the single-pan balance.

V. Weighing Devices

A. Weighing by Means of a Microboat.
Microboats (Fig. 5.5) made of platinum, quartz, or porcelain are commercially available.[4] The micro-boat should be handled with forceps having flat tips. If the boat can be placed in the reaction vessel during the analysis, the empty boat is first weighed accurately. Then it is removed from the microbalance and the solid sample is added into the boat by means of a microspatula.[5] After the amount has been adjusted approximately, the microboat containing the sample is again weighed accurately and the exact weight of the sample taken for analysis is calculated by difference. On the other hand, if it is not advisable to keep the microboat in the reaction vessel during the analysis, the approximate weight of the boat is predetermined (e.g., by using a tare), and the proper amount of sample is introduced into the boat outside the balance. After the exact weight of the boat plus the sample has been taken, the boat is transferred to the reaction vessel and turned upside down to empty its contents. The boat is then reverted to the upright position, replaced on the balance pan, and again weighed accurately. The difference between the two weighings gives the exact amount of sample which has been introduced into the reaction vessel.

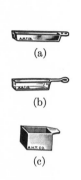

(a)

(b)

(c)

Fig. 5.5. Microboats. Courtesy of A.H.Thomas Co.

B. The Weighing Tube.
The microweighing tube (Fig. 5.6) is also known as the charging tube. It is commercially available, but can easily be made from 10-mm. glass tubing and 2-mm. glass rod. The tubing is heated in the flame and drawn to thin out the wall and to provide a taper. A section which has the narrow end of about 5 mm. outside diameter (2–3 mm. inside), wide end 7 mm., and a length of 20–25 mm. is selected. The narrow end is then sealed and joined to the glass rod which serves as the handle. The length of the handle varies from 35 to 120 mm. depending

[4] Arthur H. Thomas Co., Philadelphia, Pennsylvania.

[5] N. D. Cheronis, *Micro and Semimicro Methods*, Interscience, New York, 1954, p. 123.

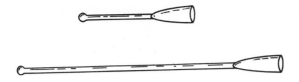

Fig. 5.6. Microweighing tubes.

on the reaction vessel. The weighing tube should be so constructed that its bottom is round instead of being pointed and can be reached by the microspatula. In using, the weighing tube is held by the knob at the end and its approximate weight is predetermined. The sample is introduced to near the bottom of the weighing tube by means of the microspatula. After the exact weight has been determined, the weighing tube is transferred to the reaction vessel and the sample is shaken out. The weighing tube is then returned to the microbalance and accurately reweighed.

C. Weighing by Means of the Capillary Tube and Plunger. The capillary tube and plunger (Fig. 5.7) are employed when the reaction vessel has an opening too small to permit passage of a microboat or weighing tube. The capillary tube, 60–100 mm. long, has inside diameter of 1–2 mm. and the plunger consists of a micro glass rod flattened at the end and fitting the capillary loosely. The finely ground solid sample is placed in the mortar or on a watch glass. On pressing the capillary tip onto the sample (the plunger being raised), a section of the capillary is packed with the solid. The capillary is removed and its outside wall is wiped with a camel's hair brush. It is then inserted into

Pulverized sample

Watch glass

Fig. 5.7. Capillary tube and plunger.

the reaction vessel which has been accurately weighed. The sample is pushed out of the capillary by means of the plunger, and the amount taken for analysis is determined by the increase in weight of the reaction vessel.

D. Weighing of Semi-Solids and Oils

1. Weighing in the Microboat. Weighing of semi-solids and oils may be

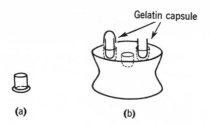

Fig. 5.8. (a) Micro glass cup. (b) Aluminum stand for gelatin capsule.

carried out in microboats (see Section V-A). The sample is added to
the boat either by means of the microspatula or glass rod.

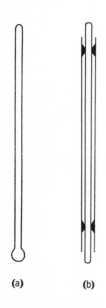

Fig. 5.9. (a) Micro glass rod with knob. (b) Micro glass rod with protecting tube.

2. *Weighing in the Glass Cup or Gelatin Capsule.*
The micro glass cup (Fig. 5.8a), about 5 mm. deep,
can be made from 4-mm. glass tubing by closing
one end and flattening it. The cup is stable and
can be placed directly on the microbalance pan.
The gelatin capsule (obtained from a drugstore)
has to be supported on a cork or an aluminum block
(Fig. 5.8b). The empty cup or capsule (with the
stand) is accurately weighed and then reweighed
after the addition of the sample. It should be noted
that in the determination of nitrogen by the Kjeldahl
method the use of gelatin capsule introduces nitrogen, the amount of which should be estimated on an
empty capsule in the blank determination.

3. *Weighing by Means of the Glass Rod.* If the
reaction vessel can be weighed on the microbalance
pan, viscous samples may be introduced directly
to the vessel without an extra container. After the
vessel has been accurately weighed, it is removed
from the balance and one of the following techniques
is used to add the sample. (a) When there is no
danger of touching the inner wall of the reaction
vessel, a simple 2-mm. glass rod with a knob at the
end (Fig. 5.9a) is employed. The glass rod is dipped
into the viscous sample until sufficient amount has
covered the knob. The rod is then brought into the
reaction vessel. As the knob touches the bottom of
the vessel, the sample will run down. (b) The glass rod shown in Figure
5.9b is used when the sample has to travel through a long narrow channel

before reaching the bottom of the reaction vessel. This device consists of a 1-mm. glass rod sealed to a capillary of 2 mm. inside diameter and protruding about 3 mm. at both ends. One end serves to carry the sample to the bottom of the reaction vessel while the other end may be used to remove the excess amount of sample from the vessel. It is apparent that the length of the glass rod depends on the depth of the reaction vessel.

E. Weighing of Liquid Samples

1. Weighing in the Microboat. The microboat (see Section V-A) may be used for weighing high-boiling liquids. The sample is added into the boat by means of a capillary.

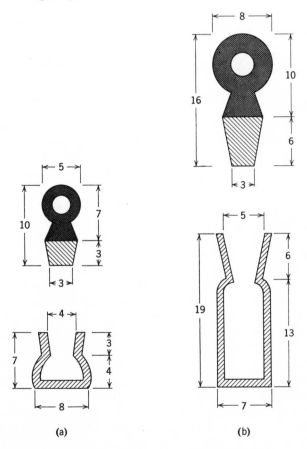

Fig. 5.10. Weighing bottles, scale in mm. (a) Micro. (b) Semimicro. Courtesy of *Microchemical Journal.*

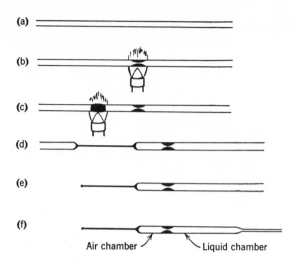

Fig. 5.11. Preparation of the weighing pipet.

2. Weighing in the Glass Cup or Gelatin Capsule. In order to prevent losses in weighing volatile liquids, the glass cup is provided with a ground glass stopper (Fig. 5.10). The stopper has an opening so that a hook can go through it to pull the stopper apart after the cup is immersed in the solvent in the reaction vessel. When the gelatin capsule is used, it should be weighed with the cap, which is placed in position after the sample has been introduced (Fig. 5.8b).

3. Weighing in the Capillary Pipet. The Ma-Eder capillary pipet[6] may be used for weighing volatile samples and keeping them for some time before analysis. The preparation of the pipet, shown in Figure 5.11 consists of the following steps: (1) a constriction (b) is made on a glass capillary of about 1–2 mm. bore; (2) one end is sealed and drawn out to form the air chamber (e) about 15 mm. long and a handle of about 1 mm. diameter and 25 mm. length; (3) the other end is then softened and drawn out to form the liquid chamber (f) about 25 mm. long and the tip of about 0.3 mm. bore and 25 mm. length. After the pipet has been accurately weighed, the air chamber is heated over a microburner, followed by dipping the tip into the liquid sample. When a suitable amount of liquid reaches the liquid chamber, the tip is lifted up and wiped with a tissue paper. The approximate weight is then taken. If the increase in weight is within the range of desirable sample size, the pipet is held with one hand and tapped upon the

[6] T. S. Ma and K. Eder, *J. Chinese Chem. Soc.*, **15**, 112 (1947).

other hand, whereby the liquid glides down the liquid chamber, but stops at the constriction. The pipet is then sealed at the tip over a flar ɛ and reweighed accurately. The liquid sample should not be brought dow ;o the constriction if the amount is too much or too little. In the former ɩse, a part of the liquid is expelled by warming the air chamber and pu ing a piece of filter paper at the tip to draw away the excess. In the latter case, the process of heating the air chamber and dipping the tip into the liquid sample is repeated. Before introducing the capillary pipet containing the sample into the reaction vessel, the tip is cut open. The handle and the air chamber may be broken off and the pipet crushed under the solvent.

4. Weighing in the Dropper or Syringe. While the dropper or syringe is usually employed for measuring volumes (see Section VI-B), it is small enough to be placed on the microbalance pan to be weighed. In order to prevent the liquid sample from dropping out while being weighed, a cap should be put on the tip of the dropper or syringe and weighed with it.

VI. Measurement of Volumes

A. Burets[7]

1. Simple Burets. Simple burets are available in various sizes and graduations.[8] The types which are needed in the micro and semi-micro determinations of functional groups are listed in Table 5.2. As

TABLE 5.2

Simple Burets Employed in Micro
or Semimicro Work

Capacity, ml.	Graduation, ml.
2	0.01
5	0.01
10	0.02
50	0.1

organic solvents have become more common in the preparation of the titrant solutions, Teflon stopcocks[9] are gaining popularity. Teflon stopcocks do not require a lubricant, thus reducing the danger of leaks due to the

[7] For review of literature on burets see N. D. Cheronis, *Micro and Semimicro Methods*, Interscience, New York, 1954, pp. 118–123.

[8] Arthur H. Thomas Co., Philadelphia, Pennsylvania.

[9] Available from Fischer & Porter Co., Hatboro, Pennsylvania.

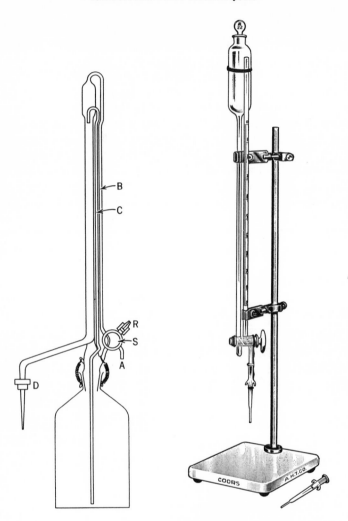

Fig. 5.12. Kirsten micro-
buret. Courtesy of *Ana-
lytical Chemistry.*

Fig. 5.13. Koch microburet.
Courtesy of A. H. Thomas Co.

action of organic solvent on the lubricant used for glass stopcocks. Teflon
stopcocks are resistant to the attack of alkalies. The screwcap type
burets[10] are also constructed for the prevention of leaking or contamination
of the titrant by the lubricant.

[10] Available from Emil Greiner Co., New York, New York.

2. Buret with Reservoir. Several types of microburets with reservoir are commercially available (Figs. 5.12–5.16). The Kirsten, Machlett, and Pregl microburets have a capacity of 10 ml. The Wiberley microburet has a capacity of 2 ml. The Koch microburet may be obtained in 2-, 5-, and 10-ml. sizes. A buret with a reservoir attachment is more expensive than the simple buret, but has the following certain advantages:

(a) It can be refilled more easily and conveniently than the simple buret. As the solution is drawn up from below the graduated portion of the buret, there is no danger of air gaps which sometimes occur in simple burets of 2–5 ml. capacity.

(b) The danger of contamination of the solution when the latter is poured from a storage bottle through a funnel into the simple buret is eliminated.

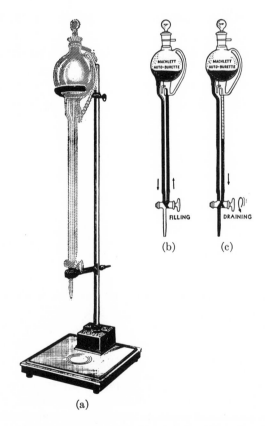

Fig. 5.14. Machlett microburet. Courtesy of Fisher Scientific Co.

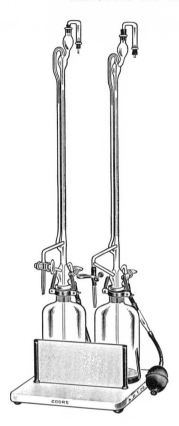

Fig. 5.15. Pregl microburet. Courtesy of A. H. Thomas Co.

Fig. 5.16.
Wiberley micro-
buret. Courtesy
of Metro Scien-
tific, Inc.

This is of serious concern when the $0.01N$ titrant is easily affected by the presence of oxygen or carbon dioxide.

(c) When the buret is provided with the automatic zero device, only one reading is taken for each measurement, thus cutting down the error in reading the volume.

B. Pipets and Syringes.   Regular pipets of capacity range from 1- to 25-ml., to deliver, are common equipment for functional group analysis, while wash-out pipets and weighing pipets are seldom used. Recently, the syringe has become a convenient tool in the analytical laboratory. It is very desirable for the measurement of volumes on the micro scale, because the syringe needle can deliver the solution from a self-sealing stock bottle into the reaction vessel without the danger of contamination due to the atmosphere. Syringe pipets of 1 ml. capacity with 0.01 ml. graduations (Fig. 5.17) are commercially available, as are syringes of larger capacities. The tip of the syringe needle should be square-cut instead of being slant like those used for injection. If the syringe is employed to measure the volume of a pure compound for microdetermination, it should be a precision type with capacity from 50 to 100 μl. and graduated in μl. Weighing this syringe pipet before and after the delivery of the liquid sample serves as a double check of the amount of the sample taken for analysis.

C. Microtitration Techniques. Microtitrations using the 5- or 10-ml. buret and $0.01N$ titrant do not involve techniques which are significantly different from the macro volumetric procedures. The titrant is added to the sample solution by carefully turning the stopcock of the microburet. Because the volume to be measured usually ranges from 2 to 8 ml., it is desirable to control the increment of the titrant near the endpoint to within 0.02 ml. This can be accomplished without difficulty since the microburet is provided with a fine tapered tip. Coating the tip with silicone or Vaseline prevents the titrant from creeping up and forming large drops.

Erlenmeyer flasks of 50–75 ml. capacity are convenient vessels for microtitration. Mixing of the solution during titration may be done by swirling the flask by hand or by using the magnetic stirring bar. If the titration endpoint is to be located visually, it should be noted that the color change may not be as intense as in macro titrations because the titrant is 10 times more dilute in microanalysis. Similarly, electrometric microtitrations will show smaller potential or conductance jumps.

D. Submicrogram Volumetric Procedures. Volumetric procedures which involve the consumption of less than 1 ml. (that is, of a few micro-

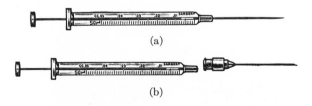

(a)

(b)

Fig. 5.17. Micro syringe. (a) With permanent needle. (b) With detachable needle. Courtesy of Sargent & Co.

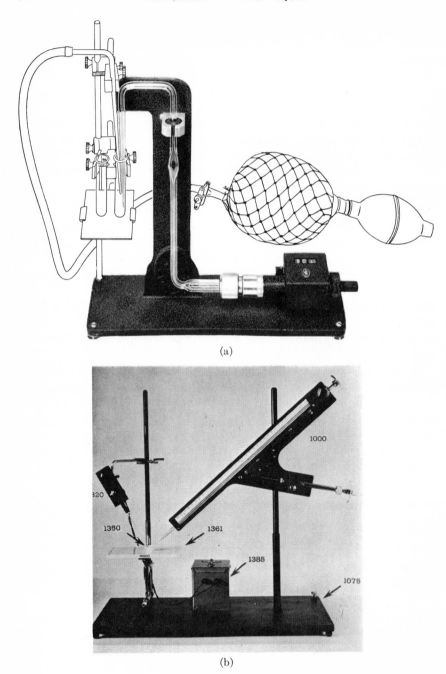

(a)

(b)

Fig. 5.18. Ultramicroburet. (a) Gilmont model. Courtesy of Manostat Corp. (b) Kirk model. Courtesy of Microchemical Specialties.

liters, μl.) of the titrant are classified as submicrogram or ultramicro methods. These procedures require a microliter buret which can deliver a volume of liquid accurate to 1 μl. Typical ultramicro burets are shown in Figures 5.18a and b.[11]

Microliter burets are considerably more expensive than 2- to 10-ml. microburets and they entail special techniques in cleaning, filling, and operating. While the buret permits the use of 0.1N titrant in functional group determination on the micro scale, it is not recommended except for special cases such as amperometric and conductometric titrations where a volume change during titration is undesirable. The reader is referred to the manuals of Benedetti-Pichler[12] and Kirk[13] for the use and care of ultramicro burets.

VII. Heating

A. Burners. Semimicro burners[14] which give a nonluminous flame 1–3 cm. long are suitable for heating the reaction mixture for functional group analysis. An ordinary Bunsen burner fitted with fine adjustments for gas and air may also be used. A large flame *should be avoided* lest there be overheating at the upper portion of the reaction vessel causing evaporation of the reaction mixture and decomposition of the sample.

B. Constant Temperature Baths. In the procedures for functional group analysis which require heating within certain temperature range, it is desirable to use a constant temperature device. For temperatures below 100°C, the water bath may serve the purpose, provided the determination is not vitiated by the very high humidity in the surrounding atmosphere. Oil baths are not recommended because it is tedious to clean the outside of the reaction vessel after heating, prior to the subsequent titration or filtration process.

The electrically heated metal block is an ideal device for controlled heating of the reaction mixture. It is conveniently machined from hard aluminum and wound with nichrome wire or heat-tape. The temperature may be regulated by means of a variable resistance and observed through a thermometer placed in a well in the metal block. An apparatus which, through an electronic circuit, automatically controls the temperature be-

[11] For review, see reference 7.

[12] A. A. Benedetti-Pichler, *Introduction to the Microtechnique of Inorganic Analysis*, Wiley, New York, 1942.

[13] P. L. Kirk, *Quantitative Ultramicro Analysis*, Wiley, New York, 1950.

[14] See N. D. Cheronis, *Micro and Semimicro Methods*, Interscience, New York, 1954, p. 21.

tween 25 and 250°C to within 3°C has been described by Ma and Schenck[15] (Fig. 5.19) and is commercially available.

C. Heating in Sealed Glass Tubes. In contrast to the macro methods, some reactions for the microdetermination of functional groups are preferably carried out in sealed glass tubes. It may be for the purpose of (a) preventing the escape of the reactants (e.g., determination of the hydroxyl group by acetylation), or (b) increasing the rate of the reaction (e.g., determination of the terminal methyl group by chromic acid oxidation). A glass reaction tube, 100–150 mm. long, may be made from soft

Fig. 5.19. Heating stage with automatic temperature control. Courtesy of Micro-Ware, Inc.

glass or borosilicate glass tubing of 8 mm. bore and 1 mm. wall thickness. The steps in preparing the sealed glass tube are shown in Figure 5.20. It is noted that the bottom as well as the tip should have the same thickness as the original tubing—hence, the formation of a lump at the bottom and the thinning of the tip on sealing should be avoided. On the other hand, it is not necessary to use the thick-walled micro-Carius tube for functional group determinations, since the reaction mixture is not heated to very high temperatures and the pressure increase inside the sealed tube is not excessive. After the reaction is completed and the tube has cooled to the room temperature, a sharp flame is applied to the tip of the sealed tube to open a tiny hole in order to equilibrate the pressure. The detailed description

[15] T. S. Ma and R. T. E. Schenck, *Mikrochemie*, **40**, 245 (1953); apparatus available from Micro-Ware, Inc., Vineland, New Jersey.

and directions for use of the sealed tube technique will be found in Chapter 12 (experiments 5, 12, and 13).

VIII. Stirring, Grinding, and Pulverizing

A. Stirring. An important requirement of the stirring device for microdeterminations of functional groups, besides the restriction of the size of the stirrer, is that it should not cause any loss of the sample or the reagent. The stirring may be accomplished by one of the following methods:

(a) Bubbling a current of inert gas through the reaction mixture.

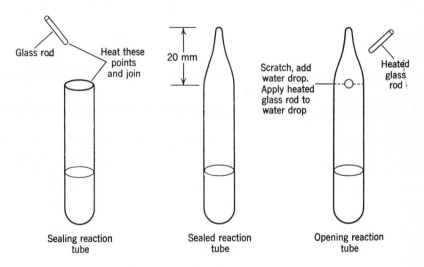

Fig. 5.20. The sealed reaction tube.

(b) Using a magnetic stirrer.

(c) Placing the reaction vessel on a shaker.

(d) Swirling the reaction flask by hand.

(e) Placing the sealed glass reaction tube in a rocking electric furnace.

Figure 5.21 shows a standard magnetic stirrer useful for micro or semimicro work. A simple magnetic stirring device is described in experiment 33.

B. Pulverizing or Grinding of Small Samples.[16] Pulverizing is employed in sampling for chemical analysis. For the purpose of functional

[16] See T. S. Ma, Quantitative Microchemical Analysis, in *Standard Methods of Chemical Analysis*, 6th ed., Vol. 2 (edited by F. J. Welcher), Van Nostrand, Princeton, 1963, p. 362.

Fig. 5.21. Commercial magnetic stirrers and stirring bars. Courtesy of Fisher Scientific Co.

group determination, the problem of taking the proper sample will depend on the question, "What is this determination for?" If it is for proof of identity of a new or known compound, the sample must be uniform and pure (with the possible contamination of some solvent which will be removed on drying before analysis); hence, no pulverizing is necessary. If it is for the elucidation of the structure of an unknown substance, the sample may be pulverized, but not mixed, since multiple determinations using sample from different parts will indicate whether the preparation is one entity or is composed of several ingredients. If it is for purity test or quality control in the production line, then the sample is suspected to be heterogeneous and the preparation of a representative sample should be the first step in the analytical procedure. The best way is to dissolve the whole sample in a suitable solvent and take aliquots for analysis. If this is not possible, the sample should be pulverized in an agate mortar and mixed and quartered by the conventional sampling technique, keeping in mind that no ingredient in the original sample is lost or destroyed during the operation.

IX. Filtration and Transfer

A. Minimal Transfer in Small Scale Work. Minimal transfer is the key to the success of small scale chemical experimentation. In all transfer there is a film left in the walls of the vessel which involves loss of material. These losses in macro work are so small compared to the total that they can be disregarded. However, in small scale work losses in transfer may introduce serious errors. The ideal analytical procedure is one which uses the same reaction vessel throughout the determination; thus, the dissolution of the sample, carrying out of the chemical transformation, and the titration of the resulting solution are performed without the transfer of the reaction mixture. However, this is not always possible and some form of transfer may be mandatory. During the process of transfer, it is essential that there be: (a) no loss of the sample or the desired reaction product, (b) no contamination of the reaction mixture, and (c) no over-dilution of the solution. Hence, the reaction vessel should be small and so shaped that it is easy to rinse the sample out. The amount of rinsing fluid should be kept to a minimum in order to avoid a very dilute final solution unsuitable for titration (in volumetric methods) or causing the dissolution of some of the precipitate (in gravimetric methods).

B. Filter Tubes. The conventional 45-degree funnel is not used in the micro methods for determining functional groups because a considerable amount of the material would be retained in the folded filter paper and on the wide surface of the funnel. The sintered glass filter tube, shown in Figure 5.22, is recommended. Instead of collecting the precipitate directly on top of the sintered glass plate, it is advantageous to select a filter tube

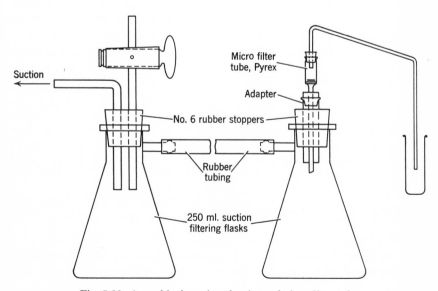

Fig. 5.22. Assembly for using the sintered glass filter tube.

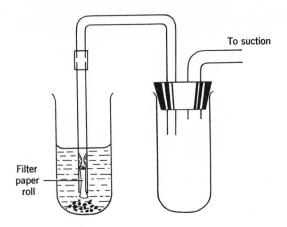

Fig. 5.23. Assembly for inverted filtration.

with a sintered glass plate of high porosity and place a disc of filter paper or glass fiber paper[17] above the sintered glass to retain the solid particles. This paper disc is cut by means of a cork borer or a puncher and is pressed onto the sintered glass plate with a glass rod flattened at the end. The paper disc should have the same diameter as the sintered glass plate so that it covers the plate completely when wet and does not crease at the edge.

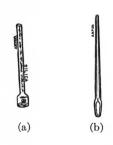

Fig. 5.24. Filtersticks. Courtesy of A. H. Thomas Co. (a) Porcelain. (b) Glass.

C. Inverted Filtration. Inverted filtration is a simple and convenient technique developed by Emich[18] for separating precipitate from its mother liquor on the micro scale. As shown in Figure 5.23, the filterstick, about 120 mm. long, is prepared from 4-mm. glass tubing (inside diameter, 2 mm.) by making a capillary constriction about 10 mm. from the bottom. The bottom is fitted with a tiny roll of filter paper with the end protruding 1 mm. beyond the filterstick. The filterstick is immersed in the solution in such position that the filter paper roll barely touches the precipitate. The

[17] T. S. Ma, I. Kaimowitz, and A. A. Benedetti-Pichler, *Mikrochimica Acta*, **1954,** 648; glass fiber paper available from Reeve Angel Co., Clifton, New Jersey.
[18] F. Emich, *Lehrbuch der Mikrochemie*, Bergmann, Munich, 1926, p. 85; A. A. Benedetti-Pichler, *Essentials of Quantitative Analysis*, Ronald Press, New York, 1956, p. 399.

solution is carried over into the clean test tube by suction. The washing liquid is then introduced, the precipitate agitated and allowed to settle down before the second filtration. Other types of filtersticks (Fig. 5.24) made with (a) porcelain porous discs or (b) constricted glass cups are commercially available. The disc should be flush with the edge of the filterstick and should not sink in; otherwise the precipitate will stick to the filter disc and cannot be washed thoroughly.

X. Preparation of the Sample

A. Purification of the Sample. Some samples which are submitted for the determination of functional groups are assumed to be relatively pure, since the purpose of the analysis is quality control or the determination of relative purity by analysis for the content of a particular function. In such cases, the sample is subjected to analysis without preliminary treatment. If no information as to the purity of the sample is available, it is necessary to fractionate it so as to obtain a relatively pure fraction.

Preliminary tests for homogeneity and purity may give considerable information as to the presence and extent of impurities and thus indicate the best approach to purification. Chromatographic examination by paper, by thin layer on

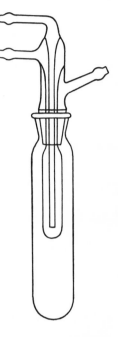

Fig. 5.25. Sublimation apparatus.

glass, or by a gas-liquid apparatus will disclose one spot or one peak if the sample is pure and several if more than one component is present. Chromatographic examination is mandatory with samples which decompose at their melting or boiling temperatures. Tests for homogeneity and purity can also be made by examination of solid samples with microscope hot stage.[19]

If the sample is a solid, either fractional crystallization or fractional sublimation (see Fig. 5.25) under reduced pressure may be used for purification. The latter procedure is preferable when the quantity of sample is below 100 mg. or when it is desired to remove solvent contamination. The details of both procedures have been published in another work by one

[19] M. Brandstätter, in *Microchemical Techniques, Microchem. J. Symposium Series,* Vol. 2, Interscience, New York, 1962, p. 221.

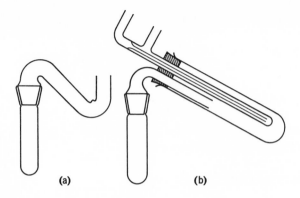

Fig. 5.26. Distillation assemblies. Courtesy of *Microchemical Journal*. (a) Fractional distillation. (b) Simple distillation.

of the authors.[20] No matter which procedure is employed, a fraction is regarded as pure when one additional fractionation yields crystals with substantially the same melting point.

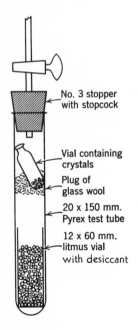

No. 3 stopper with stopcock

Vial containing crystals

Plug of glass wool

20 x 150 mm. Pyrex test tube

12 x 60 mm. litmus vial with desiccant

Fig. 5.27. Test tube desiccator.

If the sample is a liquid and the volume is more than 2 ml. it is fractionated using a small scale assembly[21,22] (see Figs. 5.26a and b). Two successive fractions which boil 1°C apart and have substantially the same refractive index are regarded as relatively pure. When the sample available is less than 1 ml. it is best to use a gas chromatograph for fractionation. A discussion on separations in organic analysis has been presented recently by Metcalfe.[23]

B. Drying of the Sample. Most solid samples should be dried prior to analysis in order to remove the last trace of solvent and surface moisture. The simple test tube vacuum microdesic-

[20] N. D. Cheronis, *Micro and Semimicro Methods*, Interscience, New York, 1954, pp. 23–50 and 88–92.

[21] N. D. Cheronis, *op. cit.*, pp. 62–81.

[22] T. S. Ma and J.M. Tien, *Microchem. J.*, **2**, 253 (1958); T. S. Ma, *J. Chinese Chem. Soc.*, Series II, **9**, 168 (1962).

[23] L. D. Metcalfe, *Symposium on Analysis via Functional Groups*, American Chemical Society Meeting, March, 1961, St. Louis, Missouri.

Fig. 5.28. Drying oven with automatic temperature control. Courtesy of Micro-Ware, Inc.

cator[24] (Fig. 5.27) serves adequately for the removal of low-boiling solvents and surface moisture. The well-known Abderhalden-type apparatus may be used for drying samples under reduced pressure at elevated temperatures. A vacuum drying apparatus provided with an automatic temperature control device[25] (Fig. 5.28) is more convenient to operate, requires less care, and is commercially available. Because this device gives the exact temperature at which the sample is heated, it is highly recommended when the sample is suspected to contain solvent of crystallization. Analysis of different samples dried at various temperatures will indicate the stability of the solvated compound.

[24] N. D. Cheronis, *Micro and Semimicro Methods*, Interscience, New York, 1954, p. 53.
[25] R. T. E. Schenck and T. S. Ma, *Mikrochemie*, **40**, 245 (1952); apparatus available from Micro-Ware, Inc., Vineland, New Jersey.

PART TWO

A Critical Survey of the Analytical Methods for Functional Group Determinations

6

The Oxygen Functions, Part I

I. General

This and the following five chapters deal with a critical survey of the various principles and methods which have been proposed for the determination of the functional groups in organic compounds. These groups which are summarized in Table 1.2 of Chapter 1 distinguish, classify, and characterize organic compounds. For the purpose of the present discussion these groups are divided into five categories: (1) oxygen; (2) nitrogen; (3) sulfur; (4) unsaturated; and (5) miscellaneous functions.

In this part of the work each function will be discussed with reference to the various methods which have been proposed for its quantitative determination and will include both chemical as well as physical methods, though the latter are not described in the practical part of this work. Particular attention will be given to micro methods which deal with samples of about 0.1 milliequivalent. In addition, when a micro method has not been described in the literature or in the practical part of this work, an approach to devise a suitable method for analysis in the 0.1 milliequivalent scale will be suggested.

A. Oxygen Functions. The oxygen functions are summarized in Table 6.1 and are treated in Chapters 6 and 7. The oxygen atom of all of these functions is involved in the chemical reactions employed for their determination and also in their estimation by physical methods. On the other hand, not all oxygen-containing functions are listed in Table 6.1. For example, the acid amide (or carbonamide) function, $—CONH_2$, is not included, since in its determination nitrogen rather than oxygen is involved in the reaction.

It should be noted that this arrangement is for the purpose of discussion of the analytical procedures rather than to establish new methods of classification. For example, the carboxyl, $—COOH$, function may be classified in the miscellaneous category with the other acidic functions or under oxy-

TABLE 6.1

List of Oxygen Functions

Function	Structure	Page reference	
		Discussion	Practical
Acetal	$=C(OR)_2$	107	504, 558
Acid anhydrides	$O=\overset{\|}{C}-O-\overset{\|}{C}=O$	109	532, 534
Acid halides	$-COX$	113	534
Acyl	$R-\overset{\|}{C}=O$	114	513
Alkoxyl	$-OR$	124	558, 622
Carbohydrate	$R-(CH_2OH)_nCOCH_2OH$; $R-(CHOH)_nCHO$ $(R=CH_2OH$ or $CH_3)$	157	507, 565
Carbonyl	$\overset{\diagdown}{\underset{\diagup}{C}}=O$	141	497, 500, 564, 590
Carboxylic ester	$-COOR$	174	510, 595
Carboxylic salt	$-COO^-Metal^+$	216	490
Epoxy	$=C\underset{\diagdown O \diagup}{\qquad}C=$	169	—
Ether	$R-O-R$	124	558, 622
Hemiacetal	$=(COHOR)$	107	558
Hydroxyl	$-OH$	183	493, 612
Inorganic ester	ROA	181	—
Lactone	$\overset{\diagdown}{\underset{\diagup}{C}}-(CH_2)_n-C=O$ $\underset{O}{\lfloor\qquad\rfloor}$	180	—
Methylene ether	$-O-CH_2-O-$	201	506
Methylol	$HOCH_2-$	197	—
Peroxy	$-O:O-$	204	529
Quinone	$O=C(Ar)C=O$	212	615

gen, since the acid-base reaction by which it is estimated involves a proton transfer from the hydroxyl-oxygen atom. Although the carboxyl group is discussed in Chapter 7 under oxygen functions, the estimation of carboxylic acids is also treated in Chapter 11 in connection with acidic functions estimated by acid-base titrimetry.

II. The Acetal Function

A. General. Acetals and ketals are the condensation products of alcohols (also glycols and polyhydroxy compounds) with aldehydes and ketones, respectively.

$$2R'OH + RCHO \rightleftharpoons RCH(OR')_2 + H_2O \qquad (1)$$

As indicated in the structure, the acetal and ketal, $[=C(OR)_2]$, function is characterized by two alkoxyl groups attached to a carbon atom and is also known as the dialkoxyl function. There is no specific method for the determination of this function. Little and Martell[1] investigated the Raman spectra of several acetals and reported that the 1541 cm^{-1} band, which is not generally found in alcohols and ethers, is a characteristic of the acetal function, but this has not been applied to quantitative analysis. Bryant, Mitchell, and Smith[2] proposed to use aquametry to determine the acetal group, based on the production of water on heating acetals or ketals with glacial acetic acid in the presence of boron trifluoride according to the following reaction:

$$=C(OR)_2 + 4CH_3COOH \xrightarrow{BF_3} =C(OOCCH_3)_2 + 2CH_3COOR + 2H_2O \qquad (2)$$

The water liberated is titrated with the Karl Fischer reagent. Low results were obtained when 5-millimole samples were used. This method has not been tested on the 0.1 meq. scale.

Two approaches are possible for the microdetermination of the acetal group: (1) analysis of the two alkoxyl groups and (2) hydrolysis of the sample to yield a carbonyl compound and a hydroxyl compound followed by the determination of one of the products.

B. Determination of Alkoxyl Groups in the Acetal Function. Two moles of alkyl iodide are produced from one mole of acetal or ketal on treatment with hydriodic acid (see alkoxyl function, p. 124). Hoffman and Wolfrom[3] described the determination of methoxyl and ethoxyl groups in acetals using about 20 mg. sample. A modified alkoxyl apparatus (see p. 134) was proposed. Good precision and accuracy were reported.

C. Determination of the Acetal Function by Hydrolysis. Acetals and ketals are hydrolyzed in an acid medium as shown in equations 3 and 4:

[1] M. H. Little and A. E. Martell, *J. Phys. and Coll. Chem.*, **53**, 472 (1949).

[2] W. M. D. Bryant, J. Mitchell, Jr., and D. M. Smith, *J. Am. Chem. Soc.*, **62**, 1 (1940).

[3] D. O. Hoffman and M. L. Wolfrom, *Anal. Chem.*, **19**, 225 (1947).

$$\begin{array}{c} \text{H} \\ \diagdown \\ \quad\quad \text{C}{=}(\text{OR})_2 + \text{H}_2\text{O} \xrightarrow{\text{H}_3\text{O}^+} \text{R}'{-}\text{CHO} + 2\text{ROH} \\ \diagup \\ \text{R}' \end{array} \qquad (3)$$

$$\text{R}_2'\text{C}{=}(\text{OR})_2 + \text{H}_2\text{O} \xrightarrow{\text{H}_3\text{O}^+} \text{R}_2'\text{CO} + 2\text{ROH} \qquad (4)$$

One of the hydrolytic products—usually the aldehyde or ketone—is then determined. Because the hydrolysis takes place in an aqueous medium, it is not feasible to determine the hydroxyl compound, even though it is produced in double molar quantity as compared to the carbonyl compound. If the hydroxyl compound were analyzable, the sensitivity of the determination would be increased.

Many macro procedures have appeared in the literature about the hydrolysis and determination acetals, and the subject has been reviewed by Mitchell.[4] It should be noted that the two methods generally recommended for the analysis of acetals and ketals, which involve hydrolysis followed by oximation or bisulfite addition, are not suitable for microdeterminations. This is because it is very difficult to obtain good endpoints using 0.1 meq. samples.

Grangaard and Purves[5] determined glyoxal tetramethylacetal using a 20-mg. sample by weighing the bis-2,4-dinitrophenylhydrazone of the glyoxal. Siegel and Weiss[6] described an argentimetric method which is applicable to acetals only. The aldehyde produced on hydrolysis is treated with known excess amount of silver nitrate, the silver oxide precipitate is separated by filtration, and the filtrate is back-titrated with $0.05N$ thiocyanate solution using ferric alum as the indicator. Cianetti[7] proposed the colorimetric estimation of dimethylacetal based on the color produced by Schiff's reagent on the aldehyde formed by the hydrolysis of the acetal. When formaldehyde is the carbonyl compound, the colorimetric method, using chromotropic acid (see experiment 9) is recommended.[8]

The accuracy of the hydrolytic method for determining the acetal function depends primarily on the completeness of the hydrolysis and the total recovery of the carbonyl compound. The rates of hydrolysis of acetals vary greatly with their structures. Cyclic acetals are usually more resistant to hydrolysis than open-chain compounds. Thus, while diethylacetal is completely hydrolyzed by boiling in $0.002N$ hydrochloric acid for a few minutes or by shaking with $1N$ acid at room temperature for 1/2 hour,

[4] J. Mitchell, Jr., in *Organic Analysis*, Vol. 1, Interscience, New York, 1953, p. 309.

[5] D. H. Grangaard and C. B. Purves, *J. Am. Chem. Soc.*, **61**, 428 (1939).

[6] H. Siegel and F. T. Weiss, *Anal. Chem.*, **26**, 917 (1954).

[7] E. Cianetti, *Ann. Chim. Applicata*, **38**, 360 (1948).

[8] C. E. Bricker and H. R. Johnson, *Ind. Eng. Chem., Anal. Ed.*, **17**, 400 (1945).

trimethylene-D-mannitol requires heating with $12N$ sulfuric acid at 90°C for 2 hours. In the estimation of acetals in wine, Kulnevich[9] reported that the amount of acetals recovered varied with the length of distillation. Hence, in order to get reproducible results, a standardized procedure should be established. Dilute phosphoric acid, if proved adequate for the hydrolysis, may advantageously replace hydrochloric or sulfuric acid, because phosphoric acid is nonvolatile and does not attack the carbonyl compound. Prolonged heating with concentrated sulfuric acid always brings complications.

III. The Acid Anhydride Function

A. General. Acid anhydrides show strong absorption in the infrared region, but the location of the absorption band depends on the molecular configuration of the compound. The macro procedures for determining acid anhydrides have been reviewed by Hammond.[10] It may be mentioned that among the macro methods the following are not readily adapted to the micro scale:

(1) Methods based on hydrolysis and measurement of the unreacted water[11,12] (eq. 5).

$$(R—CO)_2O + H_2O \xrightarrow{\text{catalyst}} 2R—COOH \tag{5}$$

(2) Methods based on anilide formation and titration of the carboxylic acid formed[13,14] (eq. 6).

$$(R—CO)_2O + H_2NC_6H_5 \rightarrow R—\underset{\underset{O}{\|}}{C}—NH—C_6H_5 + R—COOH \tag{6}$$

(3) Methods based on measurement of heat of reaction on hydrolysis[15] or anilide formation.[16]

Microdetermination of the acid anhydride function may be accomplished by the methods listed below. In some of the references cited, the procedure is given for macro analysis, but it can be readily converted to the micro range using the technique described in the practical part of this work. It

[9] V. G. Kulnevich, *Vinodelie i Vinograd*, **15**, 17 (1955).

[10] C. W. Hammond, in *Organic Analysis, Vol. 3*, Interscience, New York, 1956, p. 97.

[11] D. M. Smith, W. M. D. Bryant, and J. Mitchell, Jr., *J. Am. Chem. Soc.*, **62**, 608 (1940); **63**, 1700 (1941).

[12] E. N. Novikova and L. N. Petrova, *Zhur. Anal. Khim.*, **12**, 534 (1957).

[13] C. P. A. Kappelmeier and W. R. van Goor, *Verfdroniek*, **21**, 136 (1948).

[14] G. V. Zavaran, *Zavodskaya Lab.*, **21**, 791 (1955).

[15] L. H. Greathouse, H. J. Janssen, and C. H. Haydel, *Anal. Chem.*, **28**, 357 (1956).

[16] T. Somiza, *J. Soc. Chem. Ind.*, **51**, 135T (1932).

should be noted that acid anhydride samples are usually contaminated with the free acid which may react in the same manner as the anhydride. The reader is referred to experiment 20 for discussion on the determination of acid anhydride in mixtures.

B. Determination of Acid Anhydrides by Acid-Base Reactions

1. Titration as a Monobasic Acid.   When the acid anhydride is dissolved in an organic solvent and titrated with sodium methoxide in methanol-benzene mixture, it acts as a monobasic acid (eq. 7):

$$(R—CO)_2O + NaOCH_3 \rightarrow R—COOCH_3 + R—COONa \tag{7}$$

Various nonaqueous media may be used, and Thymol Blue is a suitable indicator for this determination.[17]

2. Titration as a Diprotic Acid.   The acid anhydride function is hydrolyzed quantitatively in the presence of water to two carboxyl groups, provided no alcohol is present. The recommended solvent is 1:1 pyridine-water mixture because pyridine acts as a catalyst for hydrolysis. After adding the sample and mixing at room temperature, the solution is immediately titrated with standard aqueous sodium hydroxide[18] (eq. 8).

$$(R—CO)_2O + 2NaOH \rightarrow 2R—COONa + H_2O \tag{8}$$

Trimethylbenzylammonium hydroxide in pyridine containing a small amount of water has also been used as the titrant[19] according to the reaction represented in the following equation:

$$(R—CO)_2O + 2(CH_3)_3N(CH_2C_6H_5)OH \rightarrow 2R—COO(CH_3)_3N(CH_2C_6H_5) + H_2O \tag{9}$$

C. Determination of Acid Anhydrides Based on Their Reaction with Morpholine.   Acid anhydrides react quantitatively with morpholine in methanol solution according to equation 10:

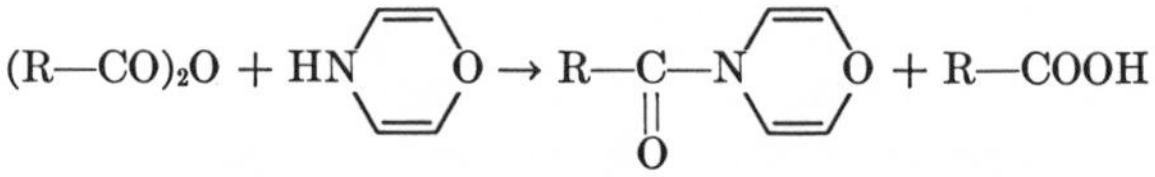

The reaction is completed at room temperature in 5–10 minutes.[20] The unreacted morpholine is then titrated with standardized methanolic hydrochloric acid. Mixed indicators consisting either of Methyl Yellow-Methyl Blue or Bromocresol Green-Methyl Red may be used. This method is not applicable to anhydrides whose parent acids have ionization

[17] A. Berger, M. Sela, and E. Katchelski, *Anal. Chem.*, **25**, 1554 (1953).

[18] D. M. Smith and W. M. D. Bryant, *J. Am. Chem. Soc.*, **58**, 2452 (1936).

[19] A. Patchornik and S. E. Rogozinski, *Anal. Chem.*, **31**, 985 (1959).

[20] J. B. Johnson and G. L. Funk, *Anal. Chem.*, **27**, 1464 (1955).

constants in water greater than 2×10^{-2} (e.g., maleic and citraconic anhydrides) because the free organic acids are acidic to the indicator. Compounds which react with morpholine (e.g., ketene, diketene, acid chlorides, mineral acids) interfere with the determination.

D. Determination of Acid Anhydrides Based on Their Reaction with Substituted Anilines. Acid anhydrides react with aniline to form an equimolar quantity of the corresponding anilide (eq. 6). On the macro scale, the excess aniline may be back-titrated with $0.2N$ hydrochloric acid in ethylene glycol-isopropanol mixture,[21] or with $0.1N$ perchloric acid in glacial acetic acid.[22] However, aniline also combines with the liberated free acid to some extent. In order to prevent this complication, substituted anilines such as m-nitroaniline,[23] p-chloroaniline,[24] and 2,4-dichloro-aniline[25] have been recommended.

Besides the determination of excess substituted aniline by acidimetry in nonaqueous medium, two other approaches are possible. Roth[25] described a micro procedure in which the anhydride sample is treated with 2,4-dichloroaniline in glacial acetic acid for 2 hours. The substituted anilide formed is not separated and the unreacted 2,4-dichloroaniline in the mixture is directly brominated with $0.02N$ bromate-bromide solution. The excess bromine is then determined iodometrically by means of $0.02N$ sodium thiosulfate:

$$(R\text{—}CO)_2O + H_2N\text{—}\underset{Cl}{\bigcirc}\text{—}Cl \rightarrow R\text{—}\underset{O}{\overset{||}{C}}\text{—}NH\text{—}\underset{Cl}{\bigcirc}\text{—}Cl + R\text{—}COOH \quad (11)$$

$$\text{excess } H_2N\text{—}\underset{Cl}{\bigcirc}\text{—}Cl + Br_2 \rightarrow H_2N\text{—}\underset{\underset{Br}{|}}{\underset{Cl}{\bigcirc}}\text{—}Cl + HBr \quad (12)$$

$$\text{excess } Br_2 + 2KI \rightarrow 2KBr + I_2 \quad (13)$$

$$I_2 + 2Na_2S_2O_3 \rightarrow 2NaI + Na_2S_4O_6 \quad (14)$$

It is apparent that no bromination at other positions or on the substituted anilide should take place.

[21] S. Siggia and J. G. Hanna, *Anal. Chem.*, **23**, 1717 (1951).

[22] T. Ellerington and J. J. Nichols, *Analyst*, **82**, 233 (1957).

[23] E. Berl and G. Lunge, eds., *Chemische-technische Untersuchungmethoden, Vol. 3*, 8th ed., Springer, Berlin, 1932, p. 770.

[24] P. Sorensen, *Anal. Chem.*, **28**, 1318 (1956).

[25] H. Roth, *Mikrochim. Acta*, **1958**, 767.

Calcott, English, and Wilbur[26] determined the excess 2,4-dichloroaniline as a primary amine by titration with $0.1N$ sodium nitrite. This method can be reduced to the 0.1 meq. scale.

E. Determination of Acid Anhydrides Based on Their Reactions with Oxalic Acid. Acid anhydride reacts with anhydrous oxalic acid in dry pyridine to liberate carbon monoxide and carbon dioxide according to the following equation:

$$(R-CO)_2O + (COOH)_2 \xrightarrow{C_5H_5N} 2R-COOH + CO_2 + CO \tag{15}$$

In the macro method described by Gottlieb,[27] the sample dissolved in pyridine is directly titrated with $0.3N$ oxalic acid in ethyl methyl ketone until a permanent turbidity is observed. This technique of end point detection is not suitable for microdeterminations. Rosenbaum and Walton[28] treated the sample with a known amount of oxalic acid and back-titrated the excess reagent with standard potassium permanganate solution. Whitford[29] collected the carbon dioxide and carbon monoxide and determined them gasometrically. Both methods can be adapted to the micro scale. The carbon dioxide formed may also be determined gravimetrically by passing the gases through an absorption tube containing Ascarite. It is to be noted that quantitative decomposition of oxalic acid by an acid anhydride is possible only in the absence of water because the latter has strong inhibitory effect on the reaction.

F. Colorimetric Methods for Determining Acid Anhydrides. Acid anhydrides react with hydroxylamine to produce hydroxamic acids which in turn form highly colored chelates with ferric ions:

$$(R-CO)_2O + H_2NOH \rightarrow R-CO(NH-OH) + R-COOH \tag{16}$$
$$3R-CO(NHOH) + FeCl_3 \rightarrow (RCONHO)_3Fe + 3HCl \tag{17}$$

A spectrophotometric method based on this reaction was described by Goddu, Le Blanc, and Wright.[30] Because the absorption maxima vary among different types of anhydrides, the calibration curve should be prepared from a pure sample of the anhydride to be determined.

Liddell and Saville[31] found that certain aromatic amines react with mixture of acid anhydride and nitrite to form diazotates which may be

[26] W. S. Calcott, F. L. English, and O. C. Wilbur, *Ind. Eng. Chem.*, **17**, 942 (1925).
[27] O. R. Gottlieb, *An. Ass. Brasil. Quim.*, **11**, 99 (1956).
[28] C. K. Rosenbaum and J. H. Walton, *J. Am. Chem. Soc.*, **52**, 3366 (1930).
[29] E. S. Whitford, *J. Am. Chem. Soc.*, **47**, 2939 (1925).
[30] R. F. Goddu, N. F. Le Blanc, and C. M. Wright, *Anal. Chem.*, **27**, 1251 (1955).
[31] H. F. Liddell and B. Saville, *Chem. & Ind.*, **16**, 493 (1957).

coupled with alkaline aminonaphtholsulfonic acid to yield intense water soluble dyes:

$$(R-CO)_2O + NO_2^- \rightarrow R-\underset{\underset{O}{\|}}{C}-ONO + R-COO^- \tag{18}$$

$$R-\underset{\underset{O}{\|}}{C}-ONO + Ar-NH_2 \rightarrow Ar-NH-N{=}O \rightleftarrows Ar-N{=}N-OH \tag{19}$$

$$Ar-N{=}N-OH + \quad \underset{H_2N\langle\ \rangle-SO_3Na}{\bigcirc\!\bigcirc} \quad \rightarrow Ar-N{=}N-\underset{H_2N-\langle\ \rangle-SO_3Na}{\bigcirc\!\bigcirc} \tag{20}$$

The colorimetric methods are recommended for the determination of micromole (μmole) quantities of anhydride. They may be adapted to the analysis of 0.1 meq. amounts when other methods prove impracticable.

IV. The Acid Halide Function

A. General. Acid halides differ from other compounds containing the acyl group by the ease with which they react with water in aqueous solution.

$$R-COX + H_2O \rightarrow RCOH + H^+X^- \tag{21}$$

Hence, both the halide ion and the acyl group may be determined in the analysis of the acid halide function.

B. Determination of the Halide Ion in Acid Halides. The halogen content of acid halide may be determined argentimetrically either by the gravimetric or by the volumetric method without preliminary decomposition of the organic compound:

$$R-\underset{\underset{O}{\|}}{C}-X + Ag^+ \rightarrow AgX + R-\underset{\underset{O}{\|}}{C}{}^+ \tag{22}$$

If the parent carboxylic acid is insoluble in water, an organic solvent such as ethanol, 2-propanol, or dioxane may be added. It should be noted that the halogen content in an acid halide sample seldom can be used as a means for purity test, because the sample is usually contaminated with halogen acid.

C. Determination of Acid Halide by Acidimetry

1. Nonaqueous Titration of Acid Halide as a Monoprotic Acid. In a completely nonaqueous system, acid halide reacts mole-per-mole with sodium methoxide according to the following equation:

$$R\!-\!\underset{\underset{O}{\|}}{C}\!-\!X + NaOCH_3 \rightarrow R\!-\!\underset{\underset{O}{\|}}{C}\!-\!OCH_3 + NaX \qquad (23)$$

Fritz and Lisicki[32] dissolved acid chlorides in benzene or benzene-methanol solution and titrated them with $0.1N$ sodium methoxide in benzene-methanol to the Thymol Blue endpoint. This can be adapted to the micro scale. Attention is called to the fact that halogen acid and free carboxylic acid, if present, will be titrated.

2. Titration of Acid Halides as Diprotic Acids. Acid halides react like diprotic acids in aqueous or semi-aqueous media towards strong alkali. Therefore, each mole of acid halide consumes 2 moles of aqueous sodium hydroxide:[33]

$$R\!-\!\underset{\underset{O}{\|}}{C}\!-\!X + 2NaOH \rightarrow R\!-\!COONa + NaX + H_2O \qquad (24)$$

Alternately, the acid halide function may be determined by titration with standardized quaternary ammonium hydroxide in pyridine:[34]

$$R\!-\!\underset{\underset{O}{\|}}{C}\!-\!X + 2R_4NOH \rightarrow R\!-\!\underset{\underset{O}{\|}}{C}\!-\!ONR_4 + R_4NX + H_2O \qquad (25)$$

Alcohols and other hydroxyl compounds should be absent to prevent the formation of ester. Unlike the titration of acid anhydride as dibasic acid, the titration of acid chloride may be performed in two stages to differentiate the endpoint of the strong acid HX from that of the carboxylic acid.

D. Colorimetric Determination of Acid Halides. Like acid anhydrides (see p. 112), acid chlorides may be determined colorimetrically through the corresponding hydroxamic acids:[35]

$$R\!-\!\underset{\underset{O}{\|}}{C}\!-\!X + H_2NOH \rightarrow R\!-\!\underset{\underset{O}{\|}}{C}\!-\!(NHOH) + HX \qquad (26)$$

V. The Acyl Function

A. General. The present section deals with the determination of the acyl function, $R\!-\!\underset{\underset{O}{\|}}{C}\!-\!$, when it is joined to an alkoxyl ($-OR'$) or to an

[32] J. S. Fritz and N. M. Lisicki, *Anal. Chem.*, **23**, 589 (1951).
[33] M. Pesey and R. Willemart, *Bull. Soc. Chim. France*, **15**, 479 (1948).
[34] A. Patchornik and S. E. Rogozinski, *Anal. Chem.*, **31**, 985 (1959).
[35] R. F. Goddu, N. F. Le Blanc, and C. M. Wright, *Anal. Chem.*, **27**, 1251 (1955).

alkimido (—NR₂′) group. Compounds containing such functions are derivatives of carboxylic acids and the purpose of the determination is to regenerate the parent acid and ascertain its proportion in the formation of the compound. The regeneration of the parent acid is always effected through hydrolytic cleavage, while the determination of the liberated acid may be carried out by several methods.

B. Hydrolytic Method for Determination of Acyl Groups

1. Reagents for Hydrolysis. The hydrolysis of esters and amides are represented by equations 27 and 28:

$$R—\underset{\underset{O}{\|}}{C}—OR' + H_2O \rightarrow R—COOH + R'OH \tag{27}$$

$$R—\underset{\underset{O}{\|}}{C}—NR_2' + H_2O \rightarrow R—COOH + R'_2NH \tag{28}$$

Unlike acid halides, the hydrolysis of esters, amides, anilides, and similar compounds do not proceed to completion without heating and the presence of a catalyst. A large variety of hydrolytic reagents for acyl group determination have been proposed and are summarized in Table 6.2.

When sulfuric acid is used, precaution should be taken so that: (1) the reaction mixture does not evaporate to the extent that concentrated sulfuric acid solution is produced, causing oxidation of the organic matter; (2) if sulfur dioxide is formed, it is removed before the determination of the carboxylic acid. p-Toluenesulfonic acid has been favored as it minimizes these two side reactions. Phosphoric acid, if proved effective for the compound in question, would be a better reagent.

The choice of solvent is dependent upon the sample. If the sample and its parent acid are water soluble, an aqueous medium will suffice. Organic solvents are indicated for water-insoluble samples or compounds which give rise to emulsion after hydrolysis. Methanol is a better solvent than ethanol for acyl group determinations since the latter alcohol may be oxidized to acetic acid which introduces errors. If high temperature is necessary for the hydrolysis, ethylene glycol, dioxane, and glycol ethers are recommended because they are miscible with water and will not cause difficulty in the subsequent titration step using aqueous standard alkali solution.

2. Rate of Hydrolysis. The first requirement for a successful determination of the acyl group is the complete cleavage of the ester or amide linkage to give a quantitative yield of the parent acid. The rate of hydrolytic cleavage depends largely on the nature of the compound. As discussed in Chapter 4 under the section on the effect of the radical on the reactivity of the functional group, O-acyl compounds are more readily hydrolyzed than

TABLE 6.2

Hydrolytic Reagents for Acyl Groups

Acidic reagents	Lit. ref.	Alkaline reagents	Lit. ref.
Dilute sulfuric acid	36, 37	Aqueous sodium hydroxide	44
Alcoholic sulfuric acid	38, 39	Sodium hydroxide in methanol	45
Aqueous p-toluenesulfonic acid	40, 41	Sodium hydroxide in ethanol	46
Alcoholic p-toluenesulfonic acid	42	Sodium hydroxide in acetone	47
Solid p-toluenesulfonic acid	41	Potassium hydroxide in ethanol	48
Phosphotungstic acid in dioxane	43	Potassium hydroxide in benzyl alcohol	49
		Potassium methoxide in methanol	50

N-acyl compounds. Alicino[51] reported that O-acetyl groups in sugar acetates are hydrolyzed in $0.01N$ sodium hydroxide solution after standing for 2 hours at 0°C while N-acetyl linkages are not attacked. According to Olsen,[52] fatty acid amides are not quantitatively hydrolyzed by alcoholic caustic, but complete cleavage is effected at the boiling point of ethylene glycol. Chaney and Wolfrom[53] recommended high temperatures for both O-acetyl and N-acetyl groups. Elek and Harte[54] prescribed heating at 100°C for 1 hour if the acetyl is linked to oxygen and for 3 hours if it is linked to nitrogen. This seems to be longer than necessary for most compounds. However, a number of N-acyl compounds may require 3 hours of heating. It is evident that acyl groups attached to a sterically hindered

[36] F. Wenzel, *Monatsh. Chem.*, **18**, 659 (1899).
[37] B. Budesinsky, *Chem. Listy*, **50**, 1936 (1956).
[38] J. Perkins, *J. Chem. Soc.*, **27**, 107 (1905).
[39] J. Phillips, *Ind. Eng. Chem., Anal. Ed.*, **6**, 321 (1934).
[40] A. F. Friedrich and A. Rappoport, *Biochem. Z.*, **251**, 432 (1932).
[41] R. B. Bradbury, *Anal. Chem.*, **21**, 1139 (1949).
[42] K. Freudenberg and W. Harder, *Ann.*, **433**, 230 (1923).
[43] F. U. Vedetz, *Mikrochim. Acta*, **1**, 326 (1937).
[44] A. J. Bailey and J. Robinson, *Mikrochemie*, **15**, 233 (1934).
[45] R. A. Kuhn and H. Roth, *Berichte*, **66**, 1274 (1935).
[46] R. A. Clark and B. E. Christensen, *Ind. Eng. Chem., Anal. Ed.*, **17**, 334 (1945).
[47] M. L. Wolfrom, *J. Am. Chem. Soc.*, **58**, 490 (1936).
[48] E. P. Clark, *Ind. Eng. Chem. Anal. Ed.*, **8**, 487 (1936).
[49] S. Sabetay and J. Sivadjian, *J. Pharm. Chim.*, **13**, 530 (1931).
[50] L. Mazor and T. Meisel, *Anal. Chim. Acta*, **20**, 130 (1959).
[51] J. F. Alicino, *Anal. Chem.*, **20**, 590 (1948).
[52] S. Olsen, *Die Chemie*, **56**, 202 (1943).
[53] A. Chaney and M. L. Wolfrom, *Anal. Chem.*, **28**, 1614 (1956).
[54] A. Elek and R. A. Harte, *Ind. Eng. Chem., Anal. Ed.*, **8**, 267 (1936).

group such as the tertiary butyl group are more difficult to hydrolyze. A general micro method for the hydrolysis of acyl compounds has been developed by Ma and Gary[55] and tested against a wide range of esters, amides, and anilides (see experiment 13).

3. Apparatus for Microhydrolysis

A. REACTION VESSEL WITH CONDENSER. Several apparatus for micro-determination of the acyl group have been described in the literature. The early reaction flask of Pregl and Soltys[56] was improved by Kuhn and Roth[57], as shown in Figure 6.1. The reaction vessel is a three-necked flask which is connected to a quartz condenser. When the condenser is placed in the upright position (dotted line) it serves as a reflux condenser. When distillation of the liberated acid is desired, the condenser is joined in the downward position.

The Wiesenberger apparatus[58] (Fig. 6.2) consists of a long necked flask connected to a reflux condenser. An adapter is inserted for distillation (Fig. 6.2B). Elek and Harte[54] used a flask with a side arm carrying a trap, as shown in Figure 6.3. The condenser is used for subsequent distillation under reduced pressure and not for reflux, since the reaction mixture is heated below the boiling point of the solvent in a water bath. It will be noted that all three apparatus are so constructed as to introduce liquid into the reaction vessel during the reflux or distillation; this is essential in order to avoid over-concentration of the reaction mixture which may cause the decomposition of the reagent or reaction products. In the apparatus of Chaney and Wolfrom[53] (Fig. 6.4), the volume of the solution is controlled by a leveling device, and the reaction flask is heated by electric tape.

It should be noted that the early assemblies of Pregl, Soltys, Roth, and others were primarily designed for elegant procedures using samples of a few milligrams. When these assemblies were modified or changed for use with samples of 10—15 mg., greater precision and accuracy were obtained.

B. HYDROLYSIS IN A SEALED VESSEL. Cleavage of the acyl group by hydrolyzing the sample in a sealed vessel has several advantages: (a) the reaction mixture has no danger of being over concentrated; (b) the reaction mixture can be heated at a temperature above its boiling point to accelerate the rate of hydrolysis; (c) volatile acids will not be lost from the condenser or through faulty joints.

Serum bottles of 50–100 ml. capacity were used by Smith, Mitchell, and

[55] T. S. Ma and H. Gary, unpublished work; H. Gary, Master's Thesis, Brooklyn College, 1960.
[56] F. Pregl and A. Soltys, Mikrochemie, 7, 1 (1929).
[57] R. Kuhn and H. Roth, Berichte, 66, 202 (1943).
[58] E. Wiesenberger, Mikrochemie, 33, 51 (1948).

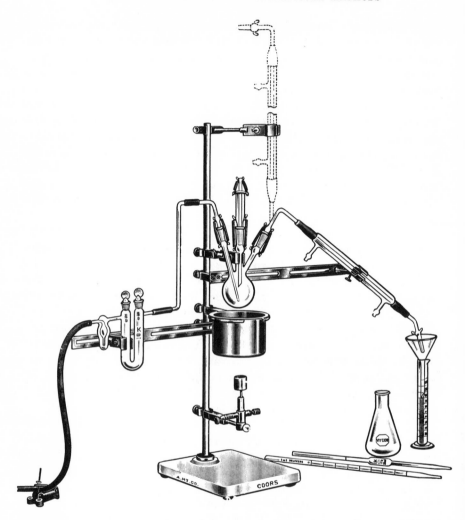

Fig. 6.1. Acetyl apparatus of Kuhn and Roth. Courtesy of A. H. Thomas Co.

Billmeyer[59] for the hydrolysis of esters on the semimicro scale. The bottle is sealed with a rubber cap and the sample taken is about 1 meq. For microdeterminations, sealed glass tubes are preferable. A simple technique of making sealed reaction tubes from glass tubing is given in Chapter 12 (see experiment 5).

[59] D. M. Smith, J. Mitchell, Jr., and A. M. Billmeyer, *Anal. Chem.*, **24**, 1847 (1952).

4. Liberation of the Acid after Hydrolysis. After the hydrolysis of the sample containing the acyl group, it is a general practice to separate the acid from the reaction mixture before the determination of the acid. Because the early micro methods for the determination of acyl groups were concerned with the acetyl group only, distillation of the acetic acid formed was the standard procedure. The solution is directly distilled after acid hydrolysis. A mineral acid, such as sulfuric acid or phosphoric acid, is added to acidify the reaction mixture after alkaline hydrolysis. The distillation method is applicable to other volatile acids, but its efficiency diminishes as the boiling point of the carboxylic acid increases. Since the ion-exchange resins have become a common reagent in the analytical laboratory, the determination of acyl groups is now extended to compounds which are derivatives of high-boiling and nonvolatile acids.

A. SEPARATION BY DISTILLATION. The apparatus discussed in Section V-B-3A includes provision for the distillation of acetic acid. In the apparatus of Kuhn and Roth[57] and Wiesenberger,[58] the acetic acid is distilled under atmospheric pressure, while distillation under reduced pressure is employed in the apparatus of Elek and Harte.[54] Comparison of these two

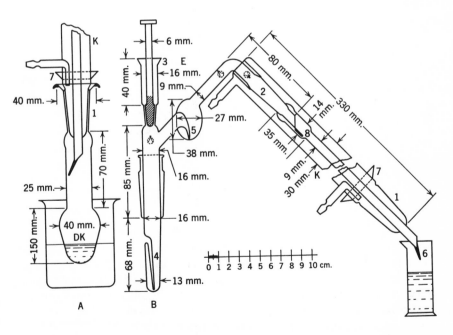

Fig. 6.2. Acetyl apparatus of Wiesenberger. Courtesy of *Mikrochimica Acta.*

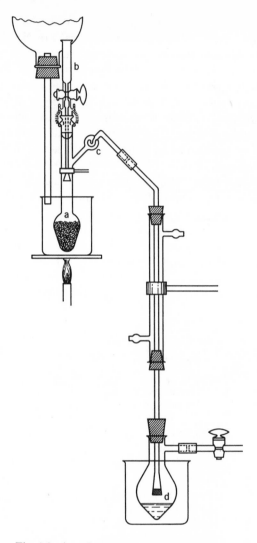

Fig. 6.3. Acetyl apparatus of Elek and Harte.

procedures did not reveal significant difference of results.[60] The volume of the reaction mixture being distilled should be controlled during distillation. If the volume is too small, decomposition of the reagent and products will take place. On the other hand, total recovery of the acetic acid is difficult to attain when the reaction mixture is too dilute.

[60] A. Steyermark and E. E. Loeschauer, *J. Ass. Official Agr. Chemists*, **37**, 433 (1954).

When the hydrolysis is carried out in a sealed vessel, the reaction mixture is transferred to a separate distilling apparatus. Liberation of acetic acid by passing a current of steam is the preferred procedure. The distilling apparatus described by Schöniger, Lieb, and Ibrahim[61] (Fig. 6.5) is similar to the conventional micro-Kjeldahl distilling flask. The apparatus of Ma and Breyer,[62] shown in Figure 6.6, is adapted from Tashinian et al.[63] Its detailed operation is given in experiment 43. This assembly is sturdy and easy to clean.

[61] W. Schöniger, H. Lieb, and M. G. D. Ibrahim, *Mikrochim. Acta*, **1954**, 96.
[62] T. S. Ma and R. Breyer, *Microchem. J.*, **4**, 484 (1960).
[63] V. H. Tashinian, M. J. Baker, and C. W. Koch, *Anal. Chem.*, **28**, 1304 (1956).

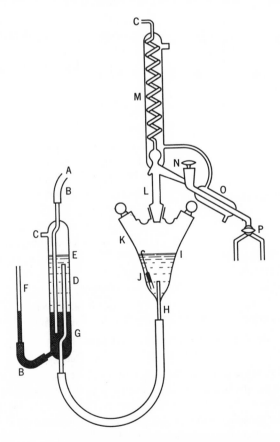

Fig. 6.4. Acetyl apparatus of Chaney and Wolfrom. Courtesy of *Analytical Chemistry*.

B. SEPARATION BY ION-EXCHANGE RESIN.   Tani and Nara[64] reported the use of cation-exchange resin for the determination of the acetyl and benzoyl groups. After hydrolysis with 5N ethanolic sodium hydroxide solution and heating in a water bath, the reaction mixture is passed through a column filled with Amberlite IR-120 and the eluate containing acetic acid or benzoic acid is collected and titrated. A thorough investigation of the ion-exchange method for acyl group microdetermination was carried out by Ma and Gary.[65] It was found that a great variety of acyl groups could be determined. The detailed procedure is given in experiment 13.

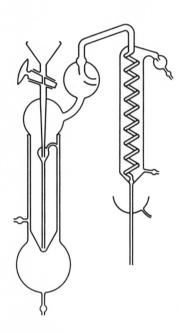

Fig. 6.5. Distilling apparatus of Schöniger, Lieb, and Ibrahim. Courtesy of *Mikrochimica Acta*.

5. Determination of the Liberated Acid

A. ACIDIMETRIC METHOD. The liberated carboxylic acid can be titrated with 0.01N sodium hydroxide using phenolphthalein as indicator. Because the solution is usually contaminated with carbon dioxide, it is generally boiled for 20 seconds immediately before titration. Kainz[66] observed that some acetic acid was lost by boiling in an open flask and he proposed to suspend a cooling cone or finger condenser in the Erlenmeyer flask to condense the acetic acid.

B. IODOMETRIC METHOD.   In this procedure, the organic acid formed is treated with an excess of potassium iodide and iodate. The liberated iodine is determined by titration with 0.01N sodium thiosulfate:

$$6RCOOH + 5KI + KIO_3 \rightarrow 6RCOOK + 3H_2O + 3I_2 \qquad (29)$$

$$3I_2 + 6Na_2S_2O_3 \rightarrow 6NaI + 3Na_2S_4O_6 \qquad (30)$$

Carbon dioxide does not interfere with the determination but sulfur dioxide, if present, will react with iodine according to the following equation:

[64] H. Tani and A. Nara, *J. Pharm. Soc. Japan*, **74**, 1399 (1954).

[65] T. S. Ma and H. Gary, unpublished work.

[66] G. Kainz, *Mikrochemie*, **35**, 89 (1950).

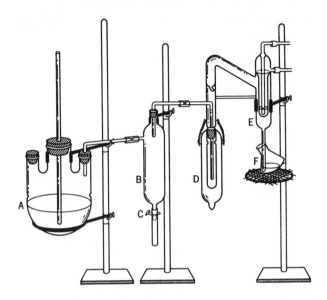

Fig. 6.6. Distilling apparatus of Ma and Breyer. Courtesy of *Microchemical Journal*.

$$SO_2 + I_2 + H_2O \rightarrow H_2SO_4 + 2HI \qquad (31)$$

The iodometric method was first recommended by Friedrich and Rappoport[40] and has been favored by various workers.[54,67-69] However, Inglis[70] reported that alkalimetric titration was better than iodometry for the determination of acetyl groups in acetylated carbohydrates.

c. BACK-TITRATION OF EXCESS ALKALI. Mazor and Meisel[50] described a method for the determination of acetyl groups by treating the sample with standard potassium methoxide and back-titrating the unreacted alkali with standard acid. In view of the corrosive nature of the strong alkali, complication is expected. This method is therefore not as accurate as those which involve the separation of the carboxylic acid formed.

C. Gas Chromatographic Method. Gas chromatography was used by Spingler and Market[71] to determine acetyl and formyl groups. Since the procedure entails the preparation of calibration curves, it is not as simple

[67] J. B. Niederl and V. Niederl, *Micromethods of Quantitative Organic Analysis*, 2nd ed., Wiley, New York, 1942, p. 257.

[68] A. Steyermark, *Quantitative Organic Microanalysis*, Blakiston, Philadelphia, 1951 p. 244.

[69] S. Mizukami, T. Ieki, and C. Koyama, *J. Pharm. Soc. Japan*, 76, 465 (1956).

[70] A. S. Inglis, *Mikrochim. Acta*, 1958, 228.

[71] H. Spingler and F. Market, *Mikrochim. Acta*, 1959, 122.

and convenient as the titration methods. However, it is useful for simultaneous microdetermination of several acyl groups present in a mixture.

D. Colorimetric Methods.   Colorimetric methods[72,73] for the determination of acetyl groups are based on the hydroxamic acid reaction (see p. 61). They are recommended for quantities in the microequivalent range. The chemistry of the formation of the hydroxamate complex was discussed in detail in Section VII of Chapter 3. Acid anhydrides, halides, and esters react with hydroxylamine to form hydroxamic acids which in presence of ferric ion form the colored complex. The reaction can be modified so that acid anhydrides and chlorides will react, whereas esters do not.[74] Alcohols and carboxylic acids must first be converted to esters for the formation of the hydroxamate complex.

VI. The Alkoxyl Function

A. General.   The alkoxyl group is a function composed of an alkyl radical attached to an oxygen atom. It is present in ethers (R'—OR), esters (R'—C—OR), acetals (R₂'═C—OR), and hemiacetals (R₂'═C—OR)

$$R'\text{—}\underset{\displaystyle O}{\overset{\displaystyle \|}{C}}\text{—OR} \qquad R_2'\text{═}\underset{\displaystyle OR}{\overset{\displaystyle |}{C}}\text{—OR} \qquad R_2'\text{═}\underset{\displaystyle OH}{\overset{\displaystyle |}{C}}\text{—OR}$$

and is generally analyzed by heating these compounds with hydriodic acid to convert the alkoxyl group to an alkyl iodide:

$$-OR + HI \rightarrow -OH + RI \qquad (32)$$

The alkyl iodide is then separated from the reaction mixture by distillation and determined by its iodine content by a gravimetric, titrimetric, or gasometric procedure.

Aliphatic alcohols (ROH) also contain the alkoxyl group and they are converted to alkyl iodides when reacted with hydriodic acid. However, they are seldom analyzed for their alkoxyl contents.

The alkoxyl group is probably the most thoroughly investigated group among all organic functions. This function was first determined by Zeisel[75] in 1885 on a macro scale. Since Pregl[76] adapted the Zeisel method to microanalysis in 1912, many workers have reinvestigated the microdetermination of alkoxyl groups and numerous publications have appeared

[72] J. L. Reissig, J. L. Strominger, and L. F. Leloir, *J. Biol. Chem.*, **217**, 959 (1955).

[73] E. A. McComb and R. M. McCready, *Anal. Chem.*, **29**, 819 (1957).

[74] N. D. Cheronis and J. B. Entrikin, *Semimicro Qualitative Organic Analysis*, Interscience, New York, 1957, p. 229.

[75] S. Zeisel, *Monatsh. Chem.*, **6**, 989 (1885).

[76] F. Pregl, *Quantitative Organic Microanalysis*, transl. by E. Fyleman, Blakiston, Philadelphia, 1924.

in the literature in which the procedures, apparatus, as well as the precision and accuracy of the analytical results are reported. A critical discussion is given below; a general method will be found in Chapter 13 (see experiment 31).

B. Cleavage of the Alkoxyl Group

1. Rate of Reaction. The rate of cleavage of the alkoxyl group on treatment with hydriodic acid varies with the type of the alkoxyl compound. Acetals and hemiacetals are readily attacked by hydriodic acid, but it should be noted that the first stage of the reaction is acid hydrolysis of the compound to give the parent aldehyde (or ketone) and alcohol:

$$R_2'{=}C(OR)_2 + HOH \xrightarrow{(HI)} R_2'C{=}O + 2ROH \qquad (33)$$

The success of the determination depends on the quantitative conversion of the alcohol to the corresponding iodide:

$$ROH + HI \rightarrow RI + H_2O \qquad (34)$$

Therefore, if the alcohol is a low boiling substance such as methanol, precaution should be taken to prevent its volatilization before reacting with hydriodic acid.

With the exception of very low boiling esters, the cleavage of alkoxyl group from this class of compound can be accomplished by gentle heating with hydriodic acid. On the other hand, ethers are difficult to cleave and two different alkyl iodides may be produced simultaneously if the radicals in the ether are different:

$$R{-}O{-}R' + HI \rightarrow RI + R'OH \qquad (35)$$
$$R{-}O{-}R' + HI \rightarrow ROH + R'I \qquad (36)$$

If R = methyl and R' = a long chain alkyl radical or an aromatic ring, the reaction will produce mainly methyl iodide and any methanol formed will also be converted to methyl iodide according to equation 34. However, if R and R' do not differ much in their chain lengths, both RI and R'I will be produced and the amount of alkyl iodide recovered depends on the boiling points of RI and R'I. For similar reason cleavage of diethyl ether $(C_2H_5{-}O{-}C_2H_5)$ will produce two equivalents of ethyl iodide when it reacts quantitatively with hydriodic acid.

2. Reagents. The hydriodic acid used for alkoxyl determination should be within certain limits of concentration. Common hydriodic acid (sp. gr. 1.57, about 47%) is not suitable. The microanalytical reagent which is commercially[77] available contains about 57% hydrogen iodide. It darkens

[77] Fisher Scientific Co., New York, lists "Hydriodic acid, 57%, special for microanalysis."

on storage, but does not affect the alkoxyl results, according to Brancone.[78] A method of obtaining a satisfactory quality of hydriodic acid was described by Steyermark.[79] Samsel and McHard[80] specified that the concentration of hydriodic acid should be of 56.7–57% concentration, while Ware[81] recommended hydriodic acid of sp. gr. 1.96. The latter variety is very difficult to keep. It should be noted that besides the initial concentration of hydriodic acid, the amount of solvent used in carrying out the cleavage reaction should be controlled in order not to over-dilute the hydriodic acid. Kirsten and Rogozinsky[82] described an iodizing mixture which consists of hydriodic acid and phosphorus. The stability of this reagent mixture has been confirmed by Nessonova and Pogosyants.[83]

The common solvents for alkoxyl compounds are anhydrous phenol and acetic anhydride. These solvents are employed because of their solvent power on solid ethers. Acetic anhydride may be preferably replaced by propionic anhydride[84] because the latter has a higher boiling point.

3. Methods of Mixing and Heating. In the microdetermination of alkoxyl groups, the sample solution is heated with the reagent in a reaction vessel of small volume so that the resulting alkyl iodide can be completely recovered by sweeping with a current of inert gas. Because the reaction vessel is provided with narrow neck and side-arm, the sample is weighed in a small container in order to introduce it into the vessel. Pregl[76] prepared a micro tin foil cup for this purpose; other workers suggested the use of cigarette paper,[85] gelatin capsules,[80] and ampoules,[86] or the introduction of solid sample in pellet form.[81] However, it is more convenient to weigh solids in a charging tube (see Fig. 5.6) and liquids in a micro glass cup (see Fig. 5.8).

Heating of the reaction mixture should be carefully controlled. Too rapid heating may remove some of the sample unchanged; heating at high temperature may cause excessive decomposition of the hydriodic acid. When heating is done by using a free flame, bumping usually occurs. Pregl relied on the precipitation of stannic iodide besides gentle tapping of the reaction vessel to prevent bumping. This method is tedious and tends to

[78] L. Brancone, private communication.

[79] A. Steyermark, *Anal. Chem.*, **20**, 368 (1948).

[80] E. P. Samsel and J. A. McHard, *Ind. Eng. Chem., Anal. Ed.*, **14**, 750 (1942).

[81] M. Ware, *Mikrochemie*, **2**, 352 (1930).

[82] W. Kirsten and S. E. Rogozinsky, *Mikrochim. Acta*, **1955**, 786.

[83] G. D. Nessonova and E. K. Pogosyants, *Zavodsk. Lab.*, **24**, 953 (1958).

[84] B. E. Christensen, L. Friedman, and Y. Sato, *Ind. Eng. Chem., Anal. Ed.*, **13**, 276 (1941).

[85] E. P. Clark, *J. Am. Chem. Soc.*, **51**, 1479 (1929).

[86] S. V. Syavtsillo and E. A. Bondarevskaya, *Zhur. Anal. Khim.*, **11**, 613 (1956).

dilute the hydriodic acid. Belcher, Fildes, and Nutten[87] used a drop of mercury or some platinum tetrahedra. A more convenient method to eliminate bumping is placing the inlet tube of the carrier gas close to the bottom of the reaction flask and keeping the temperature of the reaction mixture below its boiling point. Constant vapor baths using xylene[88] or cyclohexanol[89] have been proposed, but the simplest way is to place the reaction flask in a metal block which is electrically heated. For some samples it is necessary to maintain different temperatures at several stages in order to get satisfactory results; a heating block which is electronically controlled (see Fig. 5.19) is ideal for such occasions.[90]

Cleavage of the alkoxyl function by heating the sample with the reagent in a sealed vessel was described by Furter.[91] Kirsten and Rogozinsky[82] heated the reaction mixture in a stoppered tube. Because these methods entail the cutting or opening the reaction vessel in the subsequent separation of alkyl iodide, they are more involved than the open vessel method. The sealed tube technique is recommended for volatile compounds which are resistant to hydrogen iodide cleavage. However, one should keep in mind that hydrogen iodide is also a reducing agent and some alkyl iodide may be converted to the hydrocarbon on prolonged heating in the sealed tube:

$$RI + HI \rightarrow RH + I_2 \tag{37}$$

4. Limitations of Alkoxyl Determination. Microdetermination of the alkoxyl function is usually known by its representative group—the methoxyl group. This is due to the fact that: (1) the methoxyl group gives the best results in nearly all apparatus and methods for alkoxyl determination, and (2) methoxyl group determination is in great demand in the analysis of methyl ethers of sugars, cellulose, and many natural products. So far as the cleavage reaction (eq. 32) is concerned, the methoxyl group and its higher homologs are cleaved in approximately equal rates. On the other hand, the ease of separation of the alkyl iodides from the reaction mixture, which contains iodine and hydriodic acid, is a function of the volatility of the iodides. Table 6.3 lists the boiling points of a number of alkyl iodides. It may be noted that the hydriodic acid reagent boils at about 130°C and vapor pressure of iodine is approximately 1 mm. at 40°C, 40 mm. at 100°C, and 100 mm. at 120°C. Therefore, while methyl iodide can be recovered easily by distillation, there are problems in dealing with

[87] R. Belcher, J. E. Fildes, and A. J. Nutten, *Anal. Chim. Acta*, **13**, 16 (1955).
[88] H. G. Arlt and K. Sarkanen, *Anal. Chem.*, **28**, 1502 (1956).
[89] A. W. Billitzer, *Lab. Practice*, **7**, 289 (1958).
[90] T. S. Ma and R. T. Schenck, *Mikrochemie*, **40**, 245 (1953).
[91] M. F. Furter, *Helv. Chim. Acta*, **21**, 1144 (1938).

TABLE 6.3

Boiling Points of Alkyl Iodides

Alkyl iodide	B.P., °C
CH_3—	42
C_2H_5—	72
iso—C_3H_7—	89
n—C_3H_7—	102
tert—C_4H_9—	100 (dec.)
sec—C_4H_9—	117
iso—C_4H_9—	120
n—C_4H_9—	131
tert—C_5H_{11}—	125
iso—C_5H_{11}—	148
act—C_5H_{11}—	148
n—C_5H_{11}—	156

alkoxyl groups containing more than three carbon atoms. However, successful determinations of butoxyl and pentoxyl groups have been reported. A method for determining the butoxyl group was described by Shaw.[92] Ditrych, Rejhova, and Ulbrich[93] determined n-butoxyl groups by placing the reaction vessel in a bath of 175°C, keeping the water condenser above the vessel at 40°C, and sweeping for 3 hours. Kuck[94] reported the complete recovery of n-butyl iodide after flushing the reaction flask with a current of carbon dioxide for a week; Clark[95] claimed that this could be accomplished in a relatively short time. Using alkyl esters of 2-methoxybenzoic acid as test samples, Yohe, Hill, and Clark[96] effected the recovery of both methoxyl and butoxyl groups in 45 minutes and both methoxyl and pentoxyl groups in 90 minutes employing the Pregl apparatus. It is apparent that the temperature of the carrier gas, speed of bubbling, distance between the reaction flask and the receiver, and the efficiency of the scrubber are all important in the recovery of the alkyl iodide. Inglis[97] ascribed a rapid flow of gas as the essential factor for good results, and he reported a case where no methoxyl group was found by one procedure while quantitative yield was obtained by another.

As alkyl bromides and chlorides have lower boiling points than the

[92] B. M. Shaw, Soc. Chem. Ind., 66, 147 (1947).

[93] Z. Ditrych, H. Rejhova, and V. Ulbrich, Chem. Listy, 49, 869 (1955).

[94] J. A. Kuck, Mikrochemie, 36–37, 65 (1951).

[95] H. S. Clark, private communication.

[96] G. F. Yohe, D. R. Hill, and H. S. Clark, Trans. Illinois State Acad. Sci., 43, 75 (1950).

[97] A. S. Inglis, Mikrochim. Acta, 1957, 677.

corresponding iodides, their formation would be useful for the determination of alkoxyl groups. Unfortunately, hydrobromic and hydrochloric acids are not suitable for the cleavage of alkoxyl groups. Recently, Gerrard, Lappert, and Silver[93] investigated the fission of ethers by boron trichloride at $-80°C$ in pentane and found that alkyl chlorides were produced exclusively from the electron-releasing group according to the following equations:

$$ROR' + BCl_3 \rightarrow RO—BCl_2 + R'Cl \qquad (38)$$
$$2ROR' + BCl_3 \rightarrow (RO)_2BCl + 2R'Cl \qquad (39)$$

These reactions have not been explored as yet for analytical application.

C. The Various Apparatus for Alkoxyl Determination. The first apparatus for microdetermination of alkoxyl groups was designed by Pregl.[76] As shown in Figure 6.7, the sample is heated with hydriodic acid in the reaction flask *SK* while a current of carbon dioxide enters by the side arm *A* and carries the vapors (alkyl iodide, hydrogen iodide, and iodine) through the air condenser *SR* into the scrubbing tube *W*. The hydrogen iodide and iodine are retained in the scrubber while alkyl iodide passes through the delivery tube *E* into the receiver *B* where precipitation of silver iodide takes place. This apparatus gives satisfactory results in expert hands. However, it is fragile, delicate to operate, and cumbersome to clean. Modifications of the Pregl apparatus in order to remove these difficulties were proposed by Rigakos,[99] Christensen and King,[100] Wright and White,[101] Neuman,[102] Belcher, Fildes, and Nutten,[87] and Inglis.[97] The apparatus described by the last worker (Fig. 6.8) appears to have the best features.

Vieböck and Schwappach[103] originated the titrimetric determination of alkyl iodide and proposed an apparatus shown in Figure 6.9. The assembly includes a condenser which is open at the top and two scrubber tubes, the one next to the delivery tube being empty. The reaction flask has a capacity larger than that of the Pregl apparatus since it holds 6 ml. of hydriodic acid instead of 2 ml. as prescribed in the Pregl procedure. Clark[104] investigated the method of Vieböck and Schwappach and suggested changes in the design. Other modifications were described by Kahovec[105] and White.[106]

[98] W. Gerrard, M. F. Lappert, and H. B. Silver, *J. Chem. Soc.*, **1956**, 4987.

[99] D. P. Rigakos, *J. Am. Chem. Soc.*, **53**, 3903 (1931).

[100] B. E. Christensen and A. King, *Ind. Eng. Chem., Anal. Ed.*, **8**, 194 (1936).

[101] B. F. Wright and E. V. White, *Can. J. Research*, **14**, 427 (1936).

[102] F. Neuman, *Berichte*, **70**, 734 (1937).

[103] F. Vieböck and A. Schwappach, *Berichte*, **63**, 2818 (1930).

[104] E. P. Clark, *J. Assoc. Official Agr. Chemists*, **15**, 136 (1932); **22**, 100, 622 (1939).

[105] L. Kahovec, *Mikrochemie*, **14**, 341 (1934).

[106] T. White, *Analyst*, **68**, 366 (1943).

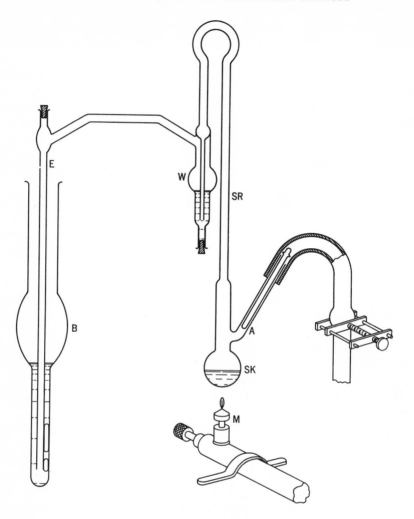

Fig. 6.7. Alkoxyl apparatus of Pregl. Reprinted from F. Pregl, *Quantitative Organic Microanalysis*, translated by E. Fyleman, Blakiston, Philadelphia, 1924.

Elek[107] described an apparatus which is shown in Figure 6.10. This apparatus is composed of three parts: (1) the reaction flask *A* which has an inlet tube for the carrier gas affixed close to the bottom of the flask; (2) the condenser-scrubber portion *B* which is connected to the reaction flask by a ground-glass joint; (3) the delivery tube which is joined to *C* by means

---

[107] A. Elek, *Ind. Eng. Chem., Anal. Ed.*, **11**, 174 (1939).

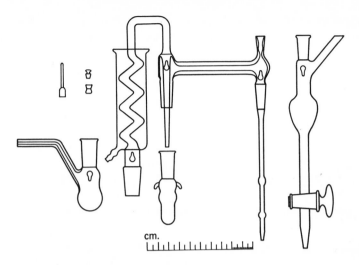

Fig. 6.8. Alkoxyl apparatus of Inglis. Courtesy of *Mikrochimica Acta*.

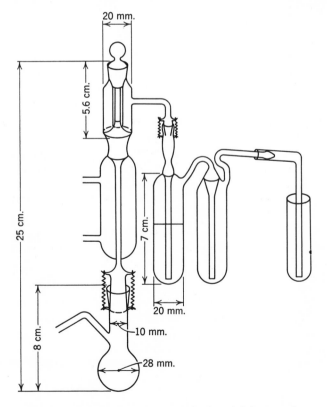

Fig. 6.9. Alkoxyl apparatus of Vieböck and Schwappach.

of a short piece of rubber tubing. When the titrimetric method is used, a delivery tube with glass spiral and a receiver with a siphon arrangement are employed, as shown in the diagram. When the gravimetric finish is desired, a simple glass tubing and the Pregl receiver are employed.

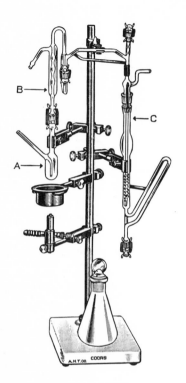

The Elek apparatus was the most popular micro alkoxyl apparatus in America until the ACS apparatus,[108] recommended by the Committee on Microchemical Apparatus of the Division of Analytical Chemistry, American Chemical Society, appeared in 1956. The ACS Committee apparatus, shown in Figure 6.11, was adapted from the apparatus of Clark.[104] It has been tested by collaborative study.[109] Attention is called to the fact that, when the ACS apparatus is used, 8 ml. of hydriodic should be delivered into the reaction flask. This is because of the large volume of the flask. When smaller amounts of hydriodic acid are used, the results tend to be low.[110]

In order to recover the sample which may escape from the reaction flask unchanged, Wiesenberger[111] attached to the flask a tube containing glass beads wetted with hydriodic acid. Steyermark[112] used an apparatus which has two reaction flasks connected to each other. Both flasks are charged with hydriodic acid, but they are heated separately by two microburners.

Fig. 6.10. Alkoxyl apparatus of Elek. Courtesy of A. H. Thomas Co.

Furter[91] designed an apparatus (Fig. 6.12) for heating the sample with hydriodic acid in a closed vessel. The reaction flask B, having a volume of about 15 ml., is sealed after the introduction of the sample, solvents, and

[108] A. Steyermark, H. K. Alber, V. A. Aluise, E. W. D. Huffman, E. L. Jolley, J. A. Kuck, J. J. Moran, and C. L. Ogg, Anal. Chem., 28, 112 (1956).

[109] A. Steyermark, J. Assoc. Official. Agr. Chemists, 39, 401 (1956).

[110] T. S. Ma and O. Phillips, unpublished work.

[111] E. Wiesenberger, Mikrochemie, 33, 51 (1947).

[112] A. Steyermark, Anal. Chem., 20, 368 (1948); Quantitative Organic Microanalysis, Blakiston, Philadelphia, 1951, p. 233.

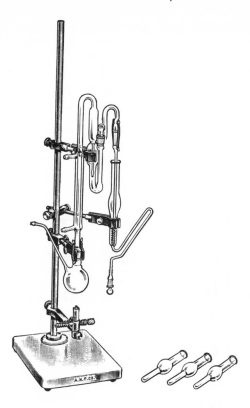

Fig. 6.11. Alkoxyl apparatus recommended by the American Chemical Society Committee. Courtesy of A. H. Thomas Co.

hydriodic acid. It is then heated for 1–4 hours at 135°C. After cooling to room temperature and in a Dewar flask containing ether-dry ice mixture, the tip D is broken and the flask is joined to the distilling head K. The side arm E is cut open, connected to the source of carbon dioxide, and the flask B is heated to distill the alkyl iodide through the scrubbing tube W and delivery tube R into the receiver.

The device for heating the reaction mixture in a glass-stoppered tube as described by Kirsten and Rogozinsky[82] is shown in Figure 6.13L. After cleavage of the alkoxyl group is completed, the reaction tube is opened and the contents transferred to the distilling unit.

Other apparatus which purported to improve and simplify the determination of alkoxyl groups were described by Slotta and Haberland,[113]

[113] K. H. Slotta and G. Haberland, *Berichte*, **65**, 127 (1932).

Houghton and Wilson,[114] and Bethge and Carlson.[115] Samsel and McHard[80] presented an assembly for analyzing methyl and ethyl cellulose. Bailey[116] described an apparatus for alkoxyl determinations in pulp and paper research. Hoffman and Wolfrom[117] proposed a unit for alkoxyl compounds which have high vapor pressure or react rapidly with hydriodic acid. Shaw[92] described an apparatus for determining butoxyl groups in resins.

D. Separation of Alkyl Iodide from Hydrogen Iodide and Iodine. Since the alkyl iodide produced by the cleavage of the alkoxyl group is

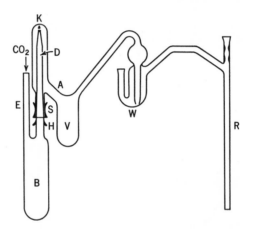

Fig. 6.12. Alkoxyl apparatus of Furter.

usually determined by its iodine content, other iodine-containing substances (hydrogen iodide and iodine) must be completely removed from the train before the gas mixture reaches the receiver. Pregl[76] filled the scrubbing tube with a suspension of red phosphorus in water; this method is retained by Roth[118] in the latest edition of Pregl's classical manual. Phosphorus reacts with iodine in water according to the following equations:

$$2P + 3I_2 \rightarrow 2PI_3 \tag{40}$$

$$PI_3 + 3H_2O \rightarrow H_3PO_3 + 3HI \tag{41}$$

[114] A. A. Houghton and H. A. B. Wilson, *Analyst*, **69**, 363 (1944); **70**, 19 (1945).

[115] P. O. Bethge and O. T. Carlson, *Anal. Chim. Acta.*, **15**, 279 (1956).

[116] A. J. Bailey, *Anal. Chem.*, **14**, 181 (1942).

[117] D. O. Hoffman and M. L. Wolfrom, *Anal. Chem.*, **19**, 225 (1947).

[118] H. Roth, *Pregl-Roth: Quantitative organische Mikroanalyse*, 7th ed., Springer, Vienna, 1958, p. 247.

Presumably a dilute solution of hydriodic acid does not liberate hydrogen iodide, but the efficacy of this method to separate alkyl iodide from both hydriodic acid and iodine is open to question. Elek[107] recommended a combination of phosphorus suspension and 5% cadmium sulfate in water, taking advantage of the formation of the cadmium complex ion $(CdI_4)^{-2}$:

$$4HI + 2CdSO_4 \rightarrow Cd(CdI_4) + 2H_2SO_4 \qquad (42)$$

While the mixture of red phosphorus and cadmium sulfate is satisfactory, it suffers from the disadvantage of being heterogeneous. The red phospho-

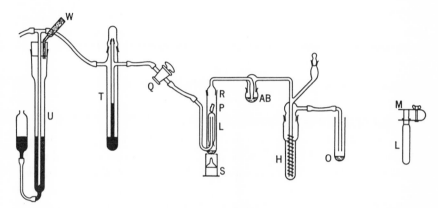

Fig. 6.13. Alkoxyl apparatus of Kirsten and Rogozinsky. Courtesy of *Mikrochimica Acta*.

rus tends to settle down below the inlet tube—this is especially true in alkoxyl apparatus which has a bent tube and ground-glass stopper. As a result, the gas mixture may bubble through the scrubbing solution without coming into contact with the red phosphorus.

Friedrich[119] proposed to replace red phosphorus with 5% sodium thiosulfate solution which removes iodine according to the reaction:

$$I_2 + 2Na_2S_2O_3 \rightarrow Na_2S_4O_6 + 2NaI \qquad (43)$$

A solution containing equal portions of 5% sodium thiosulfate and 5% cadmium sulfate became the favorite scrubbing medium until some workers suspected that the use of sodium thiosulfate caused low methoxyl values due to the solubility of methyl iodide in this reagent. White[120] reported that, when sodium thiosulfate was used alone in the scrubber, the results

[119] H. Friedrich, *Z. Physiol. Chem.*, **163**, 141 (1927).
[120] E. P. White, *Ind. Eng. Chem., Anal. Ed.*, **16**, 207 (1944).

were 55–70% lower than theory. He proposed to suppress the solubility of methyl iodide by adding a salt solution containing sodium chloride, sodium carbonate, and cadmium sulfate. Heron and co-workers[121] made a critical study of the methoxyl determination and reported that erratic results were traced to the use of thiosulfate. However, Inglis[97] claimed that perfect methoxyl values were obtained when 1 ml. of 5% sodium thiosulfate was placed in the scrubbing chamber.

Recently, alkaline solutions have been recommended as the scrubbing agent. Heron and co-workers[121] used a 5% sodium acetate solution. Belcher and co-workers[87] favored sodium antimony tartrate, while Kirsten and Rogozinsky[82] employed potassium bicarbonate. It should be realized that hydrogen iodide and iodine are converted to the stable iodide and iodate ions in an alkaline medium (eqs. 44 and 45), but iodine will be regenerated if the solution becomes acidic:

$$HI + OH^- \rightarrow I^- + H_2O \tag{44}$$
$$3I_2 + 6OH^- \rightarrow 5I^- + IO_3^- + 3H_2O \tag{45}$$

The use of solid alkaline absorber was described by Vecera and Spevak[122] who prepared a scrubbing medium by impregnating antimony potassium tartrate on kieselguhr, and by Filipovic and Stefanac,[123] who filled the scrubber chamber with Ascarite (sodium hydroxide on abestos). Ma and Schachter[123a] have designed a scrubber filled with cationic ion-exchange resin (see experiment 52). Solid absorbers have a great advantage over scrubbing fluids since the latter may be sucked back into the reaction flask and spoil the determination.

E. Determination of Alkyl Iodide.   The determination of the alkyl iodide produced from the cleavage of the alkoxyl group is effected by determining its iodine content. This may be performed by a gravimetric, titrimetric, or gasometric procedure.

1. Gravimetric Methods.   Pregl[76] used the microgravimetric method by absorbing the alkyl iodide in 2 ml. of 4% silver nitrate solution in 95% ethanol. Precipitation of silver iodide takes place while the gas mixture bubbles through the receiver (see Fig. 6.7). Water and nitric acid are added and the precipitate is digested by warming in a water bath, transferred onto a filter, dried, and weighed. A double salt is first formed (eq. 46); it then decomposes on digestion (eq. 47):

[121] A. E. Heron, R. H. Reed, H. E. Stagg, and H. Watson, *Analyst*, **79**, 671 (1954).

[122] M. Vecera and A. Spevak, *Chem. Listy*, **52**, 1520 (1958).

[123] L. Filipovic and Z. Stefanac, *Croat. Chim. Acta*, **30**, 149 (1958).

[123a] T. S. Ma and M. M. Schachter, unpublished work; M. M. Schachter, *Master's Thesis, Brooklyn College of the City University of New York*, 1962.

$$RI + 2AgNO_3 \xrightarrow{95\% \ C_2H_5OH} AgI \cdot AgNO_3 + RNO_3 \qquad (46)$$

$$AgI \cdot AgNO_3 \xrightarrow{H_2O \ + \ HNO_3} AgI + AgNO_3 \qquad (47)$$

Friedrich[119] observed that the precipitation of silver iodide from alcoholic silver nitrate solution is incomplete and he suggested a correction factor of 0.06–0.07 mg. for each ml. of silver nitrate solution delivered into the receiver. This correction factor was accepted by Pregl,[124] Roth,[125] and Steyermark.[112] While the microgravimetric method is satisfactory, the application of a correction factor, irrespective of the weight of the silver iodide obtained, affects the precision and accuracy of the alkoxyl determination. Mitsui[125a] weighed the alkyl iodide adsorbed on a molecular sieve.

Recently Fukuda[126] described a procedure in which the alkyl iodide is driven from the reaction flask by a stream of air into a combustion tube containing platinum catalyst. The iodine formed is absorbed by silver gauze and weighed. This method is rather involved, and the use of oxygen may cause decomposition of the hydriodic acid.

2. Titrimetric Methods

A. IODOMETRIC METHOD. Vieböck and Brecher[127] proposed the iodometric procedure for the microdetermination of alkoxyl groups. The alkyl iodide is absorbed in a buffered solution containing acetic acid and sodium acetate, and is oxidized by bromine to yield iodic acid (eq. 48). After the removal of the excess bromine by means of formic acid (eq. 49), potassium iodide and sulfuric acid are added to liberate iodine (eq. 50) which is titrated with 0.01N sodium thiosulfate (eq. 51) using starch as indicator.

$$RI + 3Br_2 + 3H_2O \xrightarrow{HAc, \ NaAc} HIO_3 + RBr + 5HBr \qquad (48)$$

Excess $Br_2 + HCOOH \rightarrow 2HBr + CO_2$ (49)

$HIO_3 + 5KI + 5H_2SO_4 \rightarrow 3I_2 + 3H_2O + 5KHSO_4$ (50)

$3I_2 + 6Na_2S_2O_3 \rightarrow 6NaI + 3Na_2S_4O_6$ (51)

This method was reinvestigated by Clark,[104] Elek,[107] Easterbrook and Hamilton,[128] Franzen, Eysell and Hack[129] and other workers.[70] Belcher, Bhatty, and West[130] used Thyodene (a commercial starch preparation), as the indicator for sodium thiosulfate titration. The iodometric method

[124] F. Pregl, *Die quantitative organische Mikroanalyse*, 3rd ed., Springer, Berlin, 1930.

[125] H. Roth, *Quantitative Organic Microanalysis of Fritz Pregl*, 3rd English ed., transl. by E. B. Daw, Blakiston, Philadelphia, 1937, p. 175.

[125a] T. Mitsui, *Microchem. J. Symposium Series*, **2**, 571 (1962).

[126] M. Fukuda, *J. Pharm. Soc. Japan*, **77**, 934 (1957); **78**, 83 (1958).

[127] F. Vieböck and C. Brecher, *Berichte*, **63**, 3207 (1930).

[128] W. C. Easterbrook and J. B. Hamilton, *Analyst*, **78**, 551 (1953).

[129] F. Franzen, K. Eysell, and H. Hack, *Mikrochim. Acta*, **1954**, 708.

[130] R. Belcher, M. K. Bhatty, and T. S. West, *J. Chem. Soc.*, **1957**, 4480.

is the preferred procedure for alkoxyl determinations, especially for multiple runs. It is to be noted that formic acid should not be added in excess; otherwise part of the iodic acid may be reduced.

B. ARGENTIMETRIC METHOD.   Direct titration of alkyl iodide (absorbed in pyridine) with silver nitrate was performed by Kripol and Buhn[131] on the macro scale. This method was adapted to the micro scale by Lieb, as reported by Pregl,[124] but it has not been used by other workers. Bürger and Balaz[132] precipitated silver iodide in the receiver containing a known amount of alcoholic silver nitrate solution, transferred the mixture into a flask, and titrated the excess silver ions with $0.02N$ potassium thiocyanate. This procedure is not recommended because of the instability of the alcoholic silver nitrate solution and the difficulty in locating the endpoint. A better approach for an argentimetric method would be to absorb the alkyl iodide in glacial acetic acid and titrate the halide with a solution of silver nitrate in the same solvent.

C. NONAQUEOUS ACIDIMETRIC METHOD.   Recently Cundiff and Markunas[132a] proposed a method in which the alkyl iodide is absorbed in pyridine to form alkyl pyridinium iodide. The quaternary iodide is then determined as an acid by titration with $0.02N$ tetrabutylammonium hydroxide in methanol-benzene. Since iodine does not interfere with the titration and hydriodic acid can be differentially titrated by the potentiometric procedure, the scrubbing reagents can be eliminated.

3. Gasometric Method.   A gasometric method was described by Takiura, Takino, and Harada.[133] The first step involves the conversion of the alkyl iodide to iodic acid, being identical to the iodometric method. After the iodic acid is produced and the excess bromine discharged by formic acid, potassium iodide and hydrazine are added. The nitrogen gas liberated by the action of iodine on hydrazine (eq. 52) is collected in a microazotometer and measured.

$$2I_2 + H_2N-NH_2 \rightarrow N_2 + 4HI \qquad (52)$$

F. Differential Determination of Methoxyl, Ethoxyl, and Other Alkoxyl Groups.   When there are more than one species of alkoxyl groups in the sample, the resulting products after the cleavage with hydriodic acid will consist of a mixture of alkyl iodides, and the differential determination of the mixed iodides becomes necessary.

1. Simultaneous Determination of Methoxyl and Ethoxyl Groups

[131] A. Kirpal and T. Buhn, *Berichte,* **48,** 1084 (1914).

[132] K. Bürger and F. Balaz, *Angew. Chem.,* **54,** 58 (1941).

[132a] R. H. Cundiff and P. C. Markunas, *Anal. Chem.,* **33,** 1208 (1961).

[133] K. Takiura, Y. Takino, and S. Harada, *J. Pharm. Soc. Japan,* **76,** 1328 (1956).

A. THE METHOD OF FRIEDRICH.[134] Friedrich used two samples for the cleavage. One sample is analyzed in the usual manner and the product is weighed as silver iodide, which gives the number of alkoxyl oxygen in the compound. The second sample is heated with hydriodic acid in the absence of carbon dioxide, and the mixed alkyl iodides formed are driven by means of air into a combustion tube. The alkyl groups are burnt to carbon dioxide. From the weight of carbon dioxide obtained, the ratio of alkyl carbon to alkoxyl oxygen is calculated. This method is tedious.

B. THE METHOD OF HOUGHTON.[114] Houghton collected the mixture containing methyl and ethyl iodide in a modified Pregl receiver and estimated the composition by the determination of boiling point and density. The results are not accurate.

C. THE METHOD OF KÜSTER AND MAAG.[135] Küster and Maag described a method to separate methyl and ethyl iodides which is based on the difference in solubility of the corresponding quaternary ammonium iodides. The mixed alkyl iodides are passed through two successive receiving tubes containing trimethylamine in absolute alcohol, whereupon tetramethylammonium iodide crystallizes out on standing, leaving the ethyltrimethylammonium salt in solution. Gran[136] suggested the substitution of isopropanol for ethanol as solvent. Makens, Lothringer, and Donia[137] found that the best solvent is nitrobenzene. Complete precipitation of 10 mg. of tetramethylammonium iodide takes place in nitrobenzene in 2 hours, whereas standing for 24 hours is necessary in alcoholic solution. After the separation of the two quaternary ammonium salts by filtration, they may be determined separately by the precipitation of silver iodide with a known amount of $0.01N$ silver nitrate, followed by the titration of the excess silver ions with $0.01N$ potassium thiocyanate.

2. Separation of Alkyl Iodides by Gas Chromatography. Vertalier and Martin[138] applied gas chromatography to separate alkyl iodides. After the hydriodic acid cleavage of the alkoxyl groups, the gas mixture is fed to a column containing octyl phthalate and Celite and resolved at 100°C. Methyl, ethyl, isopropyl, *n*-propyl, isobutyl, and *n*-butyl iodides are differentiated in one sample. However, there is a loss of 25–50%.

While quantitative gas chromatography entails expensive equipment and the preparation of calibration curves, it provides a rapid method for multiple determinations. Furthermore, this is the only method available

[134] A. Friedrich, *Mikrochemie*, **7**, 185 (1929).
[135] W. Küster and W. Maag, *Z. Physiol. Chem.*, **127**, 190 (1923).
[136] G. Gran, *Svensk Papperstidning*, **57**, 702 (1954).
[137] F. F. Makens, R. L. Lothringer, and R. A. Donia, *Anal. Chem.*, **31**, 1265 (1959).
[138] S. Vertalier and F. Martin, *Chim. Anal.*, **40**, 80 (1958).

for the simultaneous determination of more than two different alkoxyl groups. The detailed procedure[123a] will be found in experiment 52.

G. Interferences in Alkoxyl Group Determinations. As mentioned before, alcohols react with hydriodic acid to produce alkyl iodides. Hence, it is not advisable to wash the reaction flask with an alcohol. Diols, glycerol, and polyhydroxy compounds are also known to give apparent alkoxyl values due to the formation of ethyl iodide, isopropyl iodide, and vinyl iodide.[139]

Methyl groups attached to carbon may yield methyl iodide on heating with hydriodic acid under certain conditions. Thus, tetramethyldiphenylmethane was reported to give apparent alkoxyl values.[140] Alkyl groups attached to sulfur will react like the alkoxyl function (see section on sulfur functions, p. 331). On the other hand, alkyl groups attached to nitrogen usually do not liberate alkyl iodide under the experimental conditions for alkoxyl group determinations. However, Gysel[141] observed that some methyl groups attached to the nitrogen atom in pyridazones rearrange to methoxyl groups on heating, leading to abnormally high methoxyl results.

Samples which do not contain the alkoxyl function were reported to produce alkoxyl values by heating at 200°C,[142] and by prolonged boiling[143] of the reaction mixture. This points to the importance of controlled heating in alkoxyl determinations.

H. Special Methods for the Methoxyl Group. Methods are available for the microdetermination of the methoxyl group which are not based on its conversion to methyl iodide. For compounds (e.g., some alkaloids) whose methoxyl groups can be hydrolyzed to methanol on heating with sulfuric acid, the methanol may be recovered by distillation, oxidized to formaldehyde and the latter compound determined by the chromotropic acid method[144,145] (see p. 157). Alexander, Bourne, and Littleball[146] determined methoxyl groups in borohydrides by hydrolyzing these compounds to produce methanol and oxidizing the alcohol with excess standard ceric ammonium nitrate solution, followed by the titration of unreacted ceric ions with standard sodium arsenite. Brown and

[139] E. V. Rudloff, *Anal. Chim. Acta*, **16**, 294 (1957).
[140] R. L. Huang and K. T. Lee, *Anal. Chem.*, **27**, 1030 (1955).
[141] H. Gysel, *Mikrochim. Acta*, **1954**, 743.
[142] A. Kirpal, *Berichte*, **41**, 819 (1908).
[143] E. P. Clark, *J. Am. Chem. Soc.*, **51**, 1479 (1929).
[144] A. P. Mathus and M. J. Pro, *Anal. Chem.*, **27**, 1662 (1955).
[145] M. Langejan, *Pharm. Weekbl.*, **92**, 667 (1957).
[146] A. P. Alexander, P. Y. Bourne, and D. S. Littleball, *Anal. Chem.*, **27**, 105 (1955).

Smith[147] determined methoxyl groups in siloxane polymers by the use of infrared spectrometry.

I. Determination of the Oxyalkylene Function.   The oxyalkylene groups are internal alkoxyl groups formed by the polymerization of epoxides. Thus, ethylene oxide yields the oxyethylene group:

$$x CH_2\text{———}CH_2 \rightarrow \text{—}(CH_2\text{—}CH_2O)_x\text{—} \tag{53}$$
$$\diagdown O \diagup$$

Siggia and co-workers[148] published a macro method for the determination of the oxyalkylene group as follows. The sample is heated for 90 minutes with 58% hydriodic acid under an atmosphere of carbon dioxide. One mole of 1,2-di-iodoalkane is produced from each equivalent of the oxyalkylene function:

$$\text{—}(CR_2\text{—}CR_2O)_x\text{—} + 2x\ HI \rightarrow x ICR_2CR_2I + x H_2O \tag{54}$$

The di-iodo compounds are unstable and form the corresponding alkylene by liberating 1 mole of iodine, which is determined by titration with standard sodium thiosulfate solution. This method has not been adapted to the micro scale.

VII. The Carbonyl Function

A. General.   The determination of the carbonyl function is concerned with the C=O linkage in aldehydes and ketones. While other types of compounds such as carboxylic acids, esters, ureas, and quinones also contain the C=O grouping, they are not determined by the methods specified for the carbonyl function.

Because many carbonyl compounds are important industrial chemicals, and because a great variety of naturally occurring substances contain the carbonyl function, the literature published on the determination of this functional group and individual carbonyl compounds is voluminous. A comprehensive survey of the methods for the determination of aldehydes and ketones has been published by Mitchell,[149] which covers publications up to 1951. It is interesting to note that among the many methods listed in this review, only one deals with the micro (0.1 meq.) scale. In the following pages the discussion deals with all micro methods as well as macro procedures which may be adapted to the micro scale.

Carbonyl compounds may be determined by chemical and physical

[147] P. Brown and A. L. Smith, *Anal. Chem.*, **30**, 549 (1958).

[148] S. Siggia, A. C. Starke, J. J. Garis, Jr., and C. R. Stahl, *Anal. Chem.*, **30**, 115 (1958).

[149] J. Mitchell, Jr., in *Organic Analysis*, Vol 1, Interscience, New York, 1953, p. 243.

methods. The chemical methods for determining the carbonyl function, as discussed in Section II of Chapter 4, are based on one of the following properties of this function:

(1) Addition reaction with or without elimination;
(2) Reduction of the carbonyl group to the hydroxyl group;
(3) Oxidation of the carbonyl group to the carboxyl group.

It should be realized that the addition reaction to the carbonyl group is reversible:

$$\begin{array}{c} \diagdown \\ \diagup \end{array} C{=}O + HB \rightleftarrows \begin{array}{c} \diagdown \\ \diagup \end{array} \underset{\underset{OH}{\mid}}{C}{-}B \tag{55}$$

Hence, all carbonyl compounds do not form addition products with the same degree of ease and completion. Thus, formaldehyde does not give quantitative yield of the hydrazone with 2,4-dinitrophenylhydrazine, a common reagent for the determination of the carbonyl function. Reduction of the carbonyl group depends on the reagent as well as the conditions. Oxidation of a carbonyl compound may yield several products simultaneously, rendering the reaction unsuitable for quantitative analysis.

Physical methods for the determination of carbonyl compounds are frequently suggested, since the C=O grouping absorbs strongly in the infrared and ultraviolet regions. Pinchas[150] reported that the aldehyde C—H stretching usually absorbs at 2720 cm.$^{-1}$. However, it should be realized that spectrophotometric procedures are as a rule designed for individual compounds and not for the carbonyl function. Similarly, the polarographic reduction of the carbonyl group is characteristic for some aldehydes and can be used for the determination of such compounds.

B. Methods Based on Addition Reactions to the Carbonyl Group

1. Addition Reaction Followed by Elimination. The majority of the publications on the determination of carbonyl compounds are based on the addition to the C=O group followed by elimination. A number of reagents and various ways for completing the determination by the measurement of the reagent or one of the products have been proposed. These are summarized below.

A. METHODS BASED ON OXIME FORMATION. The formation of oxime has been used for the determination of aldehydes and ketones for several decades.[151] It is the most favored method on the macro scale, and the term

---

[150] S. Pinchas, *Anal. Chem.*, **27**, 2 (1955).

[151] See review by R. C. Stillman and R. M. Reed, *Perfumery Essent. Oil Record*, **23**, 228 (1932).

"oximation" was coined to designate this procedure. The carbonyl compound is treated with a solution containing hydroxylamine hydrochloride (or hydroxylamine sulfate[152]) to produce the oxime, accompanied by the elimination of molar equivalent quantity of water and the liberation of molar equivalent of the free acid:

$$\ce{>C=O + H2NOH\cdot HCl -> >C=NOH + H2O + HCl} \qquad (56)$$

The usual procedure involves the measurement of the free mineral acid by potentiometric titration with standard sodium hydroxide in 90% methanol solution.[153] Alternately, the hydroxylamine reagent may be incorporated with a known amount of potassium hydroxide[154] or a high boiling aliphatic amine,[155] and, after the oximation, the excess base is back-titrated with standard hydrochloric acid. A third modification[156] is to measure the pH of the solution before and after oximation and calculate the concentration of the carbonyl compound present in the original sample against a standard working curve which should be prepared individually for each compound under investigation.

Roe and Mitchell[157] determined 0.2 meq. quantities of carbonyl compounds by the differential pH method. Maute and Owens[158] titrated the liberated hydrochloric acid with $0.03N$ methanolic sodium hydroxide. Attempts to adapt these procedures to the micro (0.1 meq.) scale were not successful.[159] The presence of water interferes with the location of the endpoint making it impossible to obtain good precision with $0.01N$ alkali. The semimicro procedure is given in experiment 6.

Higuchi and Barnstein[160] proposed hydroxylammonium acetate as a substitute for hydroxylamine hydrochloride for macro oximation, while Fritz, Yamamura, and Bradford[161] recommended the corresponding formate. These workers used nonaqueous media and determined the

[152] M. Sawamura, *Koryo*, **21**, 40 (1952).

[153] D. M. Smith and J. Mitchell, Jr., *Anal. Chem.*, **22**, 750 (1950).

[154] A. Trozzolo and E. Lieber, *Anal. Chem.*, **22**, 764 (1950).

[155] L. D. Metcalfe and A. A. Schnitz, *Anal. Chem.*, **27**, 138 (1955).

[156] M. H. Hashmi, *Anal. Chim. Acta*, **17**, 383 (1957).

[157] H. R. Roe and J. Mitchell, Jr., *Anal. Chem.*, **23**, 1758 (1951).

[158] R. L. Maute and M. L. Owens, Jr., *Anal. Chem.*, **28**, 1312 (1956).

[159] T. S. Ma and R. Schnetzinger, unpublished data; R. Schnetzinger, *Master's Thesis, Brooklyn College*, 1959.

[160] T. Higuchi and C. H. Barnstein, *Anal. Chem.*, **28**, 1022 (1956).

[161] J. S. Fritz, S. S. Yamamura, and E. C. Bradford, *Anal. Chem.*, **31**, 260 (1959).

residual hydroxylamine salt by titration with $0.1N$ perchloric acid in acetic acid. Recently, Ruch, Johnson, and Critchfield[161a] reported on the macro and semimicro determination of aldehydes and ketones with hydroxylamine formate. The concentration of the hydroxylamine reagent cannot be less than $0.1M$ and the volume of the sample added should not exceed 10 ml. The titrant for the unreacted hydroxylamine is $0.02N$ nitric acid, using methyl cellosolve as the solvent. The standard solution should be prepared weekly, and to be certain of quantitative results, each carbonyl compound must be studied individually in its matrix. This, of course, means determining the proper reaction time for a given mixture experimentally rather than assuming a reaction time based upon a particular compound and ignoring the effects of all foreign matter present in the sample.

Mitchell[162] applied aquametry to the determination of the carbonyl function. The oximation reaction is carried out in methanol solution and the water formed is titrated with the Karl Fischer reagent. Vonesch and Guagnini[163] proposed a colorimetric method which is based on the difference between sample and blank on heating the hydroxylamine reagent with alcoholic potassium hydroxide. These two methods are not readily adaptable to the 0.1 meq. scale.

Veibel and Andersen[164] compared five oximation methods and reported that steric hindrance reduces the accuracy in all methods. On the other hand, the presence of hydrogen cyanide, another reagent which adds to the carbonyl group, was shown by Sasuga[165] to have no interference on the oximation of free acetone in acetone cyanhydrin.

B. METHODS BASED ON HYDRAZONE FORMATION. Phenylhydrazine and various substituted phenylhydrazines have been suggested as reagents for the determination of the carbonyl function. 2,4-dinitrophenylhydrazine is commonly employed because it is stable and forms the least soluble and highly colored hydrazones (eq. 57).

$$\text{C=O} + H_2N\text{—NH—}C_6H_3(NO_2)_2 \rightarrow \text{C=N—NH—}C_6H_3(NO_2)_2 + H_2O \quad (57)$$

[161a] J. E. Ruch, J. B. Johnson, and F. E. Critchfield, *Anal. Chem.*, **33**, 1566 (1961).

[162] J. Mitchell, Jr., *J. Am. Chem. Soc.*, **63**, 573 (1941).

[163] E. E. Vonesch and O. A. Guagnini, *An. Asoc. Quim. Argentina*, **43**, 185 (1955).

[164] S. Veibel and I. G. K. Andersen, *Anal. Chim. Acta*, **14**, 320 (1956).

[165] H. Sasuga, *J. Chem. Soc. Japan, Ind. Chem. Sect.*, **59**, 1117 (1956).

Publications on the macro and micro (including μmole) range formation of 2,4-dinitrophenylhydrazones are numerous.

The hydrazone produced from the carbonyl compound and the amount of the reagent consumed by the sample may be determined in several ways. Gravimetric, titrimetric, and gasometric methods have been employed for macro determinations. For example, Iddles and co-workers[166] collected the hydrazone on a filter and weighed the product, while Hughes[167] prepared a soluble hydrazone and then converted it to the insoluble hydrazone mercuric iodide salt to be weighed. Falkenhausen[168] treated the carbonyl compound with a known quantity of phenylhydrazine reagent and determined the excess hydrazine by measuring the volume of nitrogen evolved on the addition of Fehling's solution. Other workers determined the residual hydrazine by potentiometric titration,[169] or by titration with standard potassium iodate.[170] Petit[171] determined the nitro group of the excess nitrophenylhydrazine by reduction with $0.1N$ potassium stannite. Cheronis and Levey,[171a] in studying the reaction rates of carbonyl compounds, employed the reduction of tetrazolium salts to formazans to determine the unreacted 2,4-dinitrophenylhydrazine and also the chromatographic estimation of the 2,4-dinitrophenylhydrazones. The former method required a sample of 75 μg., while the latter used quantities as low as 0.2 μg.

Spectrophotometric methods[172–176] involve the measurement of the absorbance of the nitro group and are generally recommended for determinations on microgram (μmole) range. Rothe and Voigt[177] proposed a nephelometric method by measuring the turbidity of the solution after the precipitation of the nitrophenylhydrazone.

Some of the methods mentioned above have been adapted to the micro

[166] H. A. Iddles, A. W. Low, B. D. Rosen, and R. T. Hart, *Ind. Eng. Chem., Anal. Ed.*, **11**, 102 (1939).

[167] H. B. Hughes, *J. Biol. Chem.*, **140**, 21 (1941).

[168] F. F. V. Falkenhausen, *Z. Anal. Chem.*, **99**, 241 (1934).

[169] M. Bano-Raffel and G. Jacini, *Olii Min.*, **33**, 381 (1956).

[170] D. J. Barke and E. R. Cole, *J. Appl. Chem.*, **5**, 477 (1955).

[171] G. Petit, *Bull. Soc. Chim. France*, **15**, 141 (1948).

[171a] N. D. Cheronis and V. M. Levey, *Microchem. J.*, **1**, 224 (1957).

[172] M. F. Pool and A. A. Klose, *J. Am. Oil Chemists Soc.*, **28**, 214 (1951).

[173] G. F. Lappin and L. C. Clark, *Anal. Chem.*, **23**, 541 (1951).

[174] J. R. Stone and N. J. Bundell, *Anal. Chem.*, **23**, 770 (1951).

[175] P. Toren and B. J. Heinrich, *Anal. Chem.*, **27**, 1986 (1955).

[176] F. H. Lohman, *Anal. Chem.*, **30**, 972 (1958).

[177] M. Rothe and I. Voigt, *Ernährungsforschung*, **2**, 444 (1957).

scale. Lieb, Schöniger, and Schivizhoffen[178] used phenylhydrazine as reagent and determined the excess hydrazine iodometrically. Berka and Zyka[179] suggested the use of 2,4-dinitrophenylhydrazine followed by the titration of the excess reagent with standard chloramine-T solution in presence of potassium bromide. Schöniger, Lieb, and Gassner[180] described a method in which the excess reagent is determined by the reduction of the nitro group with titanous chloride solution. These micro methods suffer from one disadvantage: the phenylhydrazine or substituted phenylhydrazine reagent is unstable and hence requires frequent standardization. Therefore, the microgravimetric method which involves the direct weighing of the 2,4-dinitrophenylhydrazone[181] is recommended (see experiment 7). After the determination, the 2,4-dinitrophenylhydrazone may be taken out for identification purpose by making physical measurements (e.g., melting point, crystallography) or converted to the original carbonyl compound.[182]

Two macro methods have been proposed to determine carbonyl compounds by hydrazone formation followed by acid-base titration. Fuchs[183] reacted cinnamaldehyde with hydrazine sulfate:

$$C_6H_5—CH=CH—CHO + H_2N—NH_2 \cdot H_2SO_4 \rightarrow$$
$$C_6H_5—CH=CH—CH=N—NH_2 + H_2O + H_2SO_4 \quad (58)$$

The precipitate was then filtered off and the sulfuric acid in the filtrate was titrated with standard sodium hydroxide. Siggia and Stahl[184] treated aldehydes with an excess known amount of unsymmetrical hydrazine (eq. 59) and determined the unreacted hydrazine by titration with $0.1N$ hydrochloric acid in methanol. These procedures have not been adapted to the micro scale.

$$R—CHO + H_2N—N(CH_3)_2 \rightarrow R—CH=N—N(CH_3)_2 + H_2O \quad (59)$$

c. MISCELLANEOUS GRAVIMETRIC METHODS. Aldehydes react with methone or dimedon reagent (5,5-dimethyl-cyclohexane-1,3-dione) to give solid derivatives according to the following equation:

[178] H. Lieb, W. Schöniger, and E. Schivizhoffen, *Mikrochim. Acta*, **35**, 407 (1950).
[179] A. Berka and J. Zyka, *Chem. Listy*, **50**, 831 (1956).
[180] W. Schöniger, H. Lieb, and K. Gassner, *Mikrochim. Acta*, **1953**, 434.
[181] T. S. Ma, J. Logun, and P. P. Mazzella, *Microchem. J.*, **1**, 67 (1957).
[182] M. Keeney, *Anal. Chem.*, **29**, 1489 (1957).
[183] L. Fuchs, *Scientia Pharm.*, **16**, 50 (1948).
[184] S. Siggia and C. R. Stahl, *Anal. Chem.*, **27**, 1975 (1955).

$$R\text{—}CHO + 2(CH_3)_2C\underset{\overset{|}{CH_2}}{\overset{H_2C\overset{\overset{O}{\|}}{\overset{C}{\diagdown}}CH_2}{\diagdown}}C\text{=}O \rightarrow$$

$$H_2C\underset{(CH_3)_2C}{}\overset{\overset{O}{\|}}{C}\cdots CH\cdots\overset{R}{CH}\cdots HC\cdots\overset{\overset{O}{\|}}{C}CH_2 \atop C\text{=}O\quad O\text{=}C\quad C(CH_3)_2 + H_2O \quad (60)$$

Careful control of the pH of the reaction mixture is essential for quantitative precipitation.[185] Comparing the methone derivatives and the corresponding 2,4-dinitrophenylhydrazones, Duval and Xuong[186] observed that although the former are less soluble, they are less stable, some of them melting below 90°C.

Cyclic aldehydes have been determined in the form of crystalline Schiff's base upon treatment with 4-amino antipyrine.[187] Thiocarbohydrazide was proposed by Duval and Xuong[183] as a reagent for the microgravimetric determination of the carbonyl function (eq. 61).

$$2 \;\diagdown C\text{=}O + H_2N\text{—}NH\text{—}\underset{\underset{S}{\|}}{C}\text{—}NH\text{—}NH_2 \rightarrow$$

$$\diagdown C\text{=}N\text{—}NH\text{—}\underset{\underset{S}{\|}}{C}\text{—}NH\text{—}N\text{=}C\diagup + 2H_2O \quad (61)$$

These workers reported that quantitative yields of yellow or red crystalline derivatives were obtained in 30 minutes. Unfortunately, the gravimetric factor is small, since two moles of the carbonyl compound combined with only one mole of the reagent.

2. Addition Reaction Without Elimination

A. ADDITION OF SODIUM BISULFITE. The bisulfite addition reaction of aldehydes and some ketones (eq. 62)

[185] J. H. Yoe and L. C. Reid, *Ind. Eng. Chem., Anal. Ed.*, **13**, 238 (1941).
[186] C. Duval and N. D. Xuong, *Anal. Chim. Acta*, **12**, 47 (1955).
[187] O. Manno and S. Pfeifer, *Mikrochim. Acta*, **1958**, 630.
[188] C. Duval and N. D. Xuong, *Mikrochim. Acta*, **1956**, 747.

$$\begin{array}{c}\diagdown \\ \diagup\end{array}C\!\!=\!\!O + HSO_3^- \rightarrow \begin{array}{c}\diagdown \\ \diagup\end{array}C\begin{array}{c}OH \\ \diagup \\ \diagdown \\ SO_3^-\end{array} \tag{62}$$

has been applied to the quantitative analysis of carbonyl compounds for more than 50 years.[189] In one method the sample is treated with sodium sulfite and the increase in alkalinity of the solution (eq. 63) is determined by titration with 0.5N hydrochloric or sulfuric acid.[190]

$$R\!\!-\!\!CHO + Na_2SO_3 + H_2O \rightarrow R\!\!-\!\!\overset{\displaystyle H}{\underset{\displaystyle OH}{C}}\!\!-\!\!SO_3Na + NaOH \tag{63}$$

In a second method, the sample is added to a mixture containing sodium sulfite and a known amount of 0.1N sulfuric acid. After the formation of the bisulfite addition product (eq. 64), the residual acid is determined by potentiometric titration against 1N sodium hydroxide.[191]

$$R\!\!-\!\!CHO + Na_2SO_3 + H_2SO_4 \rightarrow R\!\!-\!\!\overset{\displaystyle H}{\underset{\displaystyle OH}{C}}\!\!-\!\!SO_3Na + NaHSO_4 \tag{64}$$

These two methods are not suitable for the determination of 0.1 meq. quantities. The third method,[192] which is based on the reaction between the carbonyl function and sodium bisulfite followed by the iodimetric determination of sulfurous acid (eqs. 65 and 66), has been adapted to the micro scale.

$$R\!\!-\!\!CHO + NaHSO_3 \rightarrow R\!\!-\!\!\overset{\displaystyle H}{\underset{\displaystyle OH}{C}}\!\!-\!\!SO_3Na \tag{65}$$

$$H_2SO_3 + H_2O + I_2 \rightarrow 2HI + H_2SO_4 \tag{66}$$

It should be noted that the formation of the addition product (eq. 62) is favored by (a) low temperature, (b) high acidity of the solution, and (c) high concentration of bisulfite ions since the amount of the carbonyl compound is restricted. Two approaches to complete the determination are usually employed; one is the measurement of unreacted bisulfite and the other is the measurement of addition product.

Measurement of the Unreacted Bisulfite. Lucas[193] described a procedure

[189] See review by M. A. Joslyn, *Ind. Eng. Chem., Anal. Ed.*, **10**, 364 (1938).
[190] A. Seyewetz and J. Bardin, *Bull. Soc. Chim.*, **33**, 1000 (1905).
[191] S. Siggia and W. Maxey, *Ind. Eng. Chem., Anal. Ed.*, **19**, 1023 (1947).
[192] M. Ripper, *Monatsh. Chem.*, **21**, 1079 (1900).
[193] J. F. C. Lucas, *Rev. Cienc. Apl. (Madrid)*, **8**, 103 (1954).

wherein the aldehyde is reacted with sodium bisulfite in a phosphate buffer at pH 7.0. The addition product is stabilized at pH 3.0 with citric acid buffer and the unreacted bisulfite is titrated with $0.04N$ iodine solution.

Measurement of the Bisulfite Addition Product. Unlike 2,4-dinitrophenyl-hydrazones, the sodium bisulfite addition products cannot be separated from the reaction mixture by filtration and determined gravimetrically. In the alternate method recommended by Lucas,[193] the bisulfite addition reaction is carried out at pH 7.0 and the acidity is then increased by adding $0.3N$ hydrochloric acid. The unreacted bisulfite is discharged by oxidation with 0.1 and $0.01N$ iodine successively. The pH of the solution is now raised to 6.9–7.6 by adding sodium bicarbonate, whereupon the addition product is converted to the free carbonyl compound and bisulfite ion (reverse of eq. 62). A known amount of standard iodine solution is added and the excess iodine is determined by titration with $0.02N$ arsenite solution. Hunter and Potter[194] described a similar procedure using sodium carbonate to increase the pH and $0.02N$ sodium thiosulfate as the titrant for the excess $0.02N$ iodine. Another modification was proposed by Schulek and Maros.[195] The aldehyde is first converted to the bisulfite addition product with sulfurous acid; the excess of the latter is then removed by titration with iodine. The solution is made alkaline and potassium cyanide is added to form the cyanhydrin. The free bisulfite ions are determined by titration with standard iodine solution after acidifying.

While the bisulfite addition reaction is used mainly for the determination of aldehydes, it should be realized that ketones also may form stable addition products. Thus, Strnad[196] observed that cyclic-ketones and mixed aliphatic-aromatic ketones, as well as aldehydes, suppressed the polarographic wave of a solution of sodium bisulfite. This worker made use of the decrease of the height of the sulfur dioxide wave to determine these carbonyl compounds.

B. ADDITION OF GRIGNARD REAGENT. The Grignard reagent (methyl magnesium iodide) adds to the carbonyl function to give an addition product:

$$\diagdown_{\diagup}C{=}O + CH_3MgI \rightarrow \diagdown_{\diagup}C\diagup^{OMgI}_{\diagdown CH_3} \tag{67}$$

Soltys[197] described a micro method wherein the carbonyl compound is treated with a known amount of the Grignard reagent, followed by the

[194] I. R. Hunter and E. F. Potter, *Anal. Chem.*, **30**, 293 (1958).
[195] E. Schulek and L. Maros, *Acta Chim. Acad. Sci. Hung.*, **17**, 369 (1958).
[196] F. Strnad, *Chem. Listy*, **46**, 16 (1949).
[197] A. Soltys, *Mikrochemie*, **20**, 107 (1936).

determination of the excess reagent by introducing aniline to liberate methane which is measured. The determination is carried out in the active hydrogen apparatus (see Fig. 11.8).

Because of the instability of the Grignard reagent and the complexity of the procedure, the method just described is seldom employed. Furthermore, it can be used only for anhydrous samples, and is interfered with by the presence of esters, nitriles, acyl halides, etc., which also react with the Grignard reagent without liberating methane. However, this method is useful when the simultaneous determination of the enol and keto groups are desired (see p. 590).

C. Colorimetric Methods. Besides the colorimetric method using 2,4-dinitrophenylhydrazone discussed in Section B-1-B, the red color produced by Schiff's reagent on aldehydes (eq. 68) has been applied to quantitative analysis, but the absorption curve varies with the aldehyde.[198] Petranek and Vecera[199] determined several aldehydes by condensing them with phloroglucinol in acetic acid solution containing sulfuric acid. Yellow or orange color develops but is not stable. A lavender color produced on treating aldehydes with 2-(4-phenylazo)phenylhydrazine sulfonic acid has been used to determine acetaldehyde.[200]

$$
2RCHO + \begin{array}{c} H_2N-C_6H_4 \quad C_6H_4-NH-SO_2H \\ \diagup C \diagdown \\ HO_3S \quad C_6H_4-NH-SO_2H \end{array} \rightarrow
$$

$$
\begin{array}{c} H_2N-C_6H_4 \quad C_6H_4-NH-SO_2-\overset{H}{\underset{OH}{C}}-R \\ \diagup C \diagdown \\ HO_3S \quad C_6H_4-NH-SO_2-\overset{H}{\underset{OH}{C}}-R \end{array}
$$

$$ \downarrow $$

$$
HN{=}C_6H_4{=}C \diagup^{C_6H_4-NH-SO_2-\overset{H}{\underset{OH}{C}}-R}_{\diagdown C_6H_4-NH-SO_2-\overset{H}{\underset{OH}{C}}-R} + H_2SO_3 \quad (68)
$$

[198] K. Fischbeck and L. Neundenbel, *Z. Anal. Chem.*, **104**, 81 (1936).

[199] J. Petranek and M. Vecera, *Chem. Listy*, **51**, 1686 (1957).

[200] E. N. Malmberg, B. Weinstein, D. O. Fishel, and R. A. Krause, *Mikrochim. Acta*, **1959**, 210.

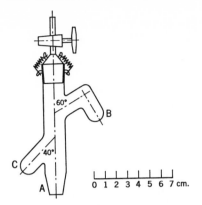

Fig. 6.14. Carbonyl apparatus of Sobotka and Trutnovsky. Courtesy of *Microchemical Journal.*

D. Methods Based on Reduction of the Carbonyl Group. Reduction of the carbonyl function by means of lithium aluminum hydride has been proposed as a method for the quantitative analysis of aldehydes and ketones.[201] After reacting the sample with a known amount of the hydride in tetrahydrofuran, the excess reagent is determined by electrometric titration with a very weak acid (e.g., propanol) in benzene. However, as lithium aluminum hydride is sensitive to moisture, oxygen, and carbon dioxide, it is not desirable for microdeterminations. Sodium and potassium borohydrides are better reductants for this purpose because these reagents are relatively stable in cold aqueous solutions of pH above 7. Jensen and Struck[202] described a macro procedure wherein a known amount of 0.5N sodium borohydride solution is added to the sample and the excess hydride is determined by oxidation with potassium bromate-potassium iodide mixture to generate iodine which is titrated with standard sodium thiosulfate. This procedure has not been adapted to the micro scale, but it is to be noted that 0.1M sodium borohydride loses about 4% of its active hydrogen in 4 days when dissolved in 1N sodium hydroxide and about 9% when dissolved in 0.1N alkali solution.[203] A microgasometric method was described by Sobotka and Trutnovsky[204] using the apparatus shown in

[201] T. Higuchi, C. J. Lintner, and R. H. Schleif, *Science*, **111**, 63 (1950).

[202] E. H. Jensen and W. A. Struck, *Anal. Chem.*, **27**, 271 (1956).

[203] E. H. Jensen, *A Study of Sodium Borohydride*, Nyt Nordisk Forlag, Copenhagen, 1954.

[204] M. Sobotka and H. Trutnovsky, *Microchem. J.*, **3**, 211 (1959).

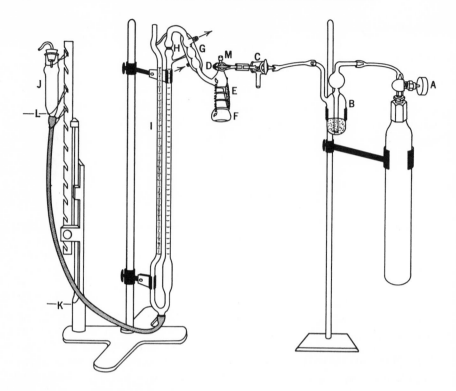

Fig. 6.15. Gasometric apparatus of Ma and Scheinthal.

Figure 6.14. The sample is placed in A; 0.1 ml. of 0.3M sodium borohydride in diglyme is measured accurately by means of an ultramicro pipet
into C, and 1.5 ml. of hydrochloric acid in propanol is introduced into B.
After connecting the reaction vessel to the gasburet, the sodium borohydride reagent is transferred from C to A by tilting the reaction vessel.
At the end of the reaction, the acid is transferred from B to A and the
volume of hydrogen evolved is measured. A simple procedure was developed by Ma and Scheinthal[205] wherein a known weight of solid sodium
borohydride is used as the reagent (see experiment 33) in order to circumvent the instability of the sodium borohydride solution. The reactions are
represented in equations 69 and 70. The apparatus is shown in Figure 6.15.

[205] T. S. Ma and B. Scheinthal, unpublished work; see B. Scheinthal, *Master's Thesis*,
Brooklyn College, 1961, apparatus available from Micro–Ware, Inc., Vineland, New
Jersey.

$$4 \quad \underset{R'}{\overset{R}{\diagdown}} C{=}O + NaBH_4 \rightarrow R{-}\underset{R'}{\overset{H}{\underset{|}{C}}}{-}ONa + 3(R{-}\underset{R'}{\overset{H}{\underset{|}{C}}}{-}O)_3B \qquad (69)$$

$$\text{excess } NaBH_4 + HCl + 3H_2O \rightarrow 4H_2 + NaCl + H_3BO_3 \qquad (70)$$

Simonyi, Tokar, and Gal[206] applied the aluminum isopropoxide reduction reaction (eq. 71) to the determination of the carbonyl function on the macro scale.

$$3 \quad \underset{R'}{\overset{R}{\diagdown}} C{=}O + Al[OCH(CH_3)_2]_3 \rightarrow (R{-}\underset{R'}{\overset{H}{\underset{|}{C}}}{-}O)_3Al + 3(CH_3)_2C{=}O \qquad (71)$$

The acetone formed is separated by distillation and determined. The validity of this method has not been proven.

Polarographic reduction of the carbonyl function has been used for the determination of aldehydes and ketones.[207–211] This method is very sensitive and may be employed for ultramicro (μmole) determinations. However, it is useful only for known compounds since the half wave potential varies with the structure of the carbonyl compound and the condition of the solvent medium.

E. Methods Based on the Oxidation of the Carbonyl Group. The oxidation of the carbonyl group in aldehydes by silver oxide has been described by Bailey and Knox[212] as a micro method for its estimation. A glass column packed with solid silver oxide is used as the oxidant. About 0.2 meq. of the aldehyde dissolved in 1–5 ml. of water or isopropyl alcohol is passed down the column and washed with 25 ml. of water. The emergent solution contains the silver salt of the fatty acid (eq. 72) and the silver content is determined by titration with $0.02N$ potassium thiocyanate using ferric alum as indicator.

$$2R{-}CHO + 3Ag_2O \rightarrow 2R{-}COOAg + H_2O + 4Ag \qquad (72)$$

These workers reported accuracy of $\pm 2\%$ for saturated aliphatic aldehydes up to hexaldehyde. However, they observed that all silver salts were not

[206] I. Simonyi, G. Tokar, and G. Gal, *Acta Chim. Acad. Sci. Hung.*, **10**, 217 (1956).
[207] G. Borchardt, *J. Am. Chem. Soc.*, **59**, 2171 (1937).
[208] J. Lupton, *J. Am. Chem. Soc.*, **66**, 697 (1944).
[209] I. A. Korshunor, *Zavodskaya Lab.*, **16**, 144 (1950).
[210] P. Zuman, *Nature*, **165**, 485 (1950).
[211] R. H. Boyd and A. P. Amell, *Anal. Chem.*, **28**, 1280 (1956).
[212] H. C. Bailey and J. H. Knox, *J. Chem. Soc.*, **1951**, 2741.

washed out in 25 ml. of water, while some silver oxide dissolved in the wash water.

Mitchell and Smith[213] heated macro quantities (5 meq.) of aldehydes with silver oxide in a flask and then introduced an excess of $0.5N$ sodium hydroxide to displace the silver salt. The reaction mixture was filtered and the filtrate was titrated with $0.2N$ hydrochloric acid. Another macro method was described by Siggia and Segal[214] who used Tollens' reagent as the oxidant (eq. 73) and determined the residual silver ions by titration with $0.1N$ potassium iodide potentiometrically.

$$R\text{—}CHO + 2Ag(NH_3)_2NO_3 + H_2O \rightarrow R\text{—}COOH + 2Ag + 2(NH_4)NO_3 \quad (73)$$

As the former method entails filtration and the latter method uses a very unstable reagent, they are not suitable for adaptation to the micro scale.

Nessler's reagent has been used for the quantitative oxidation of carbonyl groups according to the following equation:

$$R\text{—}CHO + K_2HgI_4 + 3KOH \rightarrow R\text{—}COOK + Hg + 4KI + 2H_2O \quad (74)$$

Ruch and Johnson[215] described a macro method wherein the precipitated mercury is redissolved in $0.1N$ iodine (eq. 75) after the reaction mixture has been acidified with acetic acid followed by titration of the excess iodine against $0.1N$ sodium thiosulfate. This method has not been tested on the 0.1 meq. scale. Yamagishi, Yokoo, and Inoue[216] proposed a micro method

$$Hg + I_2 \rightarrow HgI_2 \quad (75)$$

which involves the determination of the unreacted Nessler's reagent indirectly. After the oxidation of the sample, hydrazine is added and the nitrogen gas liberated is measured. These workers reported that hydroxy ketones were oxidized on heating while some aldehydes such as vanillin and salicylaldehyde failed to react.

Hawthorne[217] oxidized the carbonyl group with standardized peroxytrifluoroacetic acid (eq. 76) in ethylene chloride solution on a macro scale and determined the residual peroxyacid iodometrically. This method is not recommended for microdeterminations because of the instability of

$$2\ \begin{matrix}R\\[-2pt]\diagdown\\[-2pt]\diagup\\[-2pt]R'\end{matrix}C{=}O + 2CF_3\text{—}C\overset{O}{\underset{OOH}{\diagup\!\!\!\diagup}} \rightarrow R\text{—}C\overset{O}{\underset{OR'}{\diagup\!\!\!\diagup}} + R'\text{—}C\overset{O}{\underset{OR}{\diagup\!\!\!\diagup}} + 2CF_3\text{—}C\overset{O}{\underset{OH}{\diagup\!\!\!\diagup}} \quad (76)$$

[213] J. Mitchell, Jr. and D. M. Smith, *Anal. Chem.*, **22**, 746 (1950).

[214] S. Siggia and E. Segal, *Anal. Chem.*, **25**, 640 (1953).

[215] J. E. Ruch and J. B. Johnson, *Anal. Chem.*, **28**, 69 (1956).

[216] M. Yamagishi, M. Yokoo, and S. Inoue, *J. Pharm. Soc. Japan*, **75**, 1384 (1956).

[217] M. F. Hawthorne, *Anal. Chem.*, **28**, 540 (1956).

the reagent. Other workers used iodine in sodium hydroxide,[218,219] or chloramine-T[220] as the oxidizing agent. It should be realized that oxidation may be accompanied by halogenation when these reagents are employed. Hence, careful control of the experimental condition is necessary.

F. Differential Determination of Aldehydic and Ketonic Functions. As mentioned above, the gravimetric procedure using methone (dimedon) reagent and the colorimetric procedure using Schiff's reagent are specific methods for the aldehydic carbonyl. Since aldehydes are more easily oxidized than ketones, the silver oxide oxidation reaction has been used to determine the aldehyde group in presence of ketones. Siegel and Weiss[221] described a procedure in which a 0.5 meq. sample is treated with $0.1N$ silver nitrate solution, the precipitated metallic silver is separated by filtration, and the residual silver ions in the filtrate are determined by titration with $0.05N$ potassium thiocyanate. These workers reported no interference from ketones with the exception of cyclopentanone and cyclohexanone.

The difference in the rate of addition to carbonyl groups has been applied to the differential determination of aldehydes and ketones. Thus, Siggia and Stahl[184] reported that when unsymmetrical dimethylhydrazine was used as a reagent, aromatic aldehydes (but not aliphatic aldehydes) could be determined in presence of ketones on the macro scale. Maute and Owens[222] determined the acetaldehyde content in acrylonitrile by oximation for 1 minute and the total carbonyl content by running the reaction for 5 minutes. Critchley, Friend, and Swain[223] proposed micro methods for differentiating between conjugated aldehydes and ketones based on the marked difference in reaction rates of these two types of carbonyl compounds towards hydroxylamine, sodium borohydride, and methylamine. A procedure for differential microdetermination of aldehydes and ketones by borohydride reduction was developed by Ma and Scheinthal.[205]

G. Special Methods. The haloform reaction (eq. 77) exhibited by the methyl carbonyl group (CH_3—CO—) has been applied to the estimation of compounds containing this function.

$$CH_3-\underset{\underset{O}{\|}}{C}-R + 3X_2 + 4NaOH \rightarrow HCX_3 + R-\underset{\underset{ONa}{\diagdown}}{\overset{\diagup O}{C}} + 3NaX + 3H_2O \quad (77)$$

[218] D. Ceausescu, *Stud. Cerset Chim. Cluj.*, **8**, 291 (1958).

[219] S. Bose, *J. Indian Chem. Soc.*, **34**, 739 (1957); *Anal. Chem.*, **30**, 1526 (1958).

[220] B. N. Afanasev, *Zavodskaya Lab.*, **15**, 1271 (1949).

[221] H. Siegel and F. T. Weiss, *Anal. Chem.*, **26**, 917 (1954).

[222] R. L. Maute and M. L. Owens, Jr., *Anal. Chem.*, **28**, 1312 (1956).

[223] J. P. Critchley, J. Friend, and T. Swain, *Chem. & Ind.*, **1958**, 596.

Goltz and Glew[224] determined 0.1–0.5 meq. of acetone in benzene by reacting it with a known amount of iodine solution and titrating the excess iodine with standard sodium thiosulfate after acidification. Grover and Mehrotra[225] determined acetone by direct titration with standardized akaline hypobromite solution. Dal Nogare, Norristo, and Mitchell[226] estimated acetone and acetaldehyde by converting them to iodoform, which is then extracted with chloroform and determined spectrophotometrically at 347 mμ. Sedivec[227] described a colorimetric method for acetone and other methyl ketones; the sample is treated with sodium hypobromide and the bromoform produced is reacted with pyridine to yield a red color which is measured photometrically.

1,2-Diketones and α-hydroxyketones can be determined by periodate oxidation,[223] according to equations 78 and 79, respectively:

$$R-\underset{\underset{O}{\|}}{C}-\underset{\underset{O}{\|}}{C}-R + HIO_4 + H_2O \rightarrow 2R-C\overset{\displaystyle O}{\underset{\displaystyle OH}{\Big\backslash}} + HIO_3 \qquad (78)$$

$$R-\underset{\underset{O}{\|}}{C}-\underset{\underset{OH}{|}}{\overset{\overset{H}{|}}{C}}-R' + HIO_4 \rightarrow R-C\overset{\displaystyle O}{\underset{\displaystyle OH}{\Big\backslash}} + R'-C\overset{\displaystyle O}{\underset{\displaystyle H}{\Big\backslash}} + HIO_3 \qquad (79)$$

The detailed procedure for this method is given in experiment 11.

1,2-Diketones form red quinoid compounds when treated with strong alkali, and O'Daniel and Parsons[229] reported that the intensity of the color is proportional to the concentration of the 1,2-dicarbonyl compound in the original solution. Harjanne[230] precipitated 1,2-dicarbonyl compounds in the form of their quinoxaline derivatives. Taylor and Smith[231] proposed 1,2-diamino-4-nitrobenzene as a reagent to determine α-keto acids as the corresponding nitroquinoxalinols.

1,3-Dicarbonyl compounds form stable copper complexes. Seaman, Woods, and Massad[232] described a method wherein the sample is treated with an excess of copper acetate and the residual cupric ions are determined iodometrically.

[224] G. E. Goltz and D. N. Glew, *Anal. Chem.*, **29**, 816 (1957).
[225] K. C. Grover and R. C. Mehrotra, *Z. Anal. Chem.*, **160**, 274 (1958).
[226] S. Dal Nogare, T. O. Norristo, and J. Mitchell, Jr., *Anal. Chem.*, **23**, 1473 (1951).
[227] V. Sedivec, *Chem. Listy*, **51**, 63 (1957).
[228] P. W. Clutterbuck and F. Reuter, *J. Chem. Soc.*, **1935**, 1467.
[229] L. O'Daniel and C. B. Parsons, *Oil and Soap*, **20**, 72 (1943).
[230] A. Harjanne, *Suomen Kem.*, **28**, 37 (1955).
[231] K. W. Taylor and M. I. H. Smith, *Analyst*, **80**, 607 (1955).
[232] W. Seaman, J. T. Woods, and E. A. Massad, *Anal. Chem.*, **19**, 250 (1947).

Formaldehyde is usually determined colorimetrically by means of 1,8-dihydroxynaphthalene-3,6-disulfonic acid, known as chromotropic acid. When formaldehyde is warmed with this reagent in concentrated sulfuric acid solution a purple color develops. The chemistry of this reaction has not been elucidated; it is assumed to be analogous to phenol-formaldehyde condensation followed by oxidation to a quinoid compound.[233] The solution is diluted with water to a given volume and the color intensity is determined photometrically. This color is not shown by other carbonyl compounds. The detailed procedure, adapted from the method of Bricker and Johnson,[234] is given on page 504. It should be noted that the optimum concentration for this determination is about 0.2 mg. of formaldehyde in 100 ml. of the final solution; hence, an aliquot of the sample containing 0.1 meq. formaldehyde is taken for analysis.

VIII. The Carbohydrate Function

A. General.   The carbohydrate function is characterized by a carbonyl group adjacent to one or more hydroxyl groups [—CO—$\overset{|}{C}$(OH)—$\overset{|}{C}$(OH)—]. This function is treated in a separate section from the carbonyl and hydroxyl functions for two reasons: (a) the carbohydrates are an important class of organic compounds and their analysis is in frequent demand in the industrial and biochemical laboratories, as well as in research work on natural products, and (b) while the adjacency of the carbonyl group does not seem to interfere with the determination of the hydroxyl group[235] (see Chapter 7, Section IV), the presence of the hydroxyl group has considerable effect on the analysis of the carbonyl group. For example, the carbonyl group in carbohydrates cannot be determined as the oximes, hydrazones, or addition products of sodium bisulfite.

The methods which have been used for the determination of the carbohydrate function are discussed below. It should be realized that these methods are also applicable to α-hydroxy aldehydes and ketones, but they are not suitable for the analysis of α-hydroxy acids or esters.

B. Methods Depending on the Oxidation of the Carbohydrate Function

1. Oxidation by Periodate.   The analytical reagent most commonly used in the quantitative investigation of carbohydrates in recent years is perio-

[233] F. Feigl, *Spot Tests in Organic Analysis*, 4th ed., Elsevier, Amsterdam, 1956, p. 241.

[234] C. E. Bricker and H. R. Johnson, *Ind. Eng. Chem., Anal. Ed.*, **17**, 400 (1945).

[235] B. E. Christensen and R. A. Clark, *Ind. Eng. Chem., Anal. Ed.*, **17**, 265 (1945).

date It was first employed by Fleury and Lange[236] after the discovery of periodate oxidation of 1,2-diols by Malaprade[237] (see p. 193). Numerous publications have appeared in the literature concerning the periodate oxidation of carbohydrates and an extensive review has been published by Bobbitt.[238] An aldose is oxidized by periodate according to equation 80, while a ketose is cleaved as shown in equation 81:

$$H-\overset{\overset{\displaystyle H}{|}}{\underset{\underset{\displaystyle O}{||}}{C}}-\overset{\overset{\displaystyle H}{|}}{\underset{\underset{\displaystyle OH}{|}}{C}}-\overset{\overset{\displaystyle}{|}}{\underset{\underset{\displaystyle OH}{|}}{C}}-R + 2IO_4^- \rightarrow 2HC\overset{\displaystyle O}{\underset{\displaystyle OH}{\diagdown}} + HC-R + 2IO_3^- \qquad (80)$$

$$H-\overset{\overset{\displaystyle H}{|}}{\underset{\underset{\displaystyle OH}{|}}{C}}-\overset{\overset{\displaystyle}{|}}{\underset{\underset{\displaystyle O}{||}}{C}}-\overset{\overset{\displaystyle H}{|}}{\underset{\underset{\displaystyle OH}{|}}{C}}-R + IO_4^- \rightarrow H-\overset{\overset{\displaystyle H}{|}}{\underset{\underset{\displaystyle OH}{|}}{C}}-C\overset{\displaystyle O}{\underset{\displaystyle OH}{\diagdown}} + HC-R + IO_3^- \qquad (81)$$

The remaining portion of the carbohydrate molecule will be oxidized by periodate by virtue of the adjacent hydroxyl groups. Thus, glucose consumes 5 equivalents of periodate (eq. 82) while fructose only 4 equivalents of the same reagent (eq. 83). It will be noted that the product $CH_2OH \cdot COOH$ is not further oxidized under the experimental condition for the determination of carbohydrates.

$$H-\overset{\overset{\displaystyle OH}{|}}{\underset{\underset{\displaystyle O}{||}}{C}}-\overset{\overset{\displaystyle H}{|}}{\underset{\underset{\displaystyle H}{|}}{C}}-\overset{\overset{\displaystyle OH}{|}}{\underset{\underset{\displaystyle OH}{|}}{C}}-\overset{\overset{\displaystyle OH}{|}}{\underset{\underset{\displaystyle H}{|}}{C}}-\overset{\overset{\displaystyle OH}{|}}{\underset{\underset{\displaystyle H}{|}}{C}}-\overset{\overset{\displaystyle}{|}}{\underset{\underset{\displaystyle H}{|}}{C}}-H + 5IO_4^- \rightarrow$$
$$5HCOOH + H_2CO + 5IO_3^- \quad (82)$$

$$H-\overset{\overset{\displaystyle OH}{|}}{\underset{\underset{\displaystyle H}{|}}{C}}-\overset{\overset{\displaystyle}{|}}{\underset{\underset{\displaystyle O}{||}}{C}}-\overset{\overset{\displaystyle H}{|}}{\underset{\underset{\displaystyle OH}{|}}{C}}-\overset{\overset{\displaystyle OH}{|}}{\underset{\underset{\displaystyle H}{|}}{C}}-\overset{\overset{\displaystyle OH}{|}}{\underset{\underset{\displaystyle H}{|}}{C}}-\overset{\overset{\displaystyle OH}{|}}{\underset{\underset{\displaystyle H}{|}}{C}}-H + 4IO_4^- \rightarrow$$
$$CH_2OH \cdot COOH + 3HCOOH + H_2CO + 4IO_3^- \quad (83)$$

Several methods are available for using periodate to determine the carbohydrate function. In one method a known amount of the periodate reagent is added to the sample. After the oxidation is complete, the residual periodate ions are determined by means of sodium arsenite. The micro procedure developed by Ma and Moss[239] is given in experiment 11. In an-

[236] P. F. Fleury and J. Lange, Compt. rend., 195, 1395 (1932); J. Pharm. Chim. [8], 17, 107 (1933).

[237] L. Malaprade, Compt. rend., 186, 382 (1928); Bull. Soc. Chim. [4], 43, 683 (1928).

[238] J. M. Bobbitt, in Advances in Carbohydrate Chemistry, Vol. 11, Academic Press, New York, 1956, p. 1.

[239] T. S. Ma and H. L. Moss, unpublished work; H. Moss, Master's Thesis, Brooklyn College, 1958.

other method, proposed by Aspinall and Ferrier,[240] the reaction mixture is measured spectrophotometrically before and after the oxidation. The decrease in light absorption due to periodate ions, after correcting for the absorption due to the iodate ions formed, is proportional to the quantity of carbohydrate function present in the original sample. In still another method, the amount of formic acid produced in the reaction is determined. Since this involves the measurement of the product obtained instead of the reagent consumed, it should be more accurate than the first two methods. Unfortunately, the course of periodate oxidation is sometimes rather complicated, resulting in products which are not stoichiometric. For example, in the periodate oxidation of the ketohexoses, reaction 84 takes place first,

$$
\begin{array}{l}
CH_2OH \\
| \\
C=O \\
| \quad\quad \xrightarrow{3IO_4^-} \\
(CHOH)_3 \\
| \\
CH_2OH
\end{array}
\quad
\begin{array}{l}
CH_2OH \\
| \\
C=O \quad + 2HCOOH + H_2C=O \\
| \\
HC=O
\end{array}
\tag{84}
$$

but in the subsequent step, two reactions, 85 and 86, can occur simultaneously to give different products.[236]

$$
\begin{array}{l}
CH_2OH \\
| \\
C=O \quad \xrightarrow{IO_4^-} \\
| \\
HC=O
\end{array}
\quad H_2C=O +
\begin{array}{l}
COOH \\
| \\
HC=O
\end{array}
\tag{85}
$$

$$
\begin{array}{l}
CH_2OH \\
| \\
C=O \quad \xrightarrow{IO_4^-} \\
| \\
HC=O
\end{array}
\quad CH_2OH +
\begin{array}{l}
HCOOH \\
| \\
COOH
\end{array}
\tag{86}
$$

It will be realized that the molar equivalent of formic acid produced from the ketose sample depends on the predominance of reaction 85 or 86. Nevertheless, quantitative results can be obtained under controlled conditions. Thus, Hirst and co-workers[241] described a procedure in which the sample is heated with sodium metaperiodate under reflux on the water bath for 20 minutes. After cooling, the excess periodate is destroyed by the addition of ethylene glycol and the formic acid is titrated with $0.01N$ sodium hydroxide using methyl red as indicator. The yield of formic acid from various carbohydrates is shown in Table 6.4.

---

[240] G. O. Aspinall and R. J. Ferrier, *Chem. Ind. (London)*, **1957**, 1216.
[241] A. E. Flood, E. L. Hirst, and J. K. N. Jones, *J. Chem. Soc.*, **1948**, 679; E. L. Hirst and J. K. N. Jones, *ibid.*, **1949**, 1659.

2. Oxidation by Other Reagents.   Sharma[242] proposed to determine carbohydrates by cerate oxidimetry. The sample is boiled with a known amount of ceric sulfate in sulfuric acid. After oxidation, the excess ceric ions are titrated with standardized ferrous sulfate. It is claimed[243] that aldoses are converted to formic acid while ketoses are oxidized to carbon dioxide and water. When a small amount of chromium salt is added, formic acid is also oxidized to carbon dioxide.

TABLE 6.4

Yield of Formic Acid by Periodate Oxidation
of Several Carbohydrates

Carbohydrate	Formic acid (mol/mol)
Glucose	5
Mannose	5
Galactose	5
Arabinose	4
Ribose	4
Xylose	4
Rhamnose	4
Fructose	3
Sorbose	3
Sucrose	1

Miller and Burton[244] determined aldoses by an iodometric method with spectrophotometric finish. The sample is oxidized with $0.02N$ iodine solution containing potassium iodide and sodium carbonate. After standing for a period of time at a temperature depending on the nature of the carbohydrate, the reaction mixture is acidified and the residual iodine is measured at 480 mμ. Yoshimura and Kiboku[245] used sodium hypobromite in sodium hydroxide solution as the oxidant. The excess hypobromite is determined by adding potassium iodide and titrating with standard sodium thiosulfate solution after acidification. It should be noted that the control of experimental condition is essential. These workers reported that one equivalent of carbohydrate reduces 2 equivalents of sodium hypobromite in $6N$ sodium hydroxide in 4 minutes at room temperature, while the same compound consumes 6 equivalents of the reagent in 2 minutes at 100°C.

[242] N. N. Sharma, *Anal. Chim. Acta*, **14**, 423 (1956).
[243] N. N. Sharma, *Z. Anal. Chem.*, **154**, 340 (1957).
[244] G. L. Miller and A. L. Burton, *Anal. Chem.*, **31**, 1790 (1959).
[245] C. Yoshimura and M. Kiboku, *J. Chem. Soc. Japan*, **77**, 1546 (1956).

Launer and Tomimatsu[246] oxidized carbohydrates with sodium chlorite in a phosphate buffer. The residual chlorite is determined by adding potassium iodide which has been acidified immediately before use and titrating the liberated iodine with $0.005-0.02N$ sodium thiosulfate. These investigators reported that sodium chlorite shows no fixed stoichiometric relationship to the aldehyde groups in reactions with aldoses, not because of over-oxidation, but presumably because of the unstable chlorine intermediates which react with chlorite to varying extent.

Potassium ferricyanide has been used as the oxidant by several investigators. Hagedorn and Jensen[247] boiled the sample with ferricyanide and the unreacted reagent was treated with potassium iodide followed by the titration of the liberated iodine with thiosulfate. Schales[248] measured the disappearance of the ferricyanide by a photoelectric method. Paschke[249] reported that the amount of ferricyanide consumed is strictly proportional to the quantity of glucose present, even for concentrated solutions.

The cupric ion is the oxidant of choice for the determination of glucose in the biochemical and clinical laboratories. Colorimetric procedures using the cupric ion are given in Section D below. A compleximetric procedure, on the macro scale, was described by Potterat and Eschmann.[250] The copper is precipitated quantitatively as cuprous oxide which is filtered off and dissolved in nitric acid. The solution is made alkaline with ammonia and titrated with standardized EDTA. Rabega[251] recommended the use of cuprithiosalicylate and measurement of the residual cupric ions iodometrically. A calibration curve is constructed from known quantities of the sugar at the range of 2-10 mg. and the amount in the unknown is determined from the working curve.

C. Methods Depending on the Reduction of the Carbohydrate Function. Sodium borohydride was employed by Lindberg and co-workers[252,253] as the reductant for determining carbohydrates. The sample was dissolved in water and treated with a solution of sodium borohydride. After the reaction is complete, the residual borohydride is determined by measuring the hydrogen evolved upon addition of acid. A similar procedure

---

[246] H. F. Launer and Y. Tomimatsu, *Anal. Chem.*, **31**, 1385, 1569 (1959).

[247] H. C. Hagedorn and B. N. Jensen, *Biochem. Z.*, **135**, 46 (1923).

[248] O. and S. Schales, *Arch. Biochem.*, **8**, 285 (1945).

[249] E. Paschke, *Mikrochim. Acta*, **1955**, 983.

[250] M. Potterat and H. Eschmann, *Ann. Falsif.*, **49**, 464 (1956).

[251] C. Rabega, *An. Univ. "C. I. Parhon" Bucuresti, Ser. Stiinf Nat.*, **1956**, 57.

[252] B. Lindberg and A. Missiorny, *Svensk. Papperstidn.*, **55**, 13 (1952).

[253] B. Lindberg and O. Theander, *ibid.*, **57**, 83 (1954).

was described by Skell and Crist.[254] It has been established that 1 mole of a monocarbonyl reducing sugar consumes 1 mole of active hydrogen from sodium borohydride[255] (see eq. 87).

$$4H-\overset{\overset{\text{O}}{\|}}{C}-\overset{\overset{\text{OH}}{|}}{C}H-R + 4H_2O + NaBH_4 \rightarrow 4H_2\overset{\overset{\text{OH}}{|}}{C}-\overset{\overset{\text{OH}}{|}}{C}H-R + NaOH + B(OH)_3 \quad (87)$$

Peat, Whelan, and Roberts[256] determined the degree of polymerization of reducing oligosaccharides by means of sodium borohydride. Using potassium borohydride as the reducing agent, Bragg and Hough[257] reported that 3-0-substituted aldoses and 4-0-substituted hexuloses are reduced slowly because of steric hindrance.

A general micro procedure for reduction using alkali borohydride as the reagent will be found in experiment 33.

D. Colorimetric Methods.   Determination of sugar in biological fluids is always performed by the colorimetric method. The first procedure was developed by Folin and Wu[258] in 1919 which is based on the conversion of cupric ions to the cuprous state by the presence of the reducing sugar. The cuprous ion subsequently reduces phosphotungstic acid to a blue complex which is measured colorimetrically. Numerous modifications of this method have been published.[259]

Dearing[260] described a micro method for the estimation of cellulose in which the sample is treated with sodium hydroxide followed by heating with sulfuric acid. The absorbance at 520 mμ is measured and the amount of carbohydrate present is obtained by comparison with a standard curve made with glucose. Wahba and co-workers[261] converted glucose to glucosazone and measured the yellow color of its solution. Shallenberger and Moores[262] developed the color with a reagent containing copper sulfate and arsenomolybdate and measured the solution at 500 mμ.

Various phenolic compounds have been recommended for the colorimetric determination of carbohydrates. Among these reagents may be

[254] P. S. Skell and J. G. Crist, *Nature*, **173**, 401 (1954).

[255] P. S. Skell, J. G. Crist, and M. T. Tornascouc, *Ind. Sugar J.*, **49**, 61 (1954).

[256] S. Peat, W. J. Whelan, and J. G. Roberts, *J. Chem. Soc.*, **1956**, 2258.

[257] P. D. Bragg and L. Hough, *J. Chem. Soc.*, **1957**, 4347.

[258] O. Folin and H. Wu, *J. Biochem.*, **38**, 110 (1919); **41**, 367 (1920).

[259] See H. Varley, *Practical Clinical Biochemistry*, Interscience, New York, 1954, for a summary and laboratory procedures.

[260] G. G. Dearing, *Nature*, **179**, 579 (1957).

[261] N. Wahba, S. Hanna, and M. M. El-Sadr, *Analyst*, **81**, 430 (1956).

[262] R. S. Shallenberger and R. G. Moores, *Anal. Chem.*, **29**, 27 (1957).

mentioned phenol,[263] thymol,[264] orcinol,[265,266] and phloroglucinol[267] for reducing sugars. The color ranges from yellow to brown and the chemistry has not been elucidated. Livingston, Maurmeyer, and Worthman[268] described a specific method for fructose which is based on the formation of a green color when the sample is treated with concentrated sulfuric acid and phenol and then diluted with glacial acetic acid.

Nitro compounds as colorimetric reagents for carbohydrates include picric acid,[269] 3,4-dinitrobenzoic acid,[270] dinitrosalicylic acid,[271] and 2,4-dinitrophenylsulfone.[272] p-Aminosalicylic acid[273] and o-aminodiphenyl[274] have been used for the determination of aldoses. Indole[275] forms a colored complex with fructose.

The color reaction between anthrone and carbohydrates has been investigated for quantitative analysis. Helbert and Brown[276] reported that the color is unstable and varies with temperature and time. Hence, strict control of experimental condition is necessary. The microdetermination of reducing sugars by using tetrazolium salts which yield colored formazans was reported by Cheronis and co-workers.[277] Methods for the microdetermination of glucose with p-Anisyl Tetrazolium Blue and also of fructose have been described.

E. Miscellaneous Methods.   Carbohydrates may be determined by biological methods.[278] A milk-sugar yeast is known to ferment lactose and sucrose completely but does not attack maltose. *Saccharomyces aspiculatus*

---

[263] M. Dubois, K. A. Gilles, J. K. Hamilton, P. A. Rebers, and R. Smith, *Anal. Chem.*, **28**, 350 (1956).

[264] J. Tillmans and K. Philippi, *Biochem. Z.*, **215**, 36 (1929).

[265] M. Sorensen and G. Haugaavo, *ibid.*, **260**, 247 (1933).

[266] H. Fisher, R. G. Hansen, and H. W. Norton, *Anal. Chem.*, **27**, 857 (1955).

[267] N. O. Lindh, *Ark. Kemi.*, **10**, 569 (1957).

[268] E. M. Livingston, R. K. Maurmeyer, and A. Worthman, *Microchem. J.*, **1**, 261 (1957).

[269] E. Kestermann, *Deut. Med. Wochschr.*, **55**, 1586 (1929).

[270] T. Takemoto, K. Daigo, and T. Takai, *J. Pharm. Soc. Japan*, **75**, 1024 (1955).

[271] G. L. Miller, *Anal. Chem.*, **31**, 426 (1959).

[272] D. H. E. Taltje, *Pharm. Weekbl.*, **93**, 245 (1958).

[273] J. Ek and E. Hultman, *Scand. J. Clin. and Lab. Invest.*, **9**, 315 (1957).

[274] R. E. Tinell, C. P. J. Glaudemans, and A. L. Currie, *Anal. Chem.*, **28**, 1916 (1956).

[275] M. J. Karvonen and M. Malm, *Scand. J. Clin. and Lab. Invest.*, **7**, 305 (1955).

[276] J. R. Helbert and K. D. Brown, *Anal. Chem.*, **27**, 1791 (1955); **28**, 1098 (1956).

[277] N. D. Cheronis et al., *Mikrochim. Acta*, **1956**, 935; **1957**, 49; see also E. M. Livingston, *Microchem. J.*, **1**, 265 (1957).

[278] See C. A. Browne and F. W. Zerban, *Physical and Chemical Methods of Sugar Analysis*, 3rd ed., Wiley, New York, 1948, p. 485.

ferments D-glucose, D-fructose, and D-mannose but has no action on sucrose, galactose, or lactose. Therefore, by employing pure cultures of specially selected organism, it is sometimes possible to ferment one or more sugars of a given mixture and from the variation in polarization thus produced to calculate the percentage of one or more of the members present. Wise and Appline[279] determined D-galactose by selective fermentation using a gravimetric finish.

A polarographic method for the determination of carbohydrates was described by Haas and Lynch.[280] The sample is added into a hydrazine sulfate solution at pH 2.3. The hydrazone is formed and the polarograph gives a single hydrazone wave.

Radioactivity was employed by Mayer and Isbell[281] for determining end groups in carbohydrates. The sugar is heated with $HC^{14}N$ in a sealed tube at 50–55°C for 24 hours. The excess hydrogen cyanide is removed by volatilization and the radioactivity of the residue is measured.

[279] L. F. Wise and J. W. Appline, *Ind. Eng. Chem., Anal. Ed.*, **16**, 28 (1944).
[280] J. W. Haas and C. C. Lynch, *Anal. Chem.*, **29**, 479 (1957).
[281] J. D. Mayer and H. S. Isbell, *ibid.*, **30**, 1975 (1958).

7

The Oxygen Functions, Part II

I. The Carboxyl Function

A. General. The carboxyl function, —COOH, is the characteristic reactive group of the vast majority of organic acids. Since this group readily donates a proton to a base, the most direct method for its estimation is by direct acid-base titrimetry. These procedures are treated in Chapter 11. The present discussion is restricted to methods which are not based upon acid-base reactions. Such procedures are often useful, particularly when the sample is contaminated with other acidic substances or when the alkalimetric titration methods are difficult.

B. Methods Based on Acidity. The reader is referred to the section on the acidic function (page 396) for the detailed discussion of the principle and technique of analytical methods based on acid-base reactions. Suffice it to mention here that the carboxyl function in all organic compounds can be determined in the "active hydrogen" apparatus using the Grignard reagent:

$$R—COOH + CH_3MgI \rightarrow CH_4 + RCOOMgI \tag{1}$$

On the other hand, the use of lithium aluminum hydride is not recommended because this reagent may partially reduce the carboxyl group.

Determination of the carboxyl function by titration with a standard base is possible in most cases. However, it should be noted that carboxylic acids as a rule are weak acids, with Ka's of the order 10^{-5} to 10^{-6} (see Tables 3.3 and 7.1). Hence, titration in aqueous media is successful only for a limited number of these compounds. This is particularly true in microdeterminations using 0.1 meq. sample and $0.01N$ base. The acidity of polyfunctional carboxylic acids is dependent on the effect of the other functions present in the molecule, as shown in Table 7.1. Therefore, the choice of the titration procedure varies with the type of carboxylic acid to be analyzed.

TABLE 7.1

Effect of the Functions on the Acidity of Carboxylic Acids

Acid	Ionization constant	Acid	Ionization constant
Acetic	1.8×10^{-5}	Benzoic	6.6×10^{-5}
Chloracetic	155×10^{-5}	p-Aminobenzoic	1.2×10^{-5}
Aminoacetic	1.7×10^{-10}	p-Nitrobenzoic	40×10^{-5}
Stearic	1.4×10^{-5}	p-Hydroxybenzoic	2.9×10^{-5}

C. Methods Based on Decarboxylation.   The decarboxylation of a carboxylic acid is represented by the general equation:

$$R—COOH \rightarrow R—H + CO_2 \qquad (2)$$

The mechanism of this reaction has been studied by many investigators.[1] The ease of decarboxylation is increased by the presence of certain neighboring groups such as the carbonyl, hydroxyl, and nitro groups. Detailed reports on the decarboxylation of formic,[2] oxalic,[3] malonic,[4] and uronic acids[5] have been published. An analytical method is feasible if the reaction proceeds to completion.

1. Titrimetric Decarboxylation Methods.   Anderson[6] proposed a method for the determination of uronic acid. The sample is heated with 35 ml. of 19% hydrochloric acid for 2.5 hours. The carbon dioxide evolved is removed by a stream of nitrogen and absorbed in $0.05N$ barium hydroxide. The unreacted base is back-titrated with $0.05N$ hydrochloric acid. If automatic titration of the carbon dioxide is desired, the conductometric method of Malissa[6a] is recommended.

Trichloroacetic acid can be determined[7] by heating with a known quantity of sulfuric acid at 100°C:

$$Cl_3CCOOH \rightarrow CHCl_3 + CO_2 \qquad (3)$$

The residual acid is determined by titration with standard sodium hydroxide.

2. Gasometric Methods.   Hubacher[8] described an apparatus to determine the carboxyl group in aromatic acids on the macro scale. The sample

[1] E. de B. Barnett, *Mechanism of Organic Reactions*, Interscience, New York, 1956, p. 208.

[2] J. D. Reid and H. D. Weihe, *Anal. Chem.*, **9**, 271 (1937).

[3] L. W. Clark, *J. Am. Chem. Soc.*, **77**, 6191 (1955).

[4] G. Fraenkel, A. L. Belford, and P. E. Yankwich, *J. Am. Chem. Soc.*, **76**, 15 (1954).

[5] R. M. McCready and H. A. Swinson, *Anal. Chem.*, **18**, 290 (1946).

[6] D. M. W. Anderson, *Talanta*, **2**, 73 (1959).

[6a] H. Malissa, *Z. Anal. Chem.* **181**, 39 (1961).

[7] W. A. Schneider and L. E. Streeter, *Anal. Chem.*, **27**, 1774 (1955).

[8] M. H. Hubacher, *Anal. Chem.*, **21**, 945 (1949).

is heated in a flask and the increase in the gas volume due to the production of carbon dioxide is measured manometrically. This method has been adapted to the 0.1 meq. scale[9] and extended to other carboxylic acids. Besides the manometric measurement of the carbon dioxide, a quantitative gas chromatographic procedure also has been developed (see experiment 44). Since the latter technique also identifies the gas as carbon dioxide, it is more specific.

D. Method Based on Esterification.   While it is not possible to apply the esterification reaction to the determination of the carboxyl function by measuring the amount of alcohol consumed, the application of aquametry permits the titration of the quantity of water produced. Mitchell, Smith, and Bryant[10] described a macro method in which the carboxylic acid is esterified with methanol in the presence of boron trifluoride:

$$R—COOH + CH_3OH \xrightarrow{BF_3} R—COOCH_3 + H_2O \tag{4}$$

The amount of the water produced is determined by titration with Karl Fischer reagent. Conversion of this method to the micro scale[11] involves an assembly which is free from interference of atmospheric moisture (see page 168). As shown in Figure 7.1 the apparatus consists of a special microburet[12] which is connected to the reaction vessel containing the methanol reagent through a ground-glass joint. The sample is weighed in a platinum boat and inserted into the trough of the plunger. After the moisture in the system has been corrected for by adding the proper amount of Karl Fischer reagent, the platinum boat with the sample is dropped into the methanol reagent by turning the plunger. The reaction mixture is heated on a hot stage. After completion of the reaction, the solution is cooled to room temperature and the water produced is titrated to the potentiometric dead-stop endpoint. This method is not recommended for the determination of aromatic acids.

E. Miscellaneous Chemical Methods

1. Oxidation Methods.   A number of readily oxidizable carboxylic acids are determined by oxidimetry. Thus, the standard methods for determining

[9] T. S. Ma, C. T. Shang, and E. Manche, unpublished work; see C. T. Shang, *Master's Thesis, Brooklyn College*, 1961.

[10] J. Mitchell, Jr., D. M. Smith, and W. M. D. Bryant, *J. Am. Chem. Soc.*, **62**, 4 (1940).

[11] T. S. Ma and B. L. Hensle, unpublished work; see B. L. Hensle, *Master's Thesis, New York University*, 1957.

[12] J. S. Wiberley, *Anal. Chem.*, **23**, 656 (1951); the complete assembly is available from Micro-Ware, Inc., Vineland, N. J.

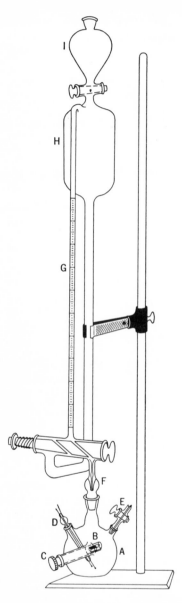

Fig. 7.1. Apparatus for aquametric determination.

oxalic, tartaric, citric, and malic acids are by titration with potassium permanganate.[13] As the reaction involves oxidation of the whole molecule and not the carboxyl function alone, it is necessary to ascertain the stoichiometry for each compound analyzed.

Lead tetraacetate was used by Berka[14] to determine mandelic acid. The excess reagent was back-titrated with Quinol using Ferroin as indicator.

Ishibashi and co-workers[15] proposed a method to determine oxalic, malonic, tartaric, citric, and salicylic acids by means of manganic pyrophosphate. However, the reactions are not stoichiometric, though the results were claimed to be reproducible.

2. Gravimetric Methods. For carboxylic acids which form insoluble salts, gravimetric determination of the salt may be practicable. Lead, magnesium, calcium, barium, and silver salts are commonly used.[16] It should be mentioned that silver salts of some acids are sometimes explosive on drying by heat and hence require caution in their handling.

3. Special Methods for α-Amino Acids. Some α-amino acids are quantitatively converted to aldehydes by the action of ninhydrin. This reaction

[13] I. M. Kolthoff and R. Belcher, *Volumetric Analysis*, Vol III, Interscience, New York, 1957.

[14] A. Berka, *Ceskosl. Farm.*, **8**, 561 (1959).

[15] M. Ishibashi, T. Shigematsu, and S. Shibata, *Japan Analyst*, **8**, 380 (1959).

[16] H. Roth, in Houben-Weyl-Müller: *Methoden der organischen Chemie*, Vol. 2, Thieme, Stuttgart, 1953, p. 502.

was applied to the gas chromatographic determination of amino acids which cannot be volatilized themselves.[17] Another approach is to decompose the amino acids to the corresponding amines, but the latter reaction is not quantitative.

F. Colorimetric Methods. There is no direct method for the colorimetric determination of the carboxyl function. However, a carboxylic acid can be determined colorimetrically by conversion to the corresponding acid chloride:[18]

$$R—COOH + SOCl_2 \rightarrow R—COCl + SO_2 + HCl \tag{5}$$

The latter is then measured by conversion to the ferric hydroxamate complex (see page 61).

Colorimetric determinations of specific carboxylic acids are available in the literature. For instance, citric acid can be determined by bromination to yield pentabromoacetone which produces color with thiourea.[19]

II. The Epoxy Function

A. General. The epoxy function has a cyclic structure composed of one oxygen atom and two or more carbon atoms. Discussions in this section are concerned mainly with the 3-membered ring, $=C\underset{\diagdown\,\diagup}{}C=$,
                                                                              O

known as 1,2-epoxy, α-epoxy, or oxirane group, and the 4-membered nucleus, $\overset{\diagdown\,\diagup}{\underset{\diagup\,\diagdown}{C—C—C}}$, known as the 1,3-epoxy, β-epoxy, or oxetane
                                        O

group. The saturated 5- and 6-membered rings—furan and pyran rings, respectively—are stable structures and hence not suitable for functional group analysis, although tetrahydrofuran has been determined by cleavage of the heterocyclic skeleton.[20] On the other hand, α,β-unsaturated 1,4- and 1,5-epoxides undergo hydrolysis readily to form aliphatic aldehydes or ketones (see Section D-2).

[17] M. Bier and P. Teitelbaum, *Ann. N. Y. Acad. Sci.*, **72**, 641 (1959).

[18] N. D. Cheronis and J. B. Entrikin, *Semimicro Qualitative Organic Analysis*, 2nd ed., Interscience, New York, 1957, p. 249.

[19] S. Natelson, J. P. Pincus, and J. K. Lugovoy, *J. Biol. Chem.*, **175**, 745 (1948); E. Beutler and M. K. Y. Yeh, *J. Lab. Clin. Med.*, **54**, 125 (1959).

[20] H. Meerwein, in Houben-Weyl-Müller: *Methoden der organischen Chemie*, Vol. 2, Thieme, Stuttgart, 1953, p. 433.

A comprehensive review of the methods for the determination of 1,2-epoxides, covering the literature up to 1952, was published by Jungnickel and co-workers.[21] Analysis of epoxy resins was reviewed by Burge and Geyer.[22] It should be noted that the methods described in these reviews are nearly all on the macro scale using 1 meq. or more of the epoxy compound. Very few micro methods are available in the literature.

B. Methods Depending on Cleavage and Addition

1. Reaction with Acid.   The reaction between epoxy group and an acid can be represented by the following equation:

$$=C\underset{\diagdown_{O}\diagup}{\underline{\hspace{1cm}}}C= + HX \rightarrow =C\underset{\overset{|}{O}H}{\underline{\hspace{0.5cm}}}\underset{\overset{|}{X}}{C}= \tag{6}$$

The acid employed is usually a halogen acid, hence the product formed is a halohydrin. Since the hydroxyl group in the latter compound is a very weak acid and the halogen attached to the molecule is not ionizable, the analysis of the epoxy compound can be accomplished by measuring either the decrease in acidity or the disappearance of the halide ions. It should be recognized, however, that the reaction does not take place instantaneously and the rate is dependent on the concentration of the reactants. For example, it was found that styrene oxide gave quantitative yields of its chlorohydrin when $0.1N$ hydrochloric acid and 1 meq. of the compound were used, but the results became erratic and the reaction incomplete when 0.1 meq. sample and $0.01N$ acid were employed.[23] Zarembo[24] reported that the determination of epoxy group was unsuccessful when the acid used was more dilute than $0.05N$. Two side reactions may also occur, namely, (a) the reaction between the halohydrin and the halogen acid (eq. 7);

$$=C\underset{\overset{|}{O}H}{\underline{\hspace{0.5cm}}}\underset{\overset{|}{X}}{C}= + HX \rightarrow =C\underset{\overset{|}{X}}{\underline{\hspace{0.5cm}}}\underset{\overset{|}{X}}{C} + H_2O \tag{7}$$

and (b) the polymerization of the epoxide (eq. 8);

$$x =C\underset{\diagdown_{O}\diagup}{\underline{\hspace{1cm}}}C= \rightarrow x =C\underset{\overset{|}{O}}{\underline{\hspace{0.3cm}}}C= \rightarrow \left(-\underset{|}{\overset{|}{C}}-\underset{|}{\overset{|}{C}}-O-\right)_x \tag{8}$$

[21] J. L. Jungnickel, E. D. Peters, A. Polgar, and F. T. Weiss, in *Organic Analysis*, Vol. 1, Interscience, New York, 1953, p. 127.

[22] R. E. Burge, Jr. and B. P. Geyer, in G. M. Kline (ed.), *Analytical Chemistry of Polymers*, Part I, Interscience, New York, 1959, p. 123.

[23] T. S. Ma and W. G. Zoellner, unpublished work.

[24] J. Zarembo, private communication.

From the point of view of quantitative analysis, these two side reactions tend to compensate for each other. However, they may not occur to the same extent.

A. DIRECT TITRATION WITH HALOGEN ACID. Durbetaki[25] described a macro procedure in which the epoxy compound is dissolved in benzene or chlorobenzene and titrated directly with 0.1N hydrobromic acid in glacial acetic acid. The endpoint can be determined potentiometrically or by using crystal violet indicator. Precision and accuracy of ±0.4% were reported for samples of 300–600 mg. This method has not been adapted to the micro scale.

B. BACK-TITRATION OF THE EXCESS ACID. Determination of the residual halogen acid by back-titration with standard alkali is the most common method for the analysis of epoxides. A micro procedure, applicable to 2 mg. of epoxy oxygen, was described by Hennart and Merlin[26] in which a nonaqueous medium is employed. The sample is placed in a stoppered flask and 0.2N hydrogen chloride in carbon tetrachloride-isopropyl ether mixed solvent is added. After standing for 6 hours, the excess acid is back-titrated by means of 0.2N sodium acetate in glacial acetic acid with methyl violet as indicator. A semimicro procedure for the determination of epoxide in drying oils using 100 mg. sample has been reported.[27] Dioxane is used as solvent and 1% hydrochloric acid in dioxane is added to the sample. After 10 minutes, ethanol is introduced, and the reaction mixture is titrated with 0.1N sodium hydroxide.

Organic solvents are preferred in the analysis of epoxy compounds. Hydrogen chloride in ether[28] has been suggested, but the volatility of the solvent is undesirable. For the determination of 1,3-epoxides, Keen[29] recommended the use of pyridinium chloride in pyridine. Heating of the reaction mixture is necessary before back-titration with aqueous alkali. Some workers used an acidic solution containing inorganic salts such as calcium chloride, magnesium chloride,[30] or potassium thiocyanate.[31] The advantage of this modification is not known. All the above methods are for macro scale determinations.

C. DETERMINATION OF THE EXCESS HALIDE. Several macro procedures used silver nitrate as the titrant to determine the excess halide ions.

[25] A. J. Durbetaki, *Anal. Chem.*, **28**, 2000 (1956).

[26] C. Hennart and E. Merlin, *Chim. Anal.*, **39**, 269 (1957).

[27] Anon., *Prakt. Chem.*, **8**, 172 (1957).

[28] D. Swern, W. Findley, N. B. Geraldine, and J. T. Scanlan, *Anal. Chem.*, **19**, 414 (1947).

[29] R. T. Keen, *Anal. Chem.*, **29**, 1041 (1957).

[30] S. H. Miller and N. E. Williams, *Analyst*, **76**, 224 (1951).

[31] M. Mousseron, J. Jullien, and A. Peyron, *Parfum Cosmet. Savons*, **13**, 3 (1958).

Krull[32] treated the sample with a known amount of collidine hydrochloride. The unreacted chloride was titrated with standardized silver nitrate solution using Congo red as indicator. Stenmark[33] used hydrochloric acid in dioxane as reagent and ferric thiocyanate as indicator for silver nitrate titration. Durbetaki[34] recommended hydrobromic acid because it reacts more readily than hydrochloric acid. The argentimetric method permits the determination of epoxy group in the presence of amines, carboxylic acids, and metal carboxylates. It probably can be adapted to the 0.1 meq. scale.

D. IODOMETRIC DETERMINATION. Dullaghan and Nord[35] determined 10–15 mg. of glycidic ester by iodometry. Hydrogen iodide gas is passed into the ethereal solution containing the epoxy compound until maximum red coloration is obtained. Then a known amount of $0.1N$ sodium thiosulfate together with a few crystals of potassium iodide is added. After removal of the ether by warming on the water bath, the residual thiosulfate is determined by titration with standardized iodine solution.

2. *Reaction with Salts.* The epoxy group has been determined on the macro scale by reacting it with a neutral solution of magnesium chloride:

$$2 =C\!\!-\!\!-\!\!-\!\!C= + \; MgCl_2 + 2H_2O \rightarrow 2 =C\!\!-\!\!-\!\!C= + \; Mg(OH)_2 \qquad (9)$$
$$\underset{O}{\diagdown\diagup} \qquad\qquad \underset{OH \;\; Cl}{| \quad |}$$

The magnesium hydroxide formed is determined by titration with standard hydrochloric acid.[36] A similar method involves the reaction of sodium sulfite on the epoxy group to produce sodium hydroxide:

$$=C\!\!-\!\!-\!\!-\!\!C= + \; Na_2SO_3 + H_2O \rightarrow =C\!\!-\!\!-\!\!C= \;\; + \; NaOH \qquad (10)$$
$$\underset{O}{\diagdown\diagup} \qquad\qquad \underset{OH \;\; SO_3Na}{| \quad |}$$

It has been shown that some epoxides react very slowly.[37] This method has not been adapted to the micro scale.

C. Methods Depending on the Conversion of the Epoxy Group to an Aldehyde

1. *By Oxidation.* 1,2-Epoxides can be determined by oxidation with perchloric acid, probably through the 1,2-diol as an intermediate step. In the case of ethylene oxide, formaldehyde is formed:

[32] L. Krull, *Fette, Seifen, Anstrichmittel*, **61**, 223 (1959).
[33] G. A. Stenmark, *Anal. Chem.*, **29**, 1367 (1957).
[34] A. J. Durbetaki, *Anal. Chem.*, **30**, 2024 (1958).
[35] M. E. Dullaghan and F. F. Nord, *Mikrochim. Acta*, **1953**, 17.
[36] A. E. K. Shafer, *J. Sci. Food Agr.*, **1**, 71 (1950).
[37] J. D. Swain, *Anal. Chem.*, **26**, 878 (1954).

$$(CH_2)_2O + H_2O \rightarrow CH_2OH—CH_2OH \tag{11}$$
$$CH_2OH—CH_2OH + HClO_4 \rightarrow 2CH_2O + HClO_3 + H_2O \tag{12}$$

Colorimetric determination of the formaldehyde produced was described by Bricker and Lee,[38] and Critchfield and Johnson.[39] Alternately, the residual perchloric acid may be determined. An iodometric macro procedure was presented by Eastman and Latremanible.[40] The latter method has general application to 1,2-epoxides. It probably can be adapted to the micro scale.

2. By Isomerization. 1,2-Epoxides containing a tertiary carbon atom are isomerized to the corresponding aldehydes by the catalytic action of zinc bromide in benzene solution. Thus, 1,2-di-isobutylene oxide is converted to 2,4,4-trimethylpentanal:

$$(CH_3)_3CH_2—\underset{\underset{O}{\diagdown\diagup}}{C(CH_3)}—CH_2 \rightarrow (CH_3)_3C—CH_2—CH(CH_3)—CHO \tag{13}$$

Durbetaki[41] presented a macro method in which the aldehyde formed is determined gravimetrically as 2,4-dinitrophenylhydrazone. This procedure can be adapted to the micro scale (see page 500).

D. Miscellaneous Methods

1. Special Methods for Ethylene Oxide. Ethylene oxide has been analyzed by heating it with 57% hydriodic acid containing 1.5% magnesium oxide. Ethyl iodide is formed, which is determined as silver iodide.[42] Another method involves the reaction of ethylene oxide with potassium ferrocyanide to form a complex, and the back-titration of the excess ferrocyanide with standardized zinc sulfate solution.[43] Still another method was proposed by Beck,[44] using the same principle.

2. Special Method for α,β-Unsaturated 1,4- and 1,5-Epoxides. α,β-Unsaturated 1,4-epoxides are readily hydrolyzed to yield γ-hydroxy aldehydes:

$$\underset{\underset{\diagdown O \diagup}{H_2C \quad\quad CH}}{\overset{H_2C—\!\!—\!\!—CH}{|\quad\quad\quad\|}} + H_2O \rightarrow HO—CH_2—CH_2—CH_2—CHO \tag{14}$$

[38] C. E. Bricker and J. K. Lee, *J. Am. Pharm. Soc.*, **41**, 346 (1952).
[39] F. E. Critchfield and J. B. Johnson, *Anal. Chem.*, **29**, 797 (1957).
[40] A. M. Eastman and G. A. Latremanible, *Can. J. Research*, **28B**, 264 (1950).
[41] A. J. Durbetaki, *Anal. Chem.*, **29**, 1666 (1957).
[42] H. Etienne, *Ind. Chim. Belge*, **22**, 1175, 1281 (1957).
[43] N. Schonfeldt, *Nature*, **172**, 820 (1953).
[44] G. Beck, *Mikrochemie*, **38**, 52 (1951).

Similar reactions occur with α,β-unsaturated 1,5-epoxides. Hence, these compounds can be determined through the aldehyde function[20] (see page 141).

E. Determination of the Epoxy Function by Physical Methods. The terminal epoxy group can be determined by infrared spectrometry. Goddu[45] reported that terminal epoxides have sharp absorption bands at 1.65 and 2.20 μ which are not exhibited by other oxygen rings. The infrared spectra of nonterminal epoxides were investigated by Bomstein.[46] It was found that the 12 μ band is most sensitive to structural changes.

III. The Ester Function

A. General. Esters are derived from the reaction of an alcohol and an organic acid or an inorganic oxyacid. In such a reaction, the organic or inorganic acid furnishes the hydroxyl function while the alcohol furnishes the hydrogen to form water. Hence, the ester function contains either the acyl function of the organic acid (or the anion of the inorganic acid) and the alkoxyl function of the alcohol. Therefore, the general formula of all esters such as the carboxylates, sulfonates, phosphonates, sulfates,

nitrates, and nitrites may be written as $R\!-\!X\!\!\underset{\diagdown OR'}{\overset{\diagup O}{}}$ where RXO represents

the acid radical, —OR′ the alkoxyl function, and X is a carbon, nitrogen, sulfur, or phosphorus atom. It should be noted that nitroglycerin and nitrocellulose are nitrate esters and not true organic nitro compounds. All esters are characterized by their hydrolysis to the parent acids and hydroxy compounds, as shown in equation 15:

$$R\!-\!\underset{O}{\overset{\|}{X}}\!-\!OR' + H_2O \rightarrow R\!-\!\underset{O}{\overset{\|}{X}}\!-\!OH + R'OH \tag{15}$$

B. Determination of Organic Esters

1. Methods Based on Saponification

A. DEFINITIONS. While organic esters can be hydrolyzed in either acid or basic media, alkaline hydrolysis is always used for analytical purposes. The hydrolysis of carboxylates may be represented in the following manner:

[45] R. F. Goddu, *Anal. Chem.*, **30**, 2013 (1958).
[46] J. Bomstein, *Anal. Chem.*, **30**, 544 (1958).

$$R\!-\!\underset{\underset{O}{\|}}{C}\!-\!OR' + NaOH \rightarrow R\!-\!\underset{\underset{O}{\|}}{C}\!-\!ONa + R'OH \tag{16}$$

This process is known as *saponification*, the term being originally derived from the fact that a soap is obtained on heating glycerol esters (fats and oils) with alkaline hydroxides. The amount of alkali consumed is a measure of the quantity of ester originally present in the sample. Since fats and oils in general consist of mixture of glycerides, it is customary to express the analytical results in terms of the alkali reagent consumed per unit weight of the sample. *Saponification number* denotes the number of milligrams of potassium hydroxide which would be required to hydrolyze completely one gram of the fat or oil sample. Hence, it is calculated by the following formula:

$$\text{Sap. no.} = \frac{\text{vol. of alkali consumed} \times \text{normality} \times 56.1}{\text{wt. of sample}}$$

where the volume of alkali is given in ml. and weight of sample in grams. For the analysis of samples which contain only a single ester, the results are more conveniently expressed as *saponification equivalents*. This term is defined as follows:

$$\text{Sap. equivalent} = \frac{\text{molecular wt. of the pure compound}}{\text{no. of ester function in the molecule}}$$

Saponification equivalent is calculated by the following formula:

$$\text{Sap. equivalent} = \frac{\text{wt. of sample} \times 1000}{\text{vol. of alkali consumed} \times \text{normality}}$$

B. General Technique for Saponification.   An excellent review of the methods for the saponification of esters has been prepared by Hall and Shaffer.[47] For macro analysis, the sample is usually heated in the alkali solution under a reflux condenser. This technique is not suitable for microdeterminations. Because the volume of solution is much smaller in the micro scale, the effect of contamination due to surface contact as well as the loss of solvent by volatilization becomes serious. While saponification on the micro scale has been described using a micro Kjeldahl flask[48] or an open vessel under reflux,[49-51] it is better carried out in a closed system using

[47] R. T. Hall and W. E. Shaffer, in *Organic Analysis*, Vol. 2, Interscience, New York, 1954, p. 19.

[48] F. A. Lee, *J. Assoc. Offi. Agric. Chemists*, **41**, 899 (1958).

[49] E. Chargaff, *Z. Physiol. Chem.*, **199**, 221 (1931).

[50] M. Furter, *Helv. Chim. Acta*, **21**, 601 (1938).

[51] G. Gorbach, in Houben-Weyl-Müller: *Methoden der organischen Chemie*, Vol. 2, Thieme, Stuttgart, 1953, p. 515.

a small container. Small serum bottles (10-ml. size) sealed with rubber caps have been proposed by Smith, Mitchell, and Billmeyer.[52] The reagent is weighed into the bottle before it is sealed. The sample is introduced through the cap by means of a hypodermic needle. Then the vessel is heated in the water bath. Van Etten[53] used thin-walled soft glass tubes as reaction vessels. The reagent and sample are weighed into the tube which is sealed and heated in an oven at 100–105°C. The tube is then dropped into a 50-ml. Erlenmeyer flask and crushed with a stirring rod. This method has been improved by using a heating block[54] with wells that fit the tubes so that the temperature can be raised to 200°C. It is also more convenient to (a) use regular glass tubing, (b) open the tube with a glass cutter, and (c) transfer the reaction mixture into the Erlenmeyer flask by rinsing. The bottom of the tube is then cut off and all sections of the tube are dropped into the Erlenmeyer flask (see experiment 12).

c. CONDITIONS OF SAPONIFICATION. Since most esters are not soluble in water, organic solvents such as ethanol, isopropyl alcohol, amyl alcohol, and ethylene glycol are used as solvents. Potassium hydroxide is the preferred reagent because it is more soluble in the organic medium and it has less tendency to form emulsions on the subsequent titration with aqueous standard acid. Some workers used alkali alkoxides for saponification.[55] Though it is possible to saponify some esters in the cold,[56] heating is generally recommended. The esters which are more difficult to saponify require higher temperatures and hence solvents of high boiling points. Thus, Shaffer and Balling[56] recommended a mixed solvent containing diethylene glycol and phenetole for esters which resist hydrolysis in other solutions. Johnson and Lawrence[57] reported that the saponification time of rosin esters in hexanolic potassium hydroxide is reduced by incorporating 2% of hydrazine hydrate in the reaction mixture. Generally, most esters may be hydrolyzed by heating with a solution of potassium hydroxide in 80–90% methanol, ethanol, or 1- or 2-propanol. For esters which are difficult to hydrolyze, such as high molecular weight esters, a solution of potassium hydroxide in diethylene glycol is recommended.

d. INTERFERENCES. The principal interferences in the determination of saponification value are acids, nitriles, amides, and amines if they are

[52] D. M. Smith, J. Mitchell, Jr., and A. Billmeyer, *Anal. Chem.*, **24**, 1847 (1954).
[53] C. H. Van Etten, *Anal. Chem.*, **23**, 1697 (1951).
[54] T. S. Ma and T. P. Flanagan, unpublished work.
[55] N. Schoorl, *Pharm. Weekblad*, **78**, 413 (1941).
[56] W. E. Shaffer and W. J. Balling, *Anal. Chem.*, **23**, 1126 (1951).
[57] A. E. Johnson and R. V. Lawrence, *Anal. Chem.*, **27**, 1345 (1955).

present in the sample. Even though the reaction is carried out in strongly basic solution, the presence of aldehydes does not affect the results.[58]

E. DETERMINATION BY BACK-TITRATION OF THE RESIDUAL BASE. Determination of saponification value is most commonly performed by back-titration of the excess base with a standard acid. For 0.1 meq. samples, $0.02N$ acid solution is suitable. The titration should be carried out in the absence of carbon dioxide. Phenolphthalein may be used as indicator, while other indicators such as α-naphtholphthalein[50] and cresol red-thymol blue mixture[53] have been recommended. Potentiometric titration is necessary when the reaction mixture turns color on heating, which occurs frequently in the case of fats and oils. Use of hydrazine in saponification sometimes serves to decolorize the solution, thus permitting a visual endpoint to be determined.[58]

Another method of back-titration aims at the determination of both the unreacted alkali and the alkali carboxylate produced. The macro procedure was developed by Rieman[59] and gives good results using $0.5N$ acid. The procedure involves the titration of the unreacted base to the phenolphthalein endpoint (colorless) followed by (a) the addition of benzene and bromophenol blue indicator and (b) continuing titration to the green endpoint to determine the carboxylate salt. The free carboxylic acid formed, shown in equation 17, is extracted in the benzene layer.

$$R—COOK + HCl \rightarrow R—COOH + KCl \qquad (17)$$

This method has been adapted to the micro scale.[60,61] However, the precision and accuracy are considerably less than those attainable in macro analysis because it is difficult to ascertain the equivalence points in dilute solutions and it is tedious to observe the color change in a two-phase system. A more accurate method to determine the alkali carboxylate is to use ion exchange as described in the following section.

F. APPLICATION OF ION-EXCHANGE. After saponification, the reaction mixture containing sodium or potassium hydroxide and carboxylate is transferred into a cation exchange column (H form). The free carboxylic acid is eluted and determined by titration with $0.02N$ alkali.[62] The detailed procedure is given on page 513. The amount of carboxylic acid found provides a direct measure of the ester group. Hence, it is not required to

[58] J. Mitchell, Jr. and D. M. Smith, Anal. Chem., 22, 746 (1950).

[59] W. Rieman III, Ind. Eng. Chem. Anal. Ed., 15, 325 (1943).

[60] K. Marcali and W. Rieman III, Ind. Eng. Chem., Anal. Ed., 18, 144 (1946).

[61] D. Ketchum, Ind. Eng. Chem. Anal. Ed., 18, 273 (1946).

[62] T. S. Ma, B. Groton, and H. Gary, unpublished work; see H. Gary, Master's Thesis, Brooklyn College, 1959.

know the exact quantity of the alkali reagent used. It is also not necessary to run blanks to correct for the contamination due to the alkaline surface of the reaction vessel.

If it is desirable to determine both the quantity of alkali consumed and the amount of alkali carboxylate produced, a known amount of the reagent should be used. After back-titration with $0.02N$ hydrochloric acid, the solution containing alkali chloride and carboxylate is transferred into a column containing an anion exchange resin. The carboxylate is eluted and determined.

G. APPLICATION OF CHELATOMETRY. Chelatometric titration can be applied for the determination of certain ester functions. Thus, a macro procedure was presented by Hennart and Merlin[63] for the analysis of oxalic esters. After saponification in ethanolic sodium hydroxide, a known amount of calcium chloride solution is added to precipitate the oxalate ions. The excess calcium is determined by back-titration with the magnesium-EDTA reagent.

2. *Methods Based on Reaction with Grignard Reagent or Lithium Aluminum Hydride*

A. USE OF GRIGNARD REAGENT. The active hydrogen apparatus of Soltys[64] (see Fig. 11.8) can be used to determine the ester function. A known amount of methyl magnesium iodide is added to the ester which reacts in the following manner:

$$R-\underset{\underset{OR}{\diagdown}}{\overset{\overset{O}{\diagup}}{C}} + 2CH_3MgI \rightarrow R-\underset{\underset{CH_3}{|}}{\overset{\overset{CH_3}{|}}{C}}-O-MgI + R'OMgI \tag{18}$$

The excess Grignard reagent is then determined by adding aniline to generate methane which is collected and measured:

$$CH_3-MgI + C_6H_5NH_2 \rightarrow C_6H_5NH-MgI + CH_4 \tag{19}$$

This method cannot be employed for samples containing alcohols or water, which liberate methane upon contact with Grignard reagent, unless the change in the gas volume of the apparatus is measured before the addition of aniline and a correction is applied.

B. USE OF LITHIUM ALUMINUM HYDRIDE. Lithium aluminum hydride reduces esters to alcohols according to equation 20:

$$4R-COOR' + 2LiAlH_4 \rightarrow LiAl(OCH_2R)_4 + LiAl(OR')_4 \tag{20}$$

[63] C. Hennart and E. Merlin, *Anal. Chim. Acta,* **17,** 534 (1957).
[64] A. Soltys, *Mikrochemie,* **20,** 107 (1936).

Higuchi and co-workers[65] described macro procedures for the titration of esters with a tetrahydrofuran solution of lithium aluminum hydride. The endpoint is located either potentiometrically or visually using p-anilinazobenzene as the indicator. It should be recognized that lithium aluminum hydride is extremely sensitive to oxygen, moisture, and carbon dioxide. Hence, it is very difficult to keep a standard $0.01N$ solution of this reagent. Zaugg and Horrom[66] employed the active hydrogen apparatus, using lithium aluminum hydride in place of the Grignard reagent. The excess reagent is determined by measuring the amount of hydrogen produced upon the addition of alcohol.

3. Colorimetric Method. As discussed in greater detail in Chapter 4, colorimetric determination of the ester function is dependent on the formation of the hydroxamic acid and its chelate complex with ferric ions according to reactions 21 and 22:

$$\underset{\displaystyle \underset{O}{\|}}{RC}-OR' + NH_2OH \rightarrow \underset{\displaystyle \underset{O}{\|}}{R-C}NHOH + R'OH \qquad (21)$$

$$3RCO(NHOH) + FeCl_3 \rightarrow (RCONHO)_3Fe + 3HCl \qquad (22)$$

Procedures using milligram amounts of samples were presented by Hill,[67] Bayer and Reuther,[68] and Goddu, LeBlanc, and Wright.[69] Since the color produced varies slightly with the hydroxamic acid, it is necessary to prepare a calibration curve using the known compound. However, this method is free from the interference of acids, nitriles, and most anilides.

4. Special Methods

A. FOR ESTERS WHICH ARE OXIDIZABLE. Esters which can be quantitatively oxidized by a suitable reagent at room temperature are conveniently determined by oxidimetry. For example, esters of malic, citric, or tartaric acid can be determined by titration with standard potassium permanganate.[70] Formates have been determined by oxidation with mercuric chloride.[71] Oxalates have been analyzed by oxidation with potassium bromate-bromide mixture, the excess reagent being back-titrated with standard arsenious oxide.[72]

[65] T. Higuchi, C. J. Lintner, and R. H. Schleif, *Science*, **111**, 63 (1950); C. J. Lintner, D. A. Zuck, and T. Higuchi, *J. Am. Pharm. Assoc. Sci. Ed.*, **39**, 418 (1950); C. J. Lintner, R. H. Schleif, and T. Higuchi, *Anal. Chem.*, **22**, 534 (1950); T. Higuchi, N. C. Hill, and G. E. Corcoran, *Anal. Chem.*, **24**, 491 (1952).

[66] H. E. Zaugg and B. W. Horrom, *Anal. Chem.*, **20**, 1026 (1948).

[67] U. T. Hill, *Ind. Eng. Chem., Anal. Ed.*, **18**, 317 (1946).

[68] E. Bayer and K. H. Reuther, *Chem. Ber.*, **89**, 2541 (1956).

[69] R. F. Goddu, N. F. LeBlanc, and C. M. Wright, *Anal. Chem.*, **27**, 1251 (1955).

[70] H. A. Schenker and W. Rieman III, *Anal. Chem.*, **25**, 1637 (1953).

[71] S. Bose, *J. Indian Chem. Soc.*, **35**, 320 (1958).

[72] L. Szekeres, M. Balazsfalvy, and L. G. Molnar, *Magyar Kem Foly*, **64**, 96 (1958).

B. FOR ESTERS WHICH CONTAIN THE ACTIVE METHYLENE GROUP. Esters which contain the active methylene group can be determined by titration with a base in a nonaqueous medium. Thus, Zaugg and Garven[73] proposed to titrate diethyl malonate with potassium methoxide in dimethylformamide using azo violet as indicator. Monosubstituted malonic esters were determined by titration with potassium methoxide in ethylene diamine using o-nitraniline as indicator (see section on weak acids, page 410).

C. FOR GLYCERIDES AND ESTERS OF POLYHYDROXY COMPOUNDS. Monoglycerides[74-76] and partial esters of polyhydroxy compounds are conveniently determined by periodate oxidation which depends on the presence of the 1,2-diol function in the ester (see page 193).

Triacetin was determined by Watts and Stalcup[77] on the macro scale by refluxing with a known amount of 0.1N hydrochloric acid, followed by titration of the liberated acetic acid together with the hydrochloric acid by means of standard sodium hydroxide. For microanalysis, it is better to separate the acetic acid by the ion-exchange method prior to titration.[62]

C. Determination of the Lactone Function. The lactone function is represented by the structure $=C-(CR_2)_n-C=O$. It is found in a num-

$$\underset{O}{\underline{}}$$

ber of natural products. For instance, all macrolide antibiotics possess a large lactone ring[78] $(n = 12)$.

Lactones may be considered as internal esters, and the methods for the determination of esters may be applied to the lactone function. Thus, a colorimetric method was proposed by Lien[79] for determining glucono- and galactonolactones by reacting them with ferric chloride in hydrochloric acid solution and measuring the color intensity of their hydroxamates at 540 mμ. Roth[80] described a micro method in which the sample is dissolved in alcohol and treated with a known amount of 0.01N sodium hydroxide at room or boiling temperatures. The excess of alkali is determined by titration with 0.01N hydrochloric acid using phenolphthalein as the indicator.

[73] H. E. Zaugg and F. C. Garven, *Anal. Chem.*, **30**, 1444 (1958).

[74] E. Handschumahe and L. Lentarn, *J. Am. Oil Chem. Soc.*, **24**, 143 (1947).

[75] L. Hartman, *Analyst*, **81**, 67 (1956).

[76] C. M. Dowse and J. A. Sandders, *Biochem. J.*, **62**, 455 (1956).

[77] J. O. Watts and H. Stalcup, *Anal. Chem.*, **28**, 975 (1956).

[78] P. F. Wiley et al., *J. Am. Chem. Soc.*, **79**, 6062 (1957).

[79] O. G. Lien, *Anal. Chem.*, **31**, 1363 (1959).

[80] H. Roth, in Pregl-Roth: *Quantitative organische Mikroanalyse*, 7th ed., Springer, Vienna, 1958, p. 272.

D. Determination of Inorganic Esters

1. *Esters of Nitrogen Acids*

A. METHODS BASED ON HYDROLYSIS AND TITRIMETRY. Hydrolysis of esters of nitric or nitrous acid is usually carried out in acetic acid solution. The nitrate and nitrite ions, respectively, produced in the reaction are then determined by one of the following methods. Simecek[81] determined nitrates by titration with standard ferrous sulfate solution in 40% sulfuric acid. The endpoint is located potentiometrically. Becker[82] reduced nitroglycerin by heating the sample with ferrous chloride in acetic acid:

$$C_3H_5(NO_3)_3 + 9FeCl_2 + 9HCl \rightarrow 9FeCl_3 + C_3H_5(OH)_3 + 3NO + 3H_2O \quad (23)$$

The ferric ions produced are determined by titration with standard titanous chloride. A semi-automatic procedure for electrometric titration of nitrocellulose was described by Sandi and Flanquart.[83] The above are all macro methods. In adapting these procedures to the micro scale, it should be noted that ferrous sulfate and titanous chloride solutions are very susceptible to atmospheric oxidation.

B. GASOMETRIC METHODS FOR NITRATE. The standard macro procedure[84] for the analysis of nitroglycerin and nitrocellulose is based on the reduction of nitrate to give nitric oxide:

$$2NO_3^- + 4H_2SO_4 + 3Hg \rightarrow 2NO + SO_4^= + 3HgSO_4 + 4H_2O \quad (24)$$

The gas evolved is measured in a nitrometer. Ferrous chloride in hydrochloric acid is used as the reagent to liberate nitric oxide in another method.[85] These procedures may be converted to the micro scale using a 5-ml. gasometer.

C. VOLUMETRIC DETERMINATION OF NITRITES. Marxova and Zyka[86] devised a titrimetric method to determine nitrites in drugs by using hydrazine as the reducing agent:

$$2HNO_2 + N_2H_4 \rightarrow N_2 + N_2O + 3H_2O \quad (25)$$

It is necessary to place the hydrazine-hydrochloric acid reagent in the titration vessel and add the nitrite sample from the buret. Titration in the

[81] J. Simecek, *Prumysl*, **7**, 285 (1957).

[82] W. W. Becker, *Ind. Eng. Chem., Anal. Ed.*, **5**, 152 (1933).

[83] S. Sandi and G. Flanquart, *Chim. Anal.*, **39**, 20 (1957).

[84] Am. Soc. for Testing Materials, *Standard Specifications and Tests for Soluble Nitrocellulose*, Designation D 301–50, Phila., 1952, Part 4, p. 362.

[85] C. Doree, *The Methods of Cellulose Chemistry*, 2nd ed., Chapman and Hall, London, 1947, p. 245.

[86] I. Marxova and J. Zyka, *Ceskosl Farm.*, **5**, 218 (1956).

conventional manner gives erroneous results as nitrite is decomposed in the acid medium more quickly than it reacts with hydrazine. The endpoint is determined potentiometrically.

Another volumetric method for nitrites has been proposed by Kellner, Szabo, and Szekeres.[87] The sample is oxidized with a known quantity of 0.05N potassium bromate-bromide mixture for 30 minutes. The excess reagent is back-titrated with 0.05N arsenious oxide.

D. METHODS BASED ON REDUCTION TO AMMONIA. Buchi and Alther[88] reported that analysis of esters of nitrous and nitric acid by hydrolysis is unreliable because the reaction is a complex one. These workers favored the modified Kjeldahl method (see page 573) by reducing the sample with Devarda's alloy prior to sulfuric acid digestion. Steyermark and co-workers[89] used tin and hydrochloric acid. Ammonia is then distilled into boric acid and titrated with 0.01N acid.

E. COLORIMETRIC METHODS. Nitric acid esters have been determined colorimetrically by the reaction with sulfuric acid and phenol.[90] The nitrophenol formed gives a yellow color with sodium hydroxide, which is measured in a spectrophotometer. Ferrous sulfate was used by Laccetti and co-workers[91] as the reagent, but the color is stable for only 2 hours.

F. POLAROGRAPHIC METHOD. Polarographic study of n-butyl nitrate has been made in organic solvents with lithium chloride as the supporting electrolyte.[92] Williams and Brooks[93] presented a method to determine isopropyl nitrate by polarography. Methanol serves as the solvent; 0.1M lithium chloride as the supporting electrolyte; Nigrosine as the maxima-suppressor.

2. Esters of Sulfuric and Phosphoric Acids

A. HYDROLYTIC METHODS. Esters of sulfuric and phosphoric acid are easily hydrolyzed in alkali solution. The sulfate and phosphate ions are stable and can be determined by several micro procedures. When sulfate is determined gravimetrically on the micro scale in form of barium sulfate, it is not necessary to ignite the precipitate.[94] Titration of sulfate with

[87] A. Kellner, C. Szabo, and L. Szekeres, Z. Anal. Chem., 157, 13 (1957).

[88] J. Buchi and R. Alther, Pharm. Acta Helv., 31, 121 (1956).

[89] A. Steyermark, B. E. McGee, E. A. Bass, and R. R. Kaup, Anal. Chem., 30, 1561 (1958).

[90] A. Holler and R. V. Huch, Anal. Chem., 21, 1385 (1949).

[91] M. A. Laccetti, S. Semel, and M. Roth, Anal. Chem., 31, 1049 (1959).

[92] N. Radin and T. DeVries, Anal. Chem., 24, 971 (1952).

[93] A. F. Williams and J. Brooks, J. Polarographic Soc., 1, 5 (1958).

[94] T. S. Ma, I. Kaimowitz, and A. A. Benedetti-Pichler, Mikrochim. Acta, 1954, 648.

barium perchlorate has been established as a micro procedure.[95] For determination of 0.1 meq. of phosphate by a colorimetric procedure, the vanadophosphomolybdate method is preferable to the molybdenum blue method.[96]

B. ION-EXCHANGE METHOD. Baldwin and Higgins[97] devised an ion-exchange method to determine phosphorus and sulfur esters. The sample is heated with ethanolamine and the reaction mixture is then passed through a cation exchange column (H form). The eluate containing the free sulfuric or phosphoric acid is titrated with standard alkali. The procedure may be reduced to the 0.1 meq. scale.

IV. The Hydroxyl Function

A. General. The hydroxyl function or hydroxyl group, —OH, treated in this section is regarded as being attached to a carbon atom that is connected to no other elements except *hydrogen* and *carbon*. Thus, the —OH

groups which are found in such functions as $-C\!\!\begin{smallmatrix}O\\ \\OH\end{smallmatrix}$, $-C\!\!\begin{smallmatrix}S\\ \\OH\end{smallmatrix}$, and

$-S\!\!\begin{smallmatrix}O\\ \\OH\end{smallmatrix}$ do not belong in this category and therefore are not to be determined by the methods discussed in the present section. Compounds containing the hydroxyl function usually have the suffix "ol," such as alcohol, glycol, phenol, or enol, or carry the prefix "hydroxy" in their names.

A review on the determination of hydroxyl groups was prepared by Mehlenbacher.[98] It covers the literature up to 1952; however, many publications have appeared since that time. This is because hydroxy compounds occupy a very important position among the industrial organic chemicals, and many methods have been developed for their estimation. The methods vary, depending on whether it is desired to determine the hydroxyl group alone or to take advantage of the structure of the molecule, such as the benzene nucleus or a neighboring group, which confers special properties to the hydroxyl function.

[95] H. Wagner, *Mikrochim. Acta*, **1957**, 19.
[96] T. S. Ma and J. D. McKinley, Jr., *Mikrochim. Acta*, **1954**, 4.
[97] W. H. Baldwin and C. E. Higgins, *Anal. Chem.*, **30**, 446 (1958).
[98] V. C. Mehlenbacher, in *Organic Analysis*, Vol. 1, Interscience, New York, 1953, p. 1.

B. Methods for Determining Single Hydroxyl Functions

1. Methods Based on Esterification. The reaction between a hydroxy compound and an acid to form an ester may be used for the estimation of the hydroxyl group:

$$R'\text{—OH} + R\text{—C}\overset{\displaystyle O}{\underset{\displaystyle OH}{\diagup\diagdown}} \rightleftarrows R\text{—C}\overset{\displaystyle O}{\underset{\displaystyle OR'}{\diagup\diagdown}} + H_2O \qquad (26)$$

If the compound contains more than one hydroxyl group, one mole of it will react with as many moles of the acid as there are hydroxyl groups. Thus, glycerol reacts in the manner shown in equation 27.

$$\begin{matrix} CH_2OH \\ | \\ CHOH \\ | \\ CH_2OH \end{matrix} + 3RC\overset{\displaystyle O}{\diagup}\text{—OH} \rightleftarrows \begin{matrix} CH_2O\text{—CR} \\ \| \\ \quad O \\ CH\text{—}O\text{—CR} \\ \| \\ O \\ CH_2O\text{—CR} \\ \| \\ O \end{matrix} + 3H_2O \qquad (27)$$

A. DEFINITIONS.   Esterification involves the union of the acyl function of the acid and the alkoxyl function of the alcohol; the process is usually called *acylation*. After the hydroxyl function has been determined by acylation, the result may be reported in several ways. For the analysis of a pure compound the result is expressed either as (a) % *hydroxyl*, which means the percentage by weight of the atom-grouping OH in the molecule, or (b) *hydroxyl equivalent*, which indicates the molecular weight of the compound divided by the number of hydroxyl groups present in the molecule. For the analysis of a sample which contains a single known hydroxy compound mixed with other materials that do not possess the hydroxyl function, the result is expressed either as (a) % *compound* or (b) % *purity*, both meaning the weight per cent of the given compound in the sample. For the analysis of unknown mixtures containing more than one hydroxy compound, e.g., fats and oils, it is required to report the result either as (a) hydroxyl value or (b) acetyl value. It should be noted that these latter two terms are not interchangeable. *Acetyl value* is defined as "the number of mg. of KOH required to neutralize the acetic acid obtained by saponifying one gram of an acetylated fat." *Hydroxyl value* is defined as "the number of mg. of KOH equivalent to the hydroxyl content of one gram of sample, based on the weight of *unacetylated* fat."

B. TECHNIQUE OF ACYLATION.   As shown in equations 26 and 27, esterification reactions involve equilibria. Hence, quantitative acylation is usually accomplished not by the free carboxylic acid, but by its chloride or anhydride, as shown in equations 28 and 29.

$$R'—OH + R—C{\overset{\displaystyle O}{\underset{\displaystyle Cl}{\big<}}} \rightarrow RC{\overset{\displaystyle O}{\underset{\displaystyle OR'}{\big<}}} + HCl \qquad (28)$$

$$R'—OH + (R—CO)_2O \rightarrow RC{\overset{\displaystyle O}{\underset{\displaystyle OR'}{\big<}}} + R—COOH \qquad (29)$$

It can be deduced from equations 26–29 that the amount of the hydroxyl function in the sample may be determined by measuring (a) the quantity of the reagent (acid chloride, anhydride) consumed, or (b) the amount of one of the products (ester, water, hydrogen chloride) formed. The former is the approach most frequently applied, while the latter has also been used. However, there is no published method which is based on the measurement of a carboxylic acid produced or consumed in the reaction.

It should be recognized that different hydroxy compounds are esterified by the same reagent at different rates. Berezin[99] studied the kinetics of acylation of alcohols by 3,5-dinitrobenzoyl chloride in pyridine-dioxane mixed solvent and found that the time varies from 10 minutes to 6 hours at 20°C. While it is desirable to find an acylating agent that serves the general purpose, modification becomes mandatory when difficulty arises. This accounts for the large variety of methods of acylation published in recent years. For example, Bring and Kadlecek[100] reported that stearoyl chloride in chloroform is the best reagent for the determination of hydroxyl groups in epoxy resins. These investigators also recommended two other reagents: (a) acetic anhydride-acetic acid mixture in the presence of sodium acetate or sulfuric acid, and (b) acetic anhydride containing pyridinium chloride or perchlorate. The catalytic effect of perchlorate in acetylation was confirmed by Fritz and Schenk[101,102] who employed ethyl acetate as solvent and found that even hindered phenols are completely acylated by acetic anhydride in presence of perchloric acid in 5 minutes at room temperature. Unfortunately, the reagents containing perchloric acid are rather unstable. The perchloric acid-ethyl acetate solution for macro scale determinations (3–4 meq.) keeps for about two weeks, and the perchloric acid-pyridine reagent has to be prepared fresh. However, Schenk and

[99] I. V. Berezin, *Dokl. Akad. Nauk SSSR*, **99**, 563 (1954).
[100] A. Bring and F. Kadlecek, *Plaste Kautschuk*, **5**, 43 (1958).
[101] J. S. Fritz and G. H. Schenk, *Anal. Chem.*, **31**, 1808 (1959).
[102] G. H. Schenk and J. S. Fritz, *Anal. Chem.*, **32**, 987 (1960).

Santiago[102a] have recently published a micro modification of the perchloric acid-catalyzed acetylation procedure which gives good results at room temperature and obviates heating. The details of the method are given in Note 5 of experiment 5, Chapter 12.

As a general rule, tertiary alcohols cannot be determined by the acylation and back-titration technique. Certain primary hydroxy functions like perfluoro alcohols are also difficult to esterify. p-Toluenesulfonic and alkyl sulfonic acids were suggested as catalysts for these alcohols,[103] using toluene and carbon tetrachloride as solvent.

An interesting observation was made by Wilson and Hughes[104] when pyridine-acetic anhydride reagent was used for acylation. The presence of water to the extent of 0.3–0.5% is shown to be necessary in order to prevent the reaction between acetic anhydride and pyridine forming a resin that cannot be decomposed by water in the subsequent titration step. Vogelenzang and Stöver[105] reported positive errors in the determination of polyoxypropylene glycols using acetic anhydride in pyridine. These workers ascribed the difficulty to the hydrolysis of the ether bond. However, they stated that the use of propionic anhydride was satisfactory.

c. DETERMINATION OF THE ACYLATING AGENT CONSUMED. When the determination of hydroxy function depends on the measurement of the acylating agent consumed, the most common reagent is acetic anhydride. Pyridine is generally used as solvent. Being a base, the latter combines with the acetic acid formed, thus helping to displace the equilibrium shown in equation 30 to the right:

$$\text{ROH} + \text{CH}_3\text{—C—O—C—CH}_3 + \text{C}_5\text{H}_5\text{N} \rightleftarrows \text{CH}_3\text{—C} \overset{\text{O}}{\underset{\text{OR}}{\diagdown}} + \text{CH}_3\text{COOH·C}_5\text{H}_5\text{N} \quad (30)$$

After the completion of esterification, the reaction mixture is treated with water to hydrolyze the residual acetic anhydride to acetic acid:

$$\text{CH}_3\text{—C—O—C—CH}_3 + \text{H}_2\text{O} + 2\text{C}_5\text{H}_5\text{N} \rightarrow 2\text{CH}_3\text{COOH·C}_5\text{H}_5\text{N} \quad (31)$$

The total amount of acetic acid is determined by titration with standard alkali according to equation 32:

$$\text{CH}_3\text{COOH·C}_5\text{H}_5\text{N} + \text{NaOH} \rightarrow \text{CH}_3\text{COONa} + \text{H}_2\text{O} + \text{C}_5\text{H}_5\text{N} \quad (32)$$

[102a] G. H. Schenk and M. Santiago, Microchem. J., 6, 77 (1962).
[103] P. D. Faurote and J. G. O. Rear, Ind. Eng. Chem., 49, 189 (1957).
[104] H. N. Wilson and W. C. Hughes, J. Soc. Chem. Ind., 58, 74 (1939).
[105] E. H. Vogelenzang and D. J. Stöver, Pharm. Weekblad, 93, 550 (1958).

It is necessary to treat the hydroxy compound with 1.5–5 times calculated excess of acetic anhydride in order to obtain quantitative esterification. It should be noted that (a) for every equivalent of hydroxyl function, one molar-equivalent of acetic anhydride is consumed and one equivalent of acetic acid is produced, and (b) one mole of acetic anhydride yields two equivalents of acetic acid to be titrated. Therefore, the success of the determination is dependent on the precise measurement of the small difference in acidity of the solution before and after esterification. Since there is no way to determine directly the amount of acid before the reaction occurs, an indirect method has to be used. This involves either running a blank under identical conditions using exactly the same volume of reagent without the sample, or predetermining the concentration of the reagent. It is important to bear these facts in mind when one evaluates a method for microanalysis. Only under ideal situations can two experiments be performed under identical conditions, and there are very few $0.01N$ solutions that are not affected by heating and exposure.

Experience in organic synthesis probably leads some workers to favor acetyl chloride (see eq. 28) as acylating agent rather than acetic anhydride. Several macro procedures for the determination of hydroxyl functions using acetyl chloride are available. Kappelmeier and Mostert[106] stated that the best method to determine hydroxyl values in resins is to dissolve the sample in toluene, acetylate with acetyl chloride in pyridine, add water and ethanol, and titrate with alcoholic potassium hydroxide. However, the application of acetyl chloride does not seem to go beyond the semimicro scale, for which the procedures presented by Lacroix[107] and Kepner and Webb[108] may be consulted. The high volatility of acetyl chloride severely limits its use for microanalysis.

Even when acetic anhydride is used, acylation is preferably carried out in sealed tubes on the micro scale. The micro procedure was first described by Christensen and co-workers.[109] This method has been extensively investigated.[110] Acylation with acetic anhydride in pyridine at 60°C for 2.5 hours is recommended for primary and secondary alcohols, glycols, and some phenols. Certain substituted phenols with high ionization constants, like 2,4-dinitrophenol and 4-hydroxy-benzoic acid, fail to react in pyridine. However, correct values can be obtained by using a neutral solvent, such

[106] C. P. A. Kappelmeier and T. Mostert, *Verfkronick*, **31**, 61 (1958).

[107] Y. Lacroix, *Mem. Poudres*, **34**, 413 (1952).

[108] R. E. Kepner and A. D. Webb, *Anal. Chem.*, **26**, 925 (1954).

[109] J. W. Petersen, K. W. Hedberg, and B. E. Christensen, *Ind. Eng. Chem., Anal. Ed.*, **15**, 225 (1943).

[110] T. S. Ma and H. Waldman, unpublished work; see H. Waldman, *Master's Thesis, Brooklyn College*, 1960.

as dimethylene glycol dimethyl ether. The detailed procedure will be found on page 493. Another micro method was described by Hamlin,[111] who also measured the acid consumed after the sample was acetylated with acetic anhydride in pyridine.

Other acid anhydrides that are used for acylation are propionic anhydride, proposed by Sezerat[112] for the analysis of polyethylene glycols, and phthalic anhydride, which was investigated by Elving and Warshowsky.[113] Siggia[114] reported that the latter reagent can be used in the presence of low molecular weight aldehydes, which for some unknown reason interfere with the determination using acetic anhydride.

D. DETERMINATION OF WATER OR HYDROGEN CHLORIDE FORMED. Bryant, Mitchell, and Smith[115] devised a method to determine aliphatic hydroxy compounds by measuring the amount of water produced in esterification (see eq. 26). By using a large excess of acetic acid in dioxane and boron trifluoride as catalyst, the reaction is completed in 2 hours at 67°C. Pyridine is added and water in the reaction mixture is determined by titration with Karl Fischer reagent according to equation 33.

$$H_2O + SO_2 + I_2 + 3C_5H_5N \rightarrow 2C_5H_5N \cdot HI + C_5H_5NSO_3 \qquad (33)$$

A procedure for determining hydroxyl groups in oils was presented by Mlejnek.[116] These investigators used samples from 1–10 grams. The micro method developed by Ma and Hensle[117] uses the same principle, but involves modifications in technique. It should be noted that less than 2 mg. of water is formed in the 0.1 meq. scale determinations. The ubiquitous moisture may cause serious errors in microanalysis. The detailed procedure is given on page 612. The advantage of this method is that it can determine tertiary aliphatic hydroxyl groups, as well as primary and secondary. On the other hand, phenols and terpenols are not quantitatively esterified.

Raymond and Bouvetier[118] proposed a scheme to determine the hydrogen chloride formed in esterification (see eq. 28). The sample is heated under reflux in an inert solvent with a nonvolatile acid chloride, while a current of inert gas passes through to remove the hydrogen chloride which is absorbed and titrated. This method can be adapted to the semimicro

[111] A. G. Hamlin, Shirley Inst. Mem., 29, 301 (1956).

[112] A. Sezerat, Ann. Pharm. France, 13, 516 (1955).

[113] P. J. Elving and B. Warshowsky, Anal. Chem., 19, 1006 (1947).

[114] S. Siggia, Quantitative Organic Analysis via Functional Groups, 2nd ed., Wiley, New York, 1954, p. 11.

[115] W. M. Bryant, J. Mitchell, Jr., and D. M. Smith, J. Am. Chem. Soc., 62, 1 (1940).

[116] O. Mlejnek, Chem. Zvesti, 9, 27 (1955).

[117] T. S. Ma and B. L. Hensle, unpublished work; see B. L. Hensle, Master's Thesis, New York University, 1957.

[118] E. Raymond and E. Bouvetier, Compt. Rend., 209, 439 (1939).

scale[119] using stearoyl or 4-nitro- or 2,4-dinitrobenzoyl chloride as the reagent, toluene as solvent, and nitrogen gas as the purger. However, the slight decomposition of these acid chlorides on heating makes them unsuitable for microanalysis. This method is not recommended for the analysis of low-boiling hydroxy compounds, but it is useful for nonvolatile substances like fats and sterols.

E. DETERMINATION OF THE ESTER FORMED. The commercial methods for the determination of hydroxyl values of fats and oils and the International Standard Method[98] for evaluation of glycerol are based on the measurement of the amount of ester formed. The sample, in gram quantity, is acetylated with acetic anhydride; the reaction mixture is then carefully neutralized, a calculated excess amount of $1N$ alkali is added and the saponification value of the ester is determined. Such roundabout way is rarely used in the analysis of a pure compound, though it is possible to adapt the procedure to the semimicro or micro scale. However, in the proof of structure of polyhydroxy compounds, it is sometimes advisable to determine the hydroxyl groups by acetylation, isolate and purify the ester, and determine the ester or acetyl groups of the latter. This serves to double check the number of hydroxyl groups present in the original compound. Weinmann and Jayle[120] proposed a scheme for the indirect determination of sterol hydroxyl groups as follows. The sample is acetylated by means of acetic anhydride in pyridine at 100°C or acetyl chloride in benzene at room temperature. The excess reagent is removed by evaporation and the dried residue is treated with hydroxylamine reagent. The amount of acetyl hydroxamic acid is determined colorimetrically through its ferric complex.

Robinson and co-workers[121] recently described a macro method for the rapid determination of hydroxyl groups by the nonaqueous titration of the esters. The sample (4 meq.) is esterified with 3,5-dinitrobenzoyl chloride in pyridine. The resulting 3,5-dinitrobenzoate is then titrated as a weak acid by means of $0.2N$ tetrabutylammonium hydroxide in benzene-methanol mixed solvent, the endpoint being located potentiometrically (see Chapter 11, Section II). This method has not been tested on the micro scale.

F. METHOD BASED ON REACTION WITH DIAZOMETHANE. The hydroxyl function reacts with diazomethane to form methyl ether, as shown in equation 34.

---

[119] T. S. Ma and D. G. Shaheen, unpublished work: see D. G. Shaheen, *Master's Thesis, New York University*, 1958.
[120] S. H. Weinmann and M. F. Jayle, *Bull. Soc. Chim. Biol.*, **39**, 65 (1957).
[121] W. T. Robinson, Jr., R. H. Cundiff, and P. C. Markunas, *Anal. Chem.*, **33**, 1030 (1961).

$$R—OH + CH_2N_2 \rightarrow R—OCH_3 + N_2 \tag{34}$$

This reaction is quantitative for most aliphatic alcohols and enols that do not form chelates.[122] Due to the instability of diazomethane, it is impractical to perform the determination by measuring the reagent consumed or the volume of nitrogen gas formed. Therefore, it is necessary to analyze the methyl ether produced. Roper and Ma[123] have devised a method to generate small quantities of diazomethane for micro synthesis. The apparatus is shown in Figure 7.2. The sample is placed in the receiving tube or some appropriate vessel. The methyl ether formed is then determined through its methoxyl content (see page 558) or by means of gas chromatography.

2. *Methods Based on Active Hydrogen Determination.* The hydrogen atom in the hydroxyl function is sufficiently labile to react with the Grignard reagent:

$$R—OH + CH_3MgI \rightarrow CH_4 + RO—MgI \tag{35}$$

or lithium aluminum hydride:

$$4R—OH + LiAlH_4 \rightarrow 4H_2 + LiOR + Al(OR)_3 \tag{36}$$

The determination can be carried out in the micro active hydrogen apparatus (see page 412), and the quantity of methane or hydrogen formed, respectively, is measured in the gasometer.

Titrimetric determination using lithium aluminum hydride was described by several workers on the macro scale. Tetrahydrofuran[124,125] or dimethoxyethane[126] is used as the solvent. The endpoint is determined either potentiometrically or visually with 4-phenylazodiphenylamine as the indicator. Small[126] reported that $0.2N$ solution of lithium aluminum hydride loses more than 10% of its normality in 6 days even when the reagent is kept under an atmosphere of nitrogen. The difficulty in adapting this method to microanalysis probably is insurmountable.

3. *Miscellaneous Methods*

A. DETERMINATION BY OXIDIMETRY.   Aliphatic hydroxy compounds are oxidized by potassium dichromate in acidic solution to form ketones, carboxylic acids, or carbon dioxide. This method is applicable only to the analysis of known substances since the stoichiometric ratio and the con-

[122] F. Arndt and C. Martius, *Ann. Chem. Liebigs*, **449**, 247 (1932); B. Eister, F. Arndt, L. Loewe, and E. Ayca, *Chem. Berichte*, **84**, 156 (1951).

[123] R. Roper and T. S. Ma, *Microchem. J.*, **1**, 246 (1957).

[124] C. J. Lintner, R. H. Schleif, and T. Higuchi, *Anal. Chem.*, **22**, 534 (1950).

[125] G. A. Stenmark and F. T. Weiss, *Anal. Chem.*, **28**, 1784 (1956).

[126] L. A. Small, *Analyst*, **84**, 17 (1959).

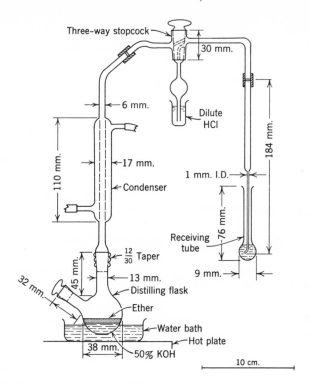

Fig. 7.2. Assembly for diazomethane reaction. Courtesy of *Microchemical Journal*.

dition of oxidation have to be established using a pure sample of the compound. Jaulmes and Mestres[127] investigated the oxidation of low molecular weight aliphatic alcohols, allyl alcohol, and hydroxyacetic acid with 0.2N potassium dichromate in sulfuric acid. The excess reagent is back-titrated with ferrous sulfate using 1,10-phenanthroline as the indicator. A micro method was developed by Griffiths and Stock[128] who oxidized the sample with 5 ml. of 0.02N potassium dichromate followed by electrometric back-titration of the excess with standard ferrous ammonium sulfate solution.

B. DETERMINATION BY INDIRECT CHELATOMETRY. Arikawa and Kato[129] described the following micro method for the determination of a few milligrams of alcohols in aqueous solutions. The hydroxy compound is first

[127] P. Jaulmes and R. Mestres, *Chim. Anal.*, **40**, 413 (1958).
[128] V. S. Griffiths and D. I. Stock, *J. Chem. Soc.*, **1956**, 1633.
[129] Y. Arikawa and T. Kato, *Techn. Repts. Tokyo Univ., Japan*, **19**, 104 (1954).

converted to the corresponding water-soluble xanthate according to reaction 37.

$$R\text{—}OH + CS_2 + NaOH \rightarrow S{=}C\begin{smallmatrix} \diagup OR \\ \diagdown SNa \end{smallmatrix} + H_2O \qquad (37)$$

Nickel acetate solution is added to precipitate the nickel salt, which is filtered off and washed. The precipitate is then redissolved in ammonium hydroxide solution and the amount of nickel is determined by titration with 0.01N EDTA using murexide as the indicator. It should be noted that only primary and secondary alcohols form stable xanthates[130,131] and this method depends on quantitative precipitation and separation. Nevertheless, it is useful for the determination of known compounds. Like the dichromate oxidation procedure, this method has an advantage over the acylation and active hydrogen methods in that it can be employed for the determination of hydroxyl function in samples which contain water.

C. DETERMINATION BY DEHYDRATION. A macro method to determine hydroxyl function by catalytic dehydration was described by Bashkirov, Loozik, and Kamzolkin.[132] The sample (3 g.) is boiled for 3 hours in 50 ml. of xylene with microspherical aluminosilicate catalyst, and the amount of water liberated is measured. The reaction may be represented as shown in equation 38.

$$\underset{\displaystyle R}{R'CH_2\text{—}CHOH} \rightarrow \underset{\displaystyle R}{R'CH{=}CH} + H_2O \qquad (38)$$

These investigators reported quantitative yields for the higher aliphatic secondary alcohols, while primary alcohols do not react. Conversion of this method to the micro scale is difficult.

D. DETERMINATION BY THE REACTION WITH DIOXANE-SULFUR TRIOXIDE. Terentev and Kupletskaya[133] proposed a new reagent to determine mono- and polyhydroxy compounds. The reagent is made from sulfur trioxide and dioxane and has the composition $O(CH_2CH_2)_2O \cdot SO_3$. The hydroxy compound (20–50 mg.) is treated with the above reagent in dioxane for 2 or 3 minutes. Water is added and the increase in acidity is determined

---

[130] F. Feigl, *Spot Tests in Organic Analysis*, 5th ed., Elsevier, Amsterdam, 1956, p. 173.

[131] N. D. Cheronis and J. B. Entrikin, *Semimicro Qualitative Organic Analysis*, 2nd ed., Interscience, New York, 1957, p. 252.

[132] A. N. Bashkirov, S. A. Lodzik, and V. V. Kamzolkin, *Trudy. Inst. Nefti, Akad. Nauk. USSR*, **12**, 297 (1958).

[133] A. P. Terentev and N. B. Kupletskaya, *Zhur. Obshch. Khim.*, **26**, 451 (1956).

by titration with standard sodium carbonate solution to the methyl orange endpoint. This method can be used to determine the hydroxyl function of primary, secondary, and tertiary aliphatic alcohols, as well as polyhydric alcohols and sugars. It cannot be applied to, or in the presence of, phenols.

C. Methods for the Determination of Multiple Hydroxyl Functions

1. Methods Based on the Periodate Oxidation of Adjacent Hydroxyl Functions. Malaprade[134] first observed the selective oxidizing power of periodate in 1928. It attacks adjacent hydroxyl functions in weakly acidic, neutral, or weakly basic solutions readily at room temperature, but it has no effect on monohydroxy compounds or polyhydroxy compounds in which the hydroxyl groups are separated by one or more carbon atoms. This specific reaction of periodate has been extensively utilized in the qualitative and quantitative analysis as well as proof of structure of hydroxy compounds and carbohydrates (see page 157). An excellent review of the application of periodate oxidation in organic analyses was prepared by Kolthoff and Belcher.[135] In the determination of multiple hydroxyl functions by means of periodate, it is well to remember that every "adjacency"—not every pair—of hydroxyl groups consumes one equivalent (mole) of periodate. The stoichiometric relationship can be represented by the following reaction:

$$CH_2OH—(CHOH)_n—CH_2OH + (n + 1)HIO_4 \rightarrow$$
$$(n + 1)HIO_3 + 2HCHO + nHCOOH + H_2O \quad (39)$$

It should be noted that formic acid is produced only when there are more than two adjacent hydroxyl functions in the molecule. Thus, glycerol yields one equivalent of formic acid according to the reaction:

$$CH_2OH—CHOH—CH_2OH + 2HIO_4 \rightarrow 2HIO_3 + 2HCHO + HCOOH + H_2O \quad (40)$$

while ethylene glycol gives only formaldehyde:

$$CH_2OH—CH_2OH + HIO_4 \rightarrow HIO_3 + 2HCHO + H_2O \quad (41)$$

If the hydrogen atom attached to the carbon is replaced by another radical, a different aldehyde will be formed. For example, 2,3-dihydroxy butane yields two equivalents of acetaldehyde, as indicated in equation 42.

$$CH_3CHOHCHOHCH_3 + HIO_4 \rightarrow HIO_3 + 2CH_3CHO + H_2O \quad (42)$$

The special feature of periodate oxidation is the cleavage of the carbon-

[134] L. Malaprade, *Compt. Rend.*, **186**, 382 (1928).

[135] I. M. Kolthoff and R. Belcher, *Volumetric Analysis*, Vol. 3, Interscience, New York, 1957, p. 475.

to-carbon bond under rather mild conditions. A mechanism proposed by
Criegee[136] involves the formation of a cyclic ester as indicated in equation 43.

$$=C-OH \atop =C-OH + HIO_4 \rightarrow \quad \begin{matrix} =C-O \\ | \quad \diagdown \\ | \quad IO(OH)_3 \\ =C-O \diagup \end{matrix} \quad (43)$$

Price and co-workers[137] observed that *cis*-cyclohexane glycol is more readily
oxidized by periodate than is the *trans* compound, and postulated the
reaction to follow a bimolecular inversion mechanism. The difference in
the reaction rate of periodate oxidation of cyclic glycols was attributed to
the conformation of the ring structures, according to Honeyman and
Shaw,[138] who also reported that the rate in alcoholic medium is slower than
that in aqueous solution.

It becomes evident by inspection of equations 39–42 that determination
of polyhydroxy compounds using periodate oxidation may be accomplished
by measuring the amount of periodate consumed, or one of the products
(iodate, formic acid, aldehyde) formed in the reaction. The aldehyde or
formic acid is determined in the analysis of known compounds or mixtures.
Measurement of the reagent consumed, or the iodate formed, is of general
application and is the necessary procedure to ascertain the number of
adjacent hydroxyl groups in a new compound. For the latter purpose,
determination of the quantity of iodate formed would be the ideal method.
Unfortunately, there is no accurate method to determine iodate in the
presence of periodate. Hess, Jordan, and Ross[139] presented a procedure
to determine ethylene glycol in water based on the formation of insoluble
silver iodate. The time of appearance of the precipitate is proportional to
the concentration of diol, under critical conditions. This method obviously
is not applicable to the analysis of unknown compounds.

Fleury and co-workers[140] investigated the various ways to determine the
amount of periodate consumed and proposed three methods on the macro
scale.

A. THE IODIDE-THIOSULFATE METHOD. The sample is treated with a
known amount of periodate. After the reaction is completed, potassium

---

[136] R. Criegee, *Angew. Chem.*, **50**, 153 (1937).

[137] C. C. Price and H. J. Kroll, *J. Am. Chem. Soc.*, **60**, 2726 (1938); C. C. Price and
M. Knell, *ibid.*, **64**, 552 (1942).

[138] J. Honeyman and C. J. G. Shaw, *J. Chem. Soc.*, **1959**, 2454.

[139] E. R. Hess, C. B. Jordan, and H. K. Ross, *Anal. Chem.*, **28**, 134 (1956).

[140] P. Fleury, *Chim. Anal.*, **35**, 197 (1935); P. Fleury, J. Courtois, and M. Grandchamp,
Bull. Soc. Chim., *France*, **1954**, 188.

iodide and sulfuric acid are added. Both the residual periodic acid and the iodic acid formed liberate iodine according to equations 44 and 45, respectively:

$$HIO_4 + 7HI \rightarrow 4I_2 + 4H_2O \tag{44}$$

$$HIO_3 + 5HI \rightarrow 3I_2 + 3H_2O \tag{45}$$

The amount of iodine liberated is determined by titration with standard sodium thiosulfate. Therefore, this method is dependent on the slight difference in the iodine liberated by periodic and iodic acid respectively.

B. THE ARSENITE METHOD.   In this method the residual periodic acid is reduced to iodate by adding a known excess of sodium arsenite in the presence of sodium bicarbonate:

$$HIO_4 + Na_3AsO_3 + NaHCO_3 \rightarrow Na_3AsO_4 + H_2CO_3 + NaIO_3 \tag{46}$$

The excess arsenite is then determined by back-titration with standard iodine solution.

C. THE MANGANOUS SULFATE METHOD.   This method is based on the reaction between manganous sulfate and the residual periodic acid in the presence of sodium carbonate to yield manganese dioxide and iodic acid:

$$HIO_4 + MnSO_4 + Na_2CO_3 + H_2O \rightarrow MnO_2 + HIO_3 + Na_2SO_4 + H_2CO_3 \tag{47}$$

The manganese dioxide is separated, redissolved in sulfuric acid, and potassium iodide is added:

$$MnO_2 + 2H_2SO_4 + 2KI \rightarrow I_2 + MnSO_4 + K_2SO_4 + 2H_2O \tag{48}$$

The iodine liberated is determined by titration with standard sodium thiosulfate.

In adapting the above methods to the micro scale, it was found that the arsenite method gave the best results.[141] The glycol sample is treated with potassium metaperiodate in dilute sulfuric acid in an Erlenmeyer flask at room temperature for 1/2 hour. Calculated excess amount of $0.05N$ sodium arsenite is then introduced, followed by a trace of potassium iodide which acts as catalyst, and solid sodium bicarbonate. The unreacted arsenite is determined by back-titration with $0.02N$ iodine solution to the blue endpoint in presence of starch. The detailed procedure is given in experiment 11.

Reddaway[142] determined glycol in alcoholic solution. The oxidation requires 70 minutes. Approximately 0.1 meq. sample is used, and the residual periodic acid is determined by means of $0.1N$ sodium arsenite.

[141] T. S. Ma and H. Moss, unpublished work; see H. Moss, *Master's Thesis, Brooklyn College*, 1958.

[142] R. J. B. Reddaway, *Analyst*, **82**, 506 (1957).

Berka and Zyka[143] proposed to measure the residual periodate by potentiometric titration with hydrazine sulfate solution, according to the following equation:

$$2IO_4^- + N_2H_4 \rightarrow 2IO_3^- + N_2 + 2H_2O \qquad (49)$$

2. Other Oxidimetric Methods for Polyhydroxy Compounds. As polyhydroxy compounds are easily oxidized, a number of oxidimetric methods have been proposed. Berka and Zyka[144] investigated the quantitative oxidation of mannitol, tartaric, and gluconic acids with lead tetraacetate, but this reagent is inferior to periodate since it tends to cause partial oxidation of the formic acid produced in the reaction.

Sharma and Mehrotra[145] described a macro procedure to determine glycerol and glycols by oxidation with $0.1N$ ceric sulfate in sulfuric acid, followed by back-titration with ferrous sulfate. The conditions should be established if this method is to be adapted to the micro scale, since Jackson and Ramamurti[146] reported that glycerol is not oxidized by $0.01N$ ceric sulfate at 100°C.

A micro method was proposed by West and Skoog[147] to determine glycerol with quinquevalent vanadium. After quantitative oxidation of the sample to formic acid, the excess of oxidant is back-titrated with ferrous sulfate using N-phenylanthranilic acid as the indicator. Ethylene glycol and trimethylene glycol also can be determined by this method. However, it cannot be applied to all polyhydroxy compounds. For instance, the oxidation of propylene glycol is not stoichiometric.[148]

Potassium dichromate oxidation has been applied to the determination of polyhydroxy compounds. After the completion of the reaction, the residual dichromate ions may be determined volumetrically by titration with potassium iodide and sodium thiosulfate,[149] or spectrophotometrically.[150]

The chief use of the methods discussed in this section is for the determination of known compounds in dilute aqueous solutions. They cannot serve the purpose of determining polyhydroxyl functions in unknown substances.

[143] A. Berka and J. Zyka, *Ceskoslov. Farm.*, **8**, 136 (1959).

[144] A. Berka and J. Zyka, *Ceskoslov. Farm.*, **7**, 141 (1958); *Collect. Czechoslov. Chem. Comm.*, **23**, 2005 (1958); *Chem. Listy*, **52**, 926 (1958).

[145] N. N. Sharma and R. C. Mehrotra, *Anal. Chim. Acta*, **13**, 419 (1955).

[146] C. P. Jackson and K. Ramamurti, *J. Sc. Food Agric.*, **9**, 787 (1956).

[147] D. M. West and D. A. Skoog, *Anal. Chem.*, **31**, 586 (1959).

[148] D. M. West and D. A. Skoog, *Am. Chem. Soc., Miami Meeting, 1957*, Abstracts, p. 23B.

[149] M. A. Amlinskaya and V. N. Erikh, *Khimgaz*, **6**, 213 (1951).

[150] R. Sargent and W. Rieman III, *Anal. Chim. Acta*, **14**, 381 (1956).

3. Colorimetric Methods for Polyhydroxy Compounds. According to Jones and Riddick,[151] propane-1,2-diol is dehydrated by sulfuric acid to give allyl alcohol and the enolic form of acetaldehyde. The latter compound yields a violet complex with ninhydrin in sulfuric acid, which is determined colorimetrically. 2-Ethyl-hexane-1,3-diol was determined by a colorimetric method which is based on its reaction with *p*-dimethylaminobenzaldehyde in concentrated sulfuric acid.[152] Ethylene glycol was determined by an indirect colorimetric method as follows.[153] The sample is heated with 2,3-diaminophenazine in $15N$ sulfuric acid. The excess of reagent is tetrazotized and the resulting tetrazonium salt is reduced with hypophosphorus acid and the intensity of the color is compared with a calibration curve. In the above methods, the authors did not state whether they are selective for 1,2- and 1,3-diols, respectively.

D. Special Methods for Certain Hydroxy Compounds

1. Determination of the Phenolic Group. When the hydroxyl function is attached to the benzene ring, it is known as a phenolic group. As mentioned above, phenols can be acetylated and the excess of acetic anhydride determined by back-titration. However, the rate of esterification of the phenolic group is much slower than that of the normal alcohols. The methods which depend on oxidation or dehydration are not applicable to the analysis of phenols. On the other hand, since the hydroxyl function activates the benzene nucleus, there are many special methods for determining phenols which are based on the reactions of the benzenoid structure. They are discussed in a different section (see Chapter 11, Section VI).

2. Determination of the Hydroxyalkyl Group. The hydroxyalkyl group is a terminal function containing the atom grouping —CH_2OH, which is known as the "methylol" or "hydroxymethyl" group. While the aliphatic primary alcohols also contain the terminal —CH_2OH, it should be noted that the methods presented below are not applicable to these alcohols.

A. DETERMINATION OF THE METHYLOL GROUP THROUGH FORMALDEHYDE. The hydroxymethyl group in glycols, polyhydroxy alcohols, and carbohydrates is converted to formaldehyde upon oxidation with periodic acid (see page 158). A micro method described by Speck and Frost[154] involves the removal of the residual periodic acid, together with the iodic acid formed in the reaction, followed by the determination of the formaldehyde colorimetrically using the chromotropic acid procedure (see page 504).

[151] L. R. Jones and J. A. Riddick, *Anal. Chem.,* **29,** 1214 (1957).

[152] M. C. Bowman, M. Beroza, and F. Acree, Jr., *J. Agric. Food Chem.,* **7,** 259 (1959).

[153] J. M. Dechary, E. Kun, and H. C. Pitot, *Anal. Chem.,* **26,** 449 (1954).

[154] J. A. Speck and A. A. Frost, *Anal. Chem.,* **26,** 1942 (1954).

The hydroxymethyl group in nitro alcohols liberates formaldehyde on treatment with sodium hydroxide, according to the following equation:

$$R\overset{\overset{\displaystyle H}{|}}{\underset{\underset{\displaystyle NO_2}{|}}{C}}-CH_2OH + NaOH \rightarrow CH_2O + R\overset{\overset{\displaystyle H}{|}}{\underset{\underset{\displaystyle O}{\parallel}}{C}}=N-ONa + H_2O \qquad (50)$$

This is the basis of a method devised by Jones and Riddick,[155] who also determined the formaldehyde by the chromotropic acid procedure.

B. DETERMINATION OF THE METHYLOL GROUP BY AQUAMETRY. Stenmark and Weiss[156] determined the methylol group in phenolic resins by its condensation with phenol in the presence of boron trifluoride, as represented by the reaction:

$$R-CH_2OH + \underset{}{\overset{OH}{\bigcirc}} \rightarrow R-CH_2-\underset{}{\overset{OH}{\bigcirc}} + H_2O \qquad (51)$$

The amount of water formed is measured by the Karl Fischer reagent. Aldehydes interfere, but not ketones or alcohols.

C. DETERMINATION OF THE HYDROXYALKYL GROUP THROUGH ETHYL IODIDE AND ETHYLENE. According to Lortz,[157] hydroxyalkyl groups in low substituted starch ethers are converted to ethyl iodide and ethylene when the sample is heated with constant boiling hydriodic acid. Ethyl iodide is absorbed in silver nitrate solution and ethylene collected in bromine solution, and these products are respectively determined by volumetric methods.

3. Determination of the Ene-Diol Function. The ene-diol function, $-\underset{\underset{\displaystyle OH}{|}}{C}=\underset{\underset{\displaystyle OH}{|}}{C}-$, is easily oxidized to the diketone. Hence, the general method to determine ene-diols is by iodine oxidation, as shown below:[158]

$$-\underset{\underset{\displaystyle OH}{|}}{C}=\underset{\underset{\displaystyle OH}{|}}{C}- + I_2 \rightarrow -\underset{\underset{\displaystyle O}{\parallel}}{C}-\underset{\underset{\displaystyle O}{\parallel}}{C}- + 2HI \qquad (52)$$

N-Bromosuccinimide has been suggested as the oxidant for the microdetermination of the ene-diol group in ascorbic acid,[159] according to the following reaction:

[155] L. R. Jones and J. A. Riddick, *Anal. Chem.*, **28**, 254 (1956).

[156] G. A. Stenmark and F. T. Weiss, *Anal. Chem.*, **28**, 260 (1956).

[157] H. J. Lortz, *Anal. Chem.*, **28**, 892 (1956).

[158] H. v. Euler and H. Hasselquist, *Reducktone*, Enke, Stuttgart, 1950.

[159] M. Z. Barakat, M. F. A. El-Wahab, and M. M. El-Sadr, *Anal. Chem.*, **27**, 536 (1955).

$$\begin{array}{c} O=C \\ HO-C \\ HO-C \\ H-C \\ HO-CH \\ CH_2OH \end{array} O + \begin{array}{c} CH_2-C=O \\ NBr \\ CH_2-C=O \end{array} \rightarrow \begin{array}{c} O=C \\ O=C \\ O=C \\ H-C \\ HO-CH \\ CH_2OH \end{array} O + \begin{array}{c} CH_2-C=O \\ NH + HBr \\ CH_2-C=O \end{array} \quad (53)$$

The endpoint is located by the use of starch-iodide mixture. A little excess of the N-bromosuccinimide liberates iodine from potassium iodide, which produces blue color in the presence of starch.

4. Determination of Low Molecular Weight Alcohols

A. COLORIMETRIC METHOD USING CERIC AMMONIUM NITRATE. Alcohols give intense red color when treated with a solution of ceric ammonium nitrate, $Ce(NH_4)_2(NO_3)_6$.[160] This reaction was adapted to the quantitative analysis of low molecular weight alcohols by Reid and co-workers.[161] The procedure works effectively when only 0.1% of the alcohol is present. Less satisfactory results are obtained at higher concentrations.

B. DETERMINATION OF ETHANOL. Small amounts of ethanol in aqueous solution, such as alcohol in blood or urine, are commonly determined by distilling it into a known quantity of standardized potassium dichromate in dilute sulfuric acid. The excess of dichromate is back-titrated iodometrically.[162] Gettler, Niederl, and Benedetti-Pichler[163] passed the ethanol vapor into a modified alkoxyl apparatus and determined the ethyl iodide formed gravimetrically as silver iodide. Other investigators converted ethanol into ethyl nitrite with nitrous acid. The nitrite is separated by distillation and determined iodometrically[164] or colorimetrically.[165] Ethanol in body fluids has been determined by a color reaction using p-nitrobenzaldehyde in dilute sodium hydroxide solution as the reagent[166] or by oxidizing the alcohol to acetaldehyde and measuring the intensity of acetaldo-thiosemicarbazone at 261 mμ.[167] Alcohol in the breath is measured

[160] F. R. Duke and G. F. Smith, *Ind. Eng. Chem., Anal. Ed.*, **12**, 201 (1940).

[161] V. W. Reid and R. K. Truelove, *Analyst*, **77**, 325 (1952); V. W. Reid and D. G. Salmon, *ibid.*, **80**, 704 (1955).

[162] H. Varley, *Practical Clinical Biochemistry*, Interscience, New York, 1954, p. 494.

[163] A. O. Gettler, J. B. Niederl, and A. A. Benedetti-Pichler, *J. Am. Chem. Soc.*, **54**, 1476 (1932).

[164] A. Wacek and F. Zeisler, *Mikrochim. Acta*, **1955**, 29.

[165] N. V. Chalov and L. P. Volskaya, *Zarodskaya Lab.*, **12**, 286 (1946).

[166] W. Schwerd, *Deut. Z. Ges. Gerichtl. Med.*, **43**, 221 (1954).

[167] O. Schmidt and R. Manz, *Klin. Wochschr.*, **33**, 82 (1955).

by the change in color intensity of permanganate or dichromate solution after the respired air has bubbled through the solution.[168]

c. DETERMINATION OF METHANOL. Methanol can be analyzed in the presence of other alcohols in very dilute solutions by oxidation with potassium permanganate in phosphoric acid.[169] The methanol is converted to formaldehyde, which is conveniently determined by the chromotropic acid method. A procedure described by Yamamura and Matsuoka[170] uses a 1-ml. sample containing up to 20 μg. of methanol, but the method is not suitable for solutions which contain more than 1.5 mg. of methanol per ml. Kubis[171] oxidized methanol with lead chromate at 600°C and determined the formaldehyde using the Schiff reagent.

5. *Determination of Long Chain Alcohols.* A semimicro method for the determination of long chain alcohols was devised by Blickenstaff, Schaffer, and Kathman.[172] The sample is sulfonated with chlorsulfonic acid. After neutralization of the reaction mixture, the sodium alkyl sulfate is titrated with cetyl trimethylammonium bromide.

E. Physical Methods for the Determination of the Hydroxyl Function

1. *Infrared Spectrometry.* The hydroxyl function shows strong absorption in the infrared region. Crisler and Burrill[173] determined the hydroxyl values of aliphatic primary alcohols on the basis of the OH stretching at 1.4 μ. Burns and Muraca[174] determined polypropylene glycols at 2.84 μ. Hilton[175] determined the hydroxyl numbers of polyesters and polyethers using the absorption in the region from 2.0 to 3.2 μ, whereas the residual hydroxyl groups in cellulose acetate were measured by Mitchell, Bockman, and Lee[176] at the 0.7–2.7 μ range. Goddu[177] reported the determination of 40 phenols using the absorption in the 2.7–3.0 μ region. Intramolecular hydrogen bonding causes shifts in the hydroxyl band. Advantage may be taken of these shifts to determine some mixtures of hydroxy compounds.[177]

[168] S. Nishiyama and N. Motohashi, *Sci. Crime Detection*, **7**, 281 (1954).

[169] A. P. Mathers, *J. Assoc. Offic. Agr. Chemists*, **38**, 753 (1955).

[170] S. Yamamura and T. Matsuoka, *J. Soc. Brewing, Japan*, **49**, 111 (1954).

[171] J. Kubis, *Casopis Lekaru Ceskych*, **98**, 851 (1959).

[172] R. T. Blickenstaff, J. R. Schaffer, and G. G. Kathman, *Anal. Chem.*, **26**, 746 (1954).

[173] R. O. Crisler and A. M. Burrill, *Anal. Chem.*, **31**, 2055 (1959).

[174] E. A. Burns and R. F. Muraca, *Anal. Chem.*, **31**, 397 (1959).

[175] C. L. Hilton, *Anal. Chem.*, **31**, 1610 (1959).

[176] J. A. Mitchell, C. D. Bockman, Jr., and A. V. Lee, *Anal. Chem.*, **29**, 499 (1957).

[177] R. F. Goddu, *Anal. Chem.*, **30**, 2009 (1958).

Kabasakalian, Townley, and Yudis[178] observed that the absorption near 3.05 μ from the hydroxyl function in steroids is linear with concentration and essentially independent of the type of the hydroxyl group. These workers used a 0.1–0.4 meq. sample, with pyridine as the solvent to eliminate hydrogen bonding.

2. Polarography. The hydroxyl function is not reducible at the dropping mercury electrode. However, polarography has been applied to the determination of hydroxy compounds by indirect methods. Thus, Kubis[171] oxidized methanol to formaldehyde and determined the latter in the polarograph using $0.1N$ lithium hydroxide as the supporting electrolyte. Monnier[179] estimated ethanol in blood by oxidizing the distillate in a mixture of nitric acid and potassium dichromate and determining the excess of dichromate polarographically. Zuman and Krupicka[180] devised a method to determine adjacent diols which is based on the polarography of iodate and periodate ions in the reaction mixture.

3. Isotopic Method. The hydroxyl function was determined by the isotopic exchange technique by Anbar and co-workers.[181] The hydroxy compound is heated with $CO_2{}^{18}$ in the presence of a trace of sulfuric acid in a sealed tube at 150–230°C. The tube is then transferred to the inlet system of a mass spectrometer and the O–18 content of the carbon dioxide is measured and the concentration of the hydroxy compound is read from a calibration curve. It should be noted that the exchange is not limited to the hydroxyl function. Other oxygen functions, like carbonyl and ester functions, also exchange with $CO_2{}^{18}$.

V. The Methylene Dioxy Function

A. General. The methylene dioxy function, $CH_2(O—)_2$, contains a CH_2 group which is attached to two oxygen atoms that are connected to adjacent carbon atoms of a benzene or other cyclic structure. This function is found in many naturally occurring substances, such as alkaloids and flavones.

The characteristic property of compounds possessing the methylene dioxy function is the liberation of formaldehyde when they are heated in 1:1 sulfuric, 80% phosphoric, or $6N$ hydrochloric acid solution. The reaction, represented by equation 54,

[178] P. Kabasakalian, E. R. Townley, and M. D. Yudis, *Anal. Chem.*, **31**, 375 (1959).

[179] D. Monnier, *Helv. Chim. Acta*, **38**, 402 (1955).

[180] P. Zuman and J. Krupicka, *Chem. Listy*, **51**, 424 (1957); K. Takiura and K. Koizumi, *J. Pharm. Soc. Japan*, **78**, 961 (1958).

[181] M. Anbar, J. Dostrovsky, F. Klein, and D. Samuel, *J. Chem. Soc.*, **1955**, 155.

$$\begin{array}{c}\text{O} \\ \diagup \quad \diagdown \\ \text{CH}_2 \end{array} + \text{H}_2\text{O} \xrightarrow{\text{strong acid}} \begin{array}{c}\text{OH} \\ \\ \text{OH}\end{array} + \text{H}_2\text{C}{=}\text{O} \qquad (54)$$

is the basis of all chemical methods for the determination of the methylene dioxy function. The apparatus of Kuck[182] for the liberation of formaldehyde is shown in Figure 7.3. The sample is placed in flask B. Acid is added from funnel A. Formaldehyde distils through C, is condensed at D, and collected in a long test tube E.

B. Gravimetric Methods. A semimicro gravimetric method described by Gadamer and co-workers[183] for the determination of the methylene dioxy function is adapted from the macro procedure of Clowes and Tollens.[184] The sample is dissolved in 0.5 ml. of water and treated with a warm solution containing 30 mg. of phloroglucinol in 3 ml. of 1:1 sulfuric acid. After the solution clarifies, 1 ml. of concentrated sulfuric acid is added and the reaction mixture is heated to boiling, then kept in the water bath at 70–80°C for 3 hours. The reaction vessel is stoppered and allowed to stand overnight, whereupon formaldehyde phloroglucide precipitates according to equation 55:

$$\text{CH}_2\text{O} + \begin{array}{c}\text{OH} \\ \\ \text{HO} \quad \text{OH}\end{array} \rightarrow \begin{array}{c}\text{O} \\ \diagup \diagdown \\ \text{HO} \quad \text{CH}_2 \\ \text{O}\end{array} + \text{H}_2\text{O} \qquad (55)$$

The product is collected on a filter, washed with water, dried at 100°C, and weighed. Resorcinol may be used in place of phloroglucinol to precipitate the analogous condensation product.[185]

While this method is suitable for determinations on the 0.1 meq. scale, it suffers from two disadvantages: (a) the possible loss of formaldehyde by volatility, and (b) condensation of formaldehyde with other substances in the reaction mixture.

C. Colorimetric Methods. Several investigators[186–188] recommended the chromotropic acid procedure to determine methylene dioxy groups. The

[182] J. Kuck, private communication.

[183] J. Gadamer and M. Theissen, *Archiv. Pharm.*, **262**, 583 (1924); J. Gadamer and K. Winterfield, *ibid.*, p. 601.

[184] V. Clowes and B. Tollens, *Berichte*, **32**, 2841 (1899).

[185] A. Lobry de Braeyn and W. A. van Eckenstein, *Rec. Trav. Chim.*, **21**, 314 (1902)

[186] M. Beroza, *Anal. Chem.*, **26**, 1970 (1954); *J. Agri. Food Chem.*, **4**, 53 (1956).

[187] L. A. Lee, *Anal. Chem.*, **28**, 1621 (1956).

[188] M. Langejan, *Pharm. Weekblad*, **92**, 693 (1957).

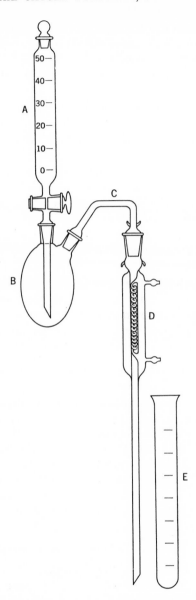

Fig. 7.3. Apparatus for liberation of formaldehyde.

sample is treated with the chromotropic acid reagent (see page 506) and concentrated sulfuric acid is added. After mixing, the reaction vessel is kept in the water bath for 10–30 minutes. The solution is diluted with water to the specified volume, cooled to room temperature and the color intensity is measured at 550–580 mμ. The procedures described in the literature are for analysis in the μ-mole range. They can be adapted to the 0.1 meq. scale. However, it should be noted that as formaldehyde and chromotropic acid are brought together in the original reaction mixture, modification will be necessary if the sample is colored or contains materials which react with formaldehyde. In such cases, the formaldehyde should be separated by distillation, followed by colorimetric determination with chromotropic acid.

Labat[189] proposed a colorimetric method for the determination of the methylene dioxy function using gallic acid as the reagent. Bovalini and Casini[190] compared this method against the chromotropic acid method for the analysis of apiole, piperonal, and safrole. The latter method was found to give higher precision and accuracy.

Pavolini and Malatester[191] used 80% phosphoric acid to decompose the methylene dioxy group and determined the formaldehyde liberated by means of Nessler's or Tollens' reagent.

The micro procedure described by Boos[192] for the determination of the methylene dioxy function is given in experiment 10.

D. Physical Methods. The infrared spectra of a number of compounds containing the methylene dioxy function have been reported.[193] This atom-grouping exhibits characteristic maxima at 1040–1020 and 943–935 cm^{-1}. Hence, it should be possible to use either region for quantitative analysis of known compounds.

Dipole moment has been applied to the measurement of the methylene dioxy group by LeFeore and Northcolt.[193a] Bernet[193b] has investigated the chromophoric group, $=C(-O-)_2$.

VI. The Peroxy Function

A. General. The peroxy function is characterized by a pair of oxygen

[189] J. A. Labat, *Bull. Soc. Chim. Bio.*, **15**, 1344 (1933).

[190] E. Bovalini and A. Casini, *Ann. Chim. Roma*, **49**, 1059 (1959).

[191] T. Pavolini and A. Malatester, *Ann. Chim. Applicata*, **37**, 495 (1947).

[192] R. Boos, private communication.

[193] L. H. Briggs, L. D. Colebrook, H. M. Fales, and W. C. Wildman, *Anal. Chem.*, **29**, 904 (1957).

[193a] R. J. W. LeFeore and J. Northcolt, *J. Chem. Soc.*, **1949**, 2374.

[193b] W. Bernet, *Monatsh.*, **85**, 287 (1954).

atoms, —O:O—, with one end attached to a carbon atom and the other end connected to either a carbon or a hydrogen atom. There is a great variety of organic compounds which contain the peroxy group.[194] A list of the classifications and typical compounds is given in Table 7.2.

TABLE 7.2

Organic Peroxides

Classification	Typical compound: Name	Structure	B.p., m.p., °C
Alkyl hydroperoxides			
Primary	ethyl hydroperoxide	C_2H_5—OOH	b. 41 (550 mm.)
Secondary	isopropyl hydroperoxide	$(CH_3)_2CH$—OOH	b. 107
Tertiary	*tert*-butyl hydroperoxide	$(CH_3)_3C$—OOH	m. 2
Acetylene hydroperoxides		CH≡C—$C(CH_3)_2$—OOH	b. 42 (170 mm.)
α-Hydroxyalkyl hydroperoxides		$R_2C(OH)$—OOH	
α-Hydroperoxy ethers		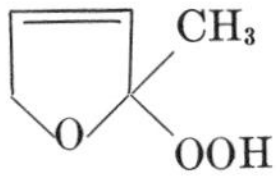	
α-Hydroperoxy ketones		CH_3—CH(OOH)—C(=O)—C_2H_5	
Dialkyl peroxides	diethyl peroxide	C_2H_5—OO—C_2H_5	b. 64
Bis-(1-hydroxyalkyl)-peroxides		$R_2C(OH)$—OO—$C(OH)R_2$	
Oxydialkyl peroxides (ozonides)		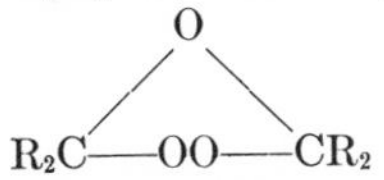	
Acyl hydroperoxides (peroxy acids)	peroxy acetic acid	$CH_3C(=O)$—OOH	m. 0.1
Diacyl peroxides	bis-(*p*-nitrobenzoyl)-peroxide	$(p\text{-}O_2NC_6H_4CO)_2O_2$	m. 158
Peroxy esters	dimethylperoxy phthalate	$p\text{-}C_6H_4(C(=O)OOCH_3)_2$	m. 125
Polymeric peroxides		—$[CR_2$—CH_2—$OO]_x$—	

[194] A. V. Tobolsky and R. B. Mesrobian, *Organic Peroxides*, Interscience, New York, 1954.

It will be noted that the peroxy compounds are either related to the corresponding oxygen functions (alcohol, ether, acid, anhydride, and ester, respectively) by insertion of one more oxygen atom, or are formed by the addition of ozone to the ethylenic function.

A property common to all peroxy compounds is thermal instability. Hence, the melting point or boiling point seldom can be used as a criterion and measure of purity of the product. Determination of "active oxygen" is the general method for the quantitative analysis of these compounds. It is based on the reduction of the peroxy function by a suitable reducing agent. The oxidizing power of the various classes of peroxy compounds decreases in the following order: peroxy acids > hydroperoxides > oxydialkyl peroxides > peroxy esters > acyl peroxides > hydroxy peroxides > dialkyl peroxides > polymeric peroxides. This may serve as a guide in selecting the optimum condition for the determination of a given peroxy compound.

It should be noted that peroxy compounds are explosive. Therefore, the use of micro methods has definite advantages, for even an explosion from decigram quantities of material can cause serious damages.

B. Iodometric Methods

1. Principle. The most common method for determining organic peroxides is dependent on their reaction with iodide ions, as represented by the general equation

$$R—OO—R' + 2I^- + 2H_2O \rightarrow I_2 + ROH + R'OH + 2OH^- \qquad (56)$$

R and R' being an alkyl or acyl group, or a hydrogen atom. Thus, each equivalent of peroxy function liberates one mole of iodine, which is determined by titration with standard sodium thiosulfate solution

$$I_2 + 2Na_2S_2O_3 \rightarrow 2NaI + Na_2S_4O_6 \qquad (57)$$

It should be noted that water molecules are shown in equation 56 for the purpose of balancing the equation only, in order to represent the organic products as neutral compounds and not ions. In actual practice, the reaction is seldom carried out in an aqueous medium, because of the insolubility of many organic peroxides in water. Chloroform and glacial acetic acid are generally used as the solvent. The former liquid has the advantage of showing the intense purple color of iodine, but also the disadvantage of two-phase titration, since aqueous solution of sodium thiosulfate is employed as the titrant. Anhydrous isopropyl alcohol[195] and acetic anhydride[196] have been recommended by some workers.

[195] C. D. Wagner, R. H. Smith, and E. D. Peters, *Anal. Chem.*, **19**, 976 (1947).
[196] K. Nozaki, *Ind. Eng. Chem., Anal. Ed.*, **18**, 583 (1946).

Potassium iodide can be used as the source of iodide ions. However, sodium iodide is a better reagent because it is more soluble in the reaction mixture and hence provides a higher concentration of iodide ions.[197] Constant boiling hydriodic acid is required for the quantitative reduction of certain peroxides[197] (see experiment 19).

Numerous macro procedures have appeared in the literature for the determination of organic peroxides using $0.1N$ sodium thiosulfate as the titrant.[198] A device for automatic titration was described by Mathews and Patchan[199] in which the iodine formed is continuously reduced by sodium thiosulfate in an automatic potentiometric titrator. Only a few micro methods have been published which involve visual titration with $0.01N$ sodium thiosulfate.[197,200,201] Determination on the μmol. scale was reported by Abrahamson and Linschitz[202] who used $0.001N$ titrant and the potentiometric dead-stop endpoint.

2. Provisions for Removing Air from the System. It is necessary to remove air from the reaction vessel which contains the organic peroxide and iodide reagent. A convenient method is to purge the system with a current of nitrogen,[197,203–205] if the latter is available. Lohaus[206] added solid carbon dioxide into the reaction mixture in order to displace the air. Carbon dioxide also can be generated by the addition of sodium bicarbonate into the reaction mixture if acetic acid is used as solvent.[207] Surrey[208] claimed that by mixing all reactants in a boiling solution of acetic acid and chloroform, necessity for de-aerating reagents and working in an inert atmosphere was obviated. This technique is not recommended for microanalysis because of the possible decomposition of the sample and loss of the iodine formed.

3. The Effect of Catalysts. While organic peroxides are unstable, their reaction with iodide ions is not instantaneous. Thus, the micro method described by Roth and Schuster[201] requires the reaction mixture to stand

[197] T. S. Ma and T. Gerstein, *Microchem. J.*, **5**, 163 (1961).

[198] See review by A. J. Martin in *Organic Analysis, Vol. 4*, Interscience, New York, 1961, p. 1.

[199] J. S. Mathews and J. F. Patchan, *Anal. Chem.*, **31**, 1003 (1959).

[200] N. Drozdov and L. Starikova, *Myasnaya Ind., S.S.S.R.*, **22**, 52 (1951).

[201] H. Roth and P. Schuster, *Mikrochim. Acta*, **1957**, 840.

[202] E. W. Abrahamson and H. Linschitz, *Anal. Chem.*, **24**, 1355 (1952).

[203] J. H. Skellon and M. N. Thurston, *Analyst*, **73**, 97 (1948).

[204] J. Mattner and R. Mattner, *Z. Anal. Chem.*, **134**, 1 (1951).

[205] L. Hartman and M. D. L. White, *Anal. Chem.*, **24**, 527 (1952).

[206] G. Lohaus, in Houben-Weyl-Müller: *Methoden der organischen Chemie*, 4th ed., Vol. 2, Thieme, Stuttgart, 1953, p. 573.

[207] J. H. Skellon and E. D. Hills, *Analyst*, **73**, 78 (1948).

[208] B. D. Surrey, *Analyst*, **79**, 86 (1954).

overnight before titration with $0.01N$ sodium thiosulfate. Prevention of air oxidation is difficult under these conditions. Skukla and Ramanjeneyulu[209] found that the reaction between peroxide and iodide is catalyzed by the presence of tungstate, vanadate, ferric, and ferrous ions. Silbert and Swern[210] reported that the addition of a trace of ferric chloride in glacial acetic acid remarkably accelerated the liberation of iodine in the macro scale determination of peresters. Hock and Kropf[211] used a granule of cuprous chloride and reported that the reaction between cumyl hydroperoxide and potassium iodide on the micro scale was complete in 5 minutes. Therefore, whenever applicable, a catalyst should be used in the iodometric determination of the peroxy function.

C. Determination with Other Reductants

1. Arsenious Oxide as Reductant.   A method using arsenious oxide as the reductant was proposed by Siggia.[212] The peroxide is treated with a known quantity of $0.1N$ arsenious oxide solution which contains sodium bicarbonate. Ethanol is added if the sample is water insoluble. The solution is then concentrated by heating until all organic solvent has been removed. After acidification with sulfuric acid, the excess of arsenious oxide is determined by titration with $0.05-0.1N$ iodine solution. Applied to the determination of benzoyl peroxide, the reactions involved are shown below.

$$2C_6H_5-\overset{\overset{\displaystyle O}{\|}}{C}-OO-\overset{\overset{\displaystyle O}{\|}}{C}-C_6H_5 + As_2O_3 + 4NaHCO_3 \rightarrow$$

$$As_2O_5 + 4C_6H_5COONa + 2H_2O + 4CO_2 \quad (58)$$

$$As_2O_3 + 2I_2 + 5H_2O \rightarrow 2HAsO_4^{-2} + 4I^- + 8H^+ \quad (59)$$

This method is limited to the most reactive peroxides. It is not suitable for conversion to the micro scale because (a) the endpoint is the disappearance of the yellow iodine color and (b) $0.01N$ iodine is difficult to keep.

2. Titanous Chloride as Reductant.   Titanous chloride was suggested as the reagent for determining organic peroxides on the macro scale by several workers,[213] and was favored by an investigator as the most sensitive method.[214] It has been adapted to the micro scale. However, this method

[209] B. K. Skukla and J. V. S. Ramanjeneyulu, *Z. Anal. Chem.*, **151**, 28 (1956); *J. Sci. Ind. Research India*, **15B**, 46 (1956).

[210] L. S. Silbert and D. Swern, *Anal. Chem.*, **30**, 385 (1958).

[211] H. Hock and H. Kropf, *Chem. Ber.*, **92**, 1115 (1959).

[212] S. Siggia, *Ind. Eng. Chem., Anal. Ed.*, **19**, 827 (1947).

[213] R. Strohecher, R. Vaubel, and A. Tenner, *Fette u. Seifen*, **44**, 246 (1937); H. Paget, *J. Chem. Soc.*, **1938**, 829; W. Kern, H. J. Jokusch, and A. Wolfram, *Makromol. Chem.*, **3**, 223 (1949).

[214] D. de Dortan-Sontag, *Chim. Anal.*, **35**, 157 (1953).

has no advantage over the iodometric method and the results are less accurate.[197] The reaction between titanous chloride and peroxide is represented by the following equation:

$$R—OO—R + 2TiCl_3 + 2HCl \rightarrow ROR + 2TiCl_4 + H_2O \tag{60}$$

The excess of titanous chloride is determined by titration with ferric ammonium sulfate using ammonium thiocyanate-neutral red mixture as the indicator.

3. *Stannous Chloride as Reductant.* Stannous chloride was an old reagent used for the determination of peroxides.[215] It was reinvestigated by Bernard and Hargrave,[216] and Egerton and co-workers.[217] The sample (1 meq.) is dissolved in 20 ml. of 30% sodium hydroxide in a long-necked 250 ml. flask which is then evacuated and refilled with nitrogen. 15 ml. of 0.1N stannous chloride is added, and the flask is again evacuated and refilled with nitrogen. After standing, 25 ml. of 7.5N sulfuric acid is added to the reaction mixture. The residual stannous chloride is titrated with 0.05N iodine under a stream of nitrogen. The 0.1N stannous chloride should be stored under hydrogen. It is apparent that this method is not suitable for adaption to the micro scale.

4. *Ferrous Ion as Reductant.* A sensitive qualitative test for peroxide is based on the appearance of intense red color when ferrous thiocyanate is added to the sample. This reaction was applied to quantitative analysis by Yule and Wilson.[218] A known amount of ferrous thiocyanate is added to the organic peroxide in a flask. The latter is stoppered and shaken vigorously. The reaction mixture is then treated with standardized titanous sulfate using the disappearance of the red color as the endpoint. Wagner, Smith, and Peters[219] reported that the results obtained by this method were invariably below theoretical, and that the manipulative variables of time of shaking and sample size showed a considerable difference in the final result of analysis. Therefore, the use of this method on the micro scale is not recommended.

Kolthoff and Medalia[220] described a method in which the peroxide is treated with an excess of ferrous ion, followed by amperometric titration of the residual reagent with standard dichromate solution. Correct results

[215] H. von Pechmann and L. Vanino, *Berichte*, **27**, 1510 (1894).

[216] D. Bernard and K. R. Hargrave, *Anal. Chim. Acta*, **5**, 476 (1951).

[217] A. C. Egerton, A. J. Everett, G. J. Minkoff, S. Rudrakanchana, and K. C. Salooja, *Anal. Chim. Acta*, **10**, 422 (1954).

[218] J. A. C. Yule and C. P. Wilson, *Ind. Eng. Chem., Anal. Ed.*, **23**, 1254 (1931).

[219] C. D. Wagner, R. H. Smith, and E. D. Peters, *Anal. Chem.*, **19**, 982 (1947).

[220] I. M. Kolthoff and A. I. Medalia, *J. Polymer Sci.*, **4**, 377 (1949); *Anal. Chem.*, **23**, 595 (1951).

are obtained if oxygen is completely absent. Acetone is used as the solvent which should be boiled to remove oxygen.

5. *Manganous Chloride as Reductant.* In the macro method described by Mattner and Mattner,[204] the peroxide sample is dissolved in aqueous sodium hydroxide solution, 20 ml. of 20% manganous chloride is added and the flask is stoppered and shaken. Then 10 ml. of 10% potassium iodide and 25 ml. of concentrated hydrochloric acid are introduced. The iodine liberated is titrated with standardized sodium thiosulfate. While these workers considered manganous chloride as a catalyst in the reaction, the amount used and the technique employed indicate that the peroxide is first completely reduced before the addition of iodide ions.

D. Miscellaneous Chemical Methods.   Chemical methods for determining organic peroxides which are not based on the reduction of the peroxy function are available. The procedures described in the literature are all on the macro scale. Some of these can be adapted to micro-determinations.

Certain peroxy compounds are hydrolyzed in the presence of mineral acids to yield hydrogen peroxide. The latter can be determined titrimetrically by oxidation with alkaline permanganate,[221] sodium hypochlorite,[222] or potassium ferricyanide.[223] On the other hand, application of trivalent manganese to the quantitative oxidation of peroxide is unsatisfactory.[224]

Higuchi and Zuck[225] investigated the potentiometric titration of hydroperoxides with lithium aluminum hydride. Martin[226] determined peracids and primary and secondary alkyl hydroperoxides by titrating them as weak acids in the presence of ethylene diamine by means of 0.25N sodium aminoethoxide. Conversion of these methods to the micro scale is difficult.

Horner and Jürgens[227] observed that diphenyl sulfide and triphenyl arsine react specifically with certain groups of peroxy compounds. By combining these reactions with the standard iodometric and acidimetric procedures, it is possible to determine mixtures containing dialkyl peroxides, peracids, and diacyl peroxides.

[221] B. R. Sant, *Anal. Chim. Acta*, **15**, 413 (1956); I. M. Issa and H. Khalifa, *J. Indian Chem. Soc.*, **33**, 778 (1956).

[222] J. Bitskei, *Acta Chim. Acad. Sci. Hung.*, **8**, 203 (1955); **10**, 327 (1957).

[223] J. Vulterin and J. Zyka, *Chem. Listy*, **48**, 619 (1954).

[224] R. Belcher and T. S. West, *Anal. Chim. Acta*, **6**, 322 (1952).

[225] T. Higuchi and D. A. Zuck, *J. Am. Chem. Soc.*, **73**, 2676 (1951).

[226] A. J. Martin, *Anal. Chem.*, **29**, 79 (1957).

[227] L. Horner and E. Jürgens, *Angew. Chem.*, **70**, 266 (1958).

E. Colorimetric Methods. Several colorimetric methods for the determination of peroxy compounds are available. These methods are recommended for the μmol. scale determinations.

Peroxides give blue color on treatment with benzoyl leuco methylene blue in benzene-trichloracetic acid solution.[228] Zirconium naphthenate is added to accelerate the decomposition of the peroxy function. The color is stable for several days if kept in the dark at 24 $\pm$1°C. This method is extremely sensitive. It has been used to determine 0.03 μg. of "active oxygen" by measuring the intensity of the color at 645 mμ.[229]

The red ferric thiocyanate complex formed in the reaction between organic peroxide and ferrous thiocyanate has been adapted to quantitative analysis. Visual comparison of the color against standards containing potassium permanganate and dichromate was suggested in one procedure.[230] Other workers used the photoelectric colorimeter and reported precision and accuracy of 5–10%.[231]

The iodine liberated by the reaction of peroxy compounds with potassium iodide was determined colorimetrically by Siddigi and Tappel.[232] Dubouloz and co-workers[233] modified the method by fixing the liberated iodine with thiofluorescein.

The yellow pertitanic complex produced from titanic sulfate by the action of peroxide was used as the basis of colorimetric analysis by two groups of investigators.[234] This method is not as sensitive as the red or blue color obtained with other color reagents. Vanillin[235] and luminol[236] have been suggested as reagents for the colorimetric determination of peroxy compounds.

An indirect colorimetric method was proposed by Laitinen and Nelson[237] for the determination of hydroperoxides in rubber and synthetic polymers. The sample is treated with ferrous iron in benzene-methanol solution.

[228] M. I. Eiss and P. Giesecke, *Anal Chem.*, **31**, 1558 (1959).

[229] K. Ueberreiter and G. Sorge, *Angew. Chem.*, **68**, 352, 479, 486 (1956).

[230] Ministry of Supply, Chemical Inspectorate, U.K., *UKAEA Rep. SCSM* Vol. 119, p. 5 (1958).

[231] C. D. Wagner, H. L. Clever, and E. D. Peters, *Anal. Chem.*, **19**, 980 (1947).

[232] A. M. Siddigi and A. L. Tappel, *Chemist-Analyst*, **44**, 52 (1955).

[233] P. Dubouloz, J. Fondaroi, J. Laurent, and R. Marville, *Anal. Chim. Acta*, **15**, 84 (1956).

[234] C. Furmanek and K. Monikowski, *Rocznik Pantstaowego Zakladu Hig.*, **1953**, 447; G. Janicek and J. Pokarny, *Chem. Listy*, **49**, 1315 (1955).

[235] A. Arrhenius, *Acta Chem. Scand.*, **9**, 715 (1955).

[236] M. Filomeni and A. J. Siesto, *Bull. Soc. Ital. Biol. Sper.*, **27**, 1096 (1951).

[237] H. A. Laitinen and J. S. Nelson, *Anal. Chem.*, **18**, 422 (1946).

The standard solution ($0.002N$ ferrous ammonium sulfate) has to be prepared fresh daily from $0.05N$ solution. The excess of ferrous ions is determined spectrophotometrically using o-phenanthroline as the color reagent.

F. Physical Methods

1. Polarography. Since the peroxy function is susceptible to reduction, a number of investigators have applied polarographic analysis to the determination of peroxy compounds.[238-240] Kuta and Quackenbush[241] performed the determinations in nonaqueous electrolyte solutions and reported that di-*tert*-butyl peroxide and 1-phenylmethyl-*tert*-butyl peroxide were not reduced in the voltage span of 0.00–2.00 volts. Comparing the iodometric, stannous chloride, and polarographic methods, Ricciuti, Coleman, and Willits[242] stated that the last method gives more reliable results for impure samples because it is more specific. Detailed analyses of mixtures of peroxides have been accomplished by polarography.[243] Determination of benzoyl peroxide in polymers was carried out polarographically.[244]

2. Infrared Spectrometry. The infrared spectra of aliphatic peroxy acids have been recorded in the vapor phase.[245] The main absorption lines are at 3.05, 6.9, and 8.5 μ. Peroxy butyric acid decomposes too quickly to be measured. Holman and co-workers studied the absorption of hydroperoxides.[246] These compounds exhibit maxima at 1.46–2.07 μ, which are not shown by dialkyl peroxides or ozonized unsaturated substances. The intensity of absorption is proportional to the peroxide content of the sample. However, detection of the —OOH group is not possible when the peroxide value falls below 0.5 meq. per gram.

VII. The Quinone Function

A. General. The quinone function is composed of two carbonyl groups in an aromatic skeleton. It can be represented by the formula

[238] M. Mikhailova, *Zavodskaya Lab.*, **9**, 166 (1940).

[239] C. O. Willits, C. Ricciuti, H. B. Knight, and D. Swern, *Anal. Chem.*, **24**, 785 (1952).

[240] E. R. Roberts and J. S. Muk, *Analyst*, **77**, 43 (1952).

[241] E. J. Kuta and F. W. Quackenbush, *Anal. Chem.*, **32**, 1069 (1960).

[242] C. Ricciuti, J. E. Coleman, and C. O. Willits, *Anal. Chem.*, **27**, 405 (1955).

[243] H. Buischweiler and G. J. Minkoff, *Anal. Chim. Acta*, **12**, 186 (1955).

[244] T. Takeuchi, N. Yokouchi, and Y. Takayama, *Japan Analyst*, **4**, 234, 290 (1955).

[245] E. R. Stephens, P. L. Hanst, and R. C. Doerr, *Anal. Chem.*, **29**, 776 (1957).

[246] R. T. Holman, C. Nickell, O. S. Privett, and P. R. Edmondson, *J. Am. Oil Chem. Soc.*, **35**, 422 (1958).

$O=C(A)C=O$ where (A) is a part of the aromatic nucleus. In most quinones the two $C=O$ groups are situated in the same aromatic ring and in the ortho or para positions. However, quinones in which the two $C=O$ groups are in different rings are found in nature and have been synthesized. On the other hand, m-quinones (the two $C=O$ groups being in meta positions) are not known. The names and structures of the common quinones are:

| o-Benzoquinone | p-Benzoquinone | α-Naphthoquinone | amphi-Naphthoquinone |

| Anthraquinone | Phenanthraquinone | 3,4-Phenanthraquinone |

The quinone function is present in an important class of synthetic dyes known as quinone dyes. Interestingly, it also constitutes the basic structure of many colored substances found in nature, although these compounds serve as catalysts in the biological system and not for coloring. More than 150 naturally occurring quinones have been reported.[247] The importance of the quinone structure in the K-vitamins is well known. Other quinones are used as pharmaceuticals and fungicides, and in leather tanning.

While quinones contain two carbonyl groups, it should be noted that the methods for the determination of the carbonyl function (see page 141) are not applicable to the quinone function. For instance, the reaction between hydroxylamine and quinone to form oxime is not quantitative. Phenylhydrazine acts as a reducing agent towards the quinone function instead of yielding the corresponding phenylhydrazone.

B. Titrimetric Methods

1. Reduction with Titanous Chloride. Titanous chloride can be used to determine the quinone structure, according to the general equation

$$O=C(A)C=O + 2TiCl_3 + 2HCl \rightarrow HO—C(A)C—OH + 2TiCl_4 \qquad (61)$$

In the macro method of Hibbert and Suida[248] the sample is dissolved in

[247] R. H. Thomson, *Naturally Occurring Quinones*, Academic Press, New York, 1958.
[248] E. Hibbert and W. Suida, *Annalen*, **416**, 119 (1918).

acetic acid and 30 ml. of 0.2N titanous chloride is added. The reaction mixture is boiled for two minutes, cooled, and the excess of titanous ion is back-titrated with 0.2N ferric sulfate. A micro procedure has been developed[249] and is described in experiment 49. Acetone is used as solvent and the solution is buffered with sodium acetate before the addition of 0.02N titanous chloride. After the reaction is completed, the solution is acidified and the residual titanous chloride is determined by titration with 0.02N ferric ammonium sulfate using neutral red-ammonium thiocyanate as indicator.

Veibel[250] stated that the reduction of quinones may be carried out in acid solution at room temperature without keeping the reaction mixture under an inert atmosphere. He also reported[251] that quinones insoluble in cold ethanol or acetone were dissolved in the boiling solvent and refluxed with titanous chloride for 15–20 minutes while a current of carbon dioxide was passed through. It should be noted that quinones differ considerably in their reduction potentials. Since titanous chloride reduces more readily at a higher pH, a buffered solution is preferred. Heating facilitates reduction, but induces other complications and renders the analysis less accurate.[249] Some quinones are resistant to titanous chloride even at the boiling temperature of the solution.

2. Iodometric Methods. Several macro iodometric procedures have been proposed for the determination of the quinone function, based on the following reaction:

$$O=C(A)C=O + 2HI \rightleftharpoons HO-C(A)C-OH + I_2 \qquad (62)$$

In one method[252] the sample is dissolved in alcohol and potassium iodide in hydrochloric acid solution is added. The iodine formed is determined by titration with 0.1N sodium thiosulfate. As the solution contains so much alcohol, starch cannot be used as the indicator.[250] Therefore the endpoint is located by the disappearance of the yellow color of iodine. In another method,[253] diethyl ether is incorporated into the reaction mixture. After the iodine color has been discharged by the addition of a measured amount of 0.1N sodium thiosulfate, the aqueous layer is separated and the excess of sodium thiosulfate is determined by titration with 0.1N iodine using

[249] T. S. Ma and T. Gerstein, unpublished work; see T. Gerstein, *Master's Thesis*, *Brooklyn College*, 1959.

[250] S. Veibel, *The Identification of Organic Compounds*, 4th ed., G. E. C. Gad Publisher, Copenhagen, 1954, p. 137.

[251] S. Veibel, private communication.

[252] K. Fries, H. Koch, and H. Stuckenbrock, *Annalen*, **468**, 179 (1929).

[253] Houben-Weyl-Müller, *Methoden der organischen Chemie*, 4th ed., Vol. 2, Thieme, Stuttgart, 1953, p. 481.

starch as indicator. In still another method,[253] the quinone is first reduced with granulated zinc in acid solution to yield the corresponding hydroquinone. The solution is filtered, neutralized with sodium bicarbonate, and the hydroquinone is determined[254] by titration with $0.1N$ iodine, applying the reverse reaction of equation 62.

It is apparent that modification of the above methods is necessary in order to convert them to the micro scale using $0.01N$ titrants. Rodopulo[255] determined small quantities of quinones in wine as follows. To a 50 ml. sample of wine is added 10 ml. of $0.1M$ potassium iodide and 10 ml. of $0.1M$ hydrochloric acid. After standing for 20 minutes in a dark place, 1 ml. of 0.5% starch solution is added and the iodine formed is titrated with $0.01N$ sodium thiosulfate. High accuracy in this procedure is not expected.

3. *Miscellaneous Titrimetric Methods.*   Schulek and Rozsa[256] put forward a micro procedure which depends on ceritometry. The quinone is dissolved in ethanol and reduced with stannous chloride in hydrochloric acid. The hydroquinone is then extracted into chloroform. Potassium bicarbonate and anhydrous sodium sulfate are added to remove hydrochloric acid and water. The solution is filtered. An aliquot portion of the filtrate is mixed with ethanol and sulfuric acid, and then titrated with $0.005N$ ceric sulfate using o-ethoxy chrysoidin as indicator. This procedure is rather involved.

α-Naphthoquinone has been determined by amperometric titration.[257] Matrka and Zdenck[258] determined anthraquinone by potentiometric titration with vanadous sulfate.

C. Gasometric Methods.   The quinone function is reduced by phenylhydrazine to yield hydroquinone and nitrogen gas, according to the following equation:

$$O{=}C(A)C{=}O + C_6H_5NHNH_2 \rightarrow HO{-}C(A)C{-}OH + N_2 + C_6H_6 \qquad (63)$$

This reaction was used by Willstätter and Cramer[259] to determine quinones on the macro scale. The nitrogen gas liberated is collected in an azotometer and measured.

A micro method described by Lindberg and Paju[260] is based on sodium

[254] I. M. Kolthoff and T. S. Lee, *Anal. Chem.*, **18**, 452 (1946); H. Wieland, *Berichte*, **43**, 715 (1910).

[255] A. K. Rodopulo, *Vinodelic i Vinogradarstvo*, S.S.S.R., **13**, 6 (1953).

[256] E. Schulek and P. Rozsa, *Magyar Chem. Foly*, **47**, 75 (1941); *Mikrochemie*, **29**, 178 (1941).

[257] M. Kurata and M. Kubota, *Japan Analyst*, **4**, 361 (1955).

[258] M. Matrka and R. Zdenck, *Chem. Listy*, **51**, 68 (1957).

[259] R. Willstätter and C. Cramer, *Berichte*, **43**, 2979 (1910).

[260] B. Lindberg and J. Paju, *Svensk. Kem. Tidskr.*, **65**, 9 (1953).

borohydride reduction of the quinone function. The sample is mixed with boric acid in ethanol; 3 ml. of 0.13M borohydride in sodium hydroxide solution is added. After completion of the reaction, the residual sodium borohydride is decomposed with sulfuric acid and the liberated hydrogen is measured.

D. Colorimetric Methods. Quinones react with amino compounds to form colored products. Some of these color reactions have been adapted to quantitative analysis. Thus Lacoste and co-workers[261] used n-butylamine as reagent for the spectrophotometric determination of benzoquinone. According to Karius and Mapstone,[262] formation of color with ethylenediamine is specific for quinones and quinone-forming materials except anthraquinone. On the other hand, the latter compound and its derivatives yield colored complexes with boric acid.[263] The intensity of the color is proportional to the concentration of the complexes.

A colorimetric method for thymoquinone described by Balcaronna and Borkowski[264] is based on the blue color produced on treating the sample with ethyl cyanoacetate.

E. Physical Methods. Polarography of quinones was investigated in nonaqueous media by Ishidate and co-workers.[265] The decreasing ease of reduction at the dropping mercury electrode was reported to be in the following order: p-benzoquinone, 1,4-naphthoquinone, 1,2,5,6-dibenzanthraquinone, 1,2-benzanthraquinone, anthraquinone.

VIII. Salts of Organic Acids

A. General. Salts of organic acids can be separated in two categories: (1) metal salts which are obtained by replacing the hydrogen atom in the acidic group of the organic acids (carboxylic, sulfonic, phosphonic, etc.) with a metallic ion; (2) amine salts which are formed by combining an organic acid and an organic base. Only metal salts of carboxylic acids, known as carboxylates, $RCOO^-M^+$, are discussed in this section, though the methods given below can be applied with discretion to the analysis of metal salts of other types of organic acids. Amine salts are classified in the nitrogen functions.

[261] R. T. Lacoste, J. R. Covington, and G. J. Frisone, *Anal. Chem.*, **32**, 990 (1960).

[262] H. Karius and G. E. Mapstone, *Chemistry & Industry*, **1956**, 266.

[263] E. C. Cogbill and J. H. Yoe, *Anal. Chim. Acta*, **12**, 455 (1955).

[264] E. Balcaronna and B. Borkowski, *Biul. Inst. Roslin Leczniczych*, **5**, 21 (1959).

[265] M. Ishidate, T. Ishiki, and K. Tada, *Pharm. Bull. Japan*, **3**, 309 (1955).

B. Methods Based on Ashing.   When a metal carboxylate is heated with concentrated sulfuric or nitric acid the organic fragment is decomposed to carbon dioxide and water, leaving the metallic element behind as a salt of the inorganic acid. A microcrucible is a convenient reaction vessel for 0.1 meq. determinations. Sulfuric acid is used when the metal (e.g., alkali or alkaline earth) forms a stable sulfate:

$$R\text{—}COONa \xrightarrow[\Delta]{H_2SO_4} Na_2SO_4 + CO_2 + H_2O \tag{64}$$

Nitric acid is employed when the metal does not form a stable sulfate but yields a stable oxide (e.g., copper, iron, aluminum), or the free metal (e.g., silver, gold, platinum).

$$(R\text{—}COO)_2Cu \xrightarrow[\Delta]{HNO_3} CuO + CO_2 + H_2O \tag{65}$$

$$R\text{—}COOAg \xrightarrow[\Delta]{HNO_3} Ag + CO_2 + H_2O \tag{66}$$

The ashing technique is applicable to metal salts of all types of organic acids. However, it is apparent that this method cannot be used for the determination of mercury salts. The latter can be determined by heating the sample in a combustion tube containing calcium oxide and passing the mercury vapor into a tube packed with shredded gold. The amalgam formed is then weighed.[266]

Some metal salts, such as those of nickel and cobalt yield metal oxides of variable composition. In such case, it is advisable to reduce the oxide by heating it in a current of hydrogen and weigh the product as the free metal.

C. Methods Based on the Liberation of the Organic Acid

1. By Steam-Distillation.   Metal salts of carboxylic acids are readily decomposed by strong acids in aqueous solutions to liberate the free organic acid.

$$2R\text{—}COOM + H_2SO_4 \rightarrow 2R\text{—}COOH + M_2SO_4 \tag{67}$$

If the carboxylic acid liberated is steam-volatile, such as acetic, stearic, and benzoic acids are, a nonvolatile strong acid like phosphoric or toluenesulfonic acid can be used as the reagent and the carboxylic acid is recovered by steam distillation.

The distillate is collected and titrated with a standard base. Sulfuric acid is not recommended for this purpose because it may act as an oxidizing

[266] T. S. Ma in F. J. Welcher (ed.), *Standard Methods of Chemical Analysis*, 6th ed., Vol. 2, Van Nostrand, Princeton, 1963, p. 403.

agent and also produce sulfur dioxide which will contaminate the distillate.

2. By Ion-Exchange. The principle involved in the liberation of organic acid by the use of ion-exchange resin is similar to that discussed in the above section (eq. 67), except that here the strong acid is in the form of an insoluble resin containing free sulfonic acid groups. Macro procedures have been described in several papers;[267-269] the salt solution is passed through a cation exchange column and the effluent is titrated with $0.1N$ alkali. Van Etten and Wiele[270] proposed a micro method to determine 0.03-0.08 meq. of organic salts as follows. The salt is dissolved in water and the solution is passed through a column filled with Dowex 50 (H) resin and washed three times with water. The eluate is collected and titrated with $0.01N$ sodium hydroxide in a carbon dioxide-free atmosphere. The indicator used is a mixture containing cresol red and thymol blue, with color change at pH 8.2–8.7. The resin employed is 20–40 mesh having 9–16% cross linking. Recovery of over 99% of the organic acid is reported.

The ion-exchange technique has the advantage of being applicable to all types of carboxylic acids irrespective of their volatility. With slight modifications, this technique can be adapted to the analysis of salts of organic acids which are either weaker or stronger than carboxylic acid. For instance, sodium phenoxide can be determined in a nonaqueous medium, such as dioxane, and the effluent titrated with standardized sodium methoxide (see Chapter 11, Section II).

3. By Solvent Extraction. Schmall, Pifer, and Wollish[271] devised a method in which the free organic acid after liberation (eq. 67) is extracted into a suitable solvent. The extractor, shown in Figure 7.4, is easy to construct and operate. The extracted acid is determined by titration in a nonaqueous medium. It is interesting to note that the common solvent diethyl ether was found to be unsuitable for titration.

D. Methods Depending on Titration of the Salt as a Base. When the metal salt of organic acid is not contaminated with other basic substances, it is convenient to determine the salt by direct alkalimetry. As a rule, the analysis is carried out in a nonaqueous medium, though aqueous titrimetry can be used for certain salts.

Standard solution of *p*-toluenesulfonic acid dissolved in acetic acid was

[267] R. N. Golovatyi, *Ukrain Khim Zhur*, **17**, 560 (1951).

[268] L. Fuchs, *J. Pharm. and Pharmacol*, **4**, 566 (1952).

[269] I. D. Burton and J. C. Bickley, *J. Soc. Leather Trades' Chemists*, **38**, 249 (1954).

[270] C. H. Van Etten and M. B. Wiele, *Anal. Chem.*, **25**, 1109 (1953).

[271] M. Schmall, C. W. Pifer, and E. G. Wollish, *Anal. Chem.*, **24**, 1446 (1952).

suggested as the titrant for sodium benzoate and salicylate by Khast.[272] However, the acid titrant which is generally used for the nonaqueous titration of bases is perchloric acid (see experiment 4). The reaction between this acid and a metal salt of organic acid is given by the following equation:

$$R—COOM + HClO_4 \rightarrow R—COOH + MClO_4 \qquad (68)$$

Macro methods for the determination of 1 meq. or larger amounts of organic salts using $0.1N$ perchloric acid in glacial acetic acid were described by Markunas and Riddick,[273] who used the potentiometric endpoint and by Beckett, Camp, and Martin,[274] who recommended crystal violet as the indicator. Pifer and co-workers[275] reported titrations with $0.01N$ perchloric acid and stated that potassium and ammonium salts can be differentiated from sodium and divalent metal salts potentiometrically because the former two are stronger bases.

Casey and Starke[276] investigated the acidimetric titration of metal acetates by means of $0.1N$ perchloric acid. It was shown that ferric, aluminum, and chromium salts gave unusual results. Blake[277] proposed a macro method for the determination of alkali salts of organic acids by residual nonaqueous titration. The sample is treated with a known amount of $0.1N$ perchloric acid in acetic acid and the excess of standard acid is back-titrated by means of $0.1N$ sodium acetate in acetic acid either potentiometrically or visually with methyl violet indicator. It is claimed that this procedure gave better results than the direct titration method.

E. Special Methods

1. Formates. A convenient method to determine formates is by oxidation. Thus the formate ions in nickel or cobalt plating solution are analyzed by treating the sample with $0.1N$ potassium permanganate.[278] The excess of reagent is determined iodometrically. Mercuric chloride was used as the oxidant by Singh and Singh.[279] The mercurous chloride formed is determined volumetrically by means of potassium periodate.

[272] G. Y. Khast, *Med. Prom S.S.S.R.*, **1949**, 388.

[273] P. C. Markunas and J. A. Riddick, *Anal. Chem.*, **23**, 337 (1951).

[274] A. H. Beckett, R. M. Camp, and H. W. Martin, *J. Pharm. and Pharmacol.*, **4**, 399 (1952).

[275] C. W. Pifer, E. G. Wollish, and M. Schmall, *Anal. Chem.*, **25**, 310 (1953); **26**, 215 (1954).

[276] A. T. Casey and K. Starke, *Anal. Chem.*, **31**, 1060 (1959).

[277] M. I. Blake, *J. Am. Pharm. Assn.*, **46**, 163 (1957).

[278] F. W. Salt, *Selec. Govt. Research Repts.* (*London*), **3**, 248 (1951).

[279] B. Singh and A. Singh, *Research Bull., East Punjab Univ.*, **17**, 51 (1951).

2. Acetates.   Two colorimetric methods have been suggested for the determinations of acetates. In one method the red color produced by ferric chloride is measured.[280] In another method,[281] the basic acetates of rare earth elements are treated with iodine and a yellowish green to bluish green color is developed in ammoniacal solutions.

3. Oxalates, Citrates, and Tartrates.   Oxalates, citrates, and tartrates are usually determined by oxidimetry. Potassium dichromate,[282] potassium permanganate,[283] and ceric sulfate[284,285] have been proposed as the oxidant.

[280] T. Brada, *Chem. Listy,* **37,** 289 (1943).
[281] K. Kimura, N. Ikeda, and M. Nomura, *Bull. Chem. Soc. Japan,* **26,** 119 (1953).
[282] H. F. Launer and Y. Tomimatsu, *Anal. Chem.,* **25,** 1767 (1953).
[283] C. J. L. Baker, *Analyst,* **77,** 340 (1952).
[284] H. T. Gordon, *Anal. Chem.,* **23,** 1853 (1951).
[285] D. Seligson and H. Seligson, *Anal. Chem.,* **23,** 1877 (1951).

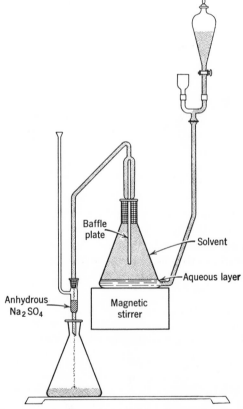

Fig. 7.4a. Extraction apparatus for solvent lighter than water. Courtesy of *Analytical Chemistry.*

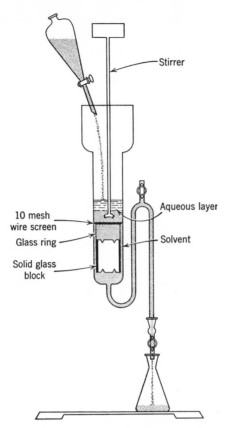

Fig. 7.4b. Extraction apparatus for solvent heavier than water. Courtesy of *Analytical Chemistry.*

Amperometric determinations of oxalates[286] and tartrates[287] have been reported. The sample is titrated with $0.1N$ lead nitrate using the dropping mercury cathode.

A macro method for the analysis of sodium citrate described by Jervain and Cooper[288] involves the precipitation of silver citrate by the addition of a known quantity of silver nitrate, and the determination of the excess silver ions by titration with standard ammonium thiocyanate. This procedure is not recommended for adaptation to the micro scale.

---

[286] M. Ishibashi and T. Fujinaga, *Sbornik mezinarod polarog. sjezdu Praze 1st congr.* Pt., **1**, 115 (1951).

[287] R. Kalvoda and J. Zyka, *Ceskoslov. Farm.*, **2**, 14 (1953).

[288] R. J. Jervain and P. Cooper, *Pharm. J.*, **160**, 480 (1951).

8

The Nitrogen Functions

I. Introduction

The functions discussed in this chapter comprise the groups that contain the element nitrogen. Most of the chemical methods employed for the estimation of this category of functional groups involve a change in the oxidation state of the nitrogen atom.

For convenience and coherence for the purpose of discussion, the numerous nitrogen functions are arranged, as far as possible, alphabetically under the following subdivisions:

1. The alkimino function.
2. The amino function.
3. The ammonium function.
4. The azido, cyano, and isocyano functions.
5. The azo, azoxy, diazo, and hydrazo functions.
6. The carbonamido, lactam, and carbonimido functions.
7. The heterocyclic nitrogen functions.
8. The hydrazino and hydrazido functions.
9. The isocyanate and isothiocyanate functions.
10. The nitro and nitroso functions.
11. The ureido and semicarbazido functions.

II. The Alkimino Function

A. General. The alkimino function is represented by $\diagdown\!\!\underset{\diagup}{N}\!R$ and has been named in various ways, such as the alkylimino, alkimido, alkyl imide, and N-alkyl group. The determination of the alkimino function is usually needed in the elucidation of the structure of naturally occurring nitrogen compounds like alkaloids. In these compounds, the alkyl group is attached to a nitrogen atom which is a part of the heterocyclic ring. The methods to be discussed, however, are applicable to other types of nitrogen compounds.

Herzig and Meyer[1] proposed the determination of the alkimino function by forming the quaternary ammonium iodide which on pyrolysis liberates alkyl iodide, as indicated in the following equations:

$$N\!-\!R + HI \rightarrow \left[\begin{array}{c} H^{+} \\ \diagdown \diagup \\ N \\ \diagup \diagdown \\ R \end{array} \right] I^{-} \tag{1}$$

$$\left[\begin{array}{c} H^{+} \\ \diagdown \diagup \\ N \\ \diagup \diagdown \\ R \end{array} \right] I \rightarrow \diagdown NH + RI \tag{2}$$

These reactions are the basis of all chemical methods for the determination of alkimino groups. In appearance the analysis is analogous to the determination of the alkoxyl function (see Chapter 6, Section VI), since the reagents employed and the reaction product to be measured are identical in both cases. Two points should be noted, however: (a) The alkimino compound does not liberate alkyl iodide when it is boiled in a solution of hydriodic acid; (b) pyrolysis of the quaternary ammonium iodide requires a temperature of 350°C and an efficient trap to remove a large amount of iodine and hydrogen iodide.

Besides hydriodic acid, Edlbacher[2] added ammonium iodide to help the formation of the quaternary salt and used gold chloride as a catalyst for decomposition. The effect of the latter reagent has not been proven,[3] although it is prescribed in many procedures.

In contrast to alkoxyl determinations, single distillations seldom yield satisfactory results for the alkimino function.[4] Haas[5] investigated the microdetermination of methylimino groups in various alkaloids and reported that some compounds under proper conditions and after several distillations will give values which approach the theoretical, whereas other compounds do not hydrolyze completely by the same experimental procedure.

Solutions of sodium antimony tartrate, hydrazine, and ascorbic acid were suggested by Franzen and co-workers[6] as absorbents for iodine and

[1] J. Herzig and J. Meyer, *Berichte*, **27**, 319 (1894).

[2] S. Edlbacher, *Z. Physiol. Chem.*, **10**, 278 (1918).

[3] A. Elek, in *Organic Analysis*, Vol. 1, Interscience, New York, 1953, p. 67.

[4] R. Kuhn and H. Roth, *Berichte*, **67**, 1458 (1934).

[5] P. Haas, *Mikrochemie*, **7**, 69 (1929).

[6] T. Franzen, W. Disse, and K. Eysell, *Mikrochim. Acta*, **1953**, 44.

hydrogen iodide, in place of the sodium thiosulfate solution. A more efficient absorber is one that uses solid reagents as a scavenger, shown in the apparatus of Ma and Schachter[7] in Section II-B which follows.

B. Assemblies. A variety of apparatus for the microdetermination of the alkimino function has been described in the literature.[8–15] The recent manuals on quantitative organic microanalysis differ in their choice of the alkimino apparatus. Thus the apparatus of Sirotenko (Fig. 8.1) is favored by Roth[13] whereas the device of Swift (Fig. 8.2) is recommended by Clark.[15] Steyermark[12] uses the alkoxyl apparatus for alkimino determinations. It may be noted that the chief concern in designing the micro alkimino apparatus is how to recover most of the hydriodic acid before it reaches the scrubber. The early models proposed by Pregl and Lieb[8] and Furter[11] were too fragile and difficult to manipulate. The apparatus described by Friedrich[9] was popular for many years and is commercially available. However, the original design of Friedrich (Fig. 8.3) suffers from two drawbacks: (a) difficulty in the passage of the hydriodic acid, and (b) no provision for adding fresh hydriodic acid to and from the condenser. These defects can be remedied[16] by using a wide-bore tubing (C) and adding a reservoir (B) as shown in Fig. 8.4. The micro alkoxyl apparatus recommended by the Committee on Microchemical Apparatus of American Chemical Society[17] can be modified for alkimino analysis by adding a reaction vessel, as shown in Fig. 8.5. A more efficient apparatus[7] is shown in Fig. 8.6, which incorporates a water condenser to recover the hydriodic acid and a siphon to return the acid into the reaction vessel. Fresh hydriodic

---

[7] T. S. Ma and M. M. Schachter, unpublished work; see M. M. Schachter, *Master's Thesis*, Brooklyn College of the City University of New York, 1962.

[8] F. Pregl, *Die quantitative organische Mikroanalyse*, Springer, Berlin, 1930, p. 210.

[9] A. Friedrich, *Mikrochemie*, **1**, 195 (1929); "Die Praxis der quantitativen organischen Mikroanalyse" Deuticke, Wein, 1933, p. 133.

[10] K. H. Slotta and G. Haberland, *Berichte*, **65**, 127 (1932).

[11] M. Furter, *Helv. Chim. Acta*, **21**, 1144 (1938); T. Sudo, D. Shimoe and T. Tsujii, *Japan Analyst*, **3**, 403 (1954).

[12] A. Steyermark, *Quantitative Organic Microanalysis*, Blakiston, Philadelphia, 1951, p. 299.

[13] A. A. Sirotenko, *Mikrochim. Acta*, **1955**, 1; H. Roth, in Pregl-Roth: *Quantitative organische Mikroanalyse*, 7th ed., Springer, Wien, 1958, p. 289.

[14] F. Franzen and H. Pauli, *Mikrochim. Acta*, **1955**, 845.

[15] H. Swift, unpublished work; see S. J. Clark, *Quantitative Methods of Organic Microanalyses*, Butterworth, London, 1956, p. 166.

[16] T. S. Ma, in *Proceedings of the International Symposium on Microchemistry 1958*, Pergamon Press, London, 1959, p. 156.

[17] A. Steyermark, *et al.*, *Anal. Chem.*, **28**, 112 (1956).

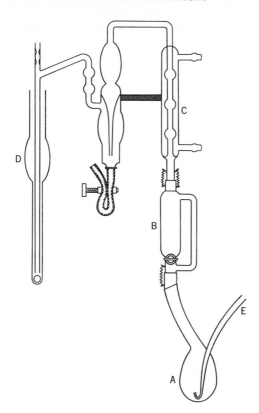

Fig. 8.1. Alkimino apparatus of Sirotenko. Courtesy of *Mikrochimica Acta*.

acid also can be added. The scrubber contains solid reagents. The detailed experimental procedure is given in experiment 52.

C. Measurement of the Alkyl Iodide Formed.   The determination of the alkyl iodide liberated in the pyrolysis of the quaternary ammonium iodide can be accomplished by (*a*) gravimetry, (*b*) iodometry, or (*c*) gas chromatography. These methods have been discussed in Chapter 6 on the alkoxyl function (see page 124). It should be remembered that sulfur-containing alkimides cannot be determined by the gravimetric procedure, which prompted Vieböck and Brecher[18] to develop the iodometric method. The application of gas chromatography to the determination of the al-kimino function involves the collection of the alkyl iodide in each stage

[18] F. Vieböck and C. Brecher, *Berichte*, **63**, 3207 (1930).

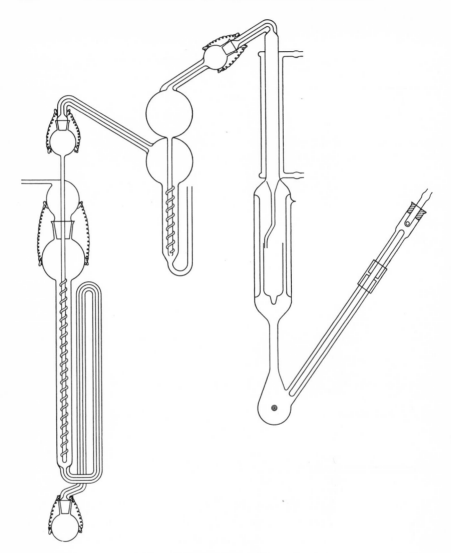

Fig. 8.2. Alkimino apparatus of Swift.

of distillation and injection of the combined distillate into the chromatographic column for quantitative measurement.[7] Franzen, Eysell and Schall reported[19] the thermal decomposition of methyl iodide and ethyl iodide as a source of error in the determination of alkylimides.

[19] F. Franzen, K. Eysell, and H. Schall, *Microchim. Acta*, **1954**, 712.

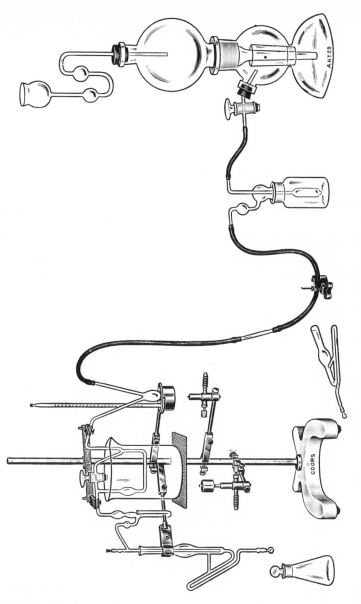

Fig. 8.3. Alkimino apparatus of Friedrich. Courtesy of A. H. Thomas Co.

D. Differential Determination of the Alkoxyl and Alkimino Functions. Since alkyl iodide is liberated from the alkoxyl function when the sample is refluxed in hydriodic acid (see p. 125) whereas the quaternary ammonium iodide remains intact, differential determination of the alkoxyl and alkimino functions is possible in the same sample. The

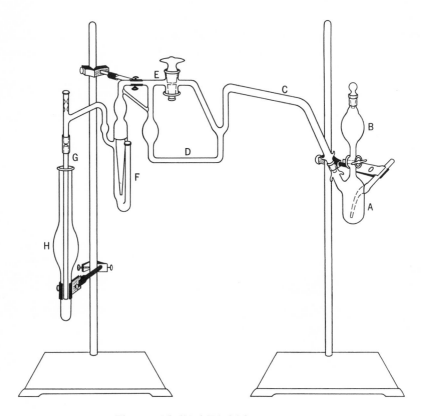

Fig. 8.4. Modified Friedrich apparatus.

reaction mixture is kept at 130°C until the alkyl iodide from the alkoxyl groups has been collected. The receiver is changed and the pyrolysis of the quaternary ammonium iodide follows. The apparatus shown in Figs. 8.4 to 8.6 are suitable for this purpose on the 0.1 meq. scale. A method for the simultaneous determination of alkoxyl and alkimino groups using 50-μg. sample was described by Belcher, Bhatty, and West,[20] who recom-

[20] R. Belcher, M. K. Bhatty, and T. S. West, *J. Chem. Soc.*, **1958**, 2393.

mended a bath temperature of 150°C for the alkoxyl group and 360°C for the alkimino group. These workers[21] also proposed a method to determine the alkimino group alone by converting the quaternary ammonium iodide to the free hydroxide by anionic exchange, and titrating the base with $0.01N$ sulfuric acid.

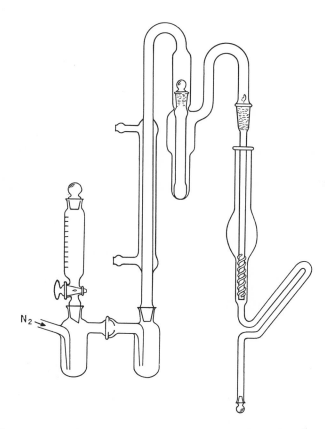

Fig. 8.5. Use of A. C. S. alkoxyl apparatus for alkimino determination.

III. The Amino Function

A. General. The amino function, $\equiv N$, discussed in this section involves primary, secondary, and tertiary amines (RNH_2, R_2NH, R_3N). Derivatives of amines are treated in other sections. Since the amino func-

[21] R. Belcher, M. K. Bhatty, and T. S. West, *J. Chem. Soc.*, **1960**, 2473.

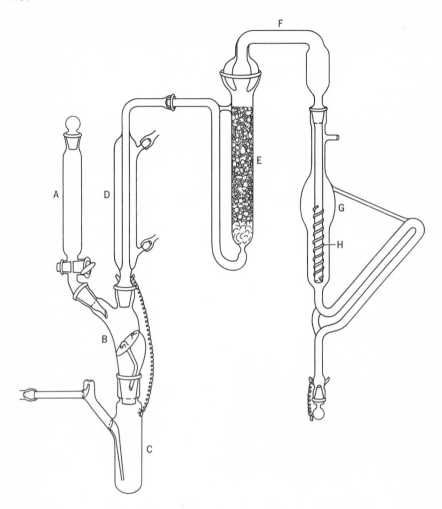

Fig. 8.6. Alkimino apparatus of Ma and Schachter.

tion and its derivatives contain an unshared pair of electrons on the nitrogen atom, they are proton acceptors. Hence a general method for the determination of these compounds is to titrate the sample as a base (see Chapter 11, Section IV). Methods for determining the amino function not dependent on direct titration with an acid are presented below.

B. Methods Based on Acetylation.   Primary and secondary amines react with acetic anhydride according to equations 3 and 4:

$$RNH_2 + (CH_3CO)_2O \rightarrow RN\!-\!\underset{H}{\overset{\text{}}{|}}\!\!-\!\!\underset{O}{\overset{||}{C}}\!\!-\!CH_3 + CH_3COOH \tag{3}$$

$$R_2NH + (CH_3CO)_2O \rightarrow R_2N\!-\!\underset{O}{\overset{||}{C}}\!\!-\!CH_3 + CH_3COOH \tag{4}$$

Pyridine, a weak base, is used as a solvent that helps to drive the reaction to completion. The reaction is carried out preferably in a sealed tube. Allowing the mixture to remain at room temperature for 30 minutes is usually sufficient for primary amines; elevated temperatures are recommended for secondary amines.

The determination may be completed in several ways. The simplest method involves the titration of the liberated acetic acid. A macro procedure using up to 10 meq. of the amine and $0.5N$ potassium hydroxide in methanol as titrant was described by Hillenbrand and Pentz.[22] This method has not been tested on the 0.1 meq. scale.

Mitchell, Hawkins, and Smith[23] devised a method by measuring the residual acetic anhydride. After the completion of the acetylation, a known amount of water is added to the reaction mixture to hydrolyze the acetic anhydride, and the excess of water is then determined by titration with the Karl Fischer reagent. Another method proposed by Angelescu and Burbulescu[24] for the determination of methylaniline is based on the measurement of the heat generated when the sample is acetylated. These two methods are not suitable for adaptation to the micro scale.

Since the hydroxyl function is also determined by acetylation in pyridine, the presence of hydroxyl groups in the sample may interfere with the determination of the amino function. However, acetylation of the hydroxyl function proceeds at a slower rate than that of the amino function. For instance, glucosamine can be determined by the exclusive acetylation of the amino group.[25] Reynolds and co-workers[26] described the photometric titration of aromatic amines at the ultraviolet range by means of $10^{-3}M$ acetic anhydride in pyridine, and reported that phenols, alcohols, and aliphatic amines do not interfere with the determination.

Acetyl chloride has been used as acetylating reagent for the determination of amines,[27] but it has no advantage over acetic anhydride. Acetyl chloride is more difficult to handle than the anhydride.

[22] E. F. Hillenbrand, Jr. and C. A. Pentz, in *Organic Analysis*, Vol. 3, Interscience, New York, 1956, p. 162.

[23] J. Mitchell, Jr., W. Hawkins, and D. M. Smith, *J. Am. Chem. Soc.*, **66**, 782 (1947).

[24] E. Angelescu and N. Burbulescu, *Commun. Acad. rep. popular Romien*, **1**, 57 (1956).

[25] G. A. Levvy and A. McAllan, *Biochem. J.*, **73**, 127 (1959).

[26] C. A. Reynolds, F. H. Walker, and E. Cochran, *Anal. Chem.*, **32**, 983 (1960).

[27] V. R. Olson and H. B. Feldman, *J. Am. Chem. Soc.*, **59**, 2003 (1937).

C. Methods Based on Nitrosation

1. For Primary Amino Group.   Determination of primary amino groups by nitrosation is dependent on the liberation of nitrogen gas, as represented by equation (5):

$$R-NH_2 + HNO_2 \rightarrow N_2 + ROH + H_2O \tag{5}$$

A. GASOMETRIC METHODS.   Van Slyke devised the first apparatus applying this reaction to the determination of primary amino groups in α-amino acids and proteins on the macro scale.[28] Because nitrous acid is unstable, it is prepared *in situ* from sodium nitrite and acetic acid. Some oxides of nitrogen are produced owing to the decomposition of the nitrous acid. These oxides are absorbed in alkaline permanganate solution before the nitrogen is collected in the gasometer and measured. The air in the system prior to analysis is either swept out by nitric oxide or in a later modification by carbon dioxide.[29] Koch's modification[30] to the micro scale employs the apparatus shown in Fig. 8.7, which has a gasometer of 3-ml. capacity. The reaction vessel is attached to the shaking device which consists of a pulley with eccentric arm. Williams and Long[31] modified the Van Slyke apparatus for the analysis of solid samples.

Kainz[32] described a simple apparatus for the determination of primary amino groups by nitrosation. As is shown in Fig. 8.8, the assembly is composed of a reaction chamber connected to a scrubber tube containing potassium bromate to remove the oxides of nitrogen. A stream of carbon dioxide is passed through the apparatus to drive the nitrogen into a micro azotometer to be measured. An improved apparatus which is less rigid has been designed by Ma, Maurmeyer, and Monaco[33] (Fig. 8.9). The detailed procedure for using this apparatus will be found in experiment 36.

A more recent modification by Hoffmann and Lysyj[34] claims greater precision and accuracy since most of the sources of errors (complicated apparatus, wash solutions and separation of nitrogen from the other gases) are eliminated. In this method the sample is introduced into a simple micro reaction flask and after the system is swept with helium, nitrous acid is added, and the evolved nitrogen-nitrogen oxide mixture is passed through

---

[28] D. D. van Slyke, *J. Biol. Chem.*, **9**, 185 (1910); **12**, 275 (1911).

[29] A. S. Hussey and J. E. Marker, *Anal. Chem.*, **22**, 1642 (1952).

[30] F. C. Koch, *J. Biol. Chem.*, **84**, 601 (1929).

[31] K. T. Williams and M. C. Long, *Anal. Chem.*, **28**, 144 (1956).

[32] G. Kainz, *Mikrochim. Acta*, **1953**, 347.

[33] T. S. Ma, R. K. Maurmeyer, and M. Monaco, unpublished work; see M. Monaco, *Master's Thesis, Brooklyn College*, 1958.

[34] E. R. Hoffmann and I. Lysyj, *Microchem. J.*, **6**, 45 (1962).

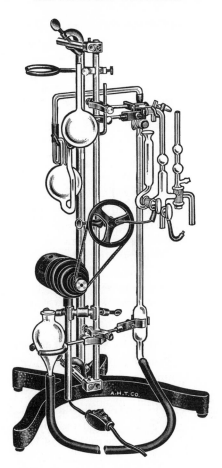

Fig. 8.7. Amino apparatus of Van Slyke and Koch. Courtesy of A. H. Thomas Co.

a suitable chromatographic column. The nitrogen peak is then read off the recorder strip chart and calculated.

It should be noted that most primary amino compounds do not react instantaneously with nitrous acid to give quantitative yields of nitrogen. Amino groups adjacent to the carbonyl group react readily at room temperature.[35] Other primary amino compounds may require elevated temperatures. Extensive investigation of the gasometric determination of the

[35] J. P. Peter and D. D. van Slyke, *Quantitative Clinical Chemistry*, Williams and Wilkins, Baltimore, 1932.

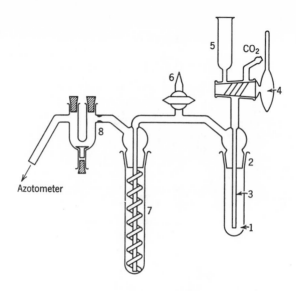

Fig. 8.8. Amino apparatus of Kainz. Courtesy of *Mikrochimica Acta.*

primary amino function was made by Shimoe[36] and Kainz and co-workers.[37] A variety of compounds such as phenols, oximes, and compounds containing the active methylene group interfere with the analysis because of the formation of nitrous oxide and/or nitrogen. Shimoe[36] reported that cupric chloride serves to suppress side reactions. Kendrick and Hanke[38] found that iodide ions have catalytic effect on nitrosation. Kainz and Schöller[39] postulated that the iodide reduces the amount of free nitrous acid present and advocated the use of dilute nitrite solution. According to Kainz, Huber, and Kasler,[40] nitrosyl bromide is a better nitrosation reagent than aqueous nitrite solution. The nitrosyl bromide reagent is prepared by dissolving sodium nitrite in glacial acetic acid followed by the addition of bromine. Since this involves the use of a nonaqueous system, aqueous solutions such as protein hydrolysates have to be evaporated to dryness before the sample is subjected to analysis.

B. TITRIMETRIC METHODS. Although both aliphatic and aromatic primary amino compounds can react with nitrous acid to liberate nitrogen

[36] D. Shimoe, *Japan Analyst,* **5,** 518, 617 (1956).
[37] G. Kainz and co-workers, *Mikrochim. Acta,* **1959,** 51, 337, 563, 875, 883, 891, 903.
[38] A. B. Kendrick and M. E. Hanke, *J. Biol. Chem.,* **117,** 161 (1937); **132,** 737 (1940).
[39] G. Kainz and F. Schöller, *Naturwissenschaften,* **42,** 209 (1955).
[40] G. Kainz, H. Huber, and F. Kasler, *Mikrochim. Acta,* **1957,** 744.

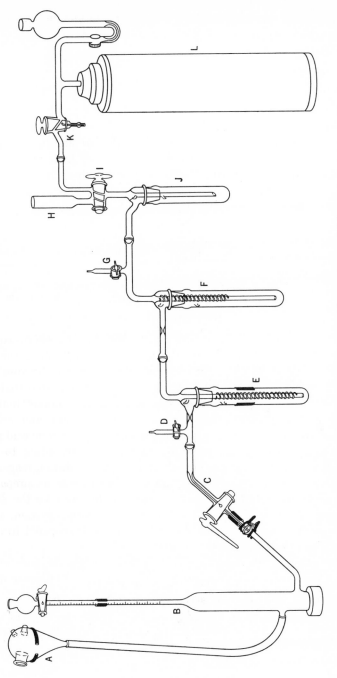

Fig. 8.9. Amino apparatus of Ma, Maurmeyer, and Monaco.

(eq. 5), aromatic primary amino groups form diazonium salts as intermediates which are stable at low temperatures.

$$RNH_2 + HNO_2 \rightarrow ROH + N_2 + H_2O \tag{6}$$

$$Ar—NH_2 + HNO_2 \rightarrow Ar—N_2^+ + OH^- + H_2O \tag{7}$$

Several methods have been proposed to apply the reaction (eq. 7) for the determination of aromatic amines by titrimetry. In general, the sample is dissolved in hydrochloric acid and titrated with a standardized solution of sodium nitrite in the cold. A review on the use of sodium nitrite as titrating agent was prepared by Matrka.[41] Most procedures are on the macro scale. Determination of the endpoint by potentiometric method is recommended by most workers.[42-44] Aromatic diamines also can be determined by this method.[45] Duenn[46] described a procedure using diphenylamine as internal indicator for diazotization titration, which is better than locating the endpoint by spotting on starch iodide paper as an external indicator.[45]

Since many aromatic primary amines undergo diazotization slowly, it has been suggested to perform the analysis by indirect titration.[42] The sample is treated with a known amount of nitrite for an appropriate period, and the residual nitrite is back-titrated with a standardized solution of p-nitroaniline which reacts with nitrous acid instantaneously. To prevent the loss of nitrous acid, concentrated nitric acid is added immediately after the sodium nitrite solution, which shifts the equilibrium of the reaction shown in equation 8 to the left.

$$3HNO_2 \rightleftharpoons HNO_3 + 2NO + H_2O \tag{8}$$

Litvinenko and Grekov[47] proposed a micro procedure using potassium bromide as catalyst. The amine is dissolved in 20 ml. of 10% hydrochloric acid. Sufficient potassium bromide to give a 0.3 to 0.4M solution is then added and the solution is titrated, during vigorous stirring, with 0.01N sodium nitrite potentiometrically by means of the platinum-quinhydrone electrodes.

[41] M. Matrka, *Chemie Prague*, **10**, 635 (1958).

[42] F. Wild, *Estimation of Organic Compounds*, Cambridge University Press, Cambridge, 1953, p. 177.

[43] M. Matrka and K. Stajner, *Chem. Prumysl*, **6**, 471 (1956).

[44] R. S. Soxena and C. S. Bhatnegar, *Naturwissenschaften*, **44**, 583 (1957).

[45] M. Matrka and Z. Sagner, *Chem. Prumsyl*, **9**, 288 (1959).

[46] T. Duenn, *Acta Pharm. Sinica*, **5**, 97 (1957).

[47] L. M. Litvinenko and A. P. Grekov, *Zhur Anal. Khim*, **10**, 164 (1955).

2. For Secondary Amino Group. The secondary amino group reacts with nitrous acid to form the N-Nitroso group as represented by equation 9:

$$\begin{array}{c} R \\ \diagdown \\ \diagup \\ R \end{array} NH + HNO_2 \rightarrow \begin{array}{c} R \\ \diagdown \\ \diagup \\ R \end{array} N{-}NO + H_2O \tag{9}$$

A macro method was described by Gassmann[48] in which the sample is dissolved in hydrochloric acid and titrated with standard sodium nitrite in the presence of potassium bromide. The endpoint is determined by using starch iodide paper.

Yokoo[49] proposed an indirect gasometric method as follows. The secondary amine is dissolved in dilute acetic acid and nitrosated with potassium nitrite solution. The reaction mixture is then treated with sulfamic acid and zinc powder, followed by concentrated hydrochloric acid and Devarda's alloy. After filtration, the solution is diluted to 50 ml.; 1 ml. is taken to react with potassium ferricyanide, and the liberated nitrogen gas is measured. The sequence of the reactions may be shown thus:

$$R_2NH \xrightarrow{HNO_2} R_2NNO \xrightarrow{[H]} R_2NNH_2 \xrightarrow{[O]} N_2 \tag{10}$$

Precision and accuracy of $\pm 1\%$ is reported for determinations on the 0.1 meq. scale, even though the analysis involves several steps that are subject to large errors.

D. Methods Based on the Formation of Schiff's Bases. The primary amino group condenses with a carbonyl group to form azomethine, usually known as Schiff's base, according to the general equation:

$$-NH_2 + O{=}C \begin{array}{c} \diagup R \\ \diagdown R \end{array} \rightarrow -N{=}C \begin{array}{c} \diagup R \\ \diagdown R \end{array} + H_2O \tag{11}$$

Hawkins, Smith, and Mitchell[50] used benzaldehyde in pyridine as a reagent and, after completion of the reaction and removal of hte excess aldehyde with hydrogen cyanide, determined the amount of water produced by means of the Karl Fischer reagent. Aliphatic, alicyclic, and aromatic primary amines have been determined by this method.

[48] C. Gassmann, *Compt. Rend.*, **123**, 313 (1896).

[49] M. Yokoo, *Chem. Pharm. Bull. Japan*, **6**, 64 (1958).

[50] W. Hawkins, D. M. Smith, and J. Mitchell, Jr., *J. Am. Chem. Soc.*, **66**, 1662 (1944).

Johnson[51] developed a method in which salicylaldehyde in pyridine is used as the reagent. The reaction is carried out in pressure bottles at room temperature, and the residual aldehyde is determined by titration with $0.1N$ sodium methoxide in pyridine. Phenolphthalein or thymolphthalein is used as the indicator, toward which the azomethine is neutral. Aromatic primary amines cannot be determined by this procedure because the reactions are not complete. On the other hand, Tsukamoto and Yuhi[52] reported that primary arylamines give quantitative yields of Schiff's bases on heating with chloro- or bromosalicylaldehyde for 10 to 30 minutes whereas analogous reactions with alkylamines are incomplete after heating for 2 to 3 hours. A similar nonaqueous titration procedure was described by Critchfield and Johnson.[53] 2,4-Pentanedione is used as the reagent for aliphatic amines, ethylenediamines, amino alcohols, and amino acids.

All methods mentioned above are macro methods. Conversion of the aquametric procedure to the micro scale is difficult. Adaptation of the nonaqueous alkalimetric method may necessitate the use of potentiometric titration equipment.

E. Precipitation Methods. Ievinsh and co-workers proposed two methods for the determination of secondary and tertiary amines based on the formation of insoluble tetraphenylborates. In one method[54] the amino compound is dissolved in nitric acid and a known amount of $0.05N$ sodium tetraphenylboron is added. After filtrating off the amine tetraphenyl borate, a known quantity of $0.05N$ silver nitrate is added to the filtrate. The silver compound is again filtered off. The excess of silver in the filtrate is determined by titration with $0.05N$ ammonium thiocyanate using ferric ion as the indicator. In another method[55] the amine tetraphenylborate is separated and treated with mercuric chloride, whereupon hydrochloric acid is liberated and determined by alkalimetric titration. These workers reported that primary amines, with the exception of n-butylamine, give soluble tetraphenylborates.

Primary amino compounds react with picryl chloride in ethyl acetate solution in the presence of sodium bicarbonate according to the following equation:

[51] J. B. Johnson, *Anal. Chem.*, **28,** 1977 (1956).

[52] T. Tsukamoto and K. Yuhi, *J. Pharm. Soc. Japan*, **78,** 706 (1958).

[53] F. E. Critchfield and J. B. Johnson, *Anal. Chem.*, **29,** 1174 (1957).

[54] A. F. Ievinsh and E. Y. Gudrinietse, *Zhur. Anal. Khim.*, **11,** 735 (1956).

[55] E. Yanson, A. F. Ievinsh, and E. Y. Gudrinietse, *Uch. Zap. Latv. Univ.*, **14,** 9 (1957).

$$RNH_2 + Cl\!\!\!\begin{array}{c} NO_2 \\ \hline \\ \end{array}\!\!\!-NO_2 + NaHCO_3 \rightarrow$$

$$R\!-\!N\!\!\!\begin{array}{c} H \quad NO_2 \\ \hline \\ NO_2 \end{array}\!\!\!-NO_2 + NaCl + CO_2 + H_2O \quad (12)$$

Macro procedures have been published[56,57] in which the sodium chloride is separated, and the chloride is determined gravimetrically or titrimetrically, but their adaptation to the micro scale is not recommended.

Certain amino compounds yield insoluble salts with perchloric, oxalic, picric, and picrolonic acid, or precipitate chromium thiocyanate complexes (called Reineckates) on treatment with Reinecke's salt. Numerous gravimetric methods based on these reactions are found in the literature. Since they are used mostly for heterocylic nitrogen compounds, these methods are discussed more fully in Section VII-E.

F. Miscellaneous Methods

1. Use of Carbon Disulfide. Primary and secondary amino groups react with carbon disulfide to form dithiocarbamic acids as represented by the following equations:

$$RNH_2 + CS_2 \rightarrow R\!-\!\overset{H}{\underset{}{N}}\!-\!\overset{S}{\underset{}{C}}\!\!\!\diagup\!\!\!-SH \quad (13)$$

$$R_2NH + CS_2 \rightarrow R_2N\!-\!C\!\!\!\begin{array}{c} S \\ \diagup \\ \diagdown \\ SH \end{array} \quad (14)$$

It is evident that tertiary amines do not react.

Critchfield and Johnson[58] described macro procedures to determine the resulting dithiocarbamic acid by nonaqueous alkalimetry. The amino compound is dissolved in pyridine or isopropyl alcohol and treated with carbon disulfide at $-10°C$. The reaction mixture is then titrated with $0.5N$ sodium hydroxide using phenolphthalein as the indicator. An ice-salt

[56] B. Linke, H. Preissecker, and J. Stadler, *Berichte.*, **65**, 1280 (1925).
[57] G. Spencer and J. E. Brimley, *J. Soc. Chem. Ind.*, **64**, 53 (1945).
[58] F. E. Critchfield and J. B. Johnson, *Anal. Chem.*, **28**, 430, 432, 436 (1956).

bath is used for cooling; solid carbon dioxide should be avoided because of its interference in the titration. This method has not been adapted to the micro scale.

Nebbia and Guerrieri[59] found that the nickel derivatives of dithiocarbamic acids from secondary amines are insoluble in sodium hydroxide. After separation, the nickel complex can be decomposed with nitric acid or exchanged with silver and the nickel ions titrated with EDTA using Murexide as the indicator. A coulometric micro method for determining secondary amino groups was devised by Przybylowicz and Rogers,[60] who titrated the dithiocarbamic acid with electrolytically generated mercury in acetone solution, according to the following equation:

$$2R_2N-C{\overset{S^-}{\underset{S}{\big<}}} + Hg^{+2} \to (R_2N-\overset{\overset{S}{\|}}{C}-S)_2Hg \qquad (15)$$

2. Use of Sulfur Trioxide. A method proposed by Terentev and co-workers[61] for determining aromatic amino compounds is based on their reaction with sulfur trioxide in dioxane:[62]

$$Ar-NH_2 + O{\overset{CH_2-CH_2}{\underset{CH_2-CH_2}{\big<}\big>}}O\cdot SO_3 \to Ar-\overset{H}{\underset{}{N}}-SO_3H + O{\overset{CH_2-CH_2}{\underset{CH_2-CH_2}{\big<}\big>}}O \qquad (16)$$

The sample is treated with a measured volume of the reagent prepared by passing a mixture of air and sulfur trioxide through dioxane. After 3 to 5 minutes, 10 ml. of water are added and the solution is titrated with sodium hydroxide using bromophenol blue or Congo red as the indicator. A similar volume of the reagent is mixed with water and titrated. 0.1 Meq. quantities of the amino compound were used, but the titrant employed was $0.1N$.

3. Oxidative Methods. Reis[63] proposed a method for determining amino groups by oxidation with sodium hypobromite. Bromamines are formed which react with potassium iodide to liberate iodine in an amount equivalent to that of the amine. This method is applicable to primary, secondary, and tertiary amines. Precision and accuracy are poor, however.

Sastri and Rao[64] determined p-methylaminophenol by titration with

[59] L. Nebbia and F. Guerrieri, *Chemica-Industria*, **35**, 896 (1953).

[60] E. P. Przybylowicz and L. B. Rogers, *Anal. Chim. Acta*, **18**, 596 (1958).

[61] A. P. Terentev, N. B. Kupletskaya, and E. V. Andreeva, *Zh. Obshch. Khim.*, **26**, 881 (1956).

[62] C. M. Suter, et al., *J. Am. Chem. Soc.*, **60**, 538 (1958).

[63] N. V. Reis, *Sb. Nauchn. Tr. Samarkandsk. Med. Inst.*, **11**, 117 (1956).

[64] T. P. Sastri and G. G. Rao, *Z. Anal. Chem.*, **163**, 263 (1958).

0.01 to 0.05N ceric sulfate. The endpoint can be located potentiometrically or by using copper phthalocyaninetetrasulfonic acid as the internal indicator.

4. The Kjeldahl Method. The time-honored method developed by Kjeldahl[65] in 1883 for the estimation of nitrogen in organic materials is based on the conversion of the organic nitrogen to ammonium sulfate by heating the compound with concentrated sulfuric acid, followed by the liberation and determination of ammonia:

$$R{-}NH_2 + H_2SO_4 \rightarrow (NH_4)_2SO_4 + CO_2 + H_2O \qquad (17)$$

$$(NH_4)_2SO_4 + 2NaOH \rightarrow 2NH_3 + Na_2SO_4 + 2H_2O \qquad (18)$$

$$NH_3 + HCl \rightarrow NH_4Cl \qquad (19)$$

It should be noted that the Kjeldahl method is not a procedure for the determination of the amino function, since other types of compounds such as oximes, nitroso,[66] and p-nitro[66a] compounds have been reported to yield ammonia on treatment with the conventional Kjeldahl procedure.

The mechanism of the Kjeldahl reaction is still unknown. Schwab and co-workers[67] studied the reaction using aniline as the model compound. It was found that sulfonation takes place followed by oxidation and decomposition, but the manner in which the C—N bond is ruptured to form the H—N bond is obscure. Because hot, concentrated sulfuric acid is a strong oxidant, Kjeldahl digestion has been called a "wet oxidation" process. So far as the nitrogen atom is concerned, however, the formation of the H—N bond cannot be the result of the oxidation of the C—N bond but that of the hydrolytic or reductive cleavage. Hence, in the determination of amino-nitrogen by the Kjeldahl method, oxidation of the amino group or the resulting ammonium ion should be prevented.

A large number of papers have appeared in the literature concerning the Kjeldahl method. Comprehensive reviews have been published by Bradstreet.[68] Various apparatus and numerous procedures have been proposed for the analysis on the macro, micro, and ultramicro scale. In general, a catalyst containing copper, selenium, and/or mercury is added, and potassium sulfate is incorporated into the digestion mixture to raise its boiling point. Alternately, the sample can be heated with concentrated

[65] C. Kjeldahl, *Z. Anal. Chem.*, **22**, 366 (1883).

[66] F. Zinneke, *Angew. Chem.*, **64**, 220 (1952).

[66a] P. R. W. Baker, *Analyst*, **80**, 481 (1955).

[67] G. M. Schwab and E. Schwab-Agallides, *J. Am. Chem. Soc.*, **73**, 803 (1951); G. M. Schwab and S. Caramos, *Monatsh.*, **86**, 341 (1955).

[68] R. B. Bradstreet, *Chem. Rev.*, **27**, 331 (1940); *Anal. Chem.*, **26**, 185 (1954).

sulfuric acid in a sealed tube[69] at 450° ± 10°C. After digestion, the reaction mixture is treated with concentrated sodium hydroxide to liberate the ammonia which is then determined titrimetrically or colorimetrically.

A micro Kjeldahl procedure[70] is given in experiment 34. The amino compound is heated with concentrated sulfuric acid to which selenium, copper sulfate, and potassium sulfate are added. It is not necessary to use mercury as catalyst for noncyclic nitrogen compounds. The ammonium sulfate solution is transferred into the steam distillation apparatus shown in Fig. 8.10. After the addition of sodium hydroxide, ammonia is driven off by steam and absorbed in 2% boric acid. The ammonia is then titrated with 0.01N hydrochloric acid using the bromocresol green-methyl red mixed indicator.

G. Special Methods for α-Amino Acids

1. *Ninhydrin Method.* α-Amino acids react with ninhydrin (1,2,3-indantrione hydrate) and related compounds to form aldehyde, carbon dioxide, and ammonia, as represented in equation 20:

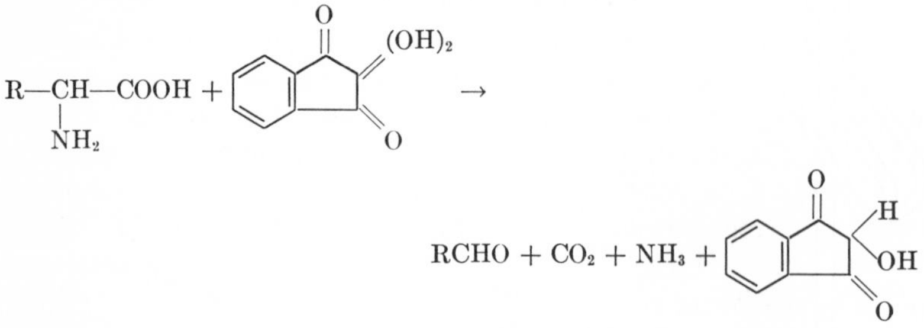

Van Slyke and co-workers proposed two procedures. In one[71] the carbon dioxide is collected and measured manometrically. In another method[72] the carbon dioxide is absorbed in a measured volume of standardized barium hydroxide solution. The excess of alkali is determined by back-titration with standard acid. Moubasher and co-workers[73] proposed pere-naphthendon-2,3,4-trione hydrate as the reagent and measured either the carbon dioxide or ammonia produced. Carbon dioxide is driven into barium

[69] F. L. Schaffer and J. C. Sprecher, *Anal. Chem.*, **29**, 437 (1957).

[70] T. S. Ma and G. Zuazaga, *Ind. Eng. Chem., Anal. Ed.*, **14**, 280 (1942).

[71] D. D. van Slyke, R. T. Dillon, D. A. MacFadyer, and P. Hamilton, *J. Biol. Chem.*, **141**, 627 (1941).

[72] D. D. van Slyke, D. A. MacFadyer, and P. Hamilton, *J. Biol. Chem.*, **141**, 671 (1941).

[73] R. Moubasher and A. Sina, *J. Biol. Chem.*, **180**, 681 (1949); R. Moubasher, A. Sina, W. A. Awad, and A. M. Othman, *J. Biol. Chem.*, **184**, 693 (1950).

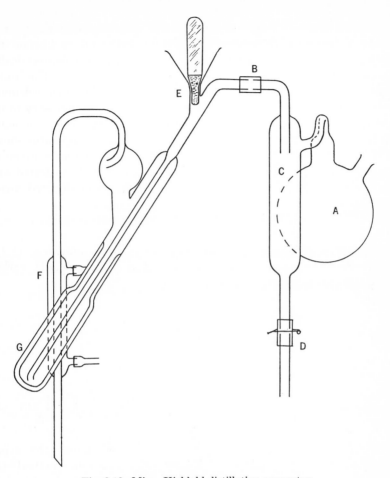

Fig. 8.10. Micro Kjeldahl distillation apparatus.

hydroxide solution which is back-titrated with $N/35$ hydrochloric acid. Ammonia is recovered by steam distillation and determined titrimetrically. Linko[74] used ninhydrin as the reagent and determined carbon dioxide and ammonia simultaneously. Gas chromatography was applied to α-amino acid analysis by Bier and Teitelbaum,[75] who measured the aldehydes produced in the ninhydrin reaction. Quantitative yields were reported, but this method is limited to compounds that form stable volatile aldehydes.

[74] P. Linko, *Suomen Kem.*, **28**, 96 (1956).
[75] M. Bier and P. Teitelbaum, *Ann. N. Y. Acad. Sci.*, **72**, 641 (1959).

2. Chelatometric Methods. α-Amino acids form soluble colored complexes with copper as indicated in equation 21.

$$2R-\underset{\underset{NH_2}{|}}{\overset{\overset{H}{|}}{C}}-\overset{\overset{O}{\diagup}}{\underset{\diagdown}{C}}_{OH} + Cu^{+2} \rightarrow \begin{matrix} O=C-O \\ | \\ R-\underset{|}{C}-NH_2 \\ H \end{matrix} Cu \begin{matrix} H \\ | \\ H_2N-C-R \\ | \\ O-C=O \end{matrix} + 2H^+ \qquad (21)$$

Kober and Sugiura[76] proposed a method by reacting the amino acid with freshly precipitated copper hydroxide. The reaction mixture is filtered and the filtrate containing the copper complex is analyzed for copper by the iodometric procedure. Pope and Stevens[77] recommended copper phosphate as the reagent, which is suspended in an alkali borate buffer. According to Bottini and co-workers,[78] this method gives reproducible results, but the values of amino group found are higher than those obtained by the Van Slyke method, probably because of the slight solubility of the copper reagent.

3. Enzymatic Methods. Since a number of α-amino acids are biologically active, various bioassays are available. Most biological methods of analysis, however, are used for the determination of specific compounds and not for a particular organic function.[79] Bioassays also require biological equipment and techniques.

Naturally occurring α-amino acids can be determined by the use of lactic acid producing bacteria. By leaving out one of the essential amino acids required for full growth of certain micro organisms, a medium for the determination of that particular amino acid is prepared. Titration of the amount of lactic acid formed is indicative of the quantity of the amino acid present.[80]

Virtanen and Laine[81] used an enzyme that decarboxylates L-α-amino acids, and determined the amount of amino acid present by measuring the quantity of carbon dioxide liberated. Several workers determined D-α-amino acids by employing D-amino acid oxidase. This enzyme is capable

---

[76] P. A. Kober and K. Sugiura, *J. Biol. Chem.*, **13**, 1 (1912).

[77] C. G. Pope and M. F. Stevens, *Biochem. J.*, **33**, 1070 (1939).

[78] E. Bottini, R. Strigini, and G. Antognoni, *Boll. Soc. Ital. Biol. Sper.*, **35**, 772 (1959).

[79] S. Colowick and N. Kaplan (eds.), *Methods of Enzymology*, Vol. 3, Academic Press, New York, 1957.

[80] J. Stokes and M. Gunness, *J. Biol. Chem.*, **157**, 651 (1945); J. Stokes and I. Dwyer, *ibid.*, **160**, 35 (1945).

[81] A. Virtanen and T. Laine, *Enzymologia*, **9**, 53 (1940).

of oxidatively deaminating a large number of α-amino acids of the D-configuration, as expressed by the following equation:

$$\underset{\underset{NH_2}{|}}{\overset{\overset{H}{|}}{R-C-COOH}} + O_2 + H_2O \xrightarrow{\text{enzyme}} \underset{\underset{O}{\|}}{R-C-COOH} + NH_3 + H_2O_2 \qquad (22)$$

Ultramicro methods were proposed that are dependent on the measurement of oxygen consumption[82,83] or the formation of the 2,4-dinitrophenylhydrazone of the ketonic acid produced. A micro method was developed by Ma and Breyer[84] in which the ammonia formed is separated from the reaction mixture by steam distillation from a borax-potassium carbonate solution. The detailed procedure is given in experiment 47.

4. Formal Titration. Amino acids are too weak to be determined by alkalimetric titration in aqueous solutions. Sörensen[85] devised a method to change the primary amino group to the neutral methylene imine. The aqueous solution of amino acid is treated with formaldehyde whereupon the following reaction takes place:

$$\underset{\underset{NH_2}{|}}{\overset{\overset{H}{|}}{R-C-COOH}} + H_2CO \rightleftharpoons \underset{\underset{N=CH_2}{|}}{\overset{\overset{H}{|}}{R-C-COOH}} + H_2O \qquad (23)$$

The resulting carboxylic acid is then titrated with aqueous standard alkali using phenolphthalein or thymol blue as the indicator. It should be noted that reaction 23 is reversible, and pH control is essential for the success of this method.[86] Since amino acids can be titrated directly in nonaqueous medium (see p. 436), the formal titration procedure is recommended only for dilute aqueous solutions such as protein hydrolysates.

H. Colorimetric Methods. The literature on the colorimetric methods for determining amines is very extensive. It should be noted, however, that each method has its limitations and there are no methods applicable to all types of amino compounds.

1. For Primary Amines. The formation of Schiff's base (see eq. 11) is the basis of most colorimetric methods for the determination of the primary amino group. Thus Milun[87] employed salicylaldehyde as the reagent and

[82] F. Lipmann, O. Behrens, E. Kabat, and D. Burk, *Science*, **91**, 21 (1940).

[83] J. Klein and P. Handler, *J. Biol. Chem.*, **139**, 103 (1941).

[84] T. S. Ma and R. Breyer, *Microchem. J.*, **4**, 481 (1960).

[85] S. P. L. Sörensen, *Bio. Z.*, **7**, 45 (1909).

[86] W. H. Taylor, *Analyst*, **82**, 488 (1957).

[87] A. J. Milun, *Anal. Chem.*, **29**, 1502 (1957).

measured the color at 410 mμ. Deeb[88] reported that only primary aromatic amines develop yellow color with vanillin at pH 0.5. The intensity is measured at 400 mμ. Critchfield and Johnson[89] described a procedure for aliphatic amino groups that is dependent on both Schiff's base and chelate formation. The sample is treated with salicylaldehyde, cupric chloride, and triethanolamine. The colored complex is extracted into n-hexanol, and the amount of copper is determined absorptiometrically by its reaction with bis-(2-hydroxymethyl)-dithiocarbamic acid. Amino compounds containing branch chain in the 2-position and aromatic amines do not react quantitatively. According to Hershenson and Hume[90] certain aliphatic amines form colored complexes with cupric chloride in alcoholic solution, which are extractable by chloroform and exhibit absorption at the range of 750 to 950 mμ.

Primary aromatic amines with free para or ortho positions can be determined colorimetrically by coupling them with a diazonium salt and measuring the intensity of the dye produced. Diazotized p-nitroaniline[91] and azobenzene-4-diazonium fluoroborate[92] have been suggested as the reagents. Aromatic amines also give colored products on oxidation. Thus Jan and co-workers[93] used lead peroxide in phosphoric acid as the oxidant. Ma and Hirsch[94] found that aromatic diamines develop color with various metal ions and inorganic anions. Smith and Swank[95] proposed a colorimetric method for aliphatic diamines based on their reaction with 3,5-dinitro-o-toluamide. It is reported that different diamines can be distinguished by this reagent.

2,4-Dinitrofluorobenzene is used frequently for the determination of the primary amino group through the formation of the substituted dinitrophenylamine according to equation 24.

$$R\!-\!NH_2 + F\!-\!\underset{}{\bigcirc}\!-\!NO_2 + NaOH \rightarrow R\!-\!\underset{H}{N}\!-\!\underset{}{\bigcirc}\!-\!NO_2 + NaF + H_2O \quad (24)$$

After the reaction is completed, the excess of reagent is hydrolyzed to 2,4-dinitrophenol. The amine derivative is separated from the sodium

[88] E. N. Deeb, *Drug Std.*, **26**, 175 (1958).

[89] F. E. Critchfield and J. B. Johnson, *Anal. Chem.*, **28**, 436 (1956).

[90] H. M. Hershenson and D. N. Hume, *Anal. Chem.*, **29**, 16 (1957).

[91] C. L. Hilton, *Rubber Age*, **84**, 263 (1958).

[92] E. Sawicki, T. W. Stanley, and T. R. Hauser, *Chemist-Analyst*, **48**, 30 (1959).

[93] J. Jan, J. Kolseck, and M. Perpar, *Z. Anal. Chem.*, **153**, 4 (1956).

[94] T. S. Ma and A. Hirsch, unpublished work; see A. Hirsch, *Master's Thesis, Brooklyn College*, 1956.

[95] G. N. Smith and M. G. Swank, *Anal. Chem.*, **32**, 978 (1960).

2,4-dinitrophenate by extraction with cyclohexane or tetrachloroethane. The yellow color of the substituted dinitrophenylamine is then determined in the spectrophotometer.[96] It should be noted that secondary amines also react with 2,4-dinitrofluorobenzene, albeit more sluggishly. Dubin[97] reported that the ratio of extinction at 350 mμ and 390 mμ can be used to differentiate primary and secondary amines. For primary amines the ratio of extinction at 350 mμ to that at 390 mμ is approximately 0.4 to 0.8; for secondary amines it ranges from 2.1 to 2.4. Instead of extracting the 2,4-dinitrophenylamine from the aqueous solution, dioxane is added to the reaction mixture to effect dissolution of the colored product, and the extinction is then determined.

2. For Secondary Amines. Clark and Morgan[98] described a spectrophotometric method for determining secondary amines which is dependent on nitrosation (eq. 9). The color is developed by heating the nitrosoamine with sodium hydroxide at 50°C and measured at 235 mμ. A correction factor is necessary if primary amines are present. Weiser and Zacherl[99] applied the dithiocarbamate reaction (eq. 14) to determine compounds containing the secondary amino group. The sample is treated with cupric acetate and carbon disulfide in ammoniacal solution. The colored complex is then extracted into chloroform and determined spectrophotometrically. These authors state that the color is stable to alkali whereas the corresponding product from a primary amine is not. According to Umbreit,[100] primary amines undergo the same reactions but give much lower color intensities.

Cullis and Waddington[101] reported that only secondary amines give a violet-blue color on treatment with sodium nitroprusside and acetaldehyde at pH 9.8. The color is measured at 565 mμ. Milun and Nelson[102] used bromocresol green as a colorimetric reagent to determine secondary amines. The extinction is measured at 627 mμ. Primary amines, if present, should be removed by conversion to the azomethine with salicylaldehyde.

3. For Tertiary Amines. Sass and co-workers[103] presented two colorimetric methods to determine tertiary amines. Aconitic anhydride is the reagent for one method and the color is measured at 500 mμ. In another method

[96] F. C. McIntire, L. M. Clements, and M. Sproull, *Anal. Chem.*, **25**, 1757 (1953).

[97] D. T. Dubin, *J. Biol. Chem.*, **235**, 783 (1960).

[98] S. J. Clark and D. J. Morgan, *Mikrochim. Acta*, **1956**, 966; D. J. Morgan, *Mikrochim. Acta*, **1958**, 104.

[99] M. Weiser and M. K. Zacherl, *Mikrochim. Acta*, **1957**, 577.

[100] G. R. Umbreit, *Anal. Chem.*, **33**, 1572 (1961).

[101] C. F. Cullis and D. J. Waddington, *Anal. Chim. Acta*, **15**, 158 (1956).

[102] A. J. Milun and J. P. Nelson, *Anal. Chem.*, **31**, 1655 (1959).

[103] S. Sass, J. J. Kaufman, A. A. Cardenas, and J. J. Martin, *Anal. Chem.*, **30**, 529 (1958).

the sample is treated with chloranil and the measurement is sensitive to 3 μg. per ml., whereas the sensitivity of the first method is 50 μg. per ml. Both reagents also give colored products with quaternary ammonium salts. However, these workers stated that the two types of amino compounds can be differentiated when the methods are used in conjunction.

4. For α-Amino Acids. 2,4-Dinitrofluorobenzene has been widely used (see eq. 24) for the colorimetric determination of α-amino acids in protein hydrolysates.[104] It is interesting to note that the ratio of the extinction at 350 mμ and 390 mμ for α-amino acid derivatives is approximately 2.1 to 2.4 and thus similar to that for secondary amines and not primary amines.

The blue-violet color which develops when α-amino acids are treated with ninhydrin[105,106] and related compounds,[107] is frequently used to determine amino acids spectrophotometrically. Since the color is not stable, the determination should be made under identical conditions as in the preparation of the calibration curve.

IV. The Ammonium Functions

A. General. The organic ammonium functions are represented by the cations: RNH_3^+, $R_2NH_2^+$, R_3NH^+, and R_4N^+. The first three cations are present in amine salts, whereas the last group is characteristic of quaternary ammonium compounds. Amine salts are also known as alkyl ammonium salts. For example, methylamine hydrochloride, $CH_3NH_3^+Cl^-$, is called methylammonium chloride. Only amine salts and quaternary ammonium salts are discussed in this section; free amines which are called by some organic ammonium hydroxides are treated as basic functions (see Chapter 11, Section IV).

Amine salts are frequently prepared in the research laboratory because they are solids and hence easier to handle than the free amines. Quaternary ammonium salts have attracted attention recently because of their antiseptic, germicidal, and surface active properties.

B. Acidimetric Titration Methods

1. Aqueous Titrimetry. Amine salts that are derived from weak acids can be determined by titration in aqueous solutions with standard hydro-

---

[104] B. B. Brodie and S. Udenfriend, *J. Biol. Chem.*, **158**, 705 (1945); G. Koch and W. Weidel, *Z. Physiol.*, **303**, 213 (1956).

[105] S. Moore and W. H. Stein, *J. Biol. Chem.*, **211**, 893 (1954); S. Moore, D. H. Spackman, and W. H. Stein, *Anal. Chem.*, **30**, 1185 (1958).

[106] S. Ishii, *J. Biochem. Japan*, **43**, 531 (1956).

[107] R. Moubasher and W. A. Awad, *J. Biol. Chem.*, **179**, 915 (1949).

chloric acid. Thus ethanolamine carbonate was titrated potentiometrically on the macro scale:[108]

$$(HOCH_2CH_2NH_3)_2CO_3 + 2HCl \rightarrow 2HOCH_2CH_2NH_3Cl + H_2O + CO_2 \quad (25)$$

Moderately strong acids, such as sulfur dioxide, interfere with the analysis.

Knabe[109] advocated a method to determine quaternary ammonium salts by the application of ion exchange. The sample is dissolved in 10 ml. of water, passed through a column containing Amberlite IRA-400 at the rate of 1 ml. per minute, and washed with 40 ml. of water. The eluate is titrated with $0.1N$ hydrochloric acid. The reactions are indicated below:

$$R_4NCl + Resin—OH \rightarrow R_4NOH + Resin—Cl \quad (26)$$

$$R_4NOH + HCl \rightarrow R_4NCl + H_2O \quad (27)$$

2. Nonaqueous Titrimetry. Amine carboxylates[110] and picrates[111,112] have been analyzed by titration in glacial acetic acid with $0.1N$ perchloric acid. The endpoint can be determined potentiometrically or visually by means of methyl violet or crystal violet. The halogen acid salts of amines cannot be titrated directly against standard perchloric acid. Pifer and Wollish[113] devised a method that is dependent on the formation of the slightly dissociable mercuric halides. The amine salt is dissolved in acetic acid and mercuric acetate is added:

$$2RNH_3X + (CH_3COO)_2Hg \rightarrow HgX_2 + 2RNH_3{}^+CH_3COO^- \quad (28)$$
$$X = I, Br, Cl$$

The resulting amine acetate is then titrated with perchloric acid in dioxane. This technique has been extended to the analysis of cationic soaps.[114] Gyenes[115] reported that the determination of amine hydrochlorides on the 0.3 to 5.5 meq. range can be accomplished by using $0.05N$ perchloric acid and crystal violet or azo red as indicator. Potentiometric titration is necessary when $0.01N$ titrant is used.[113]

An indirect acidimetric titration method proposed by Gautier and co-workers[116] for the determination of quaternary ammonium salts on the 0.2 meq. scale is as follows. The sample is dissolved in water and treated with sodium tetraphenylboron at pH 4–5. Aluminum chloride is added to aid the

[108] N. Y. C. Chang, *Anal. Chem.*, **30**, 1095 (1958).

[109] J. Knabe, *Deüt Apotheker-Zt.*, **96**, 874 (1956).

[110] P. C. Markunas and J. A. Riddick, *Anal. Chem.*, **24**, 312 (1952).

[111] J. R. Clark and S. M. Wang, *Anal. Chem.*, **26**, 1230 (1954).

[112] C. Bergamini and G. Mattei, *Sperimentale*, **6**, 13 (1956).

[113] C. W. Pifer, and E. G. Wollish, *Anal. Chem.*, **24**, 300 (1952).

[114] K. K. Kunov and M. N. Das, *Anal. Chem.*, **31**, 1358 (1959).

[115] I. Gyenes, *Magy. Kem. Folyoirat*, **63**, 94 (1957); **65**, 264 (1959).

[116] J. A. Gautier, J. Renault, and F. Pellerin, *Ann. Pharm. Franc.*, **13**, 725 (1955).

coagulation of the precipitate. The ammonium tetraphenylboron is collected on a filter, redissolved in acetone, and titrated with $0.04N$ perchloric acid in acetic acid using methyl violet as the indicator. Precision and accuracy of $\pm 1\%$ are reported. The reactions are given below:

$$R_4NX + Na(C_6H_5)_4B \rightarrow R_4N(C_6H_5)_4B + NaX \tag{29}$$

$$R_4N(C_6H_5)_4B + HClO_4 \rightarrow R_4N^+ClO_4^- + (C_6H_5)_3B + C_6H_6 \tag{30}$$

C. Alkalimetric Titration Methods. Amine salts of strong acids may be determined by titration with standard aqueous alkali on the macro scale, but the endpoint is difficult to discern when $0.01N$ titrant is used for microdeterminations. Therefore nonaqueous titration is recommended. A suitable procedure (see experiment 4) is to dissolve the sample in methanol or dimethylformamide and titrate the solution with standardized sodium methoxide in methanol:[117]

$$RNH_3X + NaOCH_3 \rightarrow RNH_2 + NaX + CH_3OH \tag{31}$$

D. Methods Based on Precipitation. Patel and Anderson[118] described a gravimetric procedure to determine quaternary ammonium salts on the 0.1 meq. scale which is dependent on the precipitation of the tetraphenylboron derivative (eq. 29). The sample is treated with 2.5% sodium tetraphenylboron solution and the precipitate is allowed to stand overnight, collected on a filter, dried at 105°C, and weighed. Filtration techniques using either the sintered glass filter tube[118a] (see experiment 26) or the filterstick (Fig. 5.23, p. 98) are applicable.

A reagent which has been used for a long time to precipitate amino compounds is Reinecke's salt, prepared from potassium dichromate and ammonium thiocyanate. Wilson[119] proposed to use this reagent for the determination of quaternary ammonium compounds according to the following reaction:

$$R_4NX + NH_4[Cr(NH_3)_2(SCN)_4] \rightarrow R_4N[Cr(NH_3)_2(SCN)_4] + NH_4X \tag{32}$$

Since the reagent is unstable and the product is rather soluble in water at room temperature,[120] this method is not recommended for microanalysis.

[117] J. S. Fritz and N. M. Lisicki, *Anal. Chem.*, **23**, 589 (1951); Fritz, *ibid.*, **24**, 306 (1952).

[118] D. M. Patel and R. A. Anderson, *Drug Standards*, **26**, 189 (1958).

[118a] T. S. Ma and L. Handler, unpublished work; L. Handler, *Master's Thesis, Eroolkyn College*, 1959.

[119] J. B. Wilson, *J. Assoc. Official Agri. Chemists*, **35**, 455 (1952).

[120] F. Wild, *Estimation of Organic Compounds*, Cambridge University Press, 1953, p. 171.

Lincoln and Chinnick[121] described a microgravimetric procedure for determining surface active quaternary ammonium compounds by the precipitation of their phosphotungstates. The precipitated complex is filtered off, dried at 105°C and weighed. It is then ignited to yield phosphotungstic acid and reweighed. Bhargava and co-workers[122] advocated sym-di-*m*-, and di-*p*-tolylthiovioluric acids as reagents for the precipitation of organic bases from their salts in acetone solution. The applicability of this method has not been established.

E. Miscellaneous Methods for Quaternary Ammonium Compounds

1. Use of Organic Sulfates and Related Anions. A number of methods have been proposed for the determination of quaternary ammonium compounds that involve the use of anionic titrants. Thus sodium lauryl sulfate[123,124] and sodium dodecyl sulfate[125] have been used to titrate quaternary ammonium compounds with eosin or dimethyl yellow as the indicator:

$$R_4NX + R'O-SO_3Na \rightarrow [R_4N^+][R'OSO_3^-] + NaX \qquad (33)$$

Rose and Bayley[126] employed sodium sulfosuccinate for the same purpose. Moseley[127] treated the quaternary ammonium salt with eosin to form the red precipitate. The reaction mixture is then titrated with an anionic reagent until the color disappears. Flanagan and co-workers[128] added sodium arylsulfonate solutions to the sample until maximum turbidity and estimated the result by comparison with standards.

2. Formation of Metal Complexes. Renard[129] reacted hexadecyltrimethyl ammonium bromide with a known amount of standardized potassium dichromate. After separation of the ammonium complex, the excess of dichromate in the filtrate is determined iodometrically. Budesinsky and Vanickova[130] devised a method to precipitate quaternary ammonium salts

[121] P. A. Lincoln and C. C. T. Chinnick, *Analyst*, **81**, 100 (1956).

[122] P. N. Bhargava, N. Veerabhadriah, and B. Satyanarayana, *J. Indian Chem. Soc.*, **34**, 889 (1957).

[123] T. E. Furlong and P. R. Elliker, *J. Dairy Sci.*, **36**, 225 (1953).

[124] M. Dolezil and J. Bulander, *Chem. Listy*, **51**, 225 (1957).

[125] E. D. Carkuff and W. F. Boyd, *J. Am. Pharm. Assoc.*, **43**, 240 (1954).

[126] G. R. F. Rose and C. H. Bayley, *Natl. Res. Council Can., Bul.*, No. 2875 (1952).

[127] W. K. Moseley, *Milk Plant Monthly*, **38**, 76 (1949).

[128] T. L. Flanagan, Jr., T. J. Drennen, and G. R. Goetchins, *Soap Sanit. Chemicals*, **24**, 163 (1948).

[129] I. Renard, *J. Pharm. Belg.*, **7**, 403 (1952).

[130] B. Budesinsky and E. Vanickova, *Chem. Listy*, **50**, 1241 (1956).

with potassium cadmium iodide, followed by the determination of the excess of cadmium by complexometric titration with 0.01M EDTA.

3. Formation of Colored Complexes. Quaternary ammonium salts produce a blue color when treated with bromophenol blue. The colored complex is extractable with chloroform. Cucci[131] presented a procedure in which a mixture of chloroform and buffered aqueous solution of bromophenol blue is titrated with the aqueous quaternary ammonium salt solution until the aqueous layer is colorless. An improved method was developed by Patel and Anderson.[118] The quaternary ammonium compound is mixed with bromophenol blue in chloroform and aqueous sodium hydroxide solution. The mixture is titrated with 0.02M sodium tetraphenylboron, with frequent shaking, until the blue color disappears from the chloroform layer.

4. Liberation of Tertiary Amine. Barber and co-workers[132] reported that quaternary ammonium salts liberate tertiary amines on treatment with morpholine according to the following equation:

$$R_4NX + \underset{\underset{O}{\bigcirc}}{\overset{\overset{H}{N}}{}} \rightarrow \left[\underset{\underset{O}{\bigcirc}}{\overset{\overset{RNH}{}}{}} \right]^+ R_3NX^- \rightarrow R_3N + \underset{\underset{O}{\bigcirc}}{\overset{RNHX}{}} \qquad (34)$$

The tertiary amine is recovered by fractional distillation and determined on the macro scale. Earlier, Bickerman[133] described a method to determine tetramethylammonium sulfate or nitrate by repeated heating with sodium hydroxide. The trimethylamine evolved is absorbed in standard acid which is then back-titrated with standard alkali. These procedures have not been adapted to the micro scale.

5. Titration of the Inorganic Anion. Most quaternary ammonium salts of inorganic acids are soluble in water and are completely ionized. Therefore the determination of the inorganic anion by the usual methods is a measure of the ammonium function for pure quaternary ammonium salts. This is also true for amine salts of inorganic acids. For instance, sulfates can be determined as barium sulfate and halides as silver halide gravimetrically on the micro scale. Kainz and Polun[134] proposed to determine hydrochlorides, hydrobromides, and iodine methylates of organic bases in ethanol

[131] M. W. Cucci, *Soap Sanit. Chemicals,* **24,** 129 (1948).
[132] A. Barber, C. C. T. Chinnick, and P. A. Lincoln, *J. Appl. Chem.,* **5,** 594 (1955).
[133] J. J. Bickerman, *Z. Anal. Chem.,* **90,** 335 (1932).
[134] G. Kainz and M. Polun, *Mikrochemie,* **35,** 189 (1950).

by titration with 0.005 to 0.01N silver nitrate using dichlorofluorescein as indicator. It should be noted that the endpoints are difficult to locate in such dilute solutions.

6. Biological Methods. The biological activity of certain quaternary ammonium compounds provides a very sensitive method for their determination. Thus Silverman and Kosikowsky[135] described a procedure to determine quaternary ammonium salts by their effect on growth of organisms using the dish assay technique. Barber[136] determined quaternary ammonium compounds in milk by adding an active lactic acid bacteria culture to the sample. The development or lack of development of lactic acid is compared with standards. These methods are recommended for trace analysis or determinations on the μeq. scale.

F. Colorimetric Methods. Auerbach[137] reported that benzyl-type quaternary ammonium salts form colored products with bromophenol blue or bromothymol blue indicator. The colored salt is extracted from aqueous alkaline solution into benzene. The intensity of the color is proportional to the amount of quaternary ammonium group present in the original sample. This method was adopted by various workers who presented a number of modifications in the procedure.[138–143] Fogh and co-workers[144] found that the blue color produced from quaternary ammonium compounds and bromocresol purple at pH 8.2 is even better. Concentrations ranging from 0 to 25 μg. per ml. can be determined by measuring the intensity at 620 mμ. The results are independent of temperature variations and uninfluenced by the presence of metal ions within certain limits.

Sass and co-workers[145] described two methods for determining tertiary and quaternary ammonium salts. Aconitic anhydride is used as the reagent in the first method shown in equation (35) and chloranil in the second method as shown in equation (36):

[135] G. J. Silverman and F. V. Kosikowsky, *J. Milk Food Technol.*, **15**, 120 (1952).

[136] F. W. Barber, *Milk Plant Monthly*, **41**, 20 (1952).

[137] M. E. Auerbach, *Ind. Eng. Chem., Anal. Ed.*, **15**, 492 (1943); **16**, 739 (1944).

[138] J. Pien, J. M. Desirant, and M. Rochelle, *Ann. Fals. Fraudes*, **44**, 290 (1951).

[139] J. B. Wilson, *J. Assoc. Offic. Agr. Chemists*, **34**, 343 (1951).

[140] D. B. Conklin, *J. Milk Food Technol.*, **15**, 22 (1952); U.S. Patent 2,599,697 (1952).

[141] R. Mitchell and B. B. Clark, *Proc. Soc. Exptl. Biol. Med.*, **81**, 105 (1952).

[142] K. R. Gottlieb, *Dansk Tidsskr. Farm.*, **27**, 199 (1953).

[143] L. D. Metcalfe, *Anal. Chem.*, **32**, 70 (1960).

[144] J. Fogh, P. O. H. Rasmussen, and K. Skadhauge, *Anal. Chem.*, **26**, 393 (1954).

[145] S. Sass, J. J. Kaufman, A. A. Cardenas, and J. J. Martin, *Anal. Chem.*, **30**, 530 (1958).

$$R_4NCl + \quad \xrightarrow{} \quad + RCl \qquad (35)$$

$$R_4NCl + \quad \xrightarrow{} \quad Cl^- + RCl \qquad (36)$$

Schill and Danielsson[146] proposed hexanitrodiphenylamine as the reagent for the photometric determination of quaternary ammonium salts. The measurement is made at 420 mμ. As low as 0.8 μeq. of the compound in 2.5 ml. solution can be determined. Reiss[147] suggested an indirect colorimetric method as follows. The quaternary ammonium compound is converted to its iodide salt by means of potassium iodide. The iodide salts are extracted with chloroform and oxidized with nitric acid to yield free iodine, which is determined colorimetrically. Weiner[148] presented a method in which the quaternary ammonium salt is titrated with standardized picric acid to the approximate equivalence point. The solution is then chilled in ice and filtered, and the intensity of the filtrate measured at 430 mμ. The latter methods do not appear to have any advantage over the other methods mentioned.

V. The Azido, Cyano and Isocyano Functions

The azido, cyano, and isocyano functions have a common characteristic: in all these groups the nitrogen atom is not linked to a hydrogen atom.

The azido function is written as $\equiv$C—N ⦗N‖N⦘ or $\equiv$C—$\overset{+}{N}$=$\overset{-}{N}$$\equiv$N and is

[146] G. Schill and B. Danielsson, *Anal. Chem. Acta*, **21**, 248, 341.

[147] R. Reiss, *Arzneimittel Forsch.*, **6**, 77 (1956).

[148] S. Weiner, *Chemist-Analyst*, **42**, 9 (1953).

present in compounds such as acyl azides, $R—\overset{\overset{\text{O}}{\|}}{C}—N_3$ and aromatic azides, $Ar—N_3$. Compounds with cyano groups —CN are also known as nitriles and are named after the carboxylic acids to which they can be converted. Thus CH_3—CN is called methylcyanide or acetonitrile; CH_2=CH—CN is vinyl cyanide or acrylonitrile. The recently discovered compound, tetracyanoethylene, $(CN)_2C$=$C(CN)_2$, exemplifies an organic molecule containing no hydrogen or halogen. The isocyano function (also called isonitrile) is represented as —N≡C or $—\overset{+}{N}=\overset{-}{C}$. Compounds that contain this function are called organic isocyanides and are noted for their penetrating and unpleasant odor and high toxicity.

Although the three functions discussed in this section have their counterparts in inorganic chemistry, it should be noted that analytical methods for inorganic azides, cyanides, and isocyanides are usually not applicable to the determination of the organic azido, cyano, and isocyano groups. Unlike halogens in organic compounds, it is seldom possible to quantitatively convert azides, nitriles, or isonitriles into azide, cyanide, or isocyanide ions.

A. Determination of Azido Groups

1. Methods Depending on Reduction. Organic azides can be reduced by arsenite ions as represented by the following equations:

$$C_6H_5N_3 + Na_3AsO_3 + H_2O \rightarrow C_6H_5NH_2 + N_2 + Na_3AsO_4 \tag{37}$$

$$R—\overset{\overset{\text{}}{\|}}{\underset{\underset{\text{O}}{\|}}{C}}—N_3 + Na_3AsO_3 + 2H_2O \rightarrow R—\overset{\overset{\text{}}{\|}}{\underset{\underset{\text{O}}{\|}}{C}}—OH + N_2 + NH_3 + Na_3AsO_4 \tag{38}$$

Gutmann[149] described a method in which the sample is decomposed with sodium arsenite and the resulting solution is analyzed for arsenate iodometrically. This procedure can be adapted to the micro scale.

2. Methods Depending on Molecular Rearrangement. Acyl azides undergo rearrangements (Curtius[150]) to yield nitrogen and isocyanate:

$$R—\overset{\|}{\underset{\underset{\text{O}}{\|}}{C}}—N\overset{\diagup N}{\underset{\diagdown N}{\big\|}} \rightarrow RNCO + N_2 \tag{39}$$

Sah and Ma[151] found that these azides are very soluble in toluene or xylene, and their solutions liberate nitrogen gas smoothly upon gentle heating in

[149] A. Gutmann, *Z. Anal. Chem.*, **66**, 24 (1925).
[150] T. Curtius, *Berichte*, **27**, 778 (1894).
[151] P. P. T. Sah, and T. S. Ma, *J. Chinese Chem. Soc.*, **2**, 159 (1934).

the presence of an amine. This reaction can be carried out in the micro hydrazine apparatus (see p. 291). The nitrogen evolved is collected in the micro azotometer and measured. Alternately, the amount of isocyanate produced can be determined by adding a known quantity of n-butylamine to the acyl azide to form the substituted urea:

$$R-\underset{\underset{O}{\|}}{C}-N\underset{N}{\overset{N}{\diagdown}} + C_4H_9NH_2 \rightarrow R-\overset{H}{\underset{}{N}}-\underset{\underset{O}{\|}}{C}-\overset{H}{\underset{}{N}}C_4H_9 + N_2 \tag{40}$$

The excess of n-butylamine is then back-titrated with standard acid (see p. 297).

B. Determination of Cyano Groups

1. Methods Depending on Conversion to Metal Cyanides. Organic cyanides as a rule do not undergo hydrolysis to form hydrogen cyanide. There are exceptions, however. For instance, tetracyanoethylene and acyl cyanides, respectively, react with water in the following manner:

$$(CN)_2C{=}C(CN)_2 + H_2O \rightarrow (CN)_2C{=}C\overset{\diagup CN}{\underset{\diagdown OH}{}} + HCN \tag{41}$$

$$R-\underset{\underset{O}{\|}}{C}-CN + H_2O \rightarrow R-COOH + HCN \tag{42}$$

In this case the cyanide in solution can be determined by titration with standard silver nitrate in the usual way.[152] Modification of the method becomes necessary for other cyano compounds. Thus Berinzaghi[153] recommended a procedure for the microdetermination of the cyano groups in acylated nitriles of aldonic acids as follows. The sample (15 to 25 mg.) is dissolved in 2 ml. of ethanol and treated with 50 mg. of silver nitrate in 2 ml. of concentrated ammonium hydroxide. The reaction mixture is allowed to stand for 24 hours before acidification with nitric acid. The silver cyanide precipitate is filtered off, washed with ethanol, dried at 90 to 100°C and weighed.

Berther and co-workers[154] proposed a method to determine cyano groups in cyanohydrins by reacting the latter with nickel cyanide complex

[152] See, for example, A. A. Benedetti-Pichler, *Essentials of Quantitative Analysis,* Ronald Press, New York, 1956, p. 517; I. M. Kolthoff and E. B. Sandell, *Textbook of Quantitative Inorganic Analysis,* Macmillan, New York, 3rd ed., 1952, p. 458.

[153] B. Berinzaghi, *An. Assoc. Quim. Argentina,* **44,** 120 (1956).

[154] C. Berther, K. Kreis, and O. Bochmann, *Z. Anal. Chem.,* **169,** 184 (1959).

$[\text{Ni(CN)}_4]^{-2}$. The excess of nickel ions is determined by titration with $0.1M$ EDTA, using Murexide as the indicator.

2. *Methods Depending on Acidimetry or Alkalimetry.* A macro method presented by Whitehurst and Johnson[155] for the determination of simple aliphatic nitriles involves the reaction with alkaline peroxide. The sample is treated with hydrogen peroxide and a known amount of $1N$ potassium hydroxide. The following reactions probably take place:

$$\text{RCN} + 2\text{H}_2\text{O}_2 \rightarrow \text{RC}\underset{\text{NH}_2}{\overset{\text{O}}{\diagup}} + \text{H}_2\text{O} + \text{O}_2 \tag{43}$$

$$\text{R--C}\underset{\text{NH}_2}{\overset{\text{O}}{\diagup}} + \text{KOH} \rightarrow \text{R--C}\underset{\text{OK}}{\overset{\text{O}}{\diagup}} + \text{NH}_3 \tag{44}$$

The reaction mixture is concentrated to a small volume by distilling with a fractionating column. The residual potassium hydroxide is determined by titration with $0.5N$ sulfuric acid using phenolphthalein as indicator. Benzonitrile, acrylonitrile, and ethylene cyanohydrin give high results. This method is not suitable for conversion to the micro scale.

Terentev and co-workers[156] proposed a micro method for the analysis of acrylonitrile which is dependent on the titration of the alkali released by its reaction with sodium sulfite. The sample (15 to 20 mg.) is weighed in a sealed ampoule and placed in a 100 ml. flask. Three ml. of dioxane and 5 ml. of $0.5N$ sodium sulfite are introduced and the ampoule is broken inside the liquid. After mixing, the solution is titrated with $0.05N$ sulfuric acid using a mixed indicator containing alizarin yellow and thymolphthalein.

3. *Method Based on Aquametry.* Mitchell and Hawkins[157] described a macro method for determining nitrile based on the measurement of the amount of water consumed in the hydrolysis of the cyano function to the amide:

$$\text{R--CN} + \text{H}_2\text{O} \rightarrow \text{R--C}\underset{\text{NH}_2}{\overset{\text{O}}{\diagup}} \tag{45}$$

The sample, dissolved in glacial acetic acid, is treated with a known amount

[155] D. H. Whitehurst, and J. B. Johnson, *Anal. Chem.*, **30**, 1332 (1958).

[156] A. P. Terentev, S. I. Obtemperanskaya, and M. M. Buzlanova, *Vestn. Moskov Univ.*, **1956**, 187.

[157] J. Mitchell, Jr., and W. Hawkins, *J. Am. Chem. Soc.*, **67**, 777 (1946).

of water and some boron trifluoride which acts as the catalyst. Heating is necessary to drive the reaction to completion. The unreacted water is then determined by titration with the Karl Fischer reagent (see p. 472).

Like other methods based on aquametry, this procedure is difficult to adapt to the 0.1 meq. scale. Furthermore, complications may be encountered here as the resulting amide may be partially hydrolyzed to form the corresponding acid unless the experimental conditions are carefully controlled.

C. Determination of Isocyano Groups.   There is no published micro method for the determination of the isocyano function. The following three methods may be applicable, but they have not been evaluated.

1. Use of Oxalic Acid.   Isonitriles react with a concentrated solution of oxalic acid in the cold to yield carbon dioxide and carbon monoxide according to the following equation:[158]

$$4R-NC + 3 \begin{array}{c} COOH \\ | \\ COOH \end{array} + H_2O \rightarrow 4R-\overset{H}{\underset{|}{N}}-\overset{H}{\underset{|}{C}}=O + 3CO + 3CO_2 \qquad (46)$$

Either the carbon dioxide or carbon monoxide can be estimated as a measure of the isocyano group. It should be noted that spontaneous decomposition of oxalic acid also leads to the formation of these two gases.

2. Method Depending on Hydrolysis.   Unlike cyanides, the isocyanides are not affected by alkalies. On the other hand, they are easily decomposed by mineral acids to amines and formic acid.[159]

$$R-NC + HCl + 2H_2O \rightarrow R-NH_3^+Cl^- + HCOOH \qquad (47)$$

Therefore the analysis can be completed by the determination of the amine (see p. 229).

3. Use of Hypobromite.   According to Guillemard,[160] alkyl isocyanides are decomposed by hypobromite to liberate carbon dioxide and nitrogen through the following sequence of reactions:

$$R-NC + NaOBr + H_2O \rightarrow R-NH_2 + CO_2 + NaBr \qquad (48)$$

$$2R-NH_2 + 3NaOBr \rightarrow 2ROH + N_2 + 3NaBr + H_2O \qquad (49)$$

It is reported that the determination of the isocyano group can be accomplished by measuring the carbon dioxide or nitrogen evolved. This method

[158] H. Guillemard, *Ann. Chim. Phys.*, [8] **14,** 330 (1908).

[159] P. Karrer, *Organic Chemistry*, 4th Eng. ed., Elsevier, Amsterdam, 1950, p. 189.

[160] H. Guillemard, *Ann. Chim. Phys.*, [8] **14,** 327 (1908).

is not applicable to aromatic isocyanides, since aromatic amines will be oxidized by hypobromite to nonidentifiable products.

D. Miscellaneous Methods for Azides, Nitriles, and Isonitriles

1. Determination of Nitrogen in Azides, Nitriles and Isonitriles by the Kjeldahl Method. As mentioned in Section III-F-4, the Kjeldahl procedure is used to determine amino nitrogen. The Kjeldahl method can be applied to the analysis of azides since these compounds can be converted to isocyanates which in turn are hydrolyzed to amines:

$$R—CN_3 \rightarrow RNCO \rightarrow RNH_2 \rightarrow (NH_4)_2SO_4 \tag{50}$$

It should be noted that two nitrogen atoms are removed as nitrogen gas during molecular rearrangement (eq. 39). Thus Pepkowitz[161] reported the recovery of one third of the nitrogen in azides when these compounds are digested with sodium thiosulfate and selenium oxychloride in sulfuric acid.

The cyano and isocyano functions are converted to the amino group either by hydrolysis (eqs. 45 and 47) or by reduction (eqs. 51 and 52):

$$R—CN + 4[H] \rightarrow RCH_2NH_2 \tag{51}$$

$$R—NC + 4[H] \rightarrow R—NH—CH_3 \tag{52}$$

Therefore the Kjeldahl method is applicable provided that the conversions are quantitative. Several papers have appeared in which the Kjeldahl procedure is proposed for the determination of nitriles. Vanetten and Wiele[162] hydrolyzed the sample by heating it with 90% sulfuric acid in a sealed tube prior to digestion. Konovalov[163] decomposed the nitrile by digesting it in the presence of mercuric oxide, selenium, and potassium sulfate. Hillenbrand and Pentz[164] boiled the sample with concentrated sulfuric acid for 30 to 60 minutes and then added hydrogen peroxide and continued heating. Rose and Ziliotto[165] recommended hydrogen iodide reduction before the Kjeldahl digestion. The sample is heated with potassium iodide and concentrated sulfuric acid on a steam bath for 45 minutes. Then potassium sulfate, copper sulfate, and selenium are added and the conventional Kjeldahl procedure is followed.

[161] L. P. Pepkowitz, *Anal. Chem.*, **24**, 900 (1952).

[162] C. H. Van Etten and M. B. Wiele, *Anal. Chem.*, **23**, 1338 (1951).

[163] A. Konovalov, *Ind. Chim. Belge*, **18**, 329 (1953).

[164] E. F. Hillenbrand, Jr., and C. A. Pentz, in *Organic Analysis*, Vol. 3, Interscience, New York, 1956, p. 138.

[165] E. L. Rose and H. Ziliotto, *Ind. Eng. Chem., Anal. Ed.*, **17**, 211 (1945).

In a study of various types of cyano compounds, Ma and Arnowich[166] found that most nitriles can be analyzed by the regular micro-Kjeldahl procedure[167] without modification. Some cyano compounds give low results, and the nitrogen values are not increased by prior reduction. Thus it appears that the incomplete recovery of nitrogen is due to partial cleavage of the C—N bond to form hydrogen cyanide which escapes as a gas. Therefore, when a low result is suspected, the nitrogen content of the sample should be checked by the micro-Dumas method instead of modifying the Kjeldahl procedure.

2. Determination of Cyano and Isocyano Groups by Means of Grignard Reagent. The cyano and isocyano functions, respectively, react with methyl magnesium iodide in the following manner:

$$R—CN + CH_3MgI \rightarrow R—\underset{\underset{CH_3}{|}}{C}=N—MgI \tag{53}$$

$$R—NC + CH_3MgI \rightarrow R—N=\underset{\underset{CH_3}{|}}{C}—MgI \tag{54}$$

Niederl and Niederl[168] and also Stone[169] advocated the application of these reactions to the determination of nitriles and isocyanides. The sample is treated with a known amount of the Grignard reagent. After the reaction is completed, the residual methyl magnesium iodide is determined gasometrically by the introduction of aniline (see p. 420).

No report of the accuracy of the method could be found in the literature. It should be noted that the Grignard reaction is usually not clear-cut.[170] Hence the addition of the Grignard reagent to the cyano and isocyano functions, respectively, may not be quantitative. Furthermore, since the Grignard reagent is sensitive to oxygen, carbon dioxide and moisture, it is difficult to maintain the concentration of an ether solution of methyl magnesium iodide for the purpose of microanalysis.

3. Determination of Azides by Titanous Chloride Reduction. Rathsburg[171] reported that picric acid azide is reduced by titanous chloride according to equation 55:

[166] T. S. Ma, and B. Arnowich, unpublished work.

[167] T. S. Ma, and G. Zuazaga, *Ind. Eng. Chem., Anal. Ed.*, **14**, 282 (1942).

[168] J. B. Niederl and V. Niederl, *Organic Quantitative Microanalysis*, 2nd ed., John Wiley and Sons, New York, 1942, p. 263.

[169] K. G. Stone, *Determination of Organic Compounds*, McGraw-Hill, New York, 1956, p. 102.

[170] M. S. Kharasch and O. Reinmuth, *The Grignard Reaction*, Prentice-Hall, Inc., Englewood Cliffs, N.J., 1954.

[171] H. Rathsburg, *Berichte*, **54**, 3183 (1921).

$$O_2N-\underset{NO_2}{\overset{NO_2}{\bigcirc}}-N_3 + 20TiCl_3 + 20HCl \rightarrow$$

$$H_2N-\underset{NH_2}{\overset{NH_2}{\bigcirc}}-N{=}N-NH_2 + 20TiCl_4 + 6H_2O \quad (55)$$

It should be noted that both the nitro and the azide functions in the compound are affected. Whether the presence of the nitro group is necessary for the application of titanous chloride to the determination of azides (as in the determination of arylhydrazines, Section IX-D) has not been investigated. The reader is referred to experiment 37 for the micro procedure of titanous chloride reduction.

E. Colorimetric Methods for Nitriles. There are no general colorimetric methods for the determination of the azido, cyano, and isocyano functions. Czerwinski[172] described a colorimetric method for determining the nitrile of isonicotinic acid, which gives a red color on treatment with sodium nitroprusside in sodium hydroxide solution. The intensity of the solution is measured at 480 mμ. A light color is also developed with nicotinonitrile.

Soloway and Lipschitz[173] suggested a colorimetric test for nitriles that is based on the formation of the ferric hydroxamates of the corresponding carboxylic acids. This test can be utilized for quantitative analysis (see Chapter 7, Section I-F).

Certain cyano compounds such as tetracyanoethylene develop intense color upon reacting with aromatic nucleus.[174] This reaction may be applied to the colorimetric determination of the cyano compounds.

F. Physical Methods for Azido and Cyano Groups. The infrared spectra of organic azides were studied by Lieber and co-workers,[175] who reported that the CN_3 vibration at 2070 to 2080 cm^{-1} is practically independent of the environmental structure. This may serve as a guide for the determination of azides by infrared spectroscopy.

[172] W. Czerwinski, *Chem. Anal. Warsaw*, **3**, 47 (1958).

[173] S. Soloway and A. Lipschitz, *Anal. Chem.*, **24**, 898 (1952).

[174] D. S. Tarbell and T. Huang, *J. Org. Chem.*, **24**, 887 (1959).

[175] E. Lieber, C. N. R. Rao, T. S. Chao, and C. W. W. Hoffman, *Anal. Chem.*, **29**, 916 (1957).

Polarographic reduction of the cyano group was reported by Bobrova and Matveeva-Kudasheva.[176] These workers claimed that the value of the limiting diffusion current is directly proportional to the concentration of the nitrile in the solution.

VI. The Azo, Diazo, Azoxy, and Hydrazo Functions

A. General. The common characteristic of azo, diazo, azoxy, and hydrazo functions is a pair of nitrogen atoms linked to each other in the organic molecule. In azo compounds the nitrogen atoms are connected to two separate carbon skeletons as shown in azobenzene, $C_6H_5—N=N—C_6H_5$. On the other hand, diazo compounds have only one carbon skeleton joined to the nitrogen function, as shown in diazomethane, benzenediazonium chloride, and p-diazobenzene sulfonic acid.

Diazomethane   Benzenediazonium chloride p-Diazobenzenesulfonic acid

$C_6H_5—N_2^+Cl^-$

The azoxy function has an oxygen atom attached to the nitrogen pair and is represented by such structures as: $—N=N—$, $—N=\overset{+}{N}—$, and

$—N———N—$, with a carbon skeleton on each nitrogen atom. The hydrazo function consists of two nitrogen atoms, each of which is joined to a hydrogen and a carbon skeleton, as shown in hydrazobenzene:

$$C_6H_5—\overset{\overset{H}{|}}{N}—\overset{\overset{H}{|}}{N}—C_6H_5$$

B. Determination of Azo Groups

1. Reduction by Means of Titanous or Chromous Ions. Titanous chloride reduction is the most common method for determining azo groups. The use

[176] M. I. Bobrova and A. N. Matveeva-Kudasheva, *Zhur. Obshch. Khim.*, **28**, 2929 (1958).

of chromous chloride as reducing agent also has been suggested.[177] The azo function is converted to two amino groups in the course of reduction. Thus one equivalent of the azo function, say in azobenzene, consumes four moles of titanous ion:

$$R—N=N—R' + 4Ti^{+3} + 4H^+ \rightarrow R—NH_2 + R'NH_2 + 4Ti^{+4} \qquad (56)$$

The macro method for the determination of azo groups by titanous chloride titration was first described by Knecht and Hibbert.[178] A large excess of standardized titanous chloride solution is added to the sample dissolved in water or alcohol, and the reaction mixture is heated with hydrochloric acid under a stream of carbon dioxide. After the reduction is complete, the residual titanous ion is determined by titration with standard ferric alum solution using ammonium thiocyanate as the indicator. In a procedure using 5 meq. samples, Siggia[179] recommended glacial acetic acid as solvent for water-insoluble compounds and the incorporation of hydrofluoric acid in the reaction mixture. The micro method (0.1 meq.) developed by Earley and Ma[180] is given in experiment 38. The azo compound is dissolved in water or 95% ethanol, and sodium acetate is added as a buffer. The reduction with $0.03N$ titanous chloride is carried out in hydrochloric acid under an atmosphere of nitrogen, and the excess of reagent is determined by titration with $0.025N$ ferric alum solution.

It should be noted that the stoichiometry given in equation 56 holds only for ideal situations. The reduction of the azo function by means of titanous ions is a complicated process and has been the subject of investigation by various workers. Fainer and co-workers[181] used titanous sulfate in sulfuric acid as the reducing agent for chlorinated azobenzenes and found that the o,o'- and m,m'-dichloro compounds consume only 2 moles of reagent. The products isolated from the reduction indicate the occurrence of benzidine rearrangement. In contrast, the reduction of p,p-dichlorazobenzene proceeds normally. According to Veibel,[182] benzidine rearrangement in the titration of azobenzene with titanous chloride occurs even in nearly neutral solutions. Blocking of p-positions by substituents prevents the benzidine rearrangement, but less than 4 equivalents of titanous chloride is consumed. The rate of titration may influence the number of equivalents of reagent

[177] A. P. Terentev and G. S. Goryacheva, *Uchemie Zapiski*, **3**, 227 (1934).

[178] E. Knecht and E. Hibbert, *Berichte*, **40**, 381 (1907). E. Knecht, *New Reduction Methods in Volumetric Analysis*, Longmans, Green and Co., New York, 1925.

[179] S. Siggia, *Quantitative Organic Analysis Via Functional Groups*, 2nd ed., John Wiley and Sons, New York, 1954, p. 130.

[180] J. V. Earley and T. S. Ma, *Mikrochim. Acta*, **1960**, 685.

[181] P. Fainer, J. L. Myers, and K. F. Keirkstead, *Can. J. Chem.*, **30**, 498 (1952).

[182] S. Veibel, *Can. J. Chem.*, **32**, 638 (1954).

used. Earley and Ma[180] tested the micro procedure with azobenzene and a number of p-substituted azo compounds. It was found that the former consumes 2 equivalents of titanous chloride:

$$C_6H_5-N{=}N-C_6H_5 + 2TiCl_3 + 2HCl \rightarrow H_2NC_6H_4-C_6H_4NH_2 + 2TiCl_4 \quad (57)$$

while the latter require 4 equivalents:

$$X{-}\langle\bigcirc\rangle{-}N{=}N{-}\langle\bigcirc\rangle + 4TiCl_3 + 4HCl \rightarrow$$

$$X{-}\langle\bigcirc\rangle{-}NH_2 + \langle\bigcirc\rangle{-}NH_2 + 4TiCl_4 \quad (58)$$

$$X = NH_2, N(CH_3)_2, OH, NO_2$$

The kinetics of the reduction of some azo compounds with titanous chloride was investigated by Large, Stubbs, and Hinshelwood.[183] In aqueous alcohol the reaction is first-order with respect to the azo compound and to titanous chloride. The influence of substituents is complex. *Trans*-azobenzene and *trans*-4-amino azobenzene are reduced by titanous chloride in a second-order reaction; the corresponding *cis*-compounds are much more rapidly reduced. The 4-amino-compound yields aniline and *p*-phenylenediamine. Azobenzene yields 16% aniline and 84% benzidine, these proportions being nearly independent of the titanous chloride or acid concentrations. The rate increases very rapidly at high acid concentrations.

The choice of buffer appears to be important in the determination of azo groups. Thus Evenson and Nagel[184] reported that sodium tartrate, sodium bitartrate, and Rochelle salt are the best buffers for the reduction of azo colors on the macro scale. Tartrate must be present for direct titration with standard titanous chloride to the yellow endpoint, but absent from the excess reagent and back-titration procedure.

2. Gasometric Methods. According to Ziegler and co-workers[185] many aliphatic azo compounds liberate nitrogen quantitatively on heating by themselves or in a suitable solvent. The following reaction probably takes place:

$$R-N{=}N-R' \rightarrow N_2 + R-R' \quad (59)$$

Thus the amount of nitrogen collected serves as a direct measure of the azo function.

[183] N. R. Large, F. J. Stubbs, and C. N. Hinshelwood, *J. Chem. Soc.*, **1954**, 2736; N. R. Large and C. N. Hinshelwood, *J. Chem. Soc.*, **1956**, 620.

[184] O. L. Evenson and R. H. Nagel, *Ind. Eng. Chem., Anal. Ed.*, **3**, 167 (1931); O. L. Evenson, *J. Assoc. Official Agr. Chemists*, **27**, 370 (1944).

[185] K. Ziegler, W. Deparade, and W. Meye, *Annalen*, **567**, 141 (1950).

Another gasometric method, proposed by Willstätter and Cramer[186] for the determination of aromatic azo compounds on the macro scale involves the reduction of the azo group by means of phenylhydrazine:

$$\text{Ar---N=N---Ar} + C_6H_5NH\text{---}NH_2 \rightarrow N_2 + C_6H_6 + \text{Ar---}\overset{\displaystyle H}{\underset{\displaystyle |}{N}}\text{---}\overset{\displaystyle H}{\underset{\displaystyle |}{N}}\text{---Ar} \qquad (60)$$

It should be noted that in this case the nitrogen comes from the reagent and not the azo group. Therefore, complication may arise if the azo compound is unstable or if other oxidant is present.

C. Determination of Diazo Groups

1. Gasometric Methods.   Since diazo compounds can be decomposed readily to liberate nitrogen, gasometric methods are usually recommended for the determination of the diazo function. Aliphatic diazo compounds are treated with dilute sulfuric acid, whereupon the following reaction occurs:

$$\text{R---}\overset{\displaystyle H}{\underset{}{C}}\text{N}_2 + H_2SO_4 \rightarrow \text{R---}\overset{\displaystyle H}{\underset{\displaystyle H}{C}}\text{---O---SO}_3H + N_2 \qquad (61)$$

Macro procedures using approximately 1 gram of material were described by Curtius,[187] Staudinger and Gaule,[188] and Nicolas and Lampei.[189] The reaction is carried out in an atmosphere of carbon dioxide and the nitrogen evolved is swept into the nitrometer and measured. This determination can be adapted to the micro scale by employing the hydrazino apparatus of Ma and Mattei[190] (see Fig. 8.11 in Section IX-B).

Quantitative liberation of nitrogen from aromatic diazo compounds and diazonium salts is conducted in the presence of a catalyst or reducing agent to prevent side reactions. Thus in the macro methods proposed by Hulle[191] and Siggia[192] the diazonium salt is decomposed by heating with cuprous chloride in hydrochloric acid:

[186] R. Willstätter and C. Cramer, *Berichte*, **43**, 2979 (1910).

[187] T. Curtius, *J. Prakt. Chem.*, [2] **38**, 417 (1888).

[188] H. Staudinger and A. Gaule, *Berichte*, **49**, 1897 (1916).

[189] L. Nicolas and P. Lampei, *Chim. Anal.*, **36**, 238 (1954).

[190] T. S. Ma and F. Mattei, unpublished work; see F. Mattei, *Master's Thesis, Brooklyn College*, 1960.

[191] E. V. Hulle, in Houben-Weyl-Müller: *Methoden der organischen Chemie*, 4th ed., Vol. 2, Theime, Stuttgart, 1953, p. 700.

[192] S. Siggia, see footnote 179, p. 124.

$$ArN_2^+Cl^- \cdot Cu_2Cl_2 \rightarrow N_2 + ArCl + Cu_2Cl_2 \tag{62}$$

Gasser[193] recommended potassium iodide as the reagent:

$$Ar\text{---}N\text{=}N\text{---}Cl + KI \rightarrow N_2 + Ar\text{---}I + KCl \tag{63}$$

Rathsburg[194] and Shaefer and Becker[195] advocated the use of titanous chloride:

$$Ar\text{---}N\text{=}N\text{---}Cl + 2TiCl_3 + HCl \rightarrow N_2 + Ar\text{---}H + 2TiCl_4 \tag{64}$$

All these determinations can be carried out on the micro scale using the hydrazino apparatus mentioned previously.

Pierce and Rising[196] described a micro procedure to determine diazo amino compounds in which the sample is boiled with hydrochloric acid, and the nitrogen produced is collected in a microazotometer. The reaction is represented in equation 65:

$$\overset{\overset{\displaystyle H}{|}}{R\text{---}N\text{=}N\text{---}N}\text{---}R' + HCl + H_2O \rightarrow N_2 + R\text{---}OH + R'NH_3Cl \tag{65}$$

2. Iodometric Methods. Aldrovandi and DeLorenzi[197] proposed an iodometric method for determining diazo compounds that is dependent on the fact that hydriodic acid acts as reducing agent to generate an equivalent of iodine:

$$Ar\text{---}N\text{=}N^+ + 2HI \rightarrow N_2 + Ar\text{---}H + H^+ + I_2 \tag{66}$$

The sample (20 to 30 mg.) is mixed with 1 ml. of 57% hydriodic acid in a sealed tube, which is then heated at 100° to 300°C for a certain length of time. When cooled, the tube is opened and the reaction mixture is diluted with water. The iodine liberated is determined by titration with $0.1N$ sodium thiosulfate using starch as indicator.

A macro method for determining aliphatic diazo esters and ketones was described by Curtius[198] and is based on the reaction of iodine:

$$N_2CH\text{---}COOR + I_2 \rightarrow I_2CH\text{---}COOR + N_2 \tag{67}$$

$$N_2CH\text{---}\overset{\overset{\displaystyle}{\|}}{\underset{\underset{\displaystyle O}{}}{C}}\text{---}R + I_2 \rightarrow I_2CH\text{---}C\overset{\nearrow O}{\searrow_R} + N_2 \tag{68}$$

[193] F. Gasser, *Chem. Zt.*, **51**, 206 (1950).

[194] H. Rathsburg, *Berichte*, **54**, 3183 (1921).

[195] W. E. Shaefer and W. W. Becker, *Anal. Chem.*, **19**, 307 (1947).

[196] A. E. Pierce and M. M. Rising, *J. Am. Chem. Soc.*, **58**, 1363 (1936).

[197] R. Aldrovandi and F. DeLorenzi, *Ann. Chim. Rome*, **42**, 298 (1952).

[198] T. Curtius, *J. Prakt. Chem.*, [2] **38**, 422 (1888).

An ethereal solution containing a known amount of iodine is used as the reagent, and the residual iodine is determined by careful evaporation of the solution and weighing. This method is not suitable for conversion to the micro scale.

D. Special Methods for Aryl Diazonium Salts

1. Use of Titanous or Chromous Ions. Knecht and Thompson[199] devised a macro titrimetric method for the determination of benzene diazonium chloride by reduction with titanous chloride. The reaction was postulated as follows:

$$2C_6H_5-N{=}N-Cl + 4TiCl_3 + 2HCl \rightarrow C_6H_5-N{=}N-N-C_6H_5 + 4TiCl_4 \quad (69)$$
$$\underset{NH_2}{\mid}$$

The sample is titrated with standard titanous chloride using H acid as the external indicator. The reaction must be carried out in dilute hydrochloric acid, since it does not occur in moderately concentrated acid solutions. Earley and Ma[180] developed a micro method in which the acidity of the reaction mixture is controlled by sodium acetate buffer. The aryl diazonium salt is treated with a known amount of $0.03N$ titanous chloride, and the excess of reagent is determined by back-titration with standard ferric-ammonium sulfate in the presence of ammonium thiocyanate, thus eliminating the use of an external indicator. The detailed procedure is found in experiment 38.

Chromous chloride was recommended by Bottei and Furman[200] for the analysis of aryl diazonium compounds. The reduction product is reported to be the corresponding aryl hydrazine:

$$Ar-N{=}N-Cl + 4CrCl_2 + 4HCl \rightarrow Ar-NH-NH_2 \cdot HCl + 4CrCl_3 \quad (70)$$

The sample is dissolved in either cold water or $0.05N$ hydrochloric acid. After the sample is placed in the ice bath and deaerated with carbon dioxide, an excess of standardized chromous chloride solution is added. The residual chromous ions are then back-titrated with ferric alum potentiometrically.

2. Methods Depending on Coupling Reaction. A common industrial method[191,201] for the analysis of aryl diazonium salts is based on the coupling reaction with 2,4-toluylenediamine (eq. 71) in acetic acid solution, or with a phenol in alkali medium.

[199] E. Knecht and L. Thompson, *J. Soc. Dyers Colourists*, **36**, 215 (1920).

[200] R. S. Bottei and N. H. Furman, *Anal. Chem.*, **29**, 119 (1957).

[201] S. Siggia, see footnote 179, p. 168.

$$\text{Ar—N=N}^+ + \text{H—}\underset{\text{NH}_2}{\overset{\text{CH}_3}{\bigcirc}}\text{—NH}_2 \rightarrow \text{Ar—N=N—}\underset{\text{NH}_2}{\overset{\text{CH}_3}{\bigcirc}}\text{—NH}_2 + \text{H}^+ \qquad (71)$$

The excess of reagent is determined by titration with a standard solution of p-toluene diazonium chloride.[191] It should be noted that 3 to 5 meq. of the diazonium compound is required in these methods, and they are not suitable for conversion to the 0.1 meq. scale. In the first place, since the product of coupling is highly colored, the endpoint has to be located by means of an external indicator. Secondly, the standardized p-toluene diazonium chloride solution is very unstable; a $0.1M$ solution of the diazonium salt deteriorates in a few hours.

E. Special Method for Diazomethane.   A convenient micro method for determining diazomethane was described by Roper and Ma.[202] It is based on acidimetry. A known amount of benzoic acid is added to the solution containing diazomethane, whereupon the acid is esterified and nitrogen is evolved:

$$\text{CH}_2\text{N}_2 + \text{C}_6\text{H}_5\text{COOH} \rightarrow \text{C}_6\text{H}_5\text{COOCH}_3 + \text{N}_2 \qquad (72)$$

The excess of benzoic acid is then determined by titration with $0.01N$ sodium hydroxide to the endpoint of phenolphthalein.

F. Bromination Method for Aromatic Diazo Compounds. Hulle[203] presented a macro method for determining certain aromatic diazo compounds by bromination. Thus diazoaminobenzene is reported to consume 3 moles of bromine (from bromide-bromate mixture):

$$\bigcirc\text{—N=N—NH—}\bigcirc + 3\text{Br}_2 + \text{HCl} \rightarrow$$

$$\bigcirc\text{—N=N—Cl} + \text{Br—}\underset{\text{Br}}{\overset{\text{Br}}{\bigcirc}}\text{—NH}_2 + 3\text{HBr} \qquad (73)$$

This method can be adapted to the micro scale. It should be noted, however, that the stoichiometry shown in equation 73 is correct only when aniline is produced from the diazoaminobenzene and no phenol is formed from the benzene diazonium chloride. Since diazonium salts decompose to phenols

[202] R. Roper and T. S. Ma, *Microchem. J.*, **1**, 247 (1957).
[203] E. V. Hulle, see footnote 191, p. 701.

readily at elevated temperatures, the determinations should be carried out in an ice bath.

G. Determination of Azoxy Groups. The determination of azoxy groups has not been extensively investigated. A macro method based on reduction with titanous chloride was suggested by Hulle,[204] who recommended the same procedure for both the nitro and azoxy functions. Therefore it can be adapted to the micro scale (see Section XI-B). Each azoxy function consumes 6 moles of titanous chloride:

$$R—N \overline{} N—R' + 6TiCl_3 + 6HCl \rightarrow RNH_2 + R'NH_2 + 6TiCl_4 + H_2O \quad (74)$$

$$\diagdown O \diagup$$

H. Determination of Hydrazo Groups

1. By Titanous Chloride Reduction. According to Hulle,[204] hydrazo groups are reduced by titanous chloride under the same conditions as for nitro groups. Two moles of titanous chloride are consumed for each hydrazo function:

$$\begin{array}{cc} H & H \\ | & | \\ R—N—N—R' \end{array} + 2TiCl_3 + 2HCl \rightarrow RNH_2 + R'NH_2 + 2TiCl_4 \quad (75)$$

The reader is referred to Section XI-B for the micro procedure. It should be remembered that hydrazobenzene undergoes molecular rearrangement in acid solution to benzidine, which is not reduced by titanous chloride.[180]

2. By Permanganate Oxidation. Reiss[205] proposed a method to determine the hydrazo function which is not affected by the presence of other nitrogen functions—azo, azoxy, nitroso, nitro—that are reducible by titanous ions. The hydrazo compound is dissolved in xylene and treated with a known amount of standard potassium permanganate, mixed with sodium hydroxide. The hydrazo group is oxidized to the azo group as depicted in equation 76:

$$3C_6H_5—NH—NH—C_6H_5 + 2KMnO_4 \rightarrow$$
$$3C_6H_5—N{=}N—C_6H_5 + 2MnO_2 + 2KOH + 2H_2O \quad (76)$$

After agitation for 10 minutes, potassium iodide and sulfuric acid are introduced. The iodine liberated by the residual permanganate is determined by titration with standard sodium thiosulfate. Samples containing 0.1 meq. of the hydrazo group were used by this investigator, but the standard solutions of permanganate and thiosulfate were both $0.1N$.

[204] E. V. Hulle, see footnote 191, p. 705.
[205] R. Reiss, *Z. Anal. Chem.*, **164**, 402 (1958).

I. Miscellaneous Methods for Azo, Diazo, Azoxy, and Hydrazo Functions

1. Use of the Modified Kjeldahl Method. Nitrogen in N—N functions cannot be quantitatively converted to ammonia by the regular Kjeldahl procedure (see Section III-F-4). Since the N—N functions can be reduced to yield amines, however, numerous publications have appeared that propose modification of the Kjeldahl method to determine the nitrogen contents in azo, diazo, azoxy, and hydrazo functions. The detailed procedure of a micro method[206] is given in experiment 35. The sample is dissolved in acetic acid and the reduction is effected slowly by means of nascent hydrogen generated from zinc powder and hydrochloric acid, as represented in equations 77 and 78:

$$R-N=N-R + 4[H] \rightarrow 2R-NH_2 \tag{77}$$

$$R-N\overset{\diagdown \diagup}{\underset{O}{\qquad}}N-R + 6[H] \rightarrow 2R-NH_2 + H_2O \tag{78}$$

The sulfuric acid digestion is carried out after the reduction, followed by the regular Kjeldahl technique. Other suggested inorganic reducing media include zinc and hydrochloric acid in aqueous[207] or formic acid[207a] solution, zinc and iron with hydrochloric acid,[208] copper powder and sulfuric acid,[209] hydriodic acid,[210] sodium hydrosulfite,[211] and titanous chloride.[212] Addition of carbohydrates, such as dextrose[213] and cotton cellulose,[214] to the concentrated sulfuric acid digestion mixture was reported to be satisfactory for azo compounds. However, the use of a large amount of organic reagent in the digestion tends to weaken the sulfuric acid.

It should be noted that N—N functions are liable to decompose by heat with the elimination of nitrogen gas. As the latter is not reducible under the experimental conditions, low nitrogen values will be obtained. It was found[215] that even for a relatively stable compound like azobenzene, erratic results were obtained when the reduction in acetic acid solution with zinc

[206] T. S. Ma, R. E. Lang, and J. D. McKinley, Jr., *Mikrochim. Acta*, **1957**, 368.

[207] C. Flamand and B. Prager, *Berichte*, **38**, 559 (1905).

[207a] W. E. Dickinson, *Anal. Chem.*, **30**, 992 (1958).

[208] A. Steyermark, B. E. McGee, E. A. Bass, and R. R. Kaup, *Anal. Chem.*, **30**, 1561 (1958).

[209] V. I. Kuznetsov, *Zavodskaya Lab.*, **9**, 1039 (1940).

[210] A. Friedrich, E. Kuhass, and R. Schnurch, *Z. Physiol. Chem.*, **216**, 68 (1933).

[211] C. E. Zoltan, F. Kenezler, and I. Gresill, *Magy Kem. Folyoirat*, **47**, 195 (1941).

[212] P. D. Somers, Jr., *Proc. Indiana Acad. Sci.*, **54**, 117 (1945).

[213] R. A. Harte, *Ind. Eng. Chem., Anal. Ed.*, **7**, 432 (1935).

[214] R. V. Bhat, *Proc. Indiana Acad. Sci.*, **134**, 269 (1941).

[215] T. S. Ma and A. T. Spencer, unpublished work.

and hydrochloric acid was not carried out slowly at room temperature.

2. The Phenylmethylpyrazolonesulfonic Acid Method for Azo and Diazo Compounds. Gracher[216] advocated phenylmethylpyrazolonesulfonic acid as the reagent for the determination of azo and diazo groups. It is based on combining the diazo compounds with excess amounts of the sulfonic acid and the subsequent nitroso formation. The endpoint of the reaction is determined either by starch-iodide paper or potentiometrically with smooth platinum electrodes.

3. Colorimetric Methods for Azo, Diazo, Azoxy, and Hydrazo Compounds. A colorimetric method for determining azobenzene[217] consists of nitrating the compound to 4,4'-dinitro-azobenzene which gives intense blue color on treatment with glucose and sodium hydroxide. It should be noted that the color is due to the nitro groups and not the azo function.

Diazonium salts can be determined colorimetrically by the coupling reaction (see Section VI-D-2) in which a suitable dye is produced and measured.[218] Certain stabilized diazonium compounds may be determined by their absorption at 380 mμ in aqueous solution without pretreatment.[219]

Azoxy compounds[220] when treated with 98% sulfuric acid give a dark colored quinoid complex in cold solution or on gentle heating. This reaction has not been applied to quantitative analysis.

Hydrazobenzene was determined colorimetrically[221] by rearrangement to benzidine, which was diazotized and coupled with N-1-naphthylethylenediamine to give the blue dye. This reaction is limited to hydrazo compounds that can undergo molecular rearrangement.

4. Physical Methods for Azo, Diazo, and Hydrazo Groups. Polarographic reduction of azo[222] and hydrazo[223] compounds have been investigated, but procedures for using this technique for quantitative analysis are not available.

Diazo compounds[224] can be analyzed by standard solutions of phenates either by following the reactions of coupling by thermometry or by conductivity. The equivalence point is located by plotting the curve. The results obtained with the diazo derivatives of sulfanilic acid, p-nitroaniline, and benzidine were reported to be within 1% of theory.

[216] F. V. Gracher, *Zavodskaya Lab.*, **11**, 154 (1945); *C.A.*, **40**, 1106 (1946).
[217] M. S. Bukhovskaya, *Org. Chem. Ind.*, *USSR*, **6**, 638 (1939).
[218] L. I. Belenkii and M. E. Kazanskaya, *Tekstil. Prom.*, **12**, 37 (1952).
[219] H. M. Rosenberger and C. J. Shoemaker, *Anal. Chem.*, **31**, 204 (1959).
[220] P. H. Gore and G. K. Hughes, *Anal. Chim. Acta*, **5**, 357 (1951).
[221] M. Vecera and J. Petranek, *Chem. Listy*, **48**, 1351 (1954).
[222] I. Tachi, *Mem. Coll. Agr.*, *Kyoto Imp. Univ.*, **42**, 36 (1938).
[223] C. A. Streuli and W. D. Cooke, *Anal. Chem.*, **26**, 963 (1954).
[224] R. A. Paris and J. Val, *Chim. Anal.*, **34**, 223 (1952).

VII. The Carbonamido, Lactam, and Carbonimido Functions

A. General. The carbonamido, lactam, and carbonimido functions are derivatives of the carboxyl function and amine or ammonia. Carbonamides are represented by the general formula $R—\overset{\|}{\underset{O}{C}}—NR'R''$ and are also known as carboxylic acid amides. Lactams are internal amides with the structure $R—\overset{\lfloor—NH—\rfloor}{C(CH_2)_n}—C{=}O$ (n = 2 to 4). Carbonimides are formed by dicarboxylic acids. Representative compounds containing these functions are shown below.

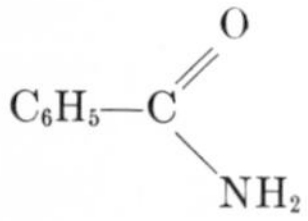

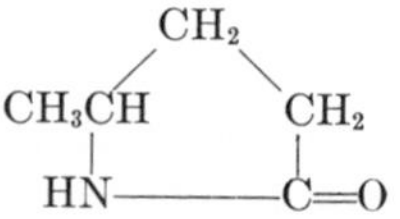

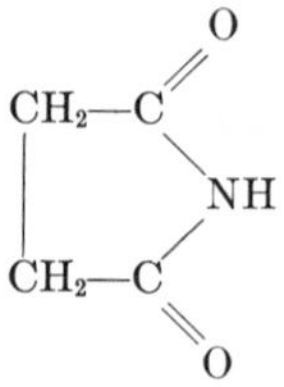

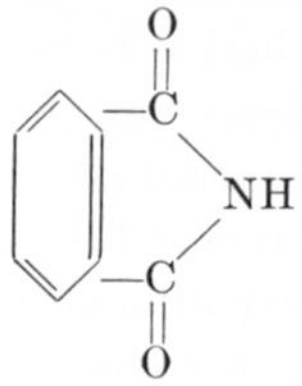

| Benzamide | γ-Valerolactam | Succinimide | Phthalimide |

When the amide contains the $—NH_2$ group, such as benzamide, it is called a primary amide or an unsubstituted amide. Amides carrying $—NHR$ groups have been called secondary amides. This nomenclature may lead to confusion, however, since the same term has been assigned to the formula $(R\overset{O}{\overset{\|}{C}}O)_2NH$, and $(R\overset{O}{\overset{\|}{C}}O)_3N$ is known as the tertiary amide structure.[225]

B. Determination of Carbonamides

1. Methods Applicable to All Types of Carbonamides

A. LITHIUM ALUMINUM HYDRIDE REDUCTION. Carbonamides can be quantitatively reduced to the corresponding amines by means of lithium aluminum hydride:[226]

$$2R—\overset{O}{\overset{\|}{\underset{NH_2}{C}}} + LiAlH_4 \rightarrow 2R—CH_2NH_2 + LiAlO_2 \qquad (79)$$

[225] P. Karrer, *Organic Chemistry*, Elsevier Publishing Co., Amsterdam, 4th Eng. ed., 1950, p. 224.

[226] N. D. Cheronis, *Micro and Semimicro Methods*, Interscience, New York, 1954, p. 254.

This reaction is the basis of a method developed by Siggia and Stahl[227] for determining amides of fatty acids. The resulting amine is steam-distilled from the reaction mixture into a known volume of standard acid, followed by the back-titration of the excess acid. This method can be adapted to the 0.1 meq. scale by using a 30-ml. micro-Kjeldahl digestion flask as the reaction vessel. After the reduction, the reaction mixture is transferred to the Kjeldahl distillation apparatus; the aliphatic amine is steam-distilled into 2% boric acid and determined by titration with 0.01N hydrochloric acid (see experiment 34).

Another approach is to treat the sample with a known amount of lithium aluminum hydride in tetrahydrofuran. The excess of reagent can be determined by measuring the volume of hydrogen produced when the residual lithium aluminum hydride is reacted with n-butyl alcohol. The analysis can be carried out in the gasometric apparatus of Ma and Scheinthal (see Fig. 6.15).[228] It should be noted, however, that a standard solution of lithium aluminum hydride in tetrahydrofuran for microanalysis is very difficult to keep, and the high-vapor pressures of short-chain amines may introduce an error in the determination. Hence this method is useful mostly for the analysis of aryl-substituted amides since the resulting aromatic amines cannot be titrated with standard acid in aqueous solution.

B. SAPONIFICATION BY ALKALI. The carbonamide function consumes one equivalent of alkali on saponification:

$$R{-}C\!\!\underset{NR_2'}{\overset{O}{<}} + KOH \rightarrow R{-}C\!\!\underset{OK}{\overset{O}{<}} + R_2'NH \tag{80}$$

Most carbonamides are difficult to hydrolyze. In the macro procedures the amide is heated with a known amount of 0.5 to 1N potassium hydroxide in ethanol or ethylene glycol under reflux for several hours. The excess of alkali is then back-titrated with standard acid. Hillenbrand and Pentz[229] recommended 0.5N hydrochloric acid as the titrant and bromophenol blue or thymol blue as the indicator, whereas Ioffe and Sergeeva[230] advocated 0.5N ethanolic acetic acid and thymolphthalein respectively. Titration of the residual alkali with a weak acid eliminates the interference of the amine present in the reaction mixture.

[227] S. Siggia and C. R. Stahl, *Anal. Chem.*, **27**, 550 (1955).

[228] T. S. Ma and B. Scheinthal, unpublished work; see B. Scheinthal, *Master's Thesis, Brooklyn College*, 1961.

[229] E. F. Hillenbrand, Jr., and C. A. Pentz, in *Organic Analysis*, Vol. 3, Interscience, New York, 1956, p. 186.

[230] B. V. Ioffe and Z. I. Sergeeva, *Zhur. Anal. Khim.*, **12**, 540 (1957).

The sealed-tube technique is recommended for determination on the micro scale (see p. 513). A 0.1 meq. sample is heated with 0.3 meq. of alkali in isopropyl alcohol at 150°C for 1 to 2 hours. The excess of alkali is determined by titration with $0.02N$ acetic acid in dioxane.

2. Method Applicable to Primary and Secondary Carbonamides. The hydrogen atom attached to the carbonamide nitrogen is sufficiently reactive to liberate methane on treatment with methyl magnesium iodide:[231]

$$R-C\underset{NH_2}{\overset{O}{\diagup}} + 2CH_3MgI \rightarrow 2CH_4 + 2R-C\underset{N(-MgI)_2}{\overset{O}{\diagup}} \tag{81}$$

$$R-\overset{O}{\overset{\|}{C}}-NHR + CH_3MgI \rightarrow CH_4 + R-\overset{O}{\overset{\|}{C}}-NMgI \tag{82}$$

The determination can be carried out on the 0.1-meq. scale in the active hydrogen apparatus (see Chapter 11, Section III-B-2). It should be noted that elevated temperature is usually needed to complete the reaction.

3. Methods Applicable to Primary Carbonamides

A. HYDROLYSIS TO AMMONIA.   Primary carbonamides are hydrolyzed by heating with concentrated sodium hydroxide to liberate ammonia:[232-234]

$$R-\overset{O}{\overset{\|}{C}}-NH_2 + NaOH \rightarrow R-\overset{O}{\overset{\|}{C}}-ONa + NH_3 \tag{83}$$

The micro procedure given on page 571 may be used; the amide is placed into the ammonia distillation apparatus, 40% sodium hydroxide solution is introduced and the ammonia is steam-distilled, collected in 2% boric acid, and determined by titration with $0.01N$ hydrochloric acid.

Breyhan[235] described a method for determining amide nitrogen in small amounts of dried organic matter as follows. The sample (< 50 mg.) is mixed with 0.7 g. of sodium hydroxide and 0.1 g. of sodium acetate trihydrate in an iron crucible. The crucible is then placed in a flask, which is heated while a current of nitrogen passes through. The ammonia liberated is collected and titrated in the usual manner. The Conway diffusion technique is recommended for the determination of the carbonamide function below the 0.1 meq. scale.[236,237]

[231] W. W. Becker, *Anal. Chem.*, **22**, 185 (1950).

[232] M. Hirai and R. Hayatsu, *J. Pharm. Sci., Japan*, **71**, 765 (1951).

[233] T. Takeuchi, M. Furusawa, and Y. Takayama, *Chem. Soc. Japan, Ind. Chem. Sect.*, **60**, 1448 (1957).

[234] H. Roth and P. Schuster, *Mikrochim. Acta*, **1957**, 837.

[235] T. Breyhan, *Zhur. Anal. Chem.*, **152**, 412 (1956).

[236] H. E. Hallam, *Analyst*, **80**, 552 (1955).

[237] H. Stegemann, *Z. Physiol. Chem.*, **312**, 255 (1958).

B. DEHYDRATION TO NITRILE. Mitchell and Ashby[238] devised a macro method based on the reaction between a primary amide and 3,5-dinitrobenzoyl chloride:

$$R-CONH_2 + \underset{\underset{O_2N}{\bigcirc}\;NO_2}{\overset{COCl}{\bigcirc}} \rightarrow \underset{\underset{O_2N}{\bigcirc}\;NO_2}{\overset{COOH}{\bigcirc}} + HCl + RCN \quad (84)$$

Ten meq. of the amide is heated with 15 ml. of the acid chloride reagent and 5 ml. of pyridine for 0.5 to 1 hour. After cooling, the excess of acid chloride is removed by esterification with 27 ml. of methanol. The 3,5-nitrobenzoic acid and hydrochloric acid in the solution are then determined by titration with $0.5N$ sodium methoxide using phenolphthalein or ethyl bis-2,4-dinitrophenyl acetate as the indicator. This procedure has not been adapted to the micro scale. It should be noted that the validity of this method depends on the difference in the rate of esterification between 3,5-dinitrobenzoyl chloride and 3,5-dinitrobenzoic acid. When 0.1 meq. sample is used, it is not feasible to reduce the amount of reagents a hundredfold. Since hydrochloric acid is present, the chance of esterification of 3,5-dinitrobenzoic acid cannot be ignored.

C. NITROSATION TO CARBOXYLIC ACID. Carbonamides react with nitrous acid to liberate nitrogen and yield the corresponding carboxylic acid:

$$R-C\overset{O}{\underset{NH_2}{\diagdown}} + HONO \rightarrow N_2 + R-C\overset{O}{\underset{OH}{\diagdown}} + H_2O \quad (85)$$

This reaction can be carried out on the 0.1 meq. scale in the primary amino group apparatus[239] (see p. 235). The nitrogen gas is purged into a nitrometer with a current of carbon dioxide and measured.

D. MOLECULAR REARRANGEMENT. Suggestions have been made to apply the Hofmann rearrangement of carbonamides to quantitative analysis:[240]

$$R-\overset{O}{\overset{\|}{C}}-NH_2 \xrightarrow{KOBr} R-\overset{O}{\overset{\|}{C}}-NHBr \xrightarrow{KOH} RNCO \xrightarrow{H_2O} RNH_2 \quad (87)$$

Theoretically, we could determine either the isocyanate or the amine

[238] J. Mitchell, Jr. and C. E. Ashby, *J. Am. Chem. Soc.*, **67**, 161 (1945).

[239] T. S. Ma, M. Gutterson, and M. Monaco, unpublished work; see M. Monaco, *Master's Thesis, Brooklyn College*, 1958.

[240] H. Roth, in Houben-Weyl-Müller: *Methoden der organischen Chemie*, 4th ed., Vol. 2, Thieme, Stuttgart, 1953, p. 530.

formed by a suitable procedure. Unfortunately this reaction seldom gives quantitative yields. Hence it cannot be recommended as a reliable method on the micro scale.

C. Determination of Lactams.   Lactams are hydrolyzed by a strong acid to yield the corresponding amino acids:

$$R{-}C{-}(CH_2)_n{-}C{=}O + H_2O \xrightarrow{H^+} R{-}C{-}(CH_2)_n{-}COOH \qquad (81)$$
$$\underset{\displaystyle \overset{|}{\underline{\hspace{1em}NH\hspace{1em}}}}{} \qquad \underset{\displaystyle \overset{|}{NH_2}}{}$$

Because the amino acid is a weak acid, it can be determined in the presence of the mineral acid by differential titration. Thus Markus and Kayser[241] proposed a macro procedure for determining ε-caprolactam as follows: The sample (0.3 to 1 g.) is heated under reflux in 20 to 30 ml. of $1N$ hydrochloric acid for 4 hours. After cooling, the reaction mixture is titrated potentiometrically with $1N$ sodium hydroxide. The difference between the two observed neutralization points is equivalent to the amount of the lactam originally present. This method can be adapted to the 0.1 meq. scale.

D. Determination of Carbonimides.   There are no specific methods for determining the carbonimide function. Carbonimides can be determined either by lithium aluminum hydride reduction or the Grignard reaction[242] described earlier for the carbonamide function (Section VII-B-1-A and B-2). On the other hand, carbonimides are not determined by the saponification procedure (see Section VII-B-1-B) since these compounds form stable salts with alkalies:

$$\text{(benzene ring)}\overset{-CO}{\underset{-CO}{\diagup}}{>}NH + KOH \rightarrow \text{(benzene ring)}\overset{-CO}{\underset{-CO}{\diagup}}{>}NK + H_2O \qquad (88)$$

$$\overset{CH_2-CO}{\underset{CH_2-CO}{|}}{>}NH + KOH \rightarrow \overset{CH_2-CONH_2}{\underset{CH_2-COOK}{|}} \qquad (89)$$

In fact, some carbonimido functions can be titrated with standard potassium hydroxide on the macro scale. However, the equivalence point is difficult to locate on the 0.1 meq. scale using $0.01N$ potassium hydroxide in aqueous solutions. Hence, nonaqueous titration is recommended (see Section VII-E-2).

[241] L. Markus and A. Kayser, *Magy. Kem. Lapja*, **15**, 86 (1960).
[242] M. Jurecek, *Chem. Listy*, **40**, 239 (1946).

E. Miscellaneous Methods for Amides and Imides

1. Use of the Kjeldahl Method. The nitrogen contents of simple carbonamides and imides can be determined by the regular Kjeldahl procedure for amino nitrogen (see experiment 34) without modification. Polyamides—synthetic (plastics) or natural (proteins)—usually require more drastic treatment to give the maximum yield of ammonia. Strong oxidizing agents like perchloric acid and hydrogen peroxide were advocated by many investigators, but the danger of explosion is a disadvantage for the use of these reagents. Heating the digestion mixture in a sealed tube is an efficient method on the micro scale. The temperature of the furnace should be kept below 450°C to prevent oxidation of ammonia. Some workers recommended hydrolysis of polyamides by means of hydrochloric acid[243] prior to the sulfuric acid digestion. In the analysis of nitrogen in proteins, it should be noted that certain amino acids containing heterocyclic nitrogen rings (see Section VIII-C) require mercury as the catalyst in the Kjeldahl digestion.

2. Nonaqueous Titration of Amides and Imides. As was mentioned earlier, the hydrogen atom of the carbonimide function is acidic and can be titrated with standard alkali, preferably in nonaqueous media. Fritz and co-worker[244] described a macro method using 0.1 to $0.2N$ sodium methylate as the titrant. The reader is referred to the section on acidic functions (see Chapter 11, Section II) for further discussion and the micro procedures.

The hydrogen atom of the carbonamide function is not titrable as an acid. On the other hand, carbonamides can act as proton acceptors in nonaqueous solvents. Wimer[245] reported that amides dissolved in acetic anhydride can be titrated with perchloric acid in acetic acid solution. This is discussed in the section on basic functions (see Chapter 11, Section IV).

3. Determination of Halogenated Carbonamides and Carbonimides. When the hydrogen atom of the amido or imido function is replaced by halogen, the compound is known as N-haloamide and N-haloimide respectively. Since the halogen atom in halogenated carbonamides and carbonimides acquires a positive valence, these compounds can be determined by the use of redox reactions. Thus Barakat and El-Wahab[246] described a micro method for determining N-halogenated imides by iodometry. The sample is treated with potassium iodide in acetic acid solution, whereupon iodine is liberated as is illustrated for N-bromosuccinimide in equation 90:

[243] R. Marenelli, *Ann. Chim. Appl.*, **30**, 243 (1940).

[244] J. Fritz and N. M. Lisicki, *Anal. Chem.*, **23**, 589 (1951); J. Fritz, *ibid.*, **24**, 674 (1952).

[245] D. C. Wimer, *Anal. Chem.*, **30**, 77 (1958).

[246] M. Z. Barakat and M. F. A. El-Wahab, *Anal. Chem.*, **26**, 1973 (1954).

$$\begin{array}{c} H_2C—CO \\ \qquad\qquad\diagdown \\ \qquad\qquad\qquad NBr \\ \diagup \\ H_2C—CO \end{array} + 2KI + CH_3COOH \rightarrow I_2 + \begin{array}{c} H_2C—CO \\ \qquad\qquad\diagdown \\ \qquad\qquad\qquad NH \\ \diagup \\ H_2C—CO \end{array} + KBr + CH_3COOK \quad (90)$$

The amount of iodine produced is determined by titration with $0.01N$ sodium thiosulfate. Freedman[247] presented a macro method for N-halo-amides and N-haloimides in which the liberated iodine is titrated with sulfur dioxide in pyridine according to the following equation:

$$I_2 + 2\left[\underset{N}{\bigcirc}\right] + SO_2 \cdot \left[\underset{N}{\bigcirc}\right] + H_2O + CH_3OH \rightarrow 2 \underset{\underset{H}{N}}{\bigcirc} \underset{I}{} + \underset{\underset{H}{N}}{\bigcirc} \underset{SO_4CH_3}{} \quad (91)$$

This is an indirect application of the Karl Fischer reaction (see p. 472), except here the presence of water does not interfere with the determination. The equivalence point has to be located electrometrically on the 0.1 meq. scale, since the color of iodine cannot serve as the indicator in a very dilute solution.

4. Determination of Amidines. Amidines have the general formula

$$R—C\begin{array}{c} \diagup NH \\ \diagdown NH_2 \end{array}$$

and may be considered to possess both the amido and imido

groups. Stephan[248] proposed two volumetric methods for determining amidines which involve precipitation. In one method, the compound is treated with 25 ml. of $0.1N$ iodine to precipitate the iodamidine:

$$R—C\begin{array}{c} \diagup NH \\ \diagdown NH_2 \end{array} + I_2 \rightarrow R—C\begin{array}{c} \diagup NI \\ \diagdown NH_2 \end{array} + HI \quad (92)$$

The solution is made alkaline, and the solid is separated by filtration. The amount of iodine in the filtrate is determined by acidifying an aliquot of the filtrate and titrating the liberated iodine with $0.05N$ sodium thiosulfate.

In another method, the amidine is precipitated as mercuriamidine by means of 25 ml. of $0.1N$ buffered mercuric acetate:

$$R—C\begin{array}{c} \diagup NH \\ \diagdown NH_2 \end{array} + Hg(OOCCH_3)_2 \rightarrow R—C\begin{array}{c} \diagup N—HgOOCCH_3 \\ \diagdown NH_2 \end{array} + CH_3COOH \quad (93)$$

[247] R. W. Freedman, *Anal. Chem.*, **28**, 247 (1956).
[248] F. H. Stephan, *Anal. Chem.*, **24**, 187 (1952).

After filtration, the excess of mercury ions is determined by titrating an aliquot of the filtrate with 0.02N ammonium thiocyanate.

F. Colorimetric and Physical Methods for Carbonamides and Carbonimides. Like esters and acid anhydrides, carbonamides and imides are converted to hydroxamic acids when they react with hydroxylamine:

$$R-C\overset{\displaystyle O}{\underset{\displaystyle NH_2}{\big<}} + NH_2OH \rightarrow R-CONHOH + NH_3 \qquad (94)$$

The hydroxamic acid is then determined colorimetrically through its ferric complex[249] (see p. 61). Polya and Tardew[250] reported the determination of diacyl amides, RCO—NR'—COR, by this reaction. It should be noted that the optimum experimental conditions and wavelength at which maximum absorption occurs vary with individual compounds. Therefore, preliminary work is necessary for each compound under investigation.

There is very little information in the literature about physical methods for the determination of carbonamides and imides. Polarographic reduction of amidines was investigated by Kane.[251] Aromatic amidines are reduced at half wave potential of 1.45 to 1.65 v., but aliphatic and aryl aliphatic amidines show no wave in the range 0 to 1.9 v. against the standard calomel electrode.

VIII. The Heterocyclic Nitrogen Functions

A. General. The heterocyclic nitrogen functions include those organic functions in which the nitrogen atom (or atoms) forms a part of the ring structure. The skeletons of some such functions are listed in Table 8.1. Compounds containing these nitrogen functions are found abundantly in nature, for example, alkaloids and purine bases. Many synthetic products of pharmaceutical and industrial importance also possess the ring —N structure, for example, barbiturates, dyes, and plastics.

B. Titrimetric Methods

1. Acidimetry. The heterocyclic nitrogen function in which the nitrogen atom is adjacent to a carbonyl group usually exhibits acidic properties.

[249] F. Bergmann, *Anal. Chem.*, **24**, 1367 (1952).
[250] J. B. Polya and P. L. Tardew, *Anal. Chem.*, **23**, 1036 (1951).
[251] P. O. Kane, *Z. Anal. Chem.*, **173**, 50 (1960).

TABLE 8.1

Heterocyclic Nitrogen Functions[a]

Name	Synonyms	Skeleton
Pyrrole	Azole	
Pyrazole	1,2-Diazole	
Osotriazole	1,2,3-Triazole	
Tetrazole	1,2,3,4-Tetrazole	
Pyridine	Azine	
Pyrimidine	1,3-Diazine; miazine	
s-Triazine	1,3,5-Triazine; cyanidine	
v-Tetrazine	1,2,3,4-Tetrazine	
Indole	1-Benzazole; benzopyrrole	
Indazole	1,2-Benzodiazole; benzopyrazole	
Benzimidazole	1,3-Benzodiazole	
Purine		
Quinoline	1-Benzazine	
Carbazole	Dibenzopyrrole; diphenyleneimide	
Acridine		

[a] See A. M. Patterson, L. T. Capell, and P. F. Walker, *The Ring Index*, 2nd ed., American Chemical Society, Washington, D.C., 1960, for complete list and numbering system.

This has been explained by enolization, as exemplified in equation 95 for barbituric acid,

$$
\begin{array}{ccc}
\text{O=C} \quad \underset{\text{H}_2\text{C}}{\overset{\overset{\text{H}}{\text{N}}}{\diagup}} \quad \text{C=O} & \rightleftarrows & \text{O=C} \quad \underset{\text{H}_2\text{C}}{\overset{\text{N}}{\diagup}} \quad \text{COH} \\
& &
\end{array}
\tag{95}
$$

or ascribed to the acidic carbonimide group (see Section VII-E-2). It should be noted that barbituric acid and its derivatives react like monoprotic acids and yield monosodium salts only.

Determination of barbituric acid and derivatives by titration in aqueous or dilute alcohol solutions using aqueous standard alkali have been reported on the macro scale.[252,253] Most substituted barbituric acids, however, are relatively weak acids (e.g., K_a of barbitol is 3.7×10^{-8}) even though barbituric acid has $K_a = 9.9 \times 10^{-5}$. Therefore, nonaqueous titration is necessary for microdetermination. Titrants ($0.1N$) ranging from potassium hydroxide in methanol,[254] sodium methoxide,[255,256] or lithium methoxide[257,258] to tetra-n-butylammonium hydroxide[259] were reported as suitable for the determination of barbituric acid derivatives in nonaqueous media. The reader is referred to the acidic functions (see Chapter 11, Section II) for the use of $0.01N$ solutions in microanalysis, and experiment 32 for micro procedures.

A number of the acidimetric methods proposed for determining heterocyclic nitrogen compounds are not based on the ionizable hydrogen attached to the ring nitrogen atom. For example, Wolf[260] determined morphine by titration with $0.1N$ potassium hydroxide potentiometrically. The hydroxyl group in the molecule is titrated. Kaye[261] presented a nonaqueous titration method for hexahydro-1,3,5-trinitro-s-triazine using

[252] W. Poethke and D. Horn, *Arch. Pharm. Berlin*, **287**, 487 (1954).

[253] H. Bräuniger and G. Borgwardt, *Pharm. Zentralhalle*, **93**, 266 (1954).

[254] L. G. Chatten, *J. Pharm. Pharmacol.*, **8**, 504 (1956).

[255] V. Vespe and J. S. Fritz, *J. Am. Pharm. Assoc.*, **42**, 338 (1953).

[256] C. J. Schwartz and N. E. Foss, *J. Am. Pharm. Assoc.*, **44**, 217 (1955).

[257] J. C. Ryan, L. K. Yanowski, and C. W. Pifer, *J. Am. Pharm. Assoc.*, **43**, 656 (1954).

[258] S. W. Goldstein and D. F. Dodgen, *Drug Standards*, **26**, 113 (1958).

[259] D. E. Leavitt and J. Austian, *Drug Standards*, **26**, 33 (1958).

[260] S. Wolf, *Naturwissenschaften*, **46**, 649 (1959).

[261] S. M. Kaye, *Anal. Chem.*, **27**, 292 (1955).

0.1N sodium methoxide. This method is based on the nitro groups present and not on the triazine structure.

2. Alkalimetry

A. DETERMINATION OF THE FREE BASE. Practically all heterocyclic nitrogen functions act as proton acceptors and hence can be determined as bases (see Chapter 11, Section IV). Gunderson and co-workers[262] presented a method for determining alkaloids in which the sample (0.5 meq.) is dissolved in 70% ethanol and titrated with 0.1N hydrochloric acid. To accommodate the weak basicity of alkaloids, these workers standardized the 0.1N acid by titrating it against borax in 70% ethanol to the bromophenol blue endpoint. Nevertheless, titration in a nonaqueous medium is preferable and should be resorted to for determinations on the 0.1 meq. scale. Tuthill and co-workers[263] described a procedure to titrate alkaloids with 0.05N perchloric acid in acetic acid using malachite green as the indicator. The color change at the equivalence point is determined visually or spectrophotometrically. Conductometric titration of alkaloids by means of naphthalene-2-sulfonic acid in acetone was proposed by Udovenko and Voedenskaya,[264] who reported that differential titration can be accomplished in this system. Gyenes[265] advocated p-toluenesulfonic acid in phenol-chloroform mixed solvent as titrant and dimethylamino-azo-benzene as indicator for the determination of alkaloids. The use of 0.005N standard solution and 0.5 to 3 mg. sample was described. Tokar and Simonyi[266] suggested chloro-aluminum-diisopropylate hydrochloride in chloroform for determining alkaloids on the macro scale, with ethyl orange or dimethyl yellow as the indicator.

B. DETERMINATION OF THE SALTS. Since heterocyclic nitrogen functions are weak bases, their salts with organic acids are titrable by means of perchloric acid in acetic acid (see Chapter 7, Section VIII-D). Thus Gyenes and Szasz[267] presented a method to determine salts of ergot alkaloids by titration with 0.05N perchloric acid. The equation for ergotamine tartrate is shown in equation 96:

$$(C_{33}H_{35}N_5O_5)_2H_2C_4H_4O_6 + 2HClO_4 \rightarrow 2(C_{33}H_{35}N_5O_5)HClO_4 + H_2C_4H_4O_6 \quad (96)$$

Alkaloid nitrates, sulfates, and perchlorates cannot be determined by neutralization reactions. On the other hand, halides can be titrated as

[262] F. O. Gunderson, R. Heiz, and R. Klevstrand, *J. Pharm. Pharmacol.*, **5**, 608 (1953).
[263] S. M. Tuthill, O. W. Kolling, and K. H. Roberts, *Anal. Chem.*, **32**, 1678 (1960).
[264] V. V. Udovenko and L. A. Voedenskaya, *Ukr. Khim. Zh.*, **20**, 648 (1954).
[265] I. Gyenes, *Magy. Kem. Folyoirat*, **56**, 383 (1950).
[266] G. Tokar and I. Simonyi, *Magy. Kem. Folyoirat*, **64**, 94, 151, 379 (1958).
[267] I. Gyenes and K. Szasz, *Magy. Kem. Folyoirat*, **61**, 356 (1955).

bases by means of perchloric acid in acetic acid after the addition of mercuric acetate:[268]

$$2(\text{Ring—NH}^+)\text{X}^- + \text{Hg(OOCCH}_3)_2 \rightarrow 2(\text{Ring—NH}^+)(\text{OOCCH}_3)^- + \text{HgX}_2 \quad (97a)$$

$$(\text{Ring—NH}^+)(\text{OOCCH}_3)^- + \text{HClO}_4 \rightarrow (\text{Ring—NH})\text{ClO}_4 + \text{CH}_3\text{COOH} \quad (97b)$$

The micro procedure is given in experiment 4.

It should be noted that carboxylic acid salts of alkaloids also can be determined by titration as acids in nonaqueous media. For instance, ergotamine tartrate, mentioned previously, was titrated by the same workers[267] in pyridine solution by means of potassium methylate in methanol, according to equation 98:

$$(\text{C}_{33}\text{H}_{35}\text{N}_5\text{O}_5)_2\text{H}_2\text{C}_4\text{H}_4\text{O}_6 + 2\text{KOCH}_3 \rightarrow 2\text{C}_{33}\text{H}_{35}\text{N}_5\text{O}_5 + \text{K}_2\text{C}_4\text{H}_4\text{O}_6 + 2\text{CH}_3\text{OH} \quad (98)$$

3. Argentimetry. Two macro methods are available for the determination of barbiturates that involve the use of silver nitrate. In one method[269] the sample is dissolved in pyridine and treated with silver nitrate in the same solvent. The hydronium ions liberated are determined with $0.1N$ ethanolic sodium hydroxide either potentiometrically or visually by using thymol blue as indicator. It is reported that free barbituric acids liberate 2 mol. of hydronium ions per mol. whereas sodium barbiturates liberate 1 mol. of hydronium ions. In another method,[270,271] the barbiturate is titrated directly with $0.1N$ silver nitrate in the presence of sodium carbonate using silver wire as electrodes. This method depends on the quantitative reaction of barbiturates with silver ions to form a slightly dissociable salt which is soluble in sodium carbonate solution. At the equivalence point the excess of silver ions precipitate as silver carbonate. Thus the endpoint potential is that of a saturated solution of silver carbonate in the presence of excess of carbonate ions. Both procedures can be adapted to the 0.1 meq. scale.

4. Use of Precipitation Agents

A. DIRECT TITRATION METHODS. Many heterocyclic nitrogen functions form insoluble complexes with a number of reagents. Determination by direct titration is possible when precipitation is instantaneous and complete. Thus $0.5N$ tungstosilicic acid has been used to titrate alkaloids, pyrazolones, and purines on the micro scale. The endpoint can be located by Congo red or metanil yellow[272] indicator or by the amperometric

[268] C. W. Pifer and E. Wollish, *Anal. Chem.*, **24**, 300 (1952).
[269] J. A. Gautier, F. Pellerin, and J. Pineau, *Ann. Pharm. France*, **16**, 625 (1958).
[270] J. I. Bodin, *J. Am. Pharm. Ass.*, **45**, 185 (1956).
[271] Y. A. M. Perelman, *Zhur. Anal. Khim.*, **11**, 241 (1956).
[272] E. Graf and E. Fiedler, *Naturwissenschaften*, **39**, 556 (1952).

method.[273] Konopik[274] proposed the application of metal salt solutions to amperometric determinations of alkaloids and barbiturates.

Bobtelsky and Cohen described micro methods for determining alkaloids and aminopyrine by heterometric titration. The sample is titrated with either 0.001 to 0.005M sodium tetraphenylboron[275] or 0.005M bismuth nitrate containing potassium iodide.[276] The equivalence point is detected by the maximum optical density of the reaction mixture. Precision and accuracy of ±2.5% were reported for samples ranging from 0.5 to 1 mg.

B. METHODS DEPENDENT ON PRECIPITATION FOLLOWED BY TITRIMETRY. Several procedures have been proposed which involve precipitation followed by titration of the product or the reagent. Hädicke[277] determined piperazine either by precipitation of the tetraphenylboron salt followed by argentimetric titration, or by precipitation of the Reineckate complex followed by hydrolysis and Volhard titration. Kranjcevic and Broz-Kajganovic[278] treated the tetraphenylboron complexes of heterocyclic nitrogen compounds with mercuric chloride, followed by titration of the liberated hydrochloric acid.

Chelatometric titration has been applied to the determination of heterocyclic nitrogen functions. Sjostrom and Rittner[279] determined alkaloid salts in aqueous solution by cation exchange with magnesium ions. The latter is collected in the eluate and titrated with EDTA using Erichrome black T as indicator. A 15 to 100 mg. sample can be determined with a mean error of 0.25%. Budesinsky and Körbl[280] treated the heterocyclic nitrogen base (20 to 40 mg.) with cadmium complexonate in presence of potassium iodide. The precipitated ring—N—CdI$_4$ complex was filtered off. The filtrate containing the liberated complex was titrated with 0.01M calcium chloride using methylthymol blue as indicator.

5. *Iodimetry.* Rapaport[281] determined barbiturates by reacting them with iodine chloride, followed by the addition of potassium iodate and titration of the liberated iodine with sodium thiosulfate. Gengrinovich and co-workers[282] determined antipyrine by amperometric titration with 0.01

[273] T. Ogawa, *J. Chem. Soc. Japan*, **76**, 739 (1955); *J. Electrochem. Soc. Japan*, **25**, 377 (1957).

[274] N. Konopik, *Öst. Chem. Ztg.*, **55**, 127 (1954).

[275] M. Bobtelsky and M. M. Cohen, *Anal. Chim. Acta*, **22**, 328 (1960).

[276] M. Bobtelsky and M. M. Cohen, *Anal. Chim. Acta*, **22**, 270 (1960).

[277] M. Hädicke, *Pharm. Zentralhalle*, **97**, 365 (1958).

[278] M. Kranjcevic and V. Broz-Kajganovic, *Croat. Chem. Acta*, **30**, 47 (1958).

[279] E. Sjostrom and W. Rittner, *Z. Anal. Chem.*, **153**, 321 (1956).

[280] B. Budesinsky and J. Körbl, *Coll. Czech. Chem. Commun.*, **25**, 76 (1960).

[281] L. I. Rapaport, *Zhur. Anal. Khim.*, **12**, 415 (1957).

[282] A. I. Gengrinovich, L. E. Korneva, and A. M. Murtazaev, *Dokl. Akad. Nauk. USSR*, **1959**, 40.

or 0.001N iodine chloride in 0.4N hydrochloric acid using the rotating platinum cathode. The accuracy reported is 0.1 to 0.5%. Alkaloids have been determined with bismuth iodide[283] or antimony iodide,[284] which forms complexes of the formula $MI_3 \cdot$ (ring—N)$\cdot$HI or MI_3(ring—N)$_2$HI. The iodine is then liberated and titrated with 0.01N sodium thiosulfate.

C. Use of the Kjeldahl Method. As mentioned in Section III-F-4, the Kjeldahl method for nitrogen determination was originally developed for amino compounds. It can be applied to the analysis of certain types of heterocyclic nitrogen functions with discretion. Barbiturates give quantitative yield of nitrogen upon digestion, with selenium as catalyst.[285] These compounds are probably hydrolyzed to urea and then to ammonia. On the other hand, the nitrogen atoms in pyrrole and pyridine nuclei are resistant to hydrolytic cleavage unless mercury is added to the digestion mixture.[286] Application of reduction prior to Kjeldahl digestion[287] also facilitates the quantitative recovery of nitrogen from such compounds as alkaloids and pyrimidines. Beet[288] advocated the addition of small amounts of potassium permanganate to the sulfuric acid for the digestion of alkaloids. This strong oxidant, which helps the destruction of the carbon chain but not the recovery of ammonia, should be handled with extreme care. Explosion usually occurs if the purple vapor of manganese heptoxide is formed.

It has not been possible to apply the Kjeldahl method to the determination of cyclic systems that have two or more nitrogen atoms in vicinal positions. Whereas open-chain N—N structures are suited to the Kjeldahl technique after reduction with nascent hydrogen (see Section VI-I-1), this method cannot be extended to the heterocyclic nitrogen functions. Thus phenylhydrazine was successfully determined by the modified Kjeldahl procedure, but its derived cyclic compounds (e.g., pyrazolones and tetrazolium salts) yielded low and erratic results with or without pretreatment.[289] It appears that these cyclic structures always liberate some nitrogen gas upon cleavage.

D. Method Dependent on Alkylation. Sackur[290] devised a micro method for determining cyclic nitrogen as follows. The sample is heated

[283] W. Poethke and H. Trabert, *Pharm. Zentralhalle*, **91**, 284 (1952); **94**, 214 (1955).

[284] S. Besson and J. J. Brignon, *Bull. Soc. Sci. Nancy*, **12**, 61 (1953); *Ann. Pharm. France*, **11**, 535 (1953).

[285] T. S. Ma and G. Zuazaga, *Ind. Eng. Chem., Anal. Ed.*, **14**, 281 (1942).

[286] T. S. Ma and E. E. Jaffe, unpublished work.

[287] T. S. Ma, R. E. Lang, and J. D. McKinley, Jr., *Mikrochim. Acta*, **1957**, 368.

[288] A. E. Beet, *Nature*, **175**, 513 (1955).

[289] T. S. Ma, A. T. Spencer, and B. Arnowich, unpublished work.

[290] O. Sackur, *Soc. Chem. France*, **1949**, 270.

with dimethyl sulfate or ethyl iodide for 2 to 4 hours. After cooling, sodium hydroxide and saturated potassium permanganate solution are added. The amine formed is steam-distilled into a known volume of $0.02N$ sulfuric acid. The excess of acid is back-titrated using methyl red-methylene blue mixed indicator. But quinoline and its derivatives do not give quantitative results.

E. Gravimetric Methods. Precipitation of heterocyclic nitrogen bases as halides, perchlorates, oxalates, picrates, or picrolonates[291] is a common practice. Other acids also can be used to obtain insoluble salts. Wachsmuth[292] recommended flavianic acid for the determination of alkaloids. Bond[293] described a macro method for determining piperazine by precipitating its diacetate in acetone solution. When quantitative precipitation is applied to the micro scale, the optimum conditions should be predetermined for each compound under investigation. The gravimetric micro procedure is given in experiment 25.

The coordinated compounds formed by alkaloids and Reinecke's salt (see Section IV-D) have been used for quantitative analysis on the macro scale.[294-297] This method is not recommended for microdeterminations, however, because of the instability of the reagent and the product.

2,4-Dinitrofluorobenzene has been used as reagent for the determination of morphine.[298] The dinitrophenyl ether that precipitates in an acetone solution containing ammonia is collected on a filter, dried at 80°C and weighed. Ma and Becker[299] have found that 2,4-dinitrofluorobenzene gives excellent solid derivatives for amines and phenols on the milligram scale, but the yields are rarely quantitative.

The precipitation of a complex with the formula $Os(OH)_3(C_8H_4NHN_2)_3$ from 1,2,3-benzotriazole and osmium tetroxide in dilute acetic acid solution has been utilized as a method for the microdetermination of osmium.[300] The conditions are not critical and the precipitate is stable below 200°C. This method may be applied to the analysis of heterocyclic nitrogen

[291] E. V. Hulle, in Houben-Weyl-Müller: *Methoden der organischen Chemie*, 4th ed., Vol. 2, Thieme, Stuttgart, 1953, p. 656.

[292] J. Wachsmuth, *J. Pharm. Belg.*, **8**, 283 (1953).

[293] G. R. Bond, *Anal. Chem.*, **32**, 1332 (1960).

[294] L. Rosenthaler, *Arch. Pharm.*, **265**, 319 (1927).

[295] P. Duquenois and M. Falley, *Bull. Soc. Chim.*, **6**, 998 (1939).

[296] L. K. Tatt and C. G. Farmilo, *Nature*, **180**, 1288 (1957).

[297] W. Poethke, P. Gebert, and E. Muller, *Pharm. Zentralhalle*, **98**, 389 (1959).

[298] D. C. Garratt, C. A. Johnson, and C. J. Lloyd, *J. Pharm. Pharmacol.*, **9**, 914 (1957).

[299] T. S. Ma and A. Becker, unpublished work.

[300] R. F. Wilson and L. J. Baye, *Talanta*, **1**, 351 (1958).

compounds related to benzotriazole. Precautions must be taken while handling osmium tetroxide.

F. Gasometric Method. A gasometric method for the determination of pyridine and its derivatives was developed by Yokoo.[301] The ring—N is hydrogenated in the presence of Raney nickel to form the secondary amine, which is nitrosated by potassium nitrite and sulfamic acid to yield the nitroso-amine. Reduction of nitroso-amine with zinc and hydrochloric acid gives aminopiperidine, which liberates nitrogen gas on ferricyanide oxidation. The sequence of reactions is indicated by the following formulas:

$$\text{(99)}$$

Samples of 0.25 to 0.5 meq. were used. Precision and accuracy of 1.3% were reported. However, the complexity of this method leaves much to be desired.

G. Colorimetric Methods. There are numerous colorimetric methods for determining heterocyclic nitrogen compounds. Some examples are given below. The pyridine nucleus can be converted to colored substances when treated with cyanogen bromide and aniline[302] or cyanogen chloride and barbituric acid.[303] These methods have been employed on the microgram scale. Pyridine derivatives produce a color with styrene oxide and sodium methoxide which is measured at 465 mμ.[304] Carbazole can be determined by its reaction with xanthydrol in acetic acid and by measurement at 525 mμ.[305]

Cross and co-workers[306] determined alkaloids by treating the sample in chloroform with 1% sodium picrate and measuring the color at 355 mμ. Pöhm[307] determined tropine alkaloids by the color produced with p-dimethylaminobenzaldehyde. Camp and Moore[308] utilized the reaction between 2,4-dinitrofluorobenzene and alkaloids and measured the color of

[301] M. Yokoo, *Chem. Pharm. Bul. Japan*, **7**, 884 (1959).

[302] B. C. Bose, H. N. De, and J. H. Dalal, *J. Indian Chem. Soc.*, **33**, 131 (1956).

[303] W. Nielsch and L. Giefer, *Z. Anal. Chem.*, **171**, 401 (1959).

[304] H. J. Roth and H. O. Schrimpf, *Mitt. Dtsch. Pharm. Ges.*, **30**, 22 (1960).

[305] G. Eilbert, R. M. Stickel, and H. M. Morgan, Jr., *Anal. Chem.*, **31**, 1981 (1959).

[306] A. H. Cross, D. McClaren, and S. G. E. Stevens, *J. Pharm. Pharmacol.*, **11**, [suppl.] 103T (1959).

[307] M. Pöhm, *Mikrochim. Acta*, **1958**, 123.

[308] B. J. Camp and J. A. Moore, *J. Am. Pharm. Ass., Sci. Ed.*, **49**, 158 (1960).

the product at 350 mμ. Ghezzi[309] precipitated the alkaloid with tungstosilicic acid and measured the color of the excess reagent after reduction with stannous chloride.

Barbiturates have been determined by precipitation with mercury, followed by colorimetric determination of mercury with dithizone.[310] The colorless tetrazolium salts are converted to intensely colored formazans on mild reduction, but the products are insoluble and separate out in a short time.[311] Hall[312] determined tetrazolium compound by treating the sample with a slight excess of picric acid, filtering the precipitate, and measuring the filtrate at 430 mμ.

H. Physical Methods. The ultraviolet absorption spectra of pyrazolones, alkaloids,[313] purines,[314] and barbiturates,[315–317] have been used for quantitative analysis. In the case of barbiturates, the shift in absorption maxima at different pH's is characteristic of individual compounds.[318,319] The infrared absorption at 10 to 15 μ has been used to determine pyridines.[320]

Fluorometric determination of ergot alkaloids was reported by Gyenes and Szasz.[321] Kirkpatrik[322] and Habersberger and Zyka[323] studied the polarographic behavior of alkaloids. Cheronis and co-workers[324] recently published a spectrofluorometric method for the microestimation of morphine and codeine in presence of each other. Both morphine and codeine in solutions of 0.1N sulfuric acid show fluorescence peaks at 350 mμ; however, at pH's 10 to 12 the fluorescence of morphine is negligible whereas that of codeine remains unchanged. This method is applicable to other alkaloids.

[309] G. Ghezzi, Ann. Chim. Rome, **43**, 48 (1953).

[310] E. Pfeil and H. J. Goldbach, Z. physiol. Chem., **302**, 263 (1955).

[311] N. D. Cheronis and J. B. Entrikin, Semimicro Qualitative Organic Analysis, 2nd ed., Interscience, New York, 1957, p. 245.

[312] W. T. Hall, Chem. Anal., **42**, 9 (1953).

[313] E. Haberli and E. Beguin, Pharm. Acta Helv., **35**, 13 (1960).

[314] A. J. Shingler and J. K. Carlton, Anal. Chem., **31**, 1679 (1959).

[315] G. W. Rock and H. N. Wright, Arch. Ind. Hyg. Occupational Med., **8**, 507 (1953).

[316] F. A. Rotondaro, J. Ass. Off. Agri. Chemists, **38**, 809 (1955).

[317] R. Hilf, G. A. Lightbourn, and F. F. Costano, J. Lab. Clin. Med., **54**, 634 (1959).

[318] G. L. Ploa, F. B. Hall, and C. H. Hine, J. Forensic Sci., **3**, 201 (1958).

[319] M. Ledvind, B. Chundela, B. Vecerek, and K. Kace, Ceskosl. Farm., **4**, 386 (1955).

[320] G. L. Cook and F. M. Church, Anal. Chem., **28**, 993 (1956).

[321] L. Gyenes and K. Szasz, Magy. Kem. Folyoirat, **61**, 393 (1955).

[322] H. F. Kirkpatrik, Quart. J. Pharm. Pharmacol., **18**, 245, 338 (1945); **19**, 8, 137, 326 (1947); **20**, 87 (1949).

[323] K. Habersberger and J. Zyka, Ceskosl. Farm., **5**, 264 (1956).

[324] R. Brandt, S. Rogozinsky, and N. D. Cheronis, Microchem. J., **5**, 215 (1961).

IX. The Hydrazino, Hydrazido, and Semicarbazido Functions

A. General. The hydrazino, hydrazido, and semicarbazido functions are characterized by the $N—NH_2$ linkage and are derived from the inorganic compound hydrazine $H_2N—NH_2$ with one or both hydrogen atoms of one of the NH_2 groups replaced by organic radicals.[325] The compound is known as hydrazine when the hydrogen is substituted by hydrocarbon radical (e.g., phenylhydrazine, $C_6H_5NH—NH_2$; unsymmetrical dimethylhydrazine, $(CH_3)_2N—NH_2$, etc.). The acyl derivatives of hydrazine are called acid hydrazides or acyl hydrazines (e.g., N⟨ ⟩—CO—NH—NH₂,

is isonicotinic hydrazide or isonicotinoyl hydrazine). The semicarbazido function is present in semicarbazide, $H_2N—CO—NHNH_2$; thiosemicarbazide, $H_2N—CS—NH—NH_2$; and aminoguanidine, $H_2N—\underset{\underset{NH}{\|}}{C}—NHNH_2$.

Compounds containing the $N—NH_2$ group may be analyzed by neutralization (see Chapter 11, Section IV) as well as redox reactions. A specific method, however, for determining hydrazino, hydrazido, and semicarbazido groups consists of measurement of the amount of nitrogen that is liberated from the respective function upon oxidation. This method is not susceptible to the interference of other oxidizing and reducing substances present, and it can be used when the compound under investigation is oxidized sluggishly. Furthermore, the redox reaction of the functions discussed in this section may be complicated by more than one possible route requiring different mole ratios of the reagent. Thus Britton and Chissold[326] reported that benzene and phenol are simultaneously produced on the oxidation of phenylhydrazine by cupric ions according to the following equations:

$$C_6H_5—\underset{\underset{H}{|}}{N}—NH_2 + 2Cu^{+2} + 2OH^- \rightarrow C_6H_6 + N_2 + 2H_2O + 2Cu^+ \qquad (100)$$

$$C_6H_5—\underset{\underset{H}{|}}{N}—NH_2 + 4Cu^{+2} + 4OH^- \rightarrow C_6H_5OH + N_2 + 3H_2O + 4Cu^+ \qquad (101)$$

Hence strict adherence to the experimental conditions is necessary to obtain reproducible results. On the other hand, one and only one mole of nitrogen is produced when the decomposition of the hydrazino function is complete.

[325] L. F. Audrieth and B. A. Ogg, *The Chemistry of Hydrazine*, John Wiley and Sons, New York, 1951.

[326] H. T. S. Britton and E. M. Chissold, *J. Chem. Soc.*, **1942**, 525.

B. Gasometric Methods.   As was mentioned previously, gasometric methods for the determination of hydrazines, hydrazides, and semicarbazones are based on the oxidative cleavage of the N—NH$_2$ linkage to liberate nitrogen gas. Strache[327] devised the first macro procedure to determine phenylhydrazine by measuring the volume of nitrogen produced on oxidation with Fehling's solution. Later, Datta[328] described the estimation of semicarbazide by oxidation with halogens and halogen oxyacids. McKennis and co-workers[329] employed the Warburg manometric apparatus and developed a technique to determine samples at the 40 μmol. range (about 1 ml. of gas).

The apparatus[330] for analysis on the 0.1 meq. scale is shown in Fig. 8.11. After the sample is placed in the reaction vessel A, the apparatus is assembled and the air in the system is displaced by carbon dioxide. The oxidizing agent is then introduced by means of a syringe through the rubber cap D. The reaction mixture is heated electrically and the nitrogen evolved is swept into the 5-ml. azotometer F. The detailed procedure will be found in experiment 39.

Extensive study[331] on a variety of compounds showed that the success of the determination depends on the choice of the oxidant and the reaction time and temperature. Potassium ferricyanide was recommended for the decomposition of acid hydrazides by Harting[332] and Wirth.[333] Reagents proposed for the decomposition of hydrazines include cupric ions in alkaline[326,327] and acid media,[334] iodine[335,336] and iodate.[329] The latter has also been used in the determination of hydrazides and semicarbazide.[329] According to Kawashiro and Hosogai,[337] hypobromite oxidation is satisfactory for semicarbazide, but not for thiosemicarbazide. The latter requires 10% copper sulfate solution which is not suitable for semicarbazide. Ferricyanide gives low results for both compounds.

[327] H. Strache, *Monatsh.*, **12**, 524 (1891); **13**, 299 (1892).

[328] R. L. Datta, *J. Am. Chem. Soc.*, **36**, 1014 (1914); **38**, 2736 (1916).

[329] H. McKennis, Jr., J. H. Weatherby, and E. P. Dellis, *Anal. Chem.*, **30**, 499 (1958).

[330] T. S. Ma, in *Proceedings of the International Symposium on Microchemistry, 1958*, Pergamon Press, London, 1959, p. 156; apparatus available from Micro-Ware, Inc., Vineland, N.J.

[331] T. S. Ma and F. Mattei, unpublished work; see F. Mattei, *Master's Thesis, Brooklyn College*, 1960.

[332] H. Harting, *J. Am. Pharm. Assoc.*, **42**, 323 (1953).

[333] C. M. P. Wirth, *Dtsch. Apoth. Ztg.*, **94**, 1289 (1954).

[334] S. Siggia, *Quantitative Organic Analysis Via Functional Groups*, 2nd ed., John Wiley and Sons, New York, 1954, p. 121.

[335] F. Kaufler and W. Suchannek, *Berichte*, **40**, 524 (1907).

[336] M. Yamagishi, M. Yokoo, and S. Inoue, *J. Pharm. Soc., Japan*, **74**, 1283 (1954).

[337] I. Kawashiro and Y. Hosogai, *Bull. Natl. Hyg. Lab. Tokyo*, **73**, 109 (1955).

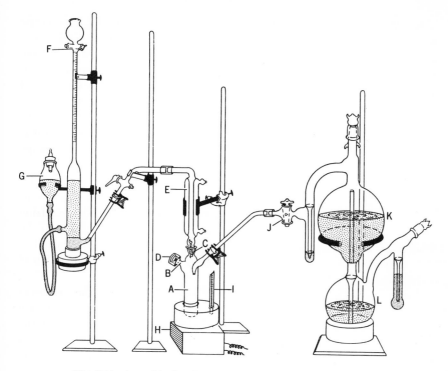

Fig. 8.11. Assembly for the determination of hydrazino groups.

C. Titrimetric Oxidative Methods

1. Iodate as Oxidant. Phenylhydrazine has been determined on the macro scale by titration with $0.1N$ potassium iodate in the presence of hydrochloric acid:[338,339]

$$3C_6H_5NH—NH_2 + IO_3^- \rightarrow 3C_6H_6 + 3N_2 + I^- + 3H_2O \qquad (102)$$

Brilliant Ponceaux R is used as the indicator, which is decolorized by a trace of iodate ions but not affected by iodine monochloride. This method has not been tested on the micro scale.

Tatsuzawa[340] described a procedure to determine isonicotinic hydrazide in hydrochloric acid solution by titration with $0.025N$ potassium iodate using indigo carmine as the redox indicator. Semicarbazide and amino-

[338] G. F. Smith and C. S. Wolcox, *Ind. Eng. Chem., Anal. Ed.,* **14,** 49 (1942).

[339] R. Belcher and C. Wilson, *New Methods in Analytical Chemistry,* Longmans, Green and Co., London, 1955, p. 179.

[340] M. Tatsuzawa, *Japan Analyst,* **7,** 790 (1958).

guanidine were determined by Hovarka[341] and Smith[342] by reacting the sample with a known volume of 0.1N potassium iodate in the presence of sulfuric acid, followed by the titration of the excess of iodate with standard sodium thiosulfate solution.

2. Molecular Halogen as Oxidant. Iodine solution was employed as oxidant for the titration of phenylhydrazine by Von Meyer[343] in 1887. This method is still advocated by some workers[344-346] for the macro determination of organic hydrazines. It should be noted, however, that the titration is conducted in a carbonate[344] or phosphate[346] buffered solution and hence restricted to water-soluble aliphatic hydrazines. Since 0.01N iodine solution is difficult to keep, the method is not suitable for adaptation to the 0.1 meq. scale.

Bromometric determination of hydrazines, hydrazides, and semicarbazide may be carried out in acidic media. Hence the potassium bromate-potassium bromide mixture technique (see p. 517) can be applied advantageously to microdeterminations. The conventional procedure of determining the excess of bromine by iodometric titration with standard sodium thiosulfate was used by Haugas and Mitchell[347] and Jancik, Cinkova, and Körbl[348] for the analysis of a number of hydrazine derivatives. Casopis[349] proposed direct titration with bromine using colloidal 2-naphthoflavone as the indicator (which gives a dark orange color when free bromine is present), but this method is not recommended for determination on the micro scale. Olson[350] presented a method for the coulometric titration of substituted hydrazine with electrolytically generated bromine. Monosubstituted hydrazine consumes two moles of bromine:

$$R-NH-NH_2 + 2Br_2 + H_2O \rightarrow ROH + N_2 + 4HBr \qquad (103)$$

On the other hand, unsymmetrical disubstituted hydrazines, R_2N-NH_2, are reported to consume 3 moles of bromine. The products of the oxidation were not identified.

[341] H. V. Hovarka, *Collection Czech. Chem. Commun.*, **3**, 285 (1931).

[342] G. S. Smith, *J. Chem. Soc.*, **1937**, 1325.

[343] E. von Meyer, *J. Prakt. Chem.*, **36**, 115 (1887).

[344] J. Rosin, *Reagent Chemicals and Standards*, Van Nostrand, Princeton, N.J., 1939, p. 194.

[345] P. Endroi, *Magy. Kem. Folyoirat*, **59**, 211 (1953).

[346] S. Siggia, *Quantitative Organic Analysis via Functional Groups*, 2nd ed., John Wiley and Sons, New York, 1954, p. 121.

[347] E. A. Haugas and B. W. Mitchell, *J. Pharm. Pharmacol.*, **4**, 687 (1952).

[348] F. Jancik, O. Cinkova, and J. Körbl, *Collection Czech. Chem. Commun.*, **24**, 2695 (1959).

[349] R. V. Casopis, *Ceskoslov., Lekarmict.*, **15**, 143 (1935).

[350] E. C. Olson, *Anal. Chem.*, **32**, 1545 (1960).

Iodine chloride was used by Cihalik and Terebova[351] to determine phenylhydrazine potentiometrically on the macro scale. Schulek and Burger[352] recommended standard bromine chloride as titrant for phenyl-hydrazine and isonicotinic hydrazide on the semimicro scale. The strength of the reagents employed was $0.1N$, but bromine chloride solutions of such strength are not very stable.

3. Vanadate or Cerate as Oxidant. Gowda and Rao[353] determined isonicotinic hydrazide by oxidizing the sample (10 to 15 mg.) with a known amount of $0.05N$ sodium vanadate in dilute sulfuric acid:

$$N \underset{}{\bigcirc} -\underset{\underset{O}{\|}}{C}-NH-NH_2 + 4VO_3^- + 4H^+ \rightarrow$$

$$N \underset{}{\bigcirc} -COOH + N_2 + 4VO_2 + 3H_2O \quad (104)$$

The excess of vanadate was back-titrated with ferrous ammonium sulfate. Singh and Sahota[354] devised a method to titrate semicarbazide, semi-carbazones, and aminoguanidine directly with $0.1M$ sodium metavanadate in hydrochloric acid or with $0.02N$ diethylenetetra-ammonium sulfatocerate in sulfuric acid[355] as follows. The sample is dissolved in 60 ml. of dilute hydrochloric acid; 5 ml. of chloroform and 5 ml. of $0.02M$ iodine chloride are added, the latter acting as a catalyst (pre-oxidizer) and internal indicator. The solution is titrated with the standard vanadate or cerate. The titration flask is shaken vigorously after each addition of the titrant. The endpoint is indicated by a change from violet to very pale yellow in the chloroform layer. It is difficult to apply this technique to micro-determinations.

4. Positive Chlorine as Oxidant. Chloramine-T has been used to deter-mine hydrazines, hydrazides, and semicarbazides[356,357] on the macro scale. The sample is oxidized in the presence of potassium iodide with a known volume of the oxidant in an alkaline medium. After the reaction is complete, the solution is acidified and the iodine liberated from the excess of chloramine-T is determined by titration with $0.1N$ sodium thiosulfate using starch as indicator. Solutions of $0.1N$ chloramine-T are stable in dark

[351] J. Cihalik and K. Terebova, *Chem. Listy,* **50,** 1774 (1956).

[352] E. Schulek and K. Burger, *Talanta,* **1,** 344 (1958).

[353] H. S. Gowda and G. G. Rao, *Z. Anal. Chem.,* **165,** 36 (1959).

[354] B. Singh and S. S. Sahota, *Anal. Chim. Acta,* **17,** 285 (1957).

[355] B. Singh, *Anal. Chim. Acta,* **17,** 467 (1957).

[356] A. Berka and J. Zyka, *Cesk. Farm.,* **5,** 335 (1956).

[357] P. Spacu, G. Teodorescu, and D. Gavanescu, *Bul. Inst. Politeh. Bucuresti.,* **18,** 51 (1956).

bottles for months,[358] but the stability of the $0.01N$ solutions has not been studied.

Sodium hypochlorite ($0.1N$ in $2N$ hydrochloric acid) was proposed by Singh and co-workers[359] as the volumetric reagent for the determination of organic derivatives of hydrazine. The endpoint is observed by the discharge of an iodine color from the chloroform layer. This method is not suitable for microanalysis.

5. Cupric or Ferrate Ions as Oxidant. Phenylhydrazine has been determined by titration with Fehling's solution[326] on the macro scale. Terentev and Zabrodina[360] used $0.1N$ cupric acetate as titrant in aqueous pyridine solution. The pyridine-cupric acetate complex is blue, and the endpoint of the titration is observed by the change of yellowish blue to bluish green. These methods have not been tested on the micro scale.

Isonicotinic hydrazide was determined by Vulterin and Zyka[361] by direct potentiometric titration with $0.1N$ potassium ferricyanide in alkaline solution. The concentration of the alkali must be controlled because the results become erratic at high pH's. The equation for the reaction is as follows:

$$\text{N} \langle \rangle - CO - NH - NH_2 + 4K_3Fe(CN)_6 + 5KOH \rightarrow$$

$$4K_4Fe(CN)_6 + N\langle \rangle - COOK + N_2 + 4H_2O \quad (105)$$

6. Use of Other Oxidants. Berka and Zyka proposed lead tetra-acetate[362] and potassium periodate[363] as oxidants for the microdetermination of hydrazine derivatives. The endpoint is located potentiometrically. The use of alkaline permanganate for the oxidation of hydrazine was investigated by Issa and Issa,[364] who reported that the stoichiometry depends on the concentration of the alkali in the reaction mixture. Sussella[365] suggested $0.1N$ selenious acid as an oxidizing agent for hydrazines according to the following equation:

$$R - NH - NH_2 + H_2SeO_3 \rightarrow ROH + N_2 + Se + 2H_2O \quad (106)$$

[358] B. N. Afanasev, *Zavodskaya Lab.*, **15**, 1271 (1949).

[359] B. Singh, S. S. Sahota, and S. Singh, *Z. Anal. Chem.*, **160**, 429 (1958).

[360] A. P. Terentev and K. S. Zabrodina, *Doklady Akad. Nauk. USSR*, **95**, 85 (1954).

[361] J. Vulterin and J. Zyka, *Chem. Listy*, **48**, 839 (1954).

[362] A. Berka and J. Zyka, *Chem. Listy*, **52**, 926 (1958).

[363] A. Berka and J. Zyka, *Chem. Listy*, **50**, 314 (1956).

[364] I. R. Issa and R. M. Issa, *Anal. Chem. Acta*, **14**, 578 (1956); *Chemist-Analyst*, **45**, 40 (1956).

[365] B. Sussella, *Chem. Ber.*, **88**, 23 (1955).

A known excess of the reagent is added to the sample. After the oxidation is complete, the residual selenious acid is determined iodometrically with standard sodium thiosulfate and starch. Alternately, the precipitated selenium can be separated and weighed. These methods have not been critically evaluated.

D. Titrimetric Reductive Methods. The reduction of phenylhydrazine was applied to quantitave analysis by Knecht and Hibbert[366] in the following manner. To 300 mg. of phenylhydrazine, dissolved in hydrochloric acid, is added 50 ml. of standard methylene blue solution. The reaction mixture is boiled in a current of carbon dioxide. After cooling, the excess of methylene blue is determined by titration with $0.1N$ titanous chloride. This method has not been extended to other hydrazines.

Previously Robinson[367] had reported that phenylhydrazine could not be quantitatively reduced by titanous chloride, and this has been confirmed by Earley and Ma.[368] Halogen substitution on the benzene ring also renders the aryl hydrazine resistant to titanous chloride reduction. On the other hand, the presence of nitro groups facilitates the reduction of the hydrazino function. Thus p-nitrophenylhydrazine can be determined on the 0.1 meq. scale by treating the sample with a known volume of $0.03N$ titanous chloride at room temperature, as shown in equation 107:

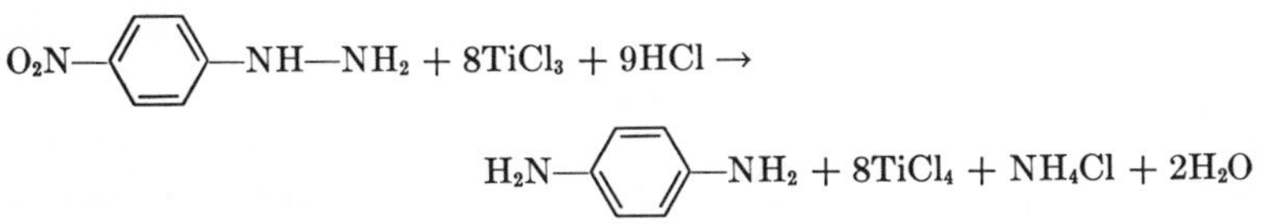

$$O_2N-\!\!\left\langle\bigcirc\right\rangle\!\!-NH\!-\!NH_2 + 8TiCl_3 + 9HCl \rightarrow$$

$$H_2N-\!\!\left\langle\bigcirc\right\rangle\!\!-NH_2 + 8TiCl_4 + NH_4Cl + 2H_2O \quad (107)$$

The excess of titanous chloride is back-titrated with $0.03N$ ferrous ammonium sulfate using thiocyanate as an indicator. It is possible to perform microdetermination of nitrophenylhydrazines in the presence of phenylhydrazine and/or halogenated phenylhydrazines. The detailed procedure is given in experiment 38.

E. Miscellaneous Methods

1. Methods Dependent on Nitrosation. Vulterin and Zyka[369] presented a method for the potentiometric determination of phenylhydrazine, semicarbazide, and thiosemicarbazide by titration with standard sodium nitrite according to equation 108:

[366] E. Knecht and E. Hibbert, *J. Chem. Soc.*, **125**, 1537 (1924).
[367] F. Robinson, *J. Soc. Chem. Ind.*, **35**, 35 (1916).
[368] J. V. Earley and T. S. Ma, *Mikrochim. Acta*, **1960**, 685.
[369] J. Vulterin and J. Zyka, *Chem. Listy*, **50**, 364 (1956).

$$\overset{\displaystyle NO}{\underset{\displaystyle |}{R-NHNH_2 + HNO_2 \rightarrow R-N-NH_2 + H_2O}} \qquad (108)$$

Hydrochloric, sulfuric, phosphoric, and perchloric acids were tried as solvents; standardized sodium nitrite solution $(0.01M)$ was found to be stable for several weeks.

Acid hydrazides were titrated potentiometrically with standard sodium nitrite in acid solutions by Litvinenko and co-workers.[370] The reaction is represented in equation 109:

$$R-CONHNH_2 + HNO_2 \rightarrow R-\underset{\displaystyle O}{\overset{\displaystyle \| }{C}}-N\overset{\diagup N}{\underset{\diagdown N}{\|}} + 2H_2O \qquad (109)$$

Satisfactory results were also reported for the determination of aldehyde condensation products of hydrazides that undergo complete hydrolysis under the experimental conditions:

$$R-CONH-N{=}CHR' + H_2O \rightarrow R-CONHNH_2 + R'-CHO \qquad (110)$$

2. Determination of Unsymmetrical Disubstituted Hydrazines. The determination of unsymmetrical disubstituted hydrazines requires further investigation in view of the conflicting statements in the literature. For instance, Rowe and Audrieth[371] described a macro method for the oxidimetric determination with standard iodine solution and proposed the following relationship to show the equimolar stoichiometry between the sample and the oxidant:

$$2R_2N-NH_2 + 2I_2 \rightarrow R_2N-N{=}N-N-R_2 + 4HI \qquad (111)$$

As was mentioned in Section IX-C-2, Olson[350] reported that one mole of unsymmetrical disubstituted hydrazine consumes 3 moles of bromine.

All the nitrogen in the hydrazino function is not liberated when the gasometric method is applied to the analysis of unsymmetrical disubstituted hydrazines. The other products formed have been reported to be either secondary amines[372] (112) or tetrasubstituted hydrazine[325] (113):

$$2R_2N-NH_2 + [O] \rightarrow 2R_2NH + N_2 + H_2O \qquad (112)$$

$$2R_2\dot{N}NH_2 \overset{(O)}{\longrightarrow} R_2N-N{=}N-NR_2 \rightarrow R_2N-NR_2 + N_2 \qquad (113)$$

F. Colorimetric Methods. Organic hydrazines can be determined by the colored hydrazones which they form on the addition of *p*-dimethyl-

[370] L. M. Litvinenko, D. G. Arlozopov, and V. I. Koroleva, *Ukrain Khim. Zhur.*, **22**, 527 (1956).

[371] R. A. Rowe and L. F. Audrieth, *J. Am. Chem. Soc.*, **78**, 563 (1955).

[372] N. V. Sedgwick, *Organic Chemistry of Nitrogen*, Clarendon, Oxford, 1910, p. 243.

amino benzaldehyde.[373] Isonicotinic hydrazide has been determined by its color reaction with sodium pentacyano-amino ferroate,[374] which is measured at 430 mμ. Another method[375] is to reduce the hydrazino group with potassium mercuric iodide in sodium hydroxide solution. Upon acidification, the orange color turns greenish yellow and is measured colorimetrically or nephelometrically. Nagai[376] determined maleic hydrazide by reductive cleavage. The sample is heated with zinc and sulfuric acid to give hydrazine, which is then condensed with p-dimethylaminobenzaldehyde and measured at 300 mμ.

G. Physical Methods. Ultraviolet spectrophotometry has been applied to the determination of maleic hydrazide.[377] The absorbance at 302 mμ seems to be characteristic of the hydrazido function, since neither maleic acid nor hydrazine absorb at this wavelength.

Polarograms of maleic hydrazide in buffer solutions of pH 3 and pH 7 give a well-defined single-reduction wave at -0.99 v. and -1.84 v., respectively.[377] This property of maleic hydrazide can be utilized for quantitative analysis. The polarographic determination of semicarbazones was reported by Coulson.[378] It should be noted that the reduction is due to the carbonyl groups and not the semicarbazido function.

X. The Isocyanate and Isothiocyanate Functions

A. General. Organic isocyanates, RNCO, and isothiocyanates, RNCS, are characterized by the —NC— linkage that undergoes addition reactions. Isocyanates are of industrial importance since they are raw materials for a number of polymers. Allyl isothiocyanate has been the subject of study for many years because it is the active principle of mustard and is present in many plants.

B. Methods Based on Addition to the —NC— Linkage

1. Addition of Primary Amines. The addition reaction between isocyanate or isothiocyanate with amines and alcohols to form substituted ureas and urethanes, respectively, is well known. Although the reaction mechanism has not been completely elucidated,[379] the reaction proceeds to

---

[373] H. McKennis, Jr. and A. S. Yard, *Anal. Chem.*, **26**, 1960 (1954).

[374] V.Scardi and V. Bonavita, *Clin. Chim. Acta*, **4**, 161 (1959).

[375] J. Wagner, P. Kraus, and B. Vecerek, *Cesk. Farm.*, **4**, 389 (1955).

[376] Y. Nagai, *J. Agr. Chem. Soc. Japan*, **32**, 851 (1958).

[377] T. Takeuchi, N. Yokouchi, and K. Onoda, *Bunseki Kagaku*, **5**, 399 (1956).

[378] D. M. Coulson, *Anal. Chim. Acta*, **19**, 284 (1958).

[379] J. W. Baker and D. N. Bailey, *J. Chem. Soc.*, **1957**, 4652.

completion and serves well for analytical purposes. Siggia and Hanna[380] investigated the addition of aliphatic and aromatic amines and recommended n-butylamine in dioxane as the reagent for the macro determination of isocyanates and isothiocyanates. The sample (2 meq.) is treated with a measured volume of the standard n-butylamine. After the reaction mixture has stood for a predetermined time, the excess of amine is determined by titration with $0.1N$ sulfuric acid using methyl red as indicator. The addition reactions are represented in equations 114 and 115 respectively:

$$R{-}NCO + nC_4H_9NH_2 \rightarrow R{-}NHCONH{-}C_4H_9(n) \qquad (114)$$

$$R{-}NCS + nC_4H_5NH_2 \rightarrow R{-}NHCSNH{-}C_4H_9(n) \qquad (115)$$

This method has been adapted to the micro scale. Roth[381] employed chlorobenzene as solvent and $0.02N$ hydrochloric acid as titrant. Since chlorobenzene is water insoluble, methanol is added before the back-titration. Karten and Ma[382] presented a simple micro procedure using dioxane as the solvent. The method is given in detail in experiment 28.

2. Addition of Secondary Amines. Dibutylamine was proposed as the reagent for the determination of isocyanates by Siefken[383] and Williamson.[384] A mixed solvent containing chlorobenzene and methanol is used. The excess of reagent is determined by titration with standard hydrochloric acid either electrometrically[384] or using bromophenol blue as an indicator.[383]

Stagg[385] determined hexamethylene-di-isocyanate on the macro scale as follows. The sample is dissolved in acetone and treated with a known amount of piperidine in the ice bath for 30 minutes. The reaction is shown in equation 116:

$$OCN(CH_2)_6NCO + 2C_5H_{10}NH \rightarrow C_5H_{10}N{-}CONH{-}(CH_2)_6{-}NHCONC_5H_{10} \quad (116)$$

A measured volume of $0.5N$ hydrochloric acid is then added to the reaction mixture, with a few drops of methylene blue to give a bright purple color. The excess acid is back-titrated with $0.5N$ sodium hydroxide to the green endpoint. A similar method was presented by Navyashskaya[386] for determining trace amounts of isocyanate in polyurethane resin. Navyashskaya used diethylamine in cyclohexane, $0.01N$ hydrochloric acid and $0.01N$ sodium hydroxide respectively. The endpoint is located potentiometrically.

[380] S. Siggia and J. G. Hanna, *Anal. Chem.*, **20**, 1084 (1948).
[381] H. Roth, *Mikrochim. Acta*, **1958**, 773.
[382] B. S. Karten and T. S. Ma, *Microchem. J.*, **3**, 507 (1959).
[383] W. Siefken, *Annalen*, **562**, 99 (1949).
[384] A. G. Williamson, *Analyst*, **77**, 372 (1952).
[385] H. E. Stagg, *Analyst*, **71**, 557 (1946).
[386] E. A. Navyashskaya, *Khim. Prom.*, **1956**, 432.

3. Addition of Ammonia. This method is used in the determination of isothiocyanates only.[387-390] For example, allyl isothiocyanate has been determined by absorption in concentrated ammonia (eq. 117), followed by the addition of a known amount of $0.1N$ silver nitrate to precipitate silver sulfide (eq. 118).

$$CH_2\!\!=\!\!CH\!-\!CH_2\!-\!NCS + NH_3 \rightarrow CH_2\!\!=\!\!CH\!-\!CH_2\!-\!\underset{\underset{H}{|}}{N}\!-\!\underset{\underset{S}{||}}{C}\!-\!NH_2 \qquad (117)$$

$$CH_2\!\!=\!\!CH\!-\!CH_2\!-\!\underset{\underset{H}{|}}{N}\!-\!\underset{\underset{S}{||}}{C}\!-\!NH_2 + 2AgNO_3 + H_2O \rightarrow$$

$$Ag_2S + CH_2\!\!=\!\!CH\!-\!CH_2\!-\!\underset{\underset{H}{|}}{N}\!-\!\underset{\underset{O}{||}}{C}\!-\!NH_2 + 2HNO_3 \qquad (118)$$

The excess of silver ions is then determined by titration with $0.1N$ ammonium thiocyanate by the Volhard method.

Other procedures which have been suggested for the determination of allyl isothiocyanate in mustard extracts involve the oxidation of the resulting substituted thiourea (see Chapter 9, Section VII-C) by iodine,[391] potassium bromide-bromate mixture,[392] and potassium iodate[393] respectively.

4. Addition of Cysteine. Fischer[394] proposed a method to determine isothiocyanate as follows. The sample is treated with cysteine or denatured ovalbumin of known sulfhydryl strength. After the reaction mixture is incubated, during which time the substituted dithiocarbamate is formed, the excess of sulfhydryl group is determined by back titration (see Chapter 9, Section II). The reaction between isothiocyanate and cysteine is represented in equation 119:

$$R\!-\!NCS + HS\!-\!\underset{\underset{NH_2}{|}}{CH}\!-\!COOH \rightarrow R\!-\!\overset{\overset{H}{|}}{N}\!-\!\underset{\underset{S}{||}}{C}\!-\!S\!-\!\underset{\underset{NH_2}{|}}{CH}\!-\!COOH \qquad (119)$$

C. Miscellaneous Methods

1. Gravimetric Method. A gravimetric method was advocated by Stagg[395] to determine hexamethylene-diisocyanate. The sample (0.5 g.) is

[387] C. Brioux, *Ann. Chim. Anal.*, **17**, 3 (1912).

[388] A. Luce and A. Doucet, *J. Pharm. Chim.*, **25**, 458 (1922).

[389] L. R. Wetter, *Can. J. Biochem. Physiol.*, **33**, 980 (1955).

[390] G. Jacini and M. B. Raffel, *Olii Minerali*, **33**, 97 (1956).

[391] M. Morvillez, *J. Pharm. Chim.*, **30**, 236 (1924).

[392] V. Mades, *Pharmacia (Estonia)*, **18**, 252 (1938).

[393] A. Berka and J. Zyka, *Cesk. Farm.*, **4**, 222 (1955).

[394] P. Fischer, *J. Belg. (New. Ser.)*, **2**, 225 (1947).

[395] H. E. Stagg, *Analyst*, **71**, 557 (1946).

heated with aniline on the steam bath, whereupon the dicarbanilide is formed:

$$OCN—(CH_2)_6—NCO + 2C_6H_5NH_2 \rightarrow$$
$$C_6H_5NHCONH—(CH_2)_6—NHCONHC_6H_5 \quad (120)$$

The excess reagent is removed by steam-distillation. The residue is filtered off, dried, and weighed. This method is not suitable for adaptation to the micro scale.

2. Conversion to Alkali Isothiocyanate. Isothiocyanates in ethanol solution are converted to sodium isocyanates on treatment with a saturated ethanolic solution of sodium sulfide in accordance with equation 121:

$$2R—NCS + Na_2S \rightarrow 2NaNCS + R_2S \quad (121)$$

This reaction has been applied for their quantitative estimation.[396] A measured volume of $0.1N$ silver nitrate is added to precipitate silver thiocyanate. After filtration, the excess of silver ions in the filtrate is determined by the Volhard titration.

3. Liberation of Isothiocyanic Acid. According to Anderson,[397] ethylsilicon isothiocyanate can be analyzed by alcoholysis, as depicted in equation 122:

$$(C_2H_5)_3SiNCS + C_2H_5OH \rightarrow (C_2H_5)_3SiOC_2H_5 + HNCS \quad (122)$$

The isothiocyanic acid liberated is determined by titration with standard sodium hydroxide using phenolphthalein as indicator.

4. Methods Based on Hydrolysis. Kemp[398] proposed a method for the analysis of isothiocyanates by alkaline hydrolysis:

$$RNCS + 3KOH \rightarrow RNH_2 + KSH + K_2CO_3 \quad (123)$$

The primary amine formed is then determined as discussed in Section III. Simet[399] proposed to determine organic isocyanates by hydrolysis in an acid medium, followed by the determination of the carbon dioxide that is liberated according to the following equation:

$$R—NCO + H_2O + H^+ \rightarrow RNH_3^+ + CO_2 \quad (124)$$

These methods have not been evaluated.

D. Colorimetric Methods. Isocyanates react with hydroxylamine to yield hydroxamic acids:[400,401]

[396] A. N. Panchenko and G. S. Smirnov, *J. Gen. Chem., USSR*, **2**, 193 (1932).

[397] H. H. Anderson, *J. Am. Chem. Soc.*, **71**, 1801 (1949).

[398] W. E. Kemp, *Analyst*, **64**, 648 (1939).

[399] L. Simet, private communication.

[400] D. J. Davidson, *J. Chem. Ed.*, **17**, 81 (1940).

[401] R. E. Buckles and C. J. Thelen, *Anal. Chem.*, **22**, 676 (1950).

$$R—NCO + H_2NOH \rightarrow R—NH—C(OH)=NOH \rightleftharpoons R—NH—CO—NHOH \quad (125)$$

The resulting acid forms colored complexes with ferric ion that may be used for their estimation as discussed on page 61.

In the method described by Kubitz[402] for the determination of traces of isocyanate in urethane-base polymers, the sample is treated with an excess of standard n-butylamine in a tetrahydrofuran solution. Excess of reagent is determined colorimetrically by Malachite green with which it forms a colorless derivative.

Bank[403] reported a color reaction for determining hexamethylene-diisocyanate by means of sodium nitrite in the presence of acetone. Funke and Hamann[404] determined the same compound by hydrolysis to the diamine, followed by diazotization and coupling reaction of the diazotate to produce color. Similar method has been used for the analysis of tolylene diisocyanate.[405]

E. Physical Methods. The ultraviolet absorption spectra of methyl, ethyl, and phenyl isocyanate have been investigated by Woo and Liu.[40] The absence of the characteristic absorption due to the carbonyl group is discussed.

The infrared absorption of the isocyanate function at 4.5 μ has been employed for their quantitative estimation.[407] Lord[408] reported the infrared absorption spectra of isomeric tolylene diisocyanates. Lieber and co-workers[409] studied the infrared absorption spectra of isothiocyanates and suggested the 2060 cm^{-1} to 2105 cm^{-1} band as suitable for identifying such compounds. Hence the determination of known isothiocyanates by infrared spectrometry is possible.

XI. The Nitro, Nitroso, and N-Oxide Functions

A. General. The nitro, nitroso, and N-oxide functions are characterized by a nitrogen atom attached to one or two oxygen atoms. In the case of N-oxides, the nitrogen atom is a part of a heterocyclic ring structure.

The technical and military importance of organic nitro compounds is responsible for a large number of publications concerning methods for

[402] K. A. Kubitz, *Anal. Chem.*, **29**, 814 (1957).

[403] H. Bank, *Chem. Ind.*, **59**, 168 (1948).

[404] W. Funke and K. Hamann, *Farbe Lack*, **64**, 120 (1958).

[405] H. Marcali, *Anal. Chem.*, **29**, 552 (1957).

[406] S. C. Woo and T. K. Liu, *J. Chem. Phys.*, **3**, 544 (1935).

[407] M. E. Bailey, V. Kirss, and R. G. Spaunburgh, *Ind. Eng. Chem.*, **48**, 794 (1956).

[408] S. S. Lord, Jr., *Anal. Chem.*, **29**, 497 (1957).

[409] E. Lieber, C. N. R. Rao, and J. Ramachandran, *Spectrochim. Acta*, **13**, 296 (1959).

their estimation, including several reviews.[410-413] It should be noted that most of the information available in the literature deals with macro procedures, and very little has been published on micro methods.

A general analytical technique that is applicable to nitro, nitroso, and N-oxide functions is based on redox reactions. In the present discussion all methods will be considered, whereas procedures that have been or can be adapted to the micro (0.1 meq.) scale will be emphasized.

B. Reductive Methods

1. Titanous Ion as Reductant. Knecht[414] proposed to use titanous chloride for the determination of nitrobenzene in 1903. Later, he and his co-worker published several papers and a monograph[415] on this subject. Although many other reductants have been suggested during the past six decades, titanous chloride remains the most commonly recommended reagent for the quantitative analysis of aromatic nitro and nitroso compounds and N-oxides.

Titanium forms salts in which its valence is $+2$, $+3$, or $+4$. It should be noted that the titanous compounds used as reductants are in the oxidation state Ti(III). Therefore the nitro function consumes six moles of titanous salt; nitroso function, four moles; and N-oxide, two moles, respectively:

$$-NO_2 + 6Ti^{+3} + 6H^+ \rightarrow -NH_2 + 6Ti^{+4} + 2H_2O \tag{126}$$

$$-NO + 4Ti^{+3} + 4H^+ \rightarrow -NH_2 + 4Ti^{+4} + H_2O \tag{127}$$

$$\underset{=/}{\diagdown N} : O + 2Ti^{+3} + 2H^+ \rightarrow \underset{=/}{\diagdown N} + 2Ti^{+4} + H_2O \tag{128}$$

Many techniques of the titanous chloride reduction procedure have appeared in the literature. The generally adopted technique is to reduce the sample with an excess known quantity of titanous chloride, followed by the determination of the excess of reagent by back-titration with standard ferric ammonium sulfate. Determinations ranging from macro to ultramicro scale have been described. The reader is referred to Kolthoff

[410] H. B. Hass and E. F. Riley, *Chem. Revs.*, **32**, 373 (1943).

[411] W. W. Becker, *Anal. Chem.*, **22**, 185 (1950).

[412] R. P. Zimmerman and E. Lieber, *Anal. Chem.*, **22**, 1151 (1950).

[413] W. W. Becker and W. E. Shaefer, in *Organic Analysis*, Vol. 2, Interscience, New York, 1954, p. 71.

[414] E. Knecht, *Berichte.*, **36**, 1667 (1903).

[415] E. Knecht and E. Hibbert, *New Reduction Methods in Volumetric Analysis*, 2nd ed., Longmans, Green, London, 1925.

and Robinson[416] and Siggia[417] for the determination of nitro and nitroso groups using 0.1 to 0.2N titanous chloride, and to Brooks and Sternglantz[418] for the determination of N-oxide groups. Maruyama[419] and Loriente and Nieto[420] determined milligram quantities of nitro compounds by heating the reaction mixture at 50 to 60°C. Blom and Caris[421] described a procedure for the determination of nitro groups in a 20 μg. sample by means of 0.003N titanous chloride. It should be noted that titanous salts are very susceptible to oxidation. Procedures that provide adequate protection of the standard solution on the macro scale usually fail when its concentration falls below 0.05N.

An extensive study of the determination of the nitro and nitroso functions by titanous chloride on the 0.1 meq. scale has been made and a micro procedure that does not involve reaction at elevated temperatures has been developed.[422] The apparatus is shown in Figure 8.12. The sample is placed in the reaction flask D, which is connected with the micro-buret E with a ground-glass joint, and is flushed with a current of purified nitrogen. Both nitro and nitroso groups are reduced in a sodium acetate buffered solution at room temperature. Nitroso groups may be determined in the presence of nitro groups by replacing the buffer with concentrated hydrochloric acid. The detailed procedures are given in experiment 37.

The kinetics of the reduction of aromatic nitro compounds by titanous chloride was investigated by Newton, Stubbs, and Hinshelwood.[423] The reaction for nitrobenzene is shown to proceed through the following sequence:

$$C_6H_5-NO_2 \xrightarrow{[H]} C_6H_5NO \xrightarrow{[H]} C_6H_5-NHOH \xrightarrow{[H]} C_6H_5-NH_2 \qquad (129)$$

The rate of reduction is proportional to $[Ti^{+3}][C_6H_5NO_2]/[H^+]^2$. Active species are thought to be $[C_6H_5-NO_2H^+]$ and a hydrolyzed form of Ti^{+3}. Nitrosobenzene and phenylhydroxylamine are reduced many times more rapidly than nitrobenzene. However, the former two compounds combine to form azoxybenzene according to equation 130:

[416] I. M. Kolthoff and C. Robinson, Rec. Trav. Chim., 45, 169 (1926).

[417] S. Siggia, Quantitative Organic Analysis Via Functional Groups, 2nd ed., John Wiley and Sons, New York, 1954, p. 128.

[418] R. T. Brooks and P. D. Sternglantz, Anal. Chem., 31, 561 (1959).

[419] S. Maruyama, Sci. Papers, Inst. Physics and Chem. Research, Tokyo, 16, 196 (1931).

[420] E. Loriente and F. Nieto, Ion, 7, 11 (1947).

[421] L. Blom and J. Caris, Nature, 184, 1313 (1959).

[422] T. S. Ma and J. V. Earley, Mikrochim. Acta, 1959, 129.

[423] S. A. Newton, Jr., F. J. Stubbs, and C. Hinshelwood, J. Chem. Soc., 1953, 3384.

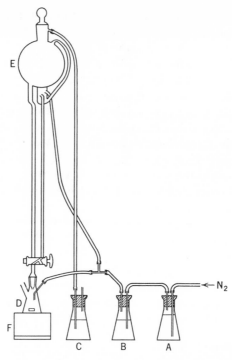

Fig. 8.12. Assembly for titanous chloride reduction. Courtesy of *Mikrochimica Acta*.

$$C_6H_5—NO + C_6H_5—NHOH \rightarrow C_6H_5—N\overset{\diagdown}{}\underset{O}{\overset{}{}}\overset{\diagup}{N}—C_6H_5 + H_2O \qquad (130)$$

Azoxybenzene, in turn, yields aniline, but at a much slower rate. The theoretical aspects of the reduction of aliphatic nitro compounds have not been studied. It is interesting to note that the analytical procedures recommended for the determination of aromatic nitro groups are not applicable to nitro paraffins.[422] Low and erratic results are obtained for nitroethane and 2-nitro-2-methyl-1-propanol. According to Fauth and Roecker[424] only one nitro group in 2,2-dinitropropane is reducible by titanous chloride, and two nitro groups are reduced for 2,2,2,-trinitroethanol.

Other titanous salts, such as the sulfate[425,426] and polyphosphate,[427] have

[424] M. I. Fauth and G. W. Roecker, *Anal. Chem.*, **33**, 894 (1961).

[425] C. F. van Duin, *Rec. Trav. Chim.*, **39**, 578 (1920).

[426] T. Callan, I. A. R. Henderson, and N. Strafford, *J. Soc. Chem. Ind.*, **39**, 86 (1920).

[427] S. Suzuki, Y. Muramoto, M. Veno, and T. Sugano, *Bull. Chem. Soc. Japan*, **30**, 775 (1957).

been suggested as the reductant to avoid chlorination of the benzene nucleus. It has been established, however, that no chlorination occurs in the micro procedure.[422] Since titanous chloride is commercially available, this salt is the reagent of choice.

Dachselt[428] reported the direct potentiometric titration of nitro and nitroso compounds with standardized titanous chloride solution. In view of the fact that the redox reaction does not take place instantaneously, it is doubtful that this method can be adapted to the micro scale.

2. Chromous Ion as Reductant. Chromous chloride was first used by Someya[429] to determine nitro groups in the following manner. Chromic chloride was reduced by zinc amalgam and hydrochloric acid. The amalgam was filtered off, and the filtrate added to a solution of the nitro compound. After 2 to 5 minutes, the excess of chromous ions was titrated with $0.1N$ ferric chloride. The reduction of the nitro function by chromous chloride is represented in equation 131:

$$Ar—NO_2 + 6CrCl_2 + 6HCl \rightarrow Ar—NH_2 + 6CrCl_3 + 2H_2O \qquad (131)$$

This method was re-investigated by Furman and Bottei[430,431] and extended to the determination of nitroso and N-nitroso groups. The N-nitroso group consumes 6 moles of chromous chloride, as illustrated by cupferron:

$$C_6H_5—\underset{\underset{NO}{|}}{N}—ONH_4 + 6CrCl_2 + 7HCl \rightarrow$$

$$C_6H_5—\underset{\underset{H}{|}}{N}—ONH_4 + 6CrCl_3 + NH_4Cl + H_2O \qquad (132)$$

The standard solution used was $0.1N$, and the back-titration with ferric alum was performed potentiometrically. Jucker[432] and Tandon[433] advocated chromous sulfate solution as the reductant.

Chromous ion is a stronger reducing agent than titanous ion and therefore is more susceptible to air oxidation. The fact that chromium assumes higher valence than $+3$ may cause complication in the analytical procedure. Standard chromous solutions less concentrated than $0.1N$ have not been reported, and the reduction method has not been tested on the micro scale.

3. Stannous Ion as Reductant. Aromatic nitro groups have been deter-

[428] E. Z. Dachselt, *Anal. Chem.*, **68**, 404 (1926).
[429] K. Someya, *Z. Anorg. Allgem. Chem.*, **169**, 293 (1928).
[430] N. H. Furman and R. S. Bottei, *Anal. Chem.*, **29**, 121 (1957).
[431] R. S. Bottei and N. H. Furman, *Anal. Chem.*, **27**, 1182 (1955).
[432] H. Jucker, *Anal. Chim. Acta*, **16**, 210 (1957).
[433] J. P. Tandon, *Z. Anal. Chem.*, **167**, 184 (1959).

mined in the macro scale by means of stannous chloride. The sample is reduced by an excess known amount of the standard solution as represented in equation 133:

$$Ar—NO_2 + 3SnCl_2 + 6HCl \rightarrow Ar—NH_2 + 3SnCl_4 + 2H_2O \qquad (133)$$

Most workers recommend the back-titration of the excess of stannous chloride with $0.1N$ iodine.[434–437] However, Florentin and Vandenberghe[438] reported that a true equivalence point is not reached when the excess stannous chloride is titrated with iodine in the presence of sodium carbonate or Rochelle salt. These workers proposed a procedure in which an excess of standard ferric chloride solution is added, followed by back-titration with $0.1N$ potassium permanganate. The pH of the solution has to be controlled to prevent the re-oxidation of the aromatic amine. Berry and Colwell[439] used standard copper sulfate solution as titrant for the excess stannous ions in a strongly acidic solution. If bromide is present, the titrant acts as its own indicator, the endpoint being a change from brownish-violet to yellow. Mercuric chloride also serves as the indicator, which ceases to give a turbidity when the equivalence point is reached.

The reduction of nitro groups by stannous chloride is a slow reaction, as is evidenced by the macro analytical procedures that prescribe heating the reaction mixture in a sealed tube[440,441] or being under reflux for 2 hours.[442,443] Judging from these facts, the stannous chloride reduction method is not suitable for adaptation to the micro scale.

4. Use of Other Ions. Vanadous sulfate has been used for the determination of aromatic nitro groups on the macro[444,445] and micro[446] scales. Gapchenko and Scheintsis described a micro method as follows.[446] The sample is dissolved in acetone in a 25-ml. Erlenmeyer flask filled with carbon dioxide, and two- to three-fold excess of a standardized vanadous

[434] E. D. W. S. Colver and E. B. R. Prideaux, *J. Soc. Chem. Ind.*, **36**, 480 (1917).

[435] J. G. F. Druce, *Chem. News*, **118**, 133 (1919).

[436] L. Desvergnes, *Ann. Chim.*, **2**, 141 (1920).

[437] G. Wallerius, *Tek. Tid. Upplc. Kemi*, **58**, 33 (1928).

[438] D. Florentin and H. Vandenberghe, *Bull. Soc. Chim.*, **27**, 158 (1920).

[439] A. J. Berry and C. K. Colwell, *Chem. News*, **112**, 1 (1915).

[440] H. Limpricht, *Berichte*, **11**, 35 (1878).

[441] A. P. Sachs, *J. Soc. Chem. Ind.*, **36**, 915 (1917).

[442] S. W. Young and R. E. Swain, *J. Am. Chem. Soc.*, **19**, 812 (1897).

[443] L. E. Hinkel, E. E. Ayling, and T. M. Walters, *J. Chem. Soc.*, **1939**, 403.

[444] P. C. Banerjee, *J. Indian Chem. Soc.*, **19**, 30 (1942).

[445] G. Witig-Schwachtgen, *Inst. Grand-Ducal Luxembourg. Sect. Sci. Nat. Arch.*, **22**, 87 (1955).

[446] M. V. Gapchenko and O. G. Scheintsis, *Zavodsk. Lab.*, **9**, 562 (1940).

sulfate solution is added, whereby the nitro function is reduced as represented in equation 134:

$$Ar—NO_2 + 6V^{+2} + 6H^+ \rightarrow Ar—NH_2 + 6V^{+3} + 2H_2O \qquad (134)$$

After 5 minutes the excess of vanadous ions is titrated with standard ferric alum using safranine as indicator.

Vanadous sulfate is a very strong reducing agent. It is even more efficient than chromous chloride for removing oxygen from a stream of nitrogen gas.[447] Like chromous ion, the difficulty in using vanadous ion for quantitative microanalysis is the instability of the $0.01N$ solution and the multiple oxidation states of the reagent.

Trivalent molybdenum was employed as the reductant for the determination of trinitrophenol and nitrosophenylhydroxylamine by Gapchenko.[448] Molybdenum is oxidized to the pentavalent state in the reaction. A two- to three-fold excess of the reagent is added to the sample in an atmosphere of carbon dioxide. Two to three minutes later, methylene blue is added as indicator, and the excess of trivalent molybdenum is determined by titration with standardized ferric ammonium sulfate.

Ferrous sulfate was used by Mitra and Srinivasan[449] to determine T.N.T. and tetryl, and by Cottrell and co-workers[450] to determine nitroguanidine. The sample is titrated directly with the reductant. The endpoint can be located either potentiometrically[450] or visually dependent on the appearance of $FeSO_4$—NO colored complex. Since the ferrous ion is a weak reducing agent, the application of this method is limited.

5. *Metallic Zinc as Reductant.* Peré and Lobunets[451,452] published a series of papers on the use of liquid zinc amalgam for the macro determination of aromatic nitro compounds. The acetic acid solution of sample (0.5 to 1.5 g.) is treated with 50 ml. of $4N$ hydrochloric acid and 15–20 ml. of 2–2.5% zinc amalgam in a flask. The reaction mixture is shaken until the solution becomes colorless. This indicates the complete reduction of the nitro groups to the amino groups, as depicted in equation 135:

$$Ar—NO_2 + 3Zn(Hg)_x + 6HCl \rightarrow Ar—NH_2 + 3ZnCl_2 + 2H_2O + xHg \qquad (135)$$

The aromatic amine produced is then determined either by nitrosation

[447] L. Meites, *Anal. Chem.*, **20**, 984 (1948).

[448] M. V. Gapchenko, *Zavodsk. Lab.*, **10**, 245 (1941).

[449] B. N. Mitra and M. Srinivasan, *Analyst*, **70**, 418 (1945).

[450] T. L. Cottrell, C. A. MacInnes, and E. M. Patterson, *Analyst*, **71**, 207 (1946).

[451] M. I. Peré and M. M. Lobunets, *Univ. état Kiev. Bull. Sci. Rec. Chim.*, **2**, 45, 73 (1936); **3**, 37, 43 (1937).

[452] M. M. Lobunets, *Univ. état Kiev Bull. Sci. Rec. Chim.*, **2**, 81 (1936); **3**, 71 (1937); **4**, 23, 41 (1939); *Z. Anal. Chem.*, **128**, 279 (1948).

(see Section III-C-1) or by bromination (see Chapter 11, Section V-D-2). A 0.1N potassium bromate-bromide mixture and 0.2N sodium nitrite, respectively, are used as the titrant. The endpoint of sodium nitrite titration is located by means of starch iodide paper. Musha[453] applied this method to the analysis of nitroso groups and determined the endpoint potentiometrically. This technique has not been tested on the micro scale. It is worthy of mention that these workers reported complete reduction of the sample by means of liquid zinc amalgam in a few seconds at room temperature. Conversely, Walthuis and co-workers[454] presented a macro method for determining nitro groups in which 0.5-g. sample is heated under reflux with zinc and hydrochloric acid for 30 minutes. The difference in the rate of reduction between these two methods is remarkable.

6. *Cadmium as Reductant.* Determination of aromatic nitro compounds by reduction with cadmium was described by Lobunets.[455] The apparatus used is a Jones reductor in which electrolytic cadmium metal is packed. The aromatic amine produced is then brominated by means of bromate-bromide mixture, and the excess of bromine is back-titrated with standard sodium thiosulfate.

Budesinsky[456] applied chelatometry to the determination of aliphatic and aromatic nitro and nitroso groups in the following way. The sample (about 1 meq.) is dissolved in methanol in a flask. Flat discs of metallic cadmium and hydrochloric acid are introduced and the flask is shaken for 90 minutes. The supernatant liquid is then transferred to a titration flask. After the addition of ammonia-ammonium chloride buffer, the cadmium ion is titrated with 0.05M EDTA using Eriochrome black-T as the indicator.

7. *Nickel as Reductant.* Ruzhentsova and Goryacheva[457] described a procedure to use Raney nickel for the determination of aromatic nitro groups on the macro scale. The sample is boiled with 3 g. of the catalyst paste in 25 ml. of 0.5N ethanolic potassium hydroxide for 1 to 2 hours. The solution is filtered into 10 ml. of concentrated hydrochloric acid and the catalyst is washed with 50 ml. of ethanol. The combined solution is then evaporated. The residue is redissolved in hydrochloric acid and titrated with 0.1N sodium nitrite. Excellent results have been reported. However, adaptation of this method to the micro scale is difficult.

[453] S. Musha, *J. Chem. Soc. Japan*, **66**, 38 (1945).
[454] E. Walthuis, S. Kolk, and L. Schaap, *Anal. Chem.*, **26**, 1238 (1954).
[455] M. M. Lobunets, *Zavodsk. Lab.*, **7**, 872 (1938).
[456] B. Budesinsky, *Chem. Listy*, **50**, 1931 (1956).
[457] A. K. Ruzhentsova and N. S. Goryacheva, *Doklady Akad. Nauk.*, *USSR*, **81**, 849 (1951).

C. Miscellaneous Titrimetric Methods

1. Modified Kjeldahl Method for Nitro and Nitroso Groups. It is interesting to note that the determination of nitro or nitroso groups as ammonia by the modified Kjeldahl method can easily be accomplished in spite of the fact that the nitrogen in these two functions is at a higher oxidation state than that in N—N functions. Certain nitroso[458] and nitro[459,460] compounds were reported to give quantitative recovery of ammonia by the regular Kjeldahl procedure. Nevertheless, it is advisable to apply the prereduction technique (see Section VI-I-1) before the concentrated sulfuric acid digestion. Dissolution of the nitro or nitroso compound in methanol or acetic acid and treatment with zinc and hydrochloric acid is a convenient method on the 0.1 meq. scale.[461] The detailed procedure is given in experiment 35. The sequence of the reactions is represented as follows:

$$R—NO_2 \xrightarrow{[H]} R—NH_2 \xrightarrow{H_2SO_4} (NH_4)_2SO_4 \xrightarrow{NaOH} NH_3 \qquad (136)$$

2. Coulometric Reduction of the Nitro Function. Electrometric determination of nitro groups was reported by Ehlers and Sease[462] and Kruse.[463] The sample is dissolved in methanol containing lithium chloride or alkyl quaternary ammonium chloride, and a current of constant potential is passed through. The number of coulombs of electricity consumed is a measure of the nitro function:

$$—NO_2 + 6e \rightarrow —N^{-2} + 2O^{-2} \qquad (137)$$

The equipment and technique required in constant potential coulometric reduction are more elaborate than the other reductometric methods. On the other hand, the electrometric method was shown to give correct results for both aliphatic and aromatic nitro groups. Since electric current can be measured with high precision, this method is applicable to determinations below the 0.1 meq. scale. It has also been employed for the differential determination of nitro compounds. Binary mixtures, whose components have reduction waves separated by at least 0.35 v., were analyzed successfully by using consecutive electrolysis at different cathode potentials.[462]

3. Acidimetric Determination of the Nitro Function. The nitro function attached to a primary or secondary carbon atom is capable of enolization to yield the aci-form as represented in equations 138 and 139 respectively:

[458] F. Zinneke, *Angew. Chem.*, **64**, 220 (1952).
[459] B. M. Margosches, W. Kirsten, and E. Scheinost, *Berichte*, **56**, 1943 (1923).
[460] P. R. W. Baker, *Analyst*, **80**, 481 (1955).
[461] T. S. Ma, R. E. Lang, and J. D. McKinley, Jr., *Mikrochim. Acta*, **1957**, 368.
[462] V. B. Ehlers and J. W. Sease, *Anal. Chem.*, **31**, 16 (1959).
[463] J. M. Kruse, *Anal. Chem.*, **31**, 1854 (1959).

$$H_3C—NO_2 \rightleftharpoons H_2C=N=O \atop \qquad\qquad\quad OH \qquad\qquad\qquad (138)$$

$$(CH_3)_2CH—NO_2 \rightleftharpoons (CH_3)_2C=N{\overset{\displaystyle O}{\underset{\textstyle OH}{\Big/}}} \qquad (139)$$

Nitro compounds are titrable as acid in nonaqueous media,[464–467] but they are too weak to be titrated in aqueous solutions. The micro procedure is given in experiment 32.

Brockmann and Meyer[465] investigated the potentiometric titration of trinitrophenol in ethylenediamine with sodium colaminate. A yellow precipitate appears after 2 moles of the base are introduced, but noticeable potential change does not show until 3 moles are added. This compound, therefore, acts like a triprotic acid. Sarson[467] reported that mono-, di-, and tri-nitrotoluene can be differentially resolved by titration in isobutyl methyl ketone and dimethylformamide.

4. Iodometric Methods

A. FOR NITROSO GROUPS. Lobunets and Gortinska[468] presented a macro procedure for iodometric determination of nitrosobenzene. The sample is dissolved in dilute alcohol; $6N$ hydrochloric acid and 20% potassium iodide are added. After a few minutes the iodine liberated is titrated with $0.1N$ sodium thiosulfate. The nitroso compound is reduced to phenylhydroxylamine as shown in equation 140:

$$C_6H_5—NO + 2KI + 2HCl \rightarrow C_6H_5NHOH + I_2 + 2KCl \qquad (140)$$

The phenylhydroxylamine then undergoes molecular rearrangement to form p-aminophenol.

Becker and Shaefer[413] reported the determination of diphenylnitrosoamine with potassium iodide and hydrochloric acid. These workers stated that 1 mole of the nitrosoamine yields 1 equivalent of iodine, but equations for the reaction were not given. It probably occurs in the following manner:

$$2(C_6H_5)_2N—NO + 2KI + 2HCl \rightarrow 2(C_6H_5)_2NH + 2NO + I_2 + 2KCl \qquad (141)$$

The iodide ion has no effect on aromatic nitro groups, although concentrated hydriodic acid reduces the latter to the amine at elevated tempera-

[464] J. S. Fritz and N. M. Lisicki, *Anal. Chem.*, **23**, 589 (1951).

[465] H. Brockmann and E. Meyer, *Naturwissenschaften*, **40**, 242 (1953).

[466] J. S. Fritz, A. J. Moye, and M. J. Richard, *Anal. Chem.*, **29**, 1685 (1957).

[467] R. D. Sarson, *Anal. Chem.*, **30**, 932 (1958).

[468] M. M. Lobunets and E. N. Gortinska, *Univ. état Kiev Bull. Sci. Rec. Chim.*, **4**, 37 (1939).

tures. Therefore the iodometric method may be used to determine the nitroso function in the presence of aromatic nitro groups.

B. FOR ALIPHATIC NITRO GROUPS. Tetranitromethane was determined by Sakamaki and co-workers[469] by means of potassium iodide and sulfamic acid. A known amount of $0.1N$ sodium thiosulfate was then added, and the excess was back-titrated with standard iodine solution.

Primary and secondary nitroparaffins can be chlorinated by sodium hypochlorite, as shown in equation 142:

$$H_3C—NO_2 + NaOCl \rightarrow ClCH_2NO_2 + NaOH \tag{142}$$

An indirect iodometric method was developed by Jones and Riddick[470] in which the sample (0.6 to 1.4 g.) is treated with a known volume of sodium hypochlorite followed by the determination of residual hypochlorite through the liberation of iodine. This method has not been tested on the micro scale.

5. *Methods Based on Aquametry.* Two methods for determining the aromatic nitro function proposed by Kissin are based on the measurement of water produced in a suitable reaction. In one method[471] the nitro compound is condensed with an aromatic amine. One mole of water is produced, as shown in equation 143:

$$Ar—NO_2 + H_2N—C_6H_5 \rightarrow Ar—\overset{\|}{\underset{O}{N}}{=}N—C_6H_5 + H_2O \tag{143}$$

In another method[472] the nitro group is reduced with zinc dust in an anhydrous medium in the presence of an amine hydrochloride. Two moles of water are obtained from each nitro group, as depicted in equation 144:

$$Ar—NO_2 + 3Zn + 6C_6H_5NH_3Cl \rightarrow ArNH_2 + 2H_2O + 3ZnCl_2 + 6C_6H_5NH_2 \tag{144}$$

Neither of these methods is suitable for adaptation to the micro scale.

D. Gasometric Methods

1. *Measurement of Nitric Oxide.* Cope and Barab[473] found that the nitro and nitroso functions attached to an amino nitrogen (known as N-nitro and N-nitroso groups respectively) liberate nitric oxide on treatment with mercury and sulfuric acid:

[469] I. Sakamaki, H. Ishikawa, and R. Nakamura, *Japan Analyst,* **6,** 626 (1957).
[470] L. R. Jones and J. A. Riddick, *Anal. Chem.,* **28,** 1137 (1956).
[471] B. I. Kissin and S. A. Vorobeichikov, *Russian Patent,* 56,179 (1939).
[472] B. I. Kissin, *Russian Patent,* 58,088 (1940).
[473] W. C. Cope and J. Barab, *J. Am. Chem. Soc.,* **38,** 2552 (1916).

$$2R_2N\text{---}NO_2 + 3Hg + 3H_2SO_4 \rightarrow 2NO + 2R_2NH + 3HgSO_4 + 2H_2O \quad (145)$$

$$2R_2N\text{---}NO + Hg + H_2SO_4 \rightarrow 2NO + 2R_2NH + HgSO_4 + H_2O \quad (146)$$

Macro and semimicro apparatus[474] have been devised to measure the nitric oxide gas. The micro method is not yet available. It should be noted that nitric oxide is slightly soluble in water and concentrated sulfuric acid. The conventional microazotometer cannot be employed for the determination of nitric oxide. The use of the gasometric apparatus of Ma and Scheinthal[475] is suggested (see p. 152).

Lehmstedt and Zumstein[476] advocated ferrous chloride in hydrochloric acid as the reagent, as represented in equation 147:

$$R_2N\text{---}NO + FeCl_2 + HCl \rightarrow NO + R_2NH + FeCl_3 \quad (147)$$

These workers reported low results by the mercury-sulfuric acid method because certain N-nitro and N-nitroso compounds undergo molecular rearrangement in concentrated sulfuric acid to give C—NO_2 and C—NO groups. These latter groups do not yield nitric oxide upon reduction. Jones and Kenner[477] described a method using cuprous chloride as the reducing agent, whereas stannous chloride was shown to be unsatisfactory. Besides nitroso derivatives of aliphatic and aromatic amines, nitroso groups attached to the heterocyclic nitrogen, such as piperidine, also liberate nitric oxide quantitatively.

2. Measurement of Nitrogen. The N-nitroso function can be reduced to hydrazine which on mild oxidation yields nitrogen gas.[478] The sequence of transformation may be indicated as follows:

$$R_2N\text{---}NO \xrightarrow{Zn + HCl} R_2N\text{---}NH_2 \xrightarrow{K_3Fe(CN)_6} N_2 \quad (148)$$

It should be noted that nitrogen is derived from both the nitroso and amino functions in this reaction, in contrast to the liberation of nitric oxide discussed in the preceding section.

Clauser[479] determined nitrosoaniline by measuring the amount of nitrogen produced on reacting the compound with a large excess of phenyl-hydrazine. In this case, the nitrogen is liberated from the reagent and not from the nitroso function.

A gasometric method for determining aromatic nitro groups was proposed

---

[474] P. J. Elving and W. R. McElroy, *Ind. Eng. Chem., Anal. Ed.,* **14,** 84 (1942).

[475] T. S. Ma and B. Scheinthal, unpublished work; see B. Scheinthal, *Master's Thesis, Brooklyn College,* 1961.

[476] K. D. Lehmstedt and O. Zumstein, *Berichte,* **58,** 2024 (1925); **60,** 1910 (1927).

[477] E. C. S. Jones and J. Kenner, *J. Chem. Soc.,* **1932,** 711.

[478] M. Yokoo, *Pharm. Bull. Japan,* **6,** 64 (1958).

[479] R. Clauser, *Berichte,* **34,** 889 (1901).

by Ohashi[480] and Takagi and Hyashi.[481] The nitro compound is reduced to the corresponding amine by iron and sulfuric acid. Oxidation of the amine by means of potassium iodate in phosphoric acid at 300°C yields nitrogen gas that is collected in the nitrometer and measured. Since this method does not differentiate nitro and amino nitrogen, it has no advantage over the modified Kjeldahl method (see Section XI-C-1).

3. *Measurement of Hydrogen.* Hörmann and co-workers[482] determined aromatic nitro compounds by quantitative hydrogenation using palladium in barium sulfate as catalyst. The Warburg apparatus was employed and a 0.1 to 0.6 mg. sample was taken for analysis. This method can be adapted to the 0.1 meq. scale by using the microhydrogenation apparatus (see Chapter 10, Section II-C-2).

The reduction of nitro,[483] nitroso, and N-oxide functions with sodium borohydride may provide a convenient gasometric micro method of analysis. The sample can be placed in the reaction vessel shown in Fig. 6.15, p. 152. A known amount of sodium borohydride is added. After the reduction is complete, the excess of reagent is determined by introducing dilute hydrochloric acid. Hydrogen gas is liberated and measured in the gasburet.

E. Gravimetric Methods. Two gravimetric methods for determining aromatic nitro and nitroso groups on the macro scale have been proposed. In one method[484] the sample and 10 g. of tin are placed in the reaction flask fitted with a reflux condenser. Methanol, 0.25M hydrochloric acid, and water are introduced, and the mixture is heated for 1 hour while a current of carbon dioxide passes through. The following reaction takes place:

$$Ar—NO_2 + 3Sn + 7HCl \rightarrow Ar—NH_3Cl + 3SnCl_2 + 2H_2O \tag{149}$$

The residual tin is then filtered off, washed, dried at 75°C, and weighed. Copper and sulfuric acid are recommended as reagents in another method.[485] Precision and accuracy of ±0.5% were claimed. Similar results are not expected, however, when these procedures are converted to the micro scale.

Erdey and co-workers[486] determined nitro compounds by using the modified Kjeldahl digestion technique (see Section XI-C-1), but they

[480] S. Ohashi, *Bull. Chem. Soc. Japan,* **28**, 537 (1955).

[481] T. Takagi and N. Hyashi, *J. Chem. Soc. Japan,* **78**, 445 (1957).

[482] H. Hörmann, J. Lamberts, and G. Fries, *Z. Physiol. Chem.,* **306**, 42 (1956).

[483] H. C. Brown, E. J. Mean, and B. C. S. Rao, *J. Am. Chem. Soc.,* **77**, 6209 (1955).

[484] C. E. Vanderzee and W. F. Edgell, *Anal. Chem.,* **22**, 572 (1950).

[485] R. S. Juvet, Jr., M. C. Twickler, and L. C. Afremow, *Anal. Chim. Acta,* **22**, 87 (1960).

[486] L. Erdey, L. Polos, and Z. Gregorowicz, *Talanta,* **3**, 6 (1959).

314   A CRITICAL SURVEY OF THE ANALYTICAL METHODS

precipitated the resulting ammonium ion with sodium tetraphenylboron. There is no advantage in this method over steam-distillation of ammonia.

F. Colorimetric Methods. Reagents reported for the colorimetric determination of aliphatic nitro compounds include resorcinol-sulfuric acid,[487] ferrous sulfate-sulfuric acid,[488] and ferric chloride-hydrochloric acid.[489] Primary nitroparaffins have been determined by their coupling reaction with diazonium salts.[490,491] Nitro alcohols[492] are hydrolyzed by alkali to yield formaldehyde, which is determined by the chromotropic acid method.

Aromatic dinitro and polynitro compounds are determined by the intensity of the color which they produce in alkali solutions. Sodium hydroxide-acetone mixture is the most commonly used reagent.[493–496] The color can be stabilized by adding an ammonium base.[497,498] The use of sodium ethoxide in benzene is also suggested.[499] Nitro phenols give color in sodium hydroxide solution when stannous chloride[500] or glucose[501] is added. Nitro derivatives of benzene, pyridine, and pyrimidine produce violet color on treatment with sodium acetate, zinc, and sodium pentacyanoammino-ferroate, but nitrofurans and nitroparaffins give no color under the same conditions.[502] Nitroso compounds form blue quinoid structures with diphenylbenzidine in sulfuric acid.[503]

G. Physical Methods. Polarographic determination of nitro and nitroso compounds has been studied by many workers. The reader is

[487] L. R. Jones and J. R. Riddick, *Anal. Chem.*, **24**, 1533 (1952).
[488] F. J. Bandelin and R. E. Pankratz, *Anal. Chem.*, **30**, 1435 (1958).
[489] E. W. Scott and J. F. Treon, *Ind. Eng. Chem., Anal. Ed.*, **12**, 189 (1940).
[490] F. Turba, R. Haul, and R. Uhlen, *Angew. Chem.*, **61**, 74 (1949).
[491] J. R. Cohen and A. P. Altshuller, *Anal. Chem.*, **31**, 1638 (1959).
[492] L. R. Jones and J. A. Riddick, *Anal. Chem.*, **28**, 254 (1956).
[493] I. M. Korenman and A. M. Fisher, *Zavodsk. Lab.*, **14**, 1058 (1948).
[494] F. L. English, *Anal. Chem.*, **20**, 745 (1948).
[495] T. Urbanski, S. Kwiatowska, and W. Kutkiewicz, *Bull. Acad. Polon. Sci. Ser. Chim.*, **7**, 397 (1959).
[496] J. P. Heotis and J. W. Cavett, *Anal. Chem.*, **31**, 1977 (1959).
[497] C. C. Porter, *Anal. Chem.*, **27**, 805 (1955).
[498] F. M. Freeman, *Analyst*, **81**, 299 (1956).
[499] K. Cruse and R. Mittag, *Z. Anal. Chem.*, **131**, 273 (1950).
[500] I. V. Kulikov and S. U. Panova, *J. Gen. Chem. USSR*, **2**, 736 (1932).
[501] R. Stöhr and F. Scheibl, *Mikrochemie*, **36**, 362 (1951).
[502] S. Okuma, *Pharm. Soc. Japan*, **75**, 1342 (1955).
[503] V. Anger, *Mikrochim. Acta*, **1960**, 58.

referred to the review by Kolthoff and Lingane.[504] Elving and Olson[505] reported the polarographic behavior of the N-nitroso function. Determination of nitroparaffins was described by several groups of investigators.[506-508]

The ultraviolet and visible absorption spectra of nitro alkylbenzenes were published by Schroeder and co-workers.[509] Jones and Thorn[510] recorded the ultraviolet absorption spectra of aliphatic nitroamines and nitrosoamines. Nitrochlorobenzenes have been determined by means of infrared spectroscopy.[511]

XII. The Ureido and Urethano Functions

A. General. The ureido and urethano functions are derived from carbamic acid, $H_2N-COOH$, whose amide is urea, NH_2CONH_2, and whose esters, H_2NCOOR, are called urethans. Urea and its derivatives (ureides) are common metabolites, and a number of urethans find use as pharmaceuticals. Substituted ureas and urethans are frequently synthesized in small amounts for the characterization of amines, alcohols, and phenols, respectively, using an aryl isocyanate[512] or azide[513] as the derivatizing reagent. Besides determining the melting point of the derivative, it is often desirable to ascertain its molecular weight through functional group analysis.

B. Nonaqueous Titrimetry

1. Titration with Perchloric Acid. Urea and substituted ureas possess very feeble basic properties (pK_a of urea = 13.82). It is not possible to determine these compounds as bases by dissolving them in acetic acid and titrating them with standard perchloric acid. On the other hand, when

[504] I. M. Kolthoff and J. Lingane, *Polarography*, 2nd ed., Interscience, New York, 1952, p. 746.

[505] P. J. Elving and E. C. Olson, *J. Am. Chem. Soc.*, **79**, 2697 (1957).

[506] N. Radin and T. DeVries, *Anal. Chem.*, **24**, 971 (1952).

[507] R. Miguel and A. Condylis, *Bull. Soc. Chim. France*, **1955**, 236.

[508] W. Kemula and D. Sybilska, *Chem. Anal. Warsaw*, 4, 123 (1959).

[509] W. A. Schroeder, P. E. Wilcox, K. N. Trueblood, and A. O. Dekker, *Anal. Chem.*, **23**, 1740 (1951).

[510] R. N. Jones and G. D. Thorn, *Can. J. Research*, **27**, 828 (1949).

[511] N. Oi and K. Miyazaki, *J. Pharm. Soc. Japan*, **77**, 1027 (1957).

[512] N. D. Cheronis and J. B. Entrikin, *Semimicro Qualitative Organic Analysis*, 2nd ed., Interscience, New York, 1957.

[513] P. P. T. Sah and T. S. Ma, *J. Chinese Chem. Soc.*, **2**, 159 (1934); *Rec. Trav. Chim.*, **58**, 453 (1939).

they are dissolved in acetic anhydride at 0°C and titrated with 0.01N perchloric acid in acetic acid, the equivalence point can be located visually or potentiometrically.[514] The detailed procedure is given in experiment 3.

The ionization constants of urethans are not available in the literature. The possibility of determining urethans as bases has not been investigated.

2. Determination of Urethans with Sodium Methoxide. Cerri and co-workers[515] proposed a method for the determination of the carbamoyl group in urethans as follows. The sample (1 to 2 meq.) is dissolved in pyridine, and a known quantity of 0.1N sodium methoxide in benzene-methanol mixture is added. The solution is heated under reflux in absence of moisture. The following reaction takes place:

$$H_2N—COOR + NaOCH_3 \rightarrow NaCNO + H_2O + ROCH_3 \qquad (150)$$

After cooling, the residual sodium methoxide is back-titrated with 0.1N benzoic acid in benzene using thymol blue as the indicator. This method is limited to urethans in which there is no substitution on the nitrogen atom. Amides, urea, biuret, thiourea, and semicarbazones do not interfere. This procedure has not been adapted to the micro scale.

C. Aqueous Titrimetry

1. Methods Dependent on Conversion to Ammonia. Determination of urea in biological fluids is usually carried out by the enzymatic method.[516] The sample is incubated with urease which hydrolyzes urea to ammonium carbonate as represented in equation 151:

$$H_2NCONH_2 + 2H_2O \xrightarrow{\text{urease}} (NH_4)_2CO_3 \qquad (151)$$

Concentrated potassium carbonate solution is then added to liberate ammonia. Sobel and co-workers[517] described an aeration technique to recover the ammonia from μeq. amounts of urea. For determinations on the 0.1 meq. scale, the steam-distillation apparatus of Ma and Breyer[518] (see Fig. 6.6, p. 123) is recommended. The ammonia is absorbed in 2% boric acid solution and titrated with 0.01N standard acid using the bromocresol green-methyl red mixed indicator.

According to Swann and Esposito,[519] urea in urea-formaldehyde resins is released as ammonia on heating with 14% potassium hydroxide in ethylene glycol. The ammonia is collected in 0.1N sulfuric acid which is

[514] M. Gutterson and T. S. Ma, *Mikrochim. Acta*, **1960**, 1.

[515] O. Cerri, A. Spialtini, and V. Gallo, *Pharm. Acta Helv.*, **34**, 13 (1959).

[516] D. D. van Slyke and G. E. Cullen, *J. Biol. Chem.*, **19**, 211 (1914).

[517] A. E. Sobel, A. Hirschman, and L. Besman, *Anal. Chem.*, **19**, 927 (1947).

[518] T. S. Ma and R. Breyer, *Microchem. J.*, **4**, 484 (1960).

[519] M. H. Swann and G. G. Esposito, *Anal. Chem.*, **28**, 1984 (1956).

back-titrated with $0.1N$ sodium hydroxide. This method can be converted to the micro scale. It is interesting to note that melamine does not give ammonia under the same conditions.

Rosenthaler[520] reported that urethans are best determined by warming with concentrated sulfuric acid until no more carbon dioxide evolves, then heating more strongly until the solution turns dark. After cooling, alkali is added, and ammonia is recovered by steam-distillation. Toth and Krasznai[521] advocated the reduction of urethans by a catalytic hydrogenation method using Raney nickel, followed by the regular Kjeldahl procedure (see Section III-F-4).

2. Methods Dependent on Oxidation. Urea is oxidized by hypobromite ions as shown in equation 152:

$$H_2NCONH_2 + 3BrO^- \rightarrow CO_2 + 3Br^- + 2H_2O + N_2 \qquad (152)$$

Wölfel[522] presented a method in which the sample is heated with a known volume of $0.5N$ hypobromite, and the excess of reagent is determined iodometrically by means of $0.5N$ sodium thiosulfate. The main source of error is due to the formation of cyanate.

Chloramine-T has been suggested as oxidant for urea, which reacts with 3 moles of the reagent in the presence of sodium bicarbonate. Direct titration with $0.1N$ solution of the oxidant was reported by two groups of workers. The endpoint was determined either visually with indigo carmine as an indicator[523] or potentiometrically[524] using platinum electrodes. These methods have not been tested on the micro scale.

D. Gasometric Methods

1. Methods Dependent on Liberation of Nitrogen. Several papers have appeared that apply the reaction given in equation 152 and measure the volume of nitrogen gas produced. According to Samoilov,[525] sodium hypobromite gives correct results, but hypochlorite yields low values. Glass[526] recommended bromine and sodium hydroxide as the oxidizing mixture. Oriol[527] described a microgasometer in which no mercury is used. However, the hypobromite method for the determination of urea has been shown to be subject to errors by several workers[528] owing to incomplete removal of

[520] L. Rosenthaler, *Pharm. Ztg.-Nache*, **88**, 252 (1952).

[521] Z. Toth and I. Krasznai, *Magy. Kem. Folyoirat*, **65**, 289 (1959).

[522] K. Wölfel, *Z. Anal. Chem.*, **90**, 170 (1932).

[523] B. N. Afanasev, *Zavodsk. Lab.*, **16**, 1011 (1950).

[524] B. Singh, A. Singh, and M. Singh, *Research Bull., East Punjab Univ.*, **30**, 55 (1953).

[525] A. F. Samoilov, *Lab. Prakt. USSR*, **13**, 1, 23 (1938); **15**, 21 (1939).

[526] A. L. Glass, *Chemist-Analyst*, **43**, 104 (1954).

[527] A. Oriol, *Bull. Soc. Chim. Biol.*, **21**, 1337 (1939).

[528] R. L. Stehle, *J. Bio. Chem.*, **51**, 89 (1922); P. Menaul, *J. Bio. Chem.*, **51**, 87 (1922).

nitrogen, formation of oxides of nitrogen, and also of carbon monoxide. A procedure in which the nitrogen generated is led through a Dumas nitrogen-type combustion furnace and then collected in a nitrometer has been described by Ronzio and Sharrah.[529]

Another approach to liberate nitrogen from the ureido function is by nitrosation (see Section III-C). Thus urea reacts with nitrous acid to give 2 moles of nitrogen:[530]

$$H_2NCONH_2 + 2HONO \rightarrow 2N_2 + CO_2 + 3H_2O \tag{153}$$

Monosubstituted and unsymmetrical disubstituted ureas yield 1 mole of nitrogen, whereas symmetrical disubstituted ureas do not liberate nitrogen gas. These determinations can be carried out on the 0.1 meq. scale in the primary amino apparatus (see Fig. 8.9, p. 000). Ninagawa[531] investigated the determination of urea in urea-formaldehyde polymers and advocated the use of 30% sodium nitrite with acetic-sulfuric acid mixture as solvent.

2. Method Dependent on Liberation of Methane. According to Zerewitnoff,[532] the hydrogen atoms in the ureido function are sufficiently labile to react with methylmagnesium iodide. Two moles of methane are liberated at room temperature, and a third mole is obtained when the reaction mixture is heated. However, this result has not been confirmed. The reader is referred to Chapter 11, Section III on the determination of active hydrogen.

E. Gravimetric Methods. Gravimetric determination of urea has been suggested by a number of workers, but it is difficult to adapt the published procedures to the micro scale. Urea forms dibenzylurea on treatment with benzylamine as shown in equation 154:

$$H_2NCONH_2 + 2C_6H_5CH_2NH_2 \rightarrow C_6H_5CH_2NHCONHCH_2C_6H_5 + 2NH_3 \tag{154}$$

The dibenzylurea is then separated and weighed.[533–535] Other reagents that have been proposed for the isolation of urea are xanthydrol[536–538] and glycine.[539]

[529] A. Ronzio and M. Sharrah, *Microchem. J.*, **6**, 233 (1962).
[530] D. D. van Slyke, *J. Bio. Chem.*, **9**, 185 (1911).
[531] E. Ninagawa, *J. Chem. Soc. Japan, Ind. Chem. Sect.*, **59**, 1227 (1956).
[532] T. Zerewitnoff, *Berichte* **41**, 2233 (1908).
[533] C. P. A. Kappelmeier, *Paint Oil Chem. Rev.*, **3**, 8, 48 (1948).
[534] P. P. Grad and R. J. Dunn, *Anal. Chem.*, **25**, 1211 (1953).
[535] G. Widmer, *Kunststoffe*, **46**, 359 (1956).
[536] A. Boivin, *Bull. Soc. Chim. Biol.*, **8**, 456 (1926).
[537] F. W. Allen and J. M. Luck, *J. Biol. Chem.*, **82**, 693 (1929).
[538] J. F. Barrett and F. B. Jones, *Biochem. J.*, **26**, 1246 (1932).
[539] F. Lippich, *Z. Physiol. Chem.*, **90**, 124 (1914).

Cerri and co-workers[515] proposed a gravimetric method to determine urethans which is dependent on the precipitation of sodium cyanate when the sample reacts with sodium methoxide in anhydrous pyridine (eq. 150). The sodium cyanate is filtered off, dried, and weighed.

F. Colorimetric Methods. Various colorimetric methods are available for the determination of urea. Most procedures are based on the condensation reaction between the primary amino group of the ureido function and a carbonyl compound. Diacetyl and acetyl-benzoyl,[540] diacetyl-monoxime,[541,542] and propiophenone oxime[543,544] have been used. Ureides give red to purple color when treated with a mixture of dimethyl-glyoxime and thiosemicarbazide in ethanolic hydrochloric acid.[545] p-Dimethylaminobenzaldehyde develops a blue color with urea.[546,547] The same reagent produces a yellow color when it reacts with methylurea[548] or urethans.[549]

Hydroxy compounds such as resorcinol in hydrochloric acid[550] and xanthydrol in sulfuric acid[551,552] have been suggested as colorimetric reagents for urea. Another method proposed involves nitrosation.[553] The sample is treated with a known quantity of nitrous acid. After the decomposition of urea (eq. 153), the excess of reagent is determined by means of the azo dye produced upon addition of sulfanilic acid and α-naphthylamine.

540 R. C. Dickenman, B. Crafts, and B. Zak, *Am. J. Clin. Path.*, **24**, 981 (1954).

541 P. Elodi, *Acta Physiol. Acad. Sci. Hung.*, **6**, 225 (1954).

542 H. L. Rosenthal, *Anal. Chem.*, **27**, 1980 (1955).

543 M. Murayama, *J. Lab. Clin. Med.*, **39**, 795 (1952).

544 S. Adachi, *J. Agr. Chem. Soc. Japan*, **30**, 126 (1956).

545 S. Okuma, *J. Pharm. Soc. Japan*, **75**, 1291 (1955).

546 G. W. Watt and J. D. Chresp, *Anal. Chem.*, **26**, 452 (1954).

547 R. E. Cline and R. M. Fink, *Anal. Chem.*, **28**, 47 (1956).

548 F. Jancik, B. Kakac, and V. Vanicek, *Chem. Listy*, **12**, 2181 (1958).

549 M. H. Swann and G. G. Esposito, *Anal. Chem.*, **30**, 107 (1958).

550 G. Fenich and A. Tommasini, *Bull. Chim. Farm.*, **91**, 391 (1952).

551 E. M. Abrahamson, *Am. J. Clin. Path.*, **26**, 103 (1956).

552 M. J. Pro, B. A. Nelson, and A. P. Mathers, *J. Ass. Off. Agri. Chemists*, **40**, 309 (1957).

553 W. Brandt, *Mikrochemie*, **22**, 181 (1937).

9

The Sulfur Functions

I. Introduction

With a few exceptions, this chapter deals with all organic functional groups that contain the element sulfur. As mentioned previously, the isothiocyanate function is treated as a nitrogen function. Sulfites and sulfates are considered as salts among the oxygen functions.

Sulfur and oxygen belong to the same group in the periodic table and, therefore, many sulfur functions are analogous to oxygen functions. However, an analytical method for an oxygen function may not be applicable to its sulfur analog. Sulfur also forms a number of functional groups for which there are no equivalent members among the oxygen functions. For convenience, this chapter is divided into the following sections:

1. The mercapto, thiol, or sulfhydryl function.
2. The sulfide and disulfide functions.
3. The sulfinic and sulfonic functions.
4. The sulfonamide functions.
5. The sulfoxide and sulfonic functions.
6. The thiocyanate and thiourea functions.
7. The xanthate, thiol acid, and dithiocarbamate functions.

II. The Mercapto Function

A. General. The mercapto function, —SH, is the sulfur analog of the hydroxyl function. It is also called the thiol or sulfhydryl group. Compounds containing this function are known as mercaptans, thiols, and thiophenols. The methods for the estimation of the mercapto or sulfhydryl function may be summarized into the following categories: (a) those which are based on the formation of an insoluble or slightly dissociated metal mercaptide; (b) those based upon oxidation of the functional —SH group; (c) gasometric methods; and (d) miscellaneous methods which include a variety of procedures such as acidimetric, reaction with colloidal sulfur, vinyl chloride, and other reagents.

B. Titrimetric Methods Based on Formation of Mercaptides

1. Reaction with Silver Ion.   Compounds containing the mercapto function react with silver nitrate to precipitate silver mercaptides according to the following equation:

$$R-SH + AgNO_3 \rightarrow R-S-Ag + HNO_3 \qquad (1)$$

Kunkel and co-workers[1] determined alkane thiols in hydrocarbons by titration with standard silver nitrate in ammoniacal ethanol using ammonium dithizonate as the indicator. Several investigators[2-5] advocated adding a known quantity of silver nitrate to the sample followed by back-titration of the excess of reagent with ammonium thiocyanate in the presence of ferric ion. For microdeterminations, electrometric titration is recommended provided the equipment is available. Amperometric titration of the mercapto function using a rotating platinum electrode was proposed by Kolthoff and co-workers.[6,7] This method is extremely sensitive and has been demonstrated to give accurate results on the μg. scale.[8-10] The reaction mixture should be protected from air since oxidation leads to low values.[11] On the other hand, neighboring amino and carboxyl groups may cause positive errors.[12] A convenient amperometric titration assembly suitable for the determination of sulfhydryl groups on the 0.1 meq. scale[13] is shown in Figure 9.1. The sample solution is placed in a 100 ml beaker, C, covered with a cardboard through which pass the microburet A, glass electrode B, nitrogen delivery tube G, and dropping mercury electrode JF. The leads from the electrodes are connected to the polarograph. The detailed procedure is given in experiment 50.

Potentiometric titration of the mercapto function in a buffered solution

[1] R. K. Kunkel, J. E. Buckley and G. Gorin, *Anal. Chem.*, **31**, 1098 (1959).

[2] P. Borgstrom and E. E. Reid, *Ind. Eng. Chem., Anal. Ed.*, **1**, 186 (1929).

[3] G. E. Mapstone, *Proc. Australian Chem. Inst.*, **13**, 373 (1946).

[4] R. Middeldorf, *Arzneimittel Forsch.*, **1**, 311 (1951).

[5] M. R. Beychoch, *Petr. Engr.*, No. 2, C 38 (1953).

[6] I. M. Kolthoff and W. E. Harris, *Ind. Eng. Chem., Anal. Ed.*, **18**, 161 (1946).

[7] I. M. Kolthoff, W. Stricks, and L. Morran, *Anal. Chem.*, **26**, 366 (1954).

[8] S. Rosenberg, C. Perrone, and P. L. Kirk, *Anal. Chem.*, **22**, 1186 (1950).

[9] S. Levine, *Instrum. and Automation*, **30**, 883 (1957).

[10] G. I. Kotlyar, *Biokhimiya*, **24**, 15 (1959).

[11] N. Strafford, F. R. Cropper, and A. Hamer, *Analyst*, **75**, 55 (1950).

[12] L. A. Sluyterman, *Biochem. Biophys. Acta*, **25**, 402 (1957).

[13] T. S. Ma and A. Faraone, unpublished work; see A. Faraone, *Master's Thesis, Brooklyn College*, 1961.

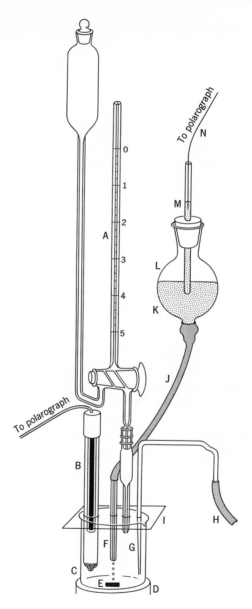

Fig. 9.1. Assembly for amperometric titration.

by means of standard silver nitrate in alcohol has been proposed.[14,15] Karchmer[16] reported that the presence of elemental sulfur interferes with the determination because of the formation of alkali polysulfide. Accuracy is improved by using a less alkaline medium and titration under nitrogen.

2. *Reaction with Mercuric Ion.* Mercaptans form insoluble or undissociable mixed-salts with mercuric compounds. For example, the reaction product between an alkyl mercaptan and mercuric chloride[17] is shown as follows:

$$R\text{—}SH + HgCl_2 \rightarrow R\text{—}SHgCl + HCl \qquad (2)$$

Stricks and Chakravarti[18] described an amperometric titration procedure for the determination of sulfhydryl groups in biological materials using ethylmercuric chloride as the titrant. This reagent is shown to be better than mercuric chloride because the latter forms a complex with glutathione. Fritz and Palmer[19] titrated 0.3 to 1 meq. samples with standard mercuric perchlorate potentiometrically or using thio-Michler's ketone as the indicator.

A coulometric method for determining mercaptans was suggested by Przybylowicz and Rogers.[20] Mercuric ion is generated electrically and the following reaction occurs:

$$2R\text{—}SH + Hg^{+2} \rightarrow (R\text{—}S)_2Hg + 2H^+ \qquad (3)$$

The procedures described above are suitable for adaptation to the 0.1 meq. scale. It should be noted that disulfides, if present, will interfere with the determination (see Section III), but sulfides have no effect.

C. Titrimetric Methods Based on Oxidation

1. *Oxidation by Iodine.* Several workers[21–23] have used standardized iodine solution to determine the mercapto function. The sample is treated with a measured volume of $0.1N$ iodine and the excess of reagent is back-titrated with $0.1N$ sodium thiosulfate to the starch endpoint. The following equation is used in the calculation:

[14] M. W. Tamele and L. B. Ryland, *Ind. Eng. Chem., Anal. Ed.*, **8**, 16 (1936).
[15] R. Cecil and S. R. McPhee, *Biochem. J.*, **59**, 235 (1955).
[16] J. H. Karchmer, *Anal. Chem.*, **29**, 425 (1957).
[17] S. Dal Nogare, in *Organic Analysis*, Vol. 2, Interscience, New York, 1953, p. 331.
[18] W. Stricks and S. K. Chakravarti, *Anal. Chem.*, **33**, 194 (1961).
[19] J. S. Fritz and T. A. Palmer, *Anal. Chem.*, **33**, 98 (1961).
[20] E. P. Przybylowicz and L. B. Rogers, *Anal. Chim. Acta*, **18**, 596 (1958).
[21] J. W. Kimball, R. L. Kramer, and E. E. Reid, *J. Am. Chem. Soc.*, **43**, 1199 (1921).
[22] I. D. Clark, *U.S. Naval Air Locket Test Sta. Rept. Fll.*, p. 1 (1951).
[23] J. A. R. Cooper and G. S. Maingot, *Anal. Chem.*, **27**, 1479 (1955).

$$2R—SH + I_2 \rightarrow R—SS—R + 2HI \qquad (4)$$

However, Kolthoff and Harris[24] have demonstrated that this stoichiometric relationship is valid only for primary mercaptans. Tertiary mercaptans react mole for mole of iodine and give sulfinyl iodides.

Because $0.01N$ iodine solution is difficult to keep, the micro method discussed in the next section is recommended for iodimetric determination of sulfhydryl groups on the 0.1 meq. scale.

2. Oxidation by Iodate or Bromate in Presence of Iodide or Bromide. Mercaptans can be determined by dissolution in methanol, mixed with acetic acid and potassium iodide, followed by titration with standardized potassium iodate. The first appearance of free iodine indicates the endpoint. The micro procedure[25] based on the following reaction will be found in experiment 22.

$$6RSH + HIO_3 \rightarrow 3RSSR + 3H_2O + HI \qquad (5)$$

Willemart and Fabre[26] investigated the electrometric determination of thiols by titrating the sample in the presence of iodide or bromide using standard potassium bromate. There is a 25 μA jump at the equivalence point when $0.1N$ titrant is used, but only 1.5 μA for $0.01N$ titrant.

3. Oxidation by Cupric Ion. Cupric ion oxidizes the mercapto function to yield cuprous mercaptide and disulfide according to the following equation:

$$4R—SH + 2Cu^{+2} \rightarrow 2R—S—Cu + R—SS—R + 4H^+ \qquad (6)$$

Standard cupric acetate,[27] oleate,[28] sulfate,[29] and alkyl phthalate[30] have been used as titrants on the macro scale. The endpoint is determined by the appearance of the blue color of the excess cupric ion,[28,30] or by the formation of a permanent yellow precipitate of the mercaptide.[29] However, these two techniques are not suitable when $0.01N$ titrant is used. Roth[31] suggested an indirect micro method as follows. The sample is treated with an excess amount of cupric butyl phthalate dissolved in a solvent mixture containing acetic acid, amyl alcohol, butanol, or hydrocarbon. After standing for 5 minutes, the residual cupric ions are determined by liberating iodine with potassium iodide and titrating the iodine with $0.01N$ sodium thiosulfate. According to Ellis,[27] part of the iodine that is liberated oxidizes

[24] I. M. Kolthoff and W. E. Harris, *Anal. Chem.*, **21**, 163 (1949).

[25] T. S. Ma, and F. Tepper, unpublished work.

[26] R. Willemart and P. Fabre, *Ann. Pharm. Françaises*, **16**, 676 (1958).

[27] E. W. Ellis, *Anal. Chem.*, **23**, 1777 (1951).

[28] G. R. Bond, Jr., *Ind. Eng. Chem., Anal. Ed.*, **5**, 257 (1933).

[29] S. B. Sant and B. R. Sant, *Anal. Chem.*, **31**, 1879 (1959).

[30] E. Turk and E. E. Reid, *Ind. Eng. Chem., Anal. Ed.*, **17**, 713 (1945).

[31] H. Roth, *Mikrochim. Acta*, **1958**, 769.

the mercaptide to the corresponding disulfide. Hence, only the remaining iodine is titrated by the standard sodium thiosulfate.

D. Gasometric Methods. The hydrogen atom of the mercapto function is sufficiently labile to react with the Grignard reagent (see page 418). Gilman and Nelson[32] reported that mercaptans also react with tetraethyl lead and triethyl bismuth which are not attacked by alcohols, amines, and acetylenic hydrogen. However, results on the microanalytical application of these reactions are not available.

Ishii[33] proposed a gasometric method for determining thiol groups which is based on the catalytic effect of mercaptans on the reaction between sodium azide and iodine to produce nitrogen gas. This method is not suitable for adaptation to the 0.1 meq. scale. Furthermore, it should be noted that other sulfur functions also catalyze this reaction.[34]

E. Miscellaneous Methods

1. Acidimetric Methods. Hopkins and Smith[35] demonstrated the quantitative extraction of thiols from petroleum distillates by absorption with sodium aminoethylate in ethylenediamine. This indicates the possibility of determining the mercapto function as acid by means of nonaqueous titration (see Chapter 11, Section II).

Benesch and Benesch[36] presented a method for the determination of mercapto groups by specific proton displacement. The sample is treated with iodo-acetamide at pH 9. The acid produced is then titrated.

2. Reaction with Colloidal Sulfur. The mercapto function liberates hydrogen sulfide when treated with colloidal sulfur at pH 7 and 30°C:[37-39]

$$2R—SH + S \rightarrow H_2S + R—SS—R \qquad (7)$$

The hydrogen sulfide can be removed by a stream of nitrogen gas, absorbed in zinc acetate solution and determined iodometrically.

3. Reaction with Vinyl Cyanide. Obtemperanskaya and co-workers[40] proposed a macro method to determine thio alcohols and thiophenols which is dependent on the addition of the mercapto function to vinyl cyanide:

[32] H. Gilman and J. F. Nelson, *J. Am. Chem. Soc.*, **59**, 935 (1937).
[33] K. Ishii, *J. Japan Biochem. Soc.*, **24**, 118 (1952).
[34] F. Feigl, *Spot Tests in Organic Analysis*, 5th ed., Elsevier, Amsterdam, 1956.
[35] R. L. Hopkins and H. M. Smith, *Anal. Chem.*, **26**, 206 (1954).
[36] R. Benesch and R. E. Benesch, *Biochem. Biophys. Acta*, **23**, 643 (1957).
[37] A. Hefter, *Med. Naturw. Arch.*, **1**, 81 (1908).
[38] J. D. Guthrie and J. Allerton, *Contrib. Boyce Thompson Inst.*, **12**, 103 (1941).
[39] M. W. Brenner, J. L. Owades, and R. Golyzniak, *Am. Soc. Brew. Chem.*, **1954**, 88.
[40] S. I. Obtemperanskaya, A. P. Terentev, and M. M. Buzlanova, *Vestn. Moskov. Univ.*, **1957**, 145.

$$R\text{---}SH + CH_2\text{=}CHCN \rightarrow CH_2\text{---}CH_2CN \atop |\atop SR \qquad (8)$$

The sample is treated with vinyl cyanide in dioxane. After 5 minutes sodium sulfite is added and the liberated alkali is titrated with $0.1N$ hydrochloric acid. This method has not been tested on the micro scale.

4. Application of Isotopic Tracer Technique. Thiol (sulfhydryl) groups in flour have been determined by means of iodosobenzoate and radioactive iodine.[41] Sodium iodide containing radioactive iodine is used. The free iodine liberated is absorbed by the starch and the unreacted sodium iodide is then determined in the supernatant liquid by a Geiger counter. This method is suitable for μg. analysis.

5. Special Method for Aminothiophenol. Ruzicka[42] reported that 2-aminothiophenol reduces ethoxyresazurin quantitatively in $4N$ hydrochloric acid. At the endpoint, the color changes from red to greenish blue. This is a special method for aminothiophenols and is not applicable to other mercapto compounds. The presence of aminophenols interferes with the determination.

6. Special Method for Sulfenyl Halides. Sulfenyl halides, R—SX, are halogen derivatives of the mercapto function. A method for the determination of certain aromatic sulfenyl halides was suggested by Kharasch and Wald.[43] The sample (1.5 meq.) is dissolved in an anhydrous solvent and sodium iodide in glacial acetic acid is added:

$$2Ar\text{---}SCl + 2NaI \rightarrow Ar\text{---}SS\text{---}Ar + I_2 + 2NaCl \qquad (9)$$

After the liberation of iodine, water is added, followed by a measured volume of standard sodium thiosulfate solution. The excess of thiosulfate is then back-titrated with standard iodine solution. It should be noted that the reaction shown in equation 9 proceeds to completion only in an anhydrous medium. This method has not been tested on the micro scale.

F. Colorimetric Methods. Mercapto compounds have been determined colorimetrically by means of phosphotungstic acid,[44] nitrous acid,[45,46] sodium nitroprusside,[47] *p*-chloromercuribenzoate,[48] 1-(4-chloromercuri-

[41] P. Nordin and E. Y. Spencer, *Cereal Chem.*, **29**, 29 (1951).

[42] E. Ruzicka, *Chem. Listy*, **51**, 969 (1957).

[43] N. Kharasch and M. M. Wald, *Anal. Chem.*, **27**, 996 (1955).

[44] K. Shinohara, *J. Biol. Chem.*, **109**, 665 (1935); **110**, 263 (1935).

[45] F. W. Woods, *Analyst*, **74**, 179 (1949).

[46] G. E. Mapstone, *Chem. and Ind.*, **36**, 1113 (1954).

[47] K. Shinohara and M. Kilpatrick, *J. Biol. Chem.*, **105**, 241 (1934).

[48] I. Fridovich and P. Handler, *Anal. Chem.*, **29**, 1219 (1957).

phenylazo)-2-naphthol,[49] and 2,6-dibromo-p-benzoquinonechlorimine.[50] When 2,4-dinitrofluorobenzene is used as the colorimetric reagent for the determination of cysteine,[51] only the mercapto group reacts below pH 5.5 to form 5-(2,4-dinitrophenyl)-cysteine whose absorption maximum is at 320 mμ. Mercapto compounds react with fluoropyruvic acid to give products absorbing at 265–275 mμ. The maximum absorption is shifted to 300 mμ when a primary amino group is in the alpha- or beta-position, and the molecular extinction is increased ten-fold.[52] Sulfhydryl groups can be measured by the extent of the reduction of the absorption peak at 300 mμ exhibited by N-ethylmaleimide[53] at pH 6. This is due to the decomposition of the reagent.[54] Thiols also give a red color on treatment with N-ethyl maleimide in alkaline solution.[55] The reaction of the mercapto function with colloidal sulfur to liberate hydrogen sulfide (page 325) can be applied to colorimetric determinations.[39] The hydrogen sulfide is absorbed in a solution of zinc acetate and p-aminodimethylaniline and ferric chloride are added to produce methylene blue.

III. The Sulfide and Disulfide Functions

A. General. The sulfide function (—S—) consists of a sulfur atom attached to two carbon atoms; the disulfide function (—S—S—) is composed of two sulfur atoms each of which is joined to the carbon atom. Aliphatic sulfides are known as dialkyl sulfides or thioethers. Aliphatic disulfides are called dialkyl disulfides. A review on the quantitative methods for certain organic sulfides was published by Sease and co-workers.[56] Hubbard and co-workers[57] evaluated four known methods for the determination of disulfides on the macro scale.

B. Oxidative Methods

1. Oxidation by Bromine. The most popular methods for determining the sulfide and disulfide functions are those which are based on oxidation

[49] L. Rausch and S. Ritter, *Klin. Wochschr.,* **33,** 1009 (1955).
[50] S. Kamiya, *Japan Analyst,* **8,** 596 (1959).
[51] H. Zuber, K. Traumann, and H. Zahn, *Z. Naturforsch.,* **10,** 457 (1955).
[52] T. Avi-Dor and J. Magyer, *J. Biol. Chem.,* **222,** 249 (1956).
[53] E. Roberts and G. Rouser, *Anal. Chem.,* **30,** 1291 (1958).
[54] J. O. Gregory, *J. Am. Chem. Soc.,* **77,** 3922 (1955).
[55] R. Benesch, R. E. Benesch, M. Gutcho, and L. Laufer, *Science,* **123,** 981 (1956).
[56] J. W. Sease, T. Lee, G. Holzman, E. H. Swift, and C. Nieman, *Anal. Chem.,* **20,** 431 (1955).
[57] R. L. Hubbard, W. E. Haines, and J. S. Ball, *Anal. Chem.,* **30,** 91 (1958).

by bromine. The reagents proposed include bromine water,[58] electrically generated bromine,[59] and bromate-bromide mixture.[60] The endpoint has been determined amperometrically,[59] potentiometrically,[61] iodometrically,[62] or by the color of bromine.[60] It is interesting to note the divergence of the reaction products. Thus, the bromine oxidation of disulfides has been reported to yield the sulfonyl bromide:[63–65]

$$R—SS—R + 5Br_2 + 4H_2O \rightarrow 2R—SO_2Br + 8HBr \tag{10}$$

or the sulfonic acid:[66]

$$R—SS—R + 5Br_2 + 6H_2O \rightarrow 2R—SO_3H + 10HBr \tag{11}$$

There is no discrepancy in the analytical results when the calculation is made on the basis of either equations 10 or 11 since the amount of bromine consumed is the same. However, certain disulfides, such as allyl propyl disulfide[67] and bis-(dialkylthiocarbamyl)-disulfide[68] have been demonstrated to give sulfate ions.

Sulfides have been reported to give either sulfoxides[58,61] or sulfones:[62,65]

$$R—S—R + Br_2 + H_2O \rightarrow R—\overset{}{\underset{\overset{\|}{O}}{S}}—R + 2HBr \tag{12}$$

$$R—S—R + 2Br_2 + 2H_2O \rightarrow R—\overset{\overset{O}{\|}}{\underset{\overset{\|}{O}}{S}}—R + 4HBr \tag{13}$$

Hence the stoichiometry of the analytical method has to be established by means of pure compounds before the determination of the unknown samples. Siggia and Edsberg[60] claimed that the use of bromate-bromide mixture limits the oxidation to the sulfoxide stage. However, Gauthier and Maillard[69] reported high results by this method due to formation of sulfones.

[58] J. R. Sampey, K. H. Slagle, and E. E. Reid, *J. Am. Chem. Soc.*, **54**, 340 (1932).

[59] J. W. Sease, C. Nieman, and E. H. Swift, *Anal. Chem.*, **19**, 197 (1947).

[60] S. Siggia and R. L. Edsberg, *Anal. Chem.*, **20**, 938 (1948).

[61] H. Landsberg and E. Escher, *Ind. Eng. Chem.*, **46**, 1422 (1954).

[62] W. Hauft and R. D. Schuetz, *Anal. Chem.*, **25**, 1258 (1953).

[63] S. Siggia, *Quantitative Organic Analysis Via Functional Groups*, 2nd ed., John Wiley and Sons, New York, 1954, p. 141.

[64] R. Willemart and P. Fabre, *Ann. Pharm. Françaises*, **16**, 676 (1958).

[65] H. Roth, *Mikrochim. Acta*, **1958**, 772.

[66] S. Dal Nogare, in *Organic Analysis*, Vol. 1, Interscience, New York, 1953, p. 363.

[67] E. F. Kohman, *Food Technol.*, **6**, 288 (1952).

[68] P. Ferreira, *Arquiv.*, **34**, 103 (1950).

[69] B. Gauthier and J. Maillard, *Compt. rend.*, **236**, 1178 (1953).

Bromometric microdetermination of sulfides[65,70] and disulfides[64,65] using 0.01–0.02N potassium bromate as titrant has been suggested by several investigators. The procedures[71] which are suitable for determination on the 0.1 meq. scale are given in experiment 23. In one method, the sample is dissolved in dilute acid, sodium bromide is added, and the solution is titrated with 0.03N potassium bromate until the first appearance of free bromine. In another method, an excess known quantity of potassium bromate is added to the acidified solution containing the sample and sodium bromide. After the oxidation is complete, the excess of bromate is determined iodometrically.

A titrimetric method for determining sulfides which entails extraction followed by acidimetry was proposed by Sampey, Slagle, and Reid.[58] The sample is dissolved in 50 ml. of benzene. An equal volume of water is introduced and saturated bromine solution is added until the bromine color persists in the reaction mixture. The reaction proceeds as shown in equation 12. After the separation of the aqueous layer, the benzene layer is washed with water to extract the hydrobromic acid dissolved in it. The combined aqueous solution is then titrated with standard sodium hydroxide. This method is not suited for microanalysis.

2. Oxidation by Hypochlorite. Leutch[72] described the chlorometric oxidation of sulfide groups. Organic sulfides are determined by means of 0.1N sodium hypochlorite. Conversion of this method to the micro scale is difficult, since 0.01N hypochlorite deteriorates rapidly.

3. Oxidation by Perbenzoic Acid. A macro method for the determination of sulfides by means of perbenzoic acid was presented by Lewin.[73] The sample is treated with a known volume of 0.2N perbenzoic acid in chloroform, which oxidizes the sulfide to sulfone:

$$R\!-\!S\!-\!R + 2C_6H_5C\!\!\overset{\displaystyle O}{\diagup}\!\!-\!OOH \rightarrow R\!-\!\overset{\displaystyle O}{\underset{\displaystyle O}{\overset{\|}{\underset{\|}{S}}}}\!-\!R + 2C_6H_5\!-\!C\!\!\overset{\displaystyle O}{\diagup}\!\!-\!OH \tag{14}$$

The excess of peroxide is then determined iodometrically (see Chapter 7, Section VI). This method is not recommended for conversion to the micro scale because of the instability of the reagent.

[70] F. Jancik, F. Buben and J. Körbl, *Ceskoslov Farmac*, **5**, 515 (1956).

[71] T. S. Ma and A. Faraone, unpublished work; see A. Faraone, *Master's Thesis, Brooklyn College*, 1961.

[72] S. L. Leutch, *J. Franklin Inst.*, **239**, 334 (1945).

[73] L. N. Lewin, *J. prakt. Chem.*, [2] **118**, 282 (1927).

C. Precipitation Procedures

1. Titration with Mercuric or Silver Ions. The disulfide function reacts with mercuric chloride in the presence of mercury to form a precipitate as shown in equation 15:

$$R—SS—R + HgCl_2 + Hg \rightarrow 2R—SHgCl \tag{15}$$

Amperometric determination of organic disulfides has been described with mercuric chloride[74,75] and ethylmercuric chloride[76] as the titrant. Potentiometric determination of the disulfide function by means of standard silver nitrate solution was described by Cecil and McPhee.[77] Though both methods are applicable to microdeterminations and serve to determine disulfide groups in the presence of sulfide, it should be noted that mercapto groups interfere with such determinations (see Section II-B-2).

2. Reactions with Sodium Plumbite or Hydroxymercuric Benzoic Acid. Two methods for determining disulfides have been proposed which are based on the cleavage of the —SS— linkage. Linnartz and Middeldorf[78] used standardized sodium plumbite as the reagent. The lead mercaptide and sulfide are filtered off and the excess of lead ions is precipitated as lead sulfate. The latter is redissolved in ammonium acetate and titrated with standardized ammonium molybdate solution using tannin as indicator. Wronski[79] heated the disulfide with sodium hydroxide and a measured amount of $0.03N$ o-hydroxymercuric benzoic acid, which forms complexes with sulfides. The excess of reagent is then back-titrated with thioglycolic acid. These methods have not been evaluated.

D. Reductive Titrimetry. The disulfide function can be quantitatively reduced to the mercapto function:

$$R—SS—R + 2[H] \rightarrow 2R—SH \tag{16}$$

Zinc amalgam,[80,81] sodium sulfite,[82] and sodium borohydride[83] have been employed as the reductant. The resulting mercaptan is then determined

---

[74] W. Stricks, I. M. Kolthoff, and N. Tanaka, *Anal. Chem.*, **26**, 299 (1954).

[75] J. R. Carter, *Science*, **120**, 895 (1954).

[76] W. Stricks and S. K. Chakravarti, *Anal. Chem.*, **33**, 194 (1961).

[77] R. Cecil and S. R. McPhee, *Biochem. J.*, **59**, 235 (1955).

[78] T. A. Linnartz and R. Middeldorf, *Süddeut, Apoth. Ztg.*, **89**, 593 (1949).

[79] M. Wronski, *Anal. Chem.*, **32**, 133 (1960).

[80] I. M. Kolthoff, D. R. May, P. Morgan, H. A. Laitinen, and A. S. O'Brien, *Ind. Eng. Chem., Anal. Ed.*, **18**, 442 (1946).

[81] I. I. Kolb and G. Toennies, *Anal. Chem.*, **24**, 1164 (1952).

[82] J. R. Carter, *J. Biol. Chem.*, **234**, 1705 (1959).

[83] C. R. Stahl and S. Siggia, *Anal. Chem.*, **29**, 154 (1957).

by an appropriate method (see Section II). The detailed procedure for the use of zinc amalgam on the 0.1 meq. scale is given on page 620.

E. Special Methods

1. Determination of Certain Thioethers. Thioethers containing a methyl or ethyl group can be determined in the form of methyl and ethyl iodide, respectively, by heating with hydriodic acid:

$$R—SCH_3 + HI \rightarrow R—SH + CH_3I \qquad (17)$$

Microdeterminations can be performed in the alkoxyl apparatus (see Chapter 6, Section VI). A microapparatus for determining methylthio groups was described by Holasek, Lieb, and Merz.[84] The iodometric method should be employed, since some gaseous sulfur compounds may form, pass into the absorber, and precipitate silver sulfide if the gravimetric method is used. Higher alkyl groups attached to sulfur are also cleaved by hydriodic acid. However, due to the high boiling point of the resulting alkyl iodide, the end measurement should be made by a gas chromatographic procedure (see page 622).

According to DuVigneaud[85] the benzyl group joined to sulfur is cleaved by sodium in liquid ammonia. It may be possible to apply this reaction to quantitative analysis.

2. Determination of Thioacetals. Gauthier and Maillard[86] proposed a method for the determination of thioacetals as follows. The sample is dissolved in a mixture of acetic acid, water, and hydrochloric acid. The solution is warmed to 30–40°C and then titrated with 0.1N potassium bromide-potassium bromate mixture to a yellow color. It is interesting to note that the oxidation stops at the disulfide stage:

$$R'CH(SR)_2 + Br_2 + H_2O \rightarrow R'CHO + R—SS—R + 2HBr \qquad (18)$$

3. Determination of Disulfide Groups by Specific Proton Displacement. Benesch and Benesch[87] developed a method to determine disulfide groups by specific proton displacement. The sample is treated with iodoacetamide at pH 9, and the acid produced is then titrated. It will be recalled that mercapto groups (see Section II-E-1) are also determined by this method.

4. Determination of Carbon Disulfide

A. CONVERSION TO DITHIOCARBAMIC ACID. Carbon disulfide reacts with a secondary amine to form dithiocarbamic acid. Romovacek[88] pro-

---

[84] A. Holasek, H. Lieb and W. Merz, *Mikrochim. Acta*, **1956**, 1216.

[85] V. DuVigneaud, *Science*, **123**, 968 (1956).

[86] B. Gauthier and J. Maillard, *Ann. Pharm. Françs.*, **11**, 509 (1953).

[87] R. Benesch and R. E. Benesch, *Biochem. Biophys. Acta*, **23**, 644 (1957).

[88] J. Romovacek, *Chem. Listy*, **52**, 1912 (1958).

posed diethanolamine or morpholine in pyridine as the reagent, followed by the titration of the product with $0.5N$ sodium hydroxide to the endpoint of thymolphthalein. For microdeterminations it is better to use di-n-butylamine in acetone solution, as shown in equation 19.

$$CS_2 + (nC_4H_9)_2NH \rightarrow (n\text{—}C_4H_9)_2N\text{—}\overset{\overset{\displaystyle S}{\|}}{C}\text{—}SH \qquad (19)$$

The resulting compound, di-n-butyldithiocarbamic acid, can be determined by titration with electrolytically generated mercury.[88a]

B. CONVERSION TO XANTHATE. Carbon disulfide is converted to potassium xanthate quantitatively when treated with anhydrous ethanolic potassium hydroxide:

$$CS_2 + KOH + C_2H_5OH \rightarrow S{=}C\overset{\displaystyle OC_2H_5}{\underset{\displaystyle SK}{\Big\backslash}} + H_2O \qquad (20)$$

The product can be determined by titration with standard iodine solution using starch as indicator[89] (see Section VIII-B-1). Johnson[90] described a gravimetric method in which the xanthate is precipitated as the copper salt. The precipitate is collected on a filter, ignited, and weighed as cupric oxide.

C. CATALYTIC EFFECT ON SODIUM AZIDE-IODINE REACTION. Kurzawa and Meybaum[91] presented a method to determine 0.05–2 mg. of carbon disulfide which is based on its catalytic effect on the sodium azide-iodine reaction:

$$2NaN_3 + I_2 \xrightarrow{CS_2} 2NaI + 3N_2 \qquad (21)$$

A measured volume of standard iodine solution is added to the sample mixed with sodium azide. The excess of iodine is then back-titrated. The amount of iodine consumed is shown to be proportional to the quantity of carbon disulfide present. The disadvantage of this method is its non-selectivity. Many sulfur compounds exhibit the same catalytic effect.[92,93]

5. *Determination of Carbonyl Sulfide.* Carbonyl sulfide, COS, is similar to carbon disulfide in structure, but requires a different method for analysis.

[88a] E. P. Przybylowicz and L. B. Rogers, *Anal. Chim. Acta*, **18**, 596 (1958).

[89] M. P. Matuszak, *Ind. Eng. Chem., Anal. Ed.*, **4**, 98 (1932).

[90] E. S. Johnson, *J. Am. Chem. Soc.*, **28**, 1209 (1906).

[91] Z. Kurzawa and Z. Meybaum, *Chem. Anal., Warsaw*, **5**, 333 (1960).

[92] T. Shiokawa and S. Suzuki, *J. Chem. Soc. Japan*, **71**, 629 (1950).

[93] F. Feigl, *Spot Tests in Organic Analysis*, 5th ed., Elsevier, Amsterdam, 1956.

According to Bruss and co-workers,[94] carbonyl sulfide is best dissolved in alcoholic ethanolamine and titrated potentiometrically with standard silver nitrate solution.

6. *Determination of Thiophene.* Thiophene may be considered as a cyclic sulfide. Like dialkyl sulfides, thiophene reacts with mercuric salts to precipitate mercury-substituted derivatives which can be used for analytical purpose. Spielman and Schotz[95] described a procedure in which the sample is dissolved in benzene and shaken with mercuric sulfate for 3 hours. The precipitate is collected on a filter, washed with hot water, dried at 110°C, and weighed as $C_4H_4S \cdot (HgO)_2 \cdot (HgSO_4)_2$. In the method proposed by Claxton and Hoffert[96] mercuric acetate is used to precipitate tetra-acetoxymercuric thiophene. After filtration, the precipitate is redissolved in aqua regia which oxidizes the sulfur to sulfate. Mercury is removed as basic mercuric oxide by the addition of ammonia. The sulfate in solution is then determined in form of barium sulfate gravimetrically.

F. Colorimetric and Physical Methods. Aliphatic sulfides react with iodine to form complexes that have unique ultraviolet absorption bands at about 308 mμ. This has been applied to quantitative analysis.[97] Disulfides are determined colorimetrically by means of phosphomolybdic acid.[98]

Carbon disulfide forms the yellow cupric diethyldithiocarbamate on treatment with diethylamine and copper acetate. Several colorimetric methods[99-101] have been suggested based on this reaction. Thiophene is usually determined by the blue color which it produces with isatin and concentrated sulfuric acid in the presence of nitric acid[102] or ferric sulfate.[103]

Polarographic studies of sulfides[104] and disulfides[105] have been reported. When the disulfide function is linked to an alkyl radical, its reduction potential is −1.25 v.; when it is linked to a phenyl radical, the potential is −0.5 v.

[94] D. B. Bruss, G. E. A. Wyld, and E. D. Peters, *Anal. Chem.*, **29**, 807 (1957).

[95] P. E. Spielman and S. P. Schotz, *J. Soc. Chem.*, **38**, 188 (1919).

[96] G. Claxton and W. H. Hoffert, *J. Soc. Chem. Ind.*, **65**, 342 (1946).

[97] S. H. Hastings and B. H. Johnson, *Anal. Chem.*, **27**, 565 (1955).

[98] N. D. Cheronis and S. Matt, unpublished work; see S. Matt, *Master's Thesis, Brooklyn College*, 1960.

[99] N. Tischler, *Ind. Eng. Chem., Anal. Ed.*, **4**, 146 (1932).

[100] F. J. Viles, *J. Ind. Hyg. Toxicol.*, **22**, 198 (1940).

[101] T. A. Dick, *J. Soc. Chem. Ind.*, **66**, 253 (1947).

[102] H. McKee, L. K. Herdon, and S. R. Withrow, *Anal. Chem.*, **20**, 30 (1948).

[103] Z. F. Solomko, *Nauch. Zap. Dnepropetrovskogo Gos. Unta*, **43**, 37 (1953).

[104] W. Furness, *J. Soc. Dyers Colourists*, **66**, 270 (1950).

[105] M. I. Guber and A. D. Shusharina, *Anal. Khim.*, **5**, 262 (1950).

IV. The Sulfinic and Sulfonic Functions

A. General. The sulfinic (R—SO—) and sulfonic (R—SO$_2$—) functions are characterized by a direct carbon to sulfur linkage and only one carbon skeleton attached to the sulfur atom which is joined to one or more oxygen atoms. These two functions are derived from sulfinic and sulfonic acids, respectively; they are also known as sulfinyl and sulfonyl groups. Aromatic sulfonic acids are important dye intermediates. Many alkylaryl sulfonates are surface active agents. A survey of the methods for the analysis of alkylbenzenesulfonates was published by Blank.[106] It should be noted that sulfonates are metal salts of sulfonic acids, while sulfonate oils are esters of sulfuric acid.

B. Acidimetric Determinations. Sulfonic acids are strong acids; sulfinic acids are moderately strong acids. Therefore, these acids can be determined on the 0.1 meq. scale by titration against aqueous 0.01N sodium hydroxide to the phenolphthalein endpoint (see Chapter 11, Section II). Electrometric titration is necessary when these acids are mixed with sulfuric acid or carboxylic acids. Both the conductometric[107] and potentiometric methods in aqueous[108] as well as nonaqueous[109] solutions have been reported.

C. Determination of the Sulfinic Function

1. Oxidative Titrimetry. Several investigators have utilized the oxidation reaction of the sulfinic function to the corresponding sulfonic group for quantitative analysis. Ackerman[110] determined sulfinic acid salts by means of standard sodium hypochlorite solution:

$$RSO_2Na + NaOCl \rightarrow R—SO_3Na + NaCl \tag{22}$$

Potassium permanganate was recommended as the oxidant by Hildrich[111] and Allen.[112] Thomas[113] and Krishna and Singh[114] favored an indirect method using ferric chloride. The sulfinate is treated with a known amount of standard ferric chloride solution. After the oxidation, a measured volume

[106] E. W. Blank, *Soap* (*N.Y.*), **34**, 41, 107 (1958).

[107] D. Ramaswamy and Y. Nayudamma, *J. Soc. Leather Trades' Chemists*, **40**, 245 (1956).

[108] V. Z. Deal and G. E. A. Wyld, *Anal. Chem.*, **27**, 47 (1955).

[109] Y. Nayudamma, *Bull. Central Leather Inst. Madras*, **2**, 197 (1956).

[110] I. Ackerman, *Ind. Eng. Chem., Anal. Ed.*, **18**, 243 (1946).

[111] J. Hildrich, *J. Chem. Soc.*, **93**, 1526 (1908).

[112] P. Allen, *J. Org. Chem.*, **7**, 23 (1942).

[113] J. Thomas, *J. Chem. Soc.*, **95**, 342 (1909).

[114] S. Krishna and H. Singh, *J. Am. Chem. Soc.*, **50**, 792 (1928).

of standard stannous chloride solution is added. The excess of stannous ion is then titrated with standardized potassium dichromate. The permanganate oxidation procedure is suitable for microdeterminations.

2. Oxidative Gasometry. Krishna and Das[115] described a gasometric method for determining the sulfinic function as follows. The sample (0.2 g.) is dissolved in 40 ml. of water, cooled in ice, and 2 g. of potassium iodide and 0.2 g. of potassium iodate are added. The reaction mixture is then brought back to room temperature. Addition of 2 ml. of 3% hydrogen peroxide and 4 ml. of 50% potassium hydroxide causes the liberation of oxygen, which is collected in the azotometer and measured. The probable sequence of reactions is shown in equations 23 and 24:

$$3R-SO_2H + KIO_3 + 2KI \rightarrow 3R-SO_2I + 3KOH \qquad (23)$$

$$R-SO_2I + H_2O_2 + 2KOH \rightarrow O_2 + R-SO_2K + KI + 2H_2O \qquad (24)$$

This method is not recommended for conversion to the micro scale, since it is subject to many complications.

D. Determination of the Sulfonic Function

1. Methods Dependent on the Formation of Amine Salts. The sulfonic function forms crystalline amine salts on reacting with aromatic amines under proper conditions.[116] This reaction has been applied to quantitative analysis. *p*-Toluidine hydrochloride was used as the reagent by Marron and Schifferli:[117]

$$ArSO_3Na + CH_3C_6H_4NH_3^+Cl^- \rightarrow ArSO_3^-H_3^+NC_6H_4CH_3 + NaCl \qquad (25)$$

The amine salt is extracted with carbon tetrachloride, alcohol is added, and the solution is then titrated with 0.1N sodium hydroxide:

$$ArSO_3^-H_3^+NC_6H_4CH_3 + NaOH \rightarrow Ar-SO_3Na + H_2NC_6H_4CH_3 + H_2O \qquad (26)$$

Benzidine dihydrochloride was proposed as the reagent by Kling and Puschal[118] and investigated by Shiraeff.[119] Two moles of the sulfonic function combine with one mole of benzidine:

$$2Ar-SO_3Na + Cl^-H_3^+NC_6H_4C_6H_4NH_3^+Cl^- \rightarrow$$
$$ArSO_3^-H_3^+NC_6H_4C_6H_4NH_3^+SO_3^-Ar + 2NaCl \qquad (27)$$

The benzidine sulfonate is precipitated from aqueous solution, collected on a filter and transferred to a beaker. After drying at 110°C, the solid

[115] S. Krishna and Q. B. Das, *J. Indian Chem. Soc.*, **4**, 367 (1927).

[116] N. D. Cheronis and J. B. Entrikin, *Semimcro Qualitative Organic Analysis*, 2nd ed., Interscience, New York, 1957, p. 524.

[117] T. V. Marron and J. Schifferli, *Ind. Eng. Chem.*, *Anal. Ed.*, **18**, 49 (1946).

[118] W. Kling and F. Puschal, *Melliand Textilber*, **15**, 21 (1934).

[119] D. A. Shiraeff, *Am. Dyestuff Reptr.*, **36**, 313 (1947); **37**, 411 (1948).

is freed from organic contaminants by extraction with petroleum ether. The amine salt is again separated by filtration, redissolved in water-alcohol mixture and titrated with standard sodium hydroxide solution.

The above procedures are not suitable for conversion to the micro scale without modification. It should be noted that the solubility of the amine salt requires prior study. Stupel and Segesser[120] reported that the carbon tetrachloride extraction technique gives good results only for sulfonic compounds containing more than nine carbon atoms. The condition for the quantitative precipitation of benzidine sulfonate should be carefully observed. Keller and Munch[121] demonstrated that benzidine sulfonate is very soluble in water when alcohol is present. Hence transferring the precipitate to a filter paper and subsequent washing are liable to cause considerable loss of the product for microdeterminations. The micro-method[122] which uses the technique described on page 98 circumvents this difficulty. The sample is dissolved in a minimum volume of water in a short test tube. Benzidine dihydrochloride reagent is added and, after complete precipitation, the supernatant liquid is removed by inverted filtration. The benzidine sulfonate is retained in the test tube and is determined—either by acid-base titration or by nitrosation—in the same vessel.

2. *Methods Dependent on Precipitation of Heavy Metal Salts.* The barium, silver, and mercury salts of many sulfonic acids are slightly soluble in water or alcohol and are commonly used as a means to isolate and purify these acids. When the solubility of such salts is known and the sample contains no interfering anions, the sulfonic compound can be determined on the 0.1 meq. scale through the heavy metal salt gravimetrically or titrimetrically.

3. *Methods Dependent on Ion-Exchange.* Neu[123] advocated a method to determine alkali sulfonates by passing the solution containing the sample through a cation exchange column, packed with Wolfatit K (H-form), followed by the titration of the free sulfonic acid in the eluate. Brauns and co-workers[124] presented a scheme to determine barium sulfonate as follows. The sample is passed through an acidic resin in a column, which retains the barium ions. The eluate containing the sulfonic acid is evaporated. The residue is oxidized to sulfuric acid and precipitated with barium chloride as usual. The ion-exchange column is then eluted with 12% hydrochloric acid and the barium ions in the eluate are precipitated with sulfuric acid. It

[120] H. Stupel and A. V. Segesser, *Helv. Chim. Acta*, **34**, 1362 (1951).
[121] R. E. Keller and R. H. Munch, *Anal. Chem.*, **26**, 1518 (1954).
[122] T. S. Ma, R. K. Maurmeyer, and M. Rafalowitz, unpublished work.
[123] R. Neu, *Fette u. Seifen*, **52**, 349 (1950).
[124] F. E. Brauns, J. B. Hlava, and H. Seiler, *Anal. Chem.*, **26**, 607 (1954).

should be noted that sulfonic acids are strong acids. Therefore, a very strongly acidic resin is required.

E. Miscellaneous Methods

1. Ignition Methods. Determination of salts of sulfonic acids by ignition in the presence of sulfuric acid has been suggested.[125] It should be noted that the metallic element—not the sulfonic function—is determined by this method. The micro procedure for ignition of alkali sulfonates is given in experiment 29.

Gardner and co-workers[126] proposed a method for the determination of sulfonates by ignition of the sample. The sulfonic function liberates one equivalent of sulfur dioxide which is collected and titrated with $0.03N$ potassium iodate.

2. Titration with Cationic Surfactant. Alkyl benzenesulfonates that are used as anionic surfactants can be determined by titration with a cationic surfactant.[127] Cetyl-pyridinium bromide[128] is commonly used as the titrant:

$$R-C_6H_4-SO_3Na + \left[\bigcirc N-C_{16}H_{13}^+ \right] Br^- \rightarrow$$

$$(R-C_6H_4SO_3)^- \left[\bigcirc N-C_{16}H_{13}^+ \right] + NaBr \quad (28)$$

Methylene blue serves as the indicator, which also forms a salt with the sulfonate until the equivalence point when it is displaced by the cetyl-pyridinium cation. The titration is performed in a two-phase system composed of water and chloroform. The endpoint is reached when the color of the two layers is the same. The use of the eosin sodium salt as a fluorescent indicator for titration in ultraviolet light has been suggested.[129]

3. Methods for Naphthalene Sulfonic Acids. A common method for the determination of naphthalene sulfonic acids is based on the halogenation of the aromatic nucleus (see Chapter 11, Section V-D). Several macro procedures are available. Some compounds can be titrated potentiometrically by means of standard iodine solution[130] or with standardized

[125] S. Siggia, *Quantitative Organic Analysis via Functional Groups*, 2nd ed., John Wiley and Sons, New York, 1954, p. 144.

[126] C. M. Gardner, C. H. Hale, E. A. Setzkorn, and W. C. Woelfel, *Anal. Chem.*, **30**, 1912 (1958).

[127] M. J. Rosen and H. A. Goldsmith, *Systematic Analysis of Surface-Active Agents*, Interscience, New York, 1960.

[128] S. R. Epton, *Trans. Faraday Soc.*, **44**, 226 (1948).

[129] M. Dolezil, *Chem. Listy*, **50**, 1588 (1956).

[130] M. Matrka and F. Nauratil, *Chem. Prumysl*, **8**, 363 (1958).

potassium bromate in the presence of bromide.[131] Alternately, the sample can be treated with a known excess of bromate-bromide mixture and the residual bromine is determined iodometrically.[132] Aminonaphthalene-sulfonic acids have been determined by diazotization and coupling.[133] These methods can be adapted to the micro scale. However, it should be remembered that they are applicable to known compounds only.

4. Methods for Sulfonyl Chloride. Barker and co-workers[134] determined the sulfonyl chloride group by hydrolyzing the sample in pyridine and titrating the pyridinium salts of sulfonic and hydrochloric acid, respectively, which are liberated:

$$R-SO_2Cl + H_2O + 2C_5H_5N \rightarrow R-SO_3H \cdot NC_5H_5 + C_5H_5N \cdot HCl \qquad (29)$$

Kirkland[135] reported that known sulfonyl chlorides can be determined by gas chromatography. These acid chlorides will not corrode the sensing apparatus under the experimental conditions. Since sulfonic acids and salts can be converted to the corresponding sulfonyl chlorides by reacting with thionyl chloride, this procedure can be utilized as a general method for the determination of the sulfonic function.

F. Colorimetric and Physical Methods. A colorimetric method for determining alkyl sulfonates was described by Harris.[136] Sodium hypochlorite and o-toluidine in 20% hydrochloric acid are used as the reagents. The color developed is measured at 525 mμ. This method is suitable for determination in the range of 5–30 p.p.m.

The polarographic determination of sulfonyl chloride has been reported[137,138] using cyclohexane as the solvent. The half-wave potential is near zero against the calomel electrode. There is a linear relation between the concentration of the sulfonyl groups and the height of the wave, unless the proportion of solvents is changed.

The infrared absorption spectra of some long chain alkyl sulfonates have been published[139] but have not been applied to quantitative analysis.

[131] S. D. Forrester and D. Bain, *J. Soc. Chem. Ind.*, **49**, 410 (1930).

[132] J. Lasylovsky, *Magyar. Kem. Foly.*, **64**, 5 (1958).

[133] K. D. Shcherbachev, *Org. Chem. Ind.*, **5**, 427 (1938).

[134] J. E. Barker, C. M. Payne, and J. Moulding, *Anal. Chem.*, **32**, 831 (1960).

[135] J. J. Kirkland, *Anal. Chem.*, **32**, 1388 (1960).

[136] S. C. Harris, *Ind. Eng. Chem.*, *Anal. Ed.*, **15**, 254 (1943).

[137] A. Stehlik, *Vozorstve*, **5**, 35 (1955).

[138] M. B. Nejman and A. Majranovskij, *Doklady Akad.*, *Nauk USSR*, **78**, 85 (1951).

[139] M. A. Smook, E. T. Pieski, and C. F. Hammer, *Ind. Eng. Chem.*, **45**, 273 (1953).

V. The Sulfonamide Function

A. General. The sulfonamide function ($-SO_2N=$) is characterized by an SO_2 grouping with a carbon skeleton on one side of the sulfur atom and an amino nitrogen on the other. Since the discovery of the chemotherapeutic activity of sulfanilamide in 1936, a large number of compounds containing this function have been synthesized as potential pharmaceutical agents.

B. Titrimetric Methods

1. Acid-Base Titrimetry

A. DETERMINATION AS ACIDS. Compounds containing the sulfonamide function in which there is at least one hydrogen atom attached to nitrogen can be determined as acids. Certain sulfonamides may be titrated in acetone with $0.1N$ sodium hydroxide to the phenolphthalein endpoint. However, titration in nonaqueous medium is generally recommended. The sample is dissolved in butylamine, ethylenediamine, or dimethylformamide and titrated with standard sodium methoxide solution. The endpoint can be located potentiometrically or visually using thymol blue or azo violet as the indicator. Determinations on the macro[140,141] to micro[142] range have been published. The detailed procedure for analysis is given on page 561. Conductometric titration of sulfonamides in nonaqueous solutions with aqueous titrants was reported by Macarovici.[143]

B. DETERMINATION AS BASES. Macro procedures for the determination of sulfonamides as bases have been described by several investigators.[144–146] Glacial acetic acid is usually used as the solvent and standard perchloric acid solution the titrant. The micro procedure is given in experiment 3. In special cases the sample may be dissolved in ethanol and titrated with $0.1N$ hydrochloric acid.[146]

2. Methods Dependent on Precipitation. The sulfonamide function carrying a hydrogen atom usually gives a precipitate with the silver ion:

$$\overset{\text{H}}{\underset{|}{\text{RSO}_2\text{NR}'}} + \text{AgNO}_3 \rightarrow \overset{\text{Ag}}{\underset{|}{\text{RSO}_2\text{NR}'}} + \text{HNO}_3 \qquad (30)$$

[140] J. S. Fritz and R. T. Keen, *Anal. Chem.*, **24**, 308 (1952).

[141] H. Conroy, *J. Ass. Official Agr. Chemists*, **37**, 697 (1954).

[142] R. K. Maurmeyer, M. Margosis, and T. S. Ma, *Mikrochim. Acta*, **1959**, 177.

[143] C. G. Macarovici, *Rev. Chim. Acad. Rep. Populaire Roumaine*, **1**, 79 (1956).

[144] O. Tomicek, *Coll. Czechoslov. Chem. Comm.*, **13**, 116 (1948).

[145] P. C. Markunas and J. A. Riddick, *Anal. Chem.*, **23**, 337 (1951).

[146] P. L. DeReeder, *Anal. Chim. Acta*, **10**, 413 (1954).

This reaction forms the basis of several published methods. In one method,[147] the sample is dissolved in alkaline ethanol and titrated with $0.1N$ silver nitrate using diphenylcarbazone as the adsorption indicator. In another method[148] the sulfonamide is dissolved in warm acetone, sodium dichromate and magnesium oxide are added, and the mixture is titrated with $0.05N$ silver nitrate to a permanent red color. Alternately, the acetone solution is treated with a known volume of $0.1N$ silver nitrate, the silver salt is filtered off, and the excess of silver ion in the filtrate is determined by back-titration with standard ammonium thiocyanate solution. A similar procedure was proposed by Parikh and Mukherji[149] for the determination of saccharin, in which acetic acid is used as solvent in place of acetone.

3. *Method Dependent on Chlorination.* Shafer and Wilde[150] proposed a method for the determination of sulfonic acid amides by thermometric titration with hypochlorite. The sample is dissolved in sodium hydroxide and placed in a Dewar flask. Sodium hypochlorite, $0.5M$, is added in small portions and the temperature of the mixture is read 30 seconds after each addition. The following reaction occurs.

$$RSO_2NH_2 + NaOCl \rightarrow RSO_2NHCl + NaOH \tag{31}$$

With the volume plotted against temperature, nearly a straight line is obtained. At the equivalence point, a bend in the curve takes place. The thermister should be used if it is desirable to adapt the method to the micro scale.

4. *Methods Dependent on Bromination.* Several workers have reported on the bromometric determination of sulfonamides. Direct titration of the sample dissolved in glacial acetic acid by means of $0.1N$ bromine in the same solvent was described by Doneyal and Simon.[151] Wojolin[152] and DeReeder[153] used dilute hydrochloric acid as the solvent. Potassium bromide is added, followed by a measured volume of $0.1N$ potassium bromate until a yellow bromine color persists. The excess of bromate is then determined by the liberation of iodine with potassium iodide and the titration of iodine with $0.1N$ sodium thiosulfate. It should be noted that the method is based on the bromination of the benzene ring (see Chapter 11, Section V-D), and the sulfonic function is not affected.

[147] C. G. Macarovici and E. Anusecu, *Anal. Acad. Rep. Populaire Roumaine,* **21,** 1 (1950).

[148] L. Kum-Tatt, *Analyst,* **82,** 185 (1957).

[149] P. M. Parikh and S. P. Mukherji, *Analyst,* **85,** 25 (1960).

[150] H. Shafer and E. Wilde, *Z. Anal. Chem.,* **130,** 396 (1950).

[151] J. Doneyal and V. Simon, *Chem. Listy,* **44,** 198 (1950).

[152] H. Wojolin, *Süddeut. Apoth. Ztg.,* **88,** 395 (1948).

[153] P. L. DeReeder, *Anal. Chim. Acta,* **9,** 314 (1953).

5. Methods Dependent on Conversion to Ammonia. Unsubstituted sulfonamides are hydrolyzed by heating with dilute sulfuric acid[154,155] to form free sulfonic acids and ammonium sulfate:

$$2RSO_2NH_2 + H_2SO_4 + 2H_2O \rightarrow 2RSO_3H + (NH_4)_2SO_4 \qquad (32)$$

Ammonia is then steam-distilled into 2% boric acid solution and titrated with $0.01N$ acid. Substituted sulfonamides[156] require the regular Kjeldahl digestion (see Chapter 8, Section III-F-4) for conversion to ammonia.

C. Gasometric Methods

1. Use of Nitric Acid. The primary sulfonamide function on reacting with concentrated nitric acid in the presence of sulfuric[157] or hydrochloric acid[158] yields one equivalent of nitrous oxide. The reaction probably proceeds through ammonium nitrate as the intermediate according to the following equations:

$$RSO_2NH_2 + HNO_3 + H_2O \rightarrow RSO_3H + NH_4NO_3 \qquad (33)$$

$$NH_4NO_3 \rightarrow N_2O + 2H_2O \qquad (34)$$

Renard and Deschamps[158] devised a micro method as follows. The sample is treated in a U-tube with 10 μl. of concentrated nitric acid and 20 μl. of concentrated hydrochloric acid. All air is removed from the apparatus by means of carbon dioxide. The reaction mixture is then heated to 70°C for 45 minutes. The volume of nitrous oxide is measured in a microazotometer containing strong potassium hydroxide solution. The apparatus designed by Ma and Mattei[159] (see Fig. 8.11) is well suited for this determination.

According to Khromov and Borisov,[157] acylated sulfonamides also give quantitative yields of nitrous oxide, indicating that the first reaction is the cleavage of the acyl group. On the other hand, these workers reported that meta aryl substituted sulfonamides fail to react.

2. Use of Nitrous Acid. Kainz and Huber[160] demonstrated that the sulfonamide function is not deaminated on treatment with nitrous acid (sodium nitrite + acetic acid) but gives approximately 1.5 mol. of nitrous

[154] E. Schulek and P. Rozsa, *Z. Anal. Chem.,* **108**, 396 (1937).

[155] Anon., *J. Ass. Official Agric. Chemists,* **22**, 97 (1939).

[156] P. L. DeReeder, *Anal. Chim. Acta,* **9**, 140 (1953).

[157] N. V. Khromov and I. Borisov, *J. Appl. Chem. USSR,* **18**, 612 (1945).

[158] M. Renard and P. Deschamps, *Mikrochemie,* **36/37**, 665 (1951).

[159] T. S. Ma and F. Mattei, unpublished work; see F. Mattei, *Master's Thesis, Brooklyn College,* 1960.

[160] G. Kainz and H. Huber, *Mikrochim. Acta,* **1960**, 38.

oxide and 0.25 mol. of nitrogen gas. It is thought that the following reactions occur:

$$RSO_2NH_2 + HNO_2 \rightarrow RSO_2H + N_2O + H_2O \tag{35}$$

$$2RSO_2H + HNO_2 \rightarrow (RSO_2)_2{=}NOH + H_2O \tag{36}$$

$$(RSO_2)_2{=}NOH + HNO_2 \rightarrow 2RSO_2{-}OH + N_2O \tag{37}$$

If iodine or iodide is present in the reaction mixture, the sulfinic acid is oxidized without giving the extra 0.5 mol. of nitrous oxide:

$$RSO_2H + I_2 + H_2O \rightarrow RSO_3H + 2HI \tag{38}$$

D. Special Methods for Aminobenzenesulfonamides

1. Diazotization Methods. Nitrosation methods have been advocated for the determination of aminobenzenesulfonamides. It should be noted that the reaction involves the aromatic amino group and not the sulfonamide function. The presence of the latter apparently facilitates the diazotization. Thus sulfanilamide and sulfaguanidine were determined by Fischbach[161] using the direct titration procedure. The sample (0.5 g.) is dissolved in hydrochloric acid. Potassium bromide and 2 drops of the internal indicator reagent containing p-dimethylaminobenzaldehyde are added. The solution is titrated with 0.1N sodium nitrite at room temperature until the yellow color of the Schiff's base formed disappears. Kakemi and co-workers[162] detected the endpoint externally using a test paper impregnated with 3% dimethylaminobenzaldehyde. Other investigators[163,164] used potentiometric titration. Yamagishi and Yokoo[165] prepared the diazonium compound of the sulfonamide by means of potassium nitrite. After removing the excess nitrite ions, the diazonium compound is decomposed and the volume of nitrogen liberated is collected and measured.

2. Acetylation Method. An acetylation method was suggested by Gaind and Punn[166] as follows. The sample is heated under reflux with a known amount of acetic anhydride in pyridine. After cooling, a measured volume of sodium hydroxide solution is added. The precipitate which forms is filtered off and the residual sodium hydroxide in the united filtrate is titrated with standardized sulfuric acid.

3. Hydrolytic Method. Hydrolysis and ion-exchange were utilized by Jindu and Sipos[167] to analyze sulfonamides. The hydrolysis is carried out

[161] C. Fischbach, *Acia Cient. Venezobana,* 7, 152 (1956).
[162] K. Kakemi, T. Uno, and I. Kegami, *J. Pharm. Soc. Japan,* 76, 11 (1956).
[163] L. T. Butt and H. E. Stagg, *Anal. Chim. Acta,* 19, 208 (1958).
[164] H. S. Conway, *J. Am. Pharm.,* 34, 236 (1945).
[165] M. Yamagishi and M. Yokoo, *J. Pharm. Soc. Japan,* 74, 961 (1954).
[166] K. N. Gaind and D. P. Punn, *Indian J. Pharm.,* 19, 279 (1957).
[167] A. Jindu and F. Sipos, *Chem. Listy,* 44, 235 (1950).

with $1N$ hydrochloric acid in a sealed tube at 100–200°C. The reaction products are chromatographed on Amberlite IR-100. The eluate containing sulfanilic acid is titrated potentiometrically with standard hydroxide solution.

4. Colorimetric Methods. All colorimetric methods reported for the determination of sulfonamides are dependent on the reaction of the aromatic amino group present in these compounds. The yellow color produced by *p*-dimethylaminobenzaldehyde on sulfanilamide was used by early workers.[168–170] Recent investigators appear to favor diazotization followed by coupling to produce intense colors. The coupling agents proposed include dimethyl-*α*-naphthylamine,[171] N-(1-naphthyl)ethylenediamine,[172,173] naphthyldiethylpropylenediamine,[174] thymol,[175] and N-sulfato-ethyl-*m*-toluidine.[176] A method which involves formation of a colored precipitate followed by colorimetry was proposed by Vonesch.[177] Sulfanilamide and *p*-aminobenzenesulfonacetamide gives an easily distinguishable red precipitate with sodium-*o*-naphthoquinone sulfate. The crystals are separated by centrifugation, redissolved in dilute sodium hydroxide solution and the color intensity measured at 445 mμ.

VI. The Sulfone and Sulfoxide Functions

A. General. The sulfone (—SO—) and sulfoxide (—SO$_2$—) functions are characterized by the presence of two carbon skeletons linked to a sulfur atom that is attached to oxygen. Many sulfones are used as pharmaceuticals, and some sulfoxides have been found in plants.

B. Methods Dependent on Conversion to Sulfate or Sulfide

All organic sulfur compounds are converted to sulfur trioxide upon exhaustive oxidation. Therefore the determination of sulfur functions by oxidation to yield sulfate ions is seldom recommended since the method is nondiscriminative. However, this appears to be the only chemical method available for the analysis of the sulfone function. Sulfones are relatively

[168] A. Werner, *Lancet*, **1**, 15 (1939).

[169] C. J. O. Morris, *Biochem. J.*, **35**, 952 (1941).

[170] C. A. Mawson, *Biochem. J.*, **36**, 845 (1942).

[171] E. K. Marshall, *J. Biol. Chem.*, **122**, 263 (1937).

[172] A. C. Brattan and E. K. Marshall, *J. Biol. Chem.*, **128**, 537 (1939).

[173] S. W. Lee, N. B. Hannay, and W. C. Hand, *Ind. Eng. Chem., Anal. Ed.*, **15**, 403 (1943).

[174] F. Servantor, *Bull. Trans. Soc. Pharm. Bordeaux*, **81**, 16 (1943).

[175] E. Zöllner and G. Vastach, *J. Am. Pharm. Ass.*, **46**, 287 (1957).

[176] D. G. Moss, *J. Clin. Path.*, **10**, 371 (1951).

[177] E. Vonesch, *Angles Farm. y Bioquim. Buenos Aires*, **14**, 81 (1943).

inert. A possible approach is the reductometric technique that Bordwell and McKellan[178] described for the reduction of sulfones. Catalytic hydrogen, sulfur, zinc and acid, and lithium aluminum hydride have been shown to affect certain sulfones, but in no case is the result quantitative. Attempts to determine the sulfone function on the 0.1 meq. scale either by reduction in the micro Jones reductor (see Section C-1 below) with zinc amalgam, or by refluxing with zinc and acetic acid were unsuccessful.[179]

Korshun and Sheveliva[180] demonstrated that sulfones give quantitative yields of sulfur trioxide in the microcombustion tube at 950°C with or without platinum catalyst. The sulfur trioxide is retained in the form of silver sulfate by a section of silver gauze kept at 700°C. These workers reported that the recovery of sulfate is incomplete if the silver gauze is maintained at a temperature of 420–600°C. Sulfones also can be oxidized to sulfate using the closed flask combustion technique,[180a] or reduced to sulfide by the potassium fusion method of Zimmermann.[180b]

A wet oxidation macro method was presented by Szabo and Orsos,[181] who analyzed aromatic sulfones by heating the sample with potassium chlorate and concentrated nitric acid in a flask. The resulting sulfate ions were then determined gravimetrically. Young[182] described a macro combustion method in which the sample (0.5 g.) is mixed with sodium carbonate and cobaltic oxide in a porcelain boat. The latter is inserted into a combustion tube and heated in a current of oxygen. After cooling, the contents of the boat are transferred into a beaker and acidified with hydrochloric acid. A small amount of bromine water is added and the solution is heated to boiling and filtered. Sulfate determination is performed on the filtrate. This method was applied to the analysis of sulfones and sulfoxides, respectively. However, it is recommended that the sulfoxide function be determined by one of the methods given in the next section.

C. Determination of Sulfoxides

1. Reduction by Zinc Amalgam. The sulfoxide function is reduced to the sulfide on reacting with zinc and hydrochloric acid:[183]

[178] L. G. Bordwell and W. McKellan, *J. Am. Chem. Soc.*, **73**, 2251 (1951).

[179] T. S. Ma and A. Faraone, unpublished work; see A. Faraone, *Master's Thesis, Brooklyn College*, 1961.

[180] M. O. Korshun and N. S. Sheveliva, *Zhur. Anal. Khim.*, **7**, 904 (1952).

[180a] T. S. Ma, in F. J. Welcher (ed.), *Standard Methods of Chemical Analysis*, 6th edition, Vol. 2, Van Nostrand, Princeton, 1963, p. 396.

[180b] W. Zimmermann, *Mikrochemie*, **40**, 162 (1952).

[181] Z. G. Szabo and S. Orsos, *Magyar Kem. Foly.*, **56**, 173 (1950).

[182] G. H. Young, *Ind. Eng. Chem., Anal. Ed.*, **10**, 686 (1938).

[183] T. S. Ma, in F. J. Welcher (ed.), *Standard Methods of Chemical Analysis*, 6th edition, Vol. 2, Van Nostrand, Princeton, 1963, p. 420.

$$\text{RSOR} + \text{Zn} + 2\text{HCl} \rightarrow \text{RSR} + \text{H}_2\text{O} + \text{ZnCl}_2 \qquad (39)$$

The micro Jones reductor (Fig. 9.2) is a convenient apparatus to carry out the reduction on the 0.1 meq. scale. The sample is dissolved in 5% ethanolic hydrochloric acid and run through the reductor in 10 minutes. The eluate containing the sulfide is determined as usual (see this chapter, Section III). Detailed description of the micro procedure is found in experiment 51.

2. *Reduction by Titanous or Stannous Ion.* Titanous ions reduce sulfoxides according to the following equation:

$$\text{R—SO—R}' + 2\text{Ti}^{+3} + 2\text{H}^+ \rightarrow \text{R—S—R}' + 2\text{Ti}^{+4} + \text{H}_2\text{O} \qquad (40)$$

However, this is a slow reaction and the resulting sulfide is easily oxidizable. Barnard and Hargrave[184] developed an indirect method using standard titanous chloride solution to determine sulfoxides in the following manner. The sample (0.7–1 meq.) is dissolved in acetic acid in a flask fitted with a three-way stopcock. The flask is evacuated to 20 mm. pressure and filled with nitrogen gas. Titanous chloride (15 ml., 0.1N) is introduced and the flask is again evacuated and refilled with nitrogen three times. After heating the reaction mixture at 80°C for 1 hour, a boiling solution of ferric alum is added and allowed to stand for 30 seconds. The flask is then cooled rapidly and phosphoric acid (10 ml.) is added, followed by carbon tetrachloride (14 ml.). The mixture is shaken vigorously to extract the sulfide into the organic phase. The amount of ferrous ion in the aqueous layer is determined by titration with 0.05N potassium dichromate using diphenylamine sulfonate as the indicator.

A modification of this method was described by Legault and Groves.[185] After reduction, addition of ferric alum and ammonium sulfate follows. Phosphoric acid is added after cooling and the reaction mixture is extracted with n-butyl alcohol followed by carbon tetrachloride. The extract is then titrated with 0.05N potassium dichromate.

While the above procedures can be adapted to the 0.1 meq. scale, the precision and accuracy will be reduced because of the extraction process. The reader is referred to page 302 for the discussion on the application of titanous chloride to microanalysis.[186]

Glynn[187] proposed a reductometric method using stannous chloride as follows. The sulfoxide (0.5 g.) solution is placed in a beaker. Stannous chloride (10 ml., 0.2N) and hot concentrated hydrochloric acid are added, and the mixture is boiled for 45 minutes. The sulfoxide function is reduced:

[184] D. Barnard and K. R. Hargrave, *Anal. Chim. Acta*, **5**, 476, 536 (1951).

[185] R. R. Legault and K. Groves, *Anal. Chem.*, **29**, 1495 (1957).

[186] T. S. Ma and J. V. Earley, *Mikrochim. Acta*, **1959**, 129.

[187] E. Glynn, *Analyst*, **72**, 248 (1947).

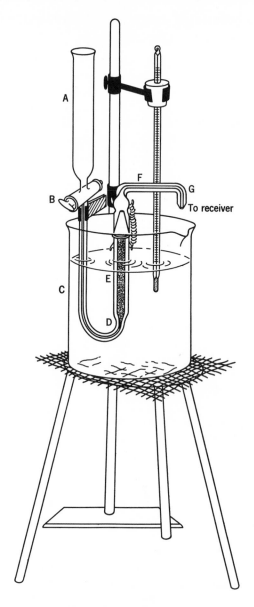

Fig. 9.2. Micro Jones reductor.

$$R—SO—R' + SnCl_2 + 2HCl \rightarrow R—S—R' + SnCl_4 + H_2O \qquad (41)$$

Upon cooling, more water and concentrated hydrochloric acid are added, together with the potassium indigo trisulfonate indicator. The residual stannous chloride is titrated with $0.1N$ ferric alum until a reddish blue color is attained. This procedure is not suitable for conversion to the micro scale.

3. Oxidation by Peracids. Böhme[188] utilized the oxidation of the sulfoxide function to sulfone for quantitative analysis. A peracid is employed as the reagent:

$$RSOR' + R''CO·O·OH \rightarrow RSO_2R' + R''COOH \qquad (42)$$

The published procedure requires a 1–5 g. sample, which is dissolved in acetic acid. A measured volume of phthalic monoperacid in ether solution is added at a reduced temperature. The reaction mixture is incubated for 24 hours. The residual peracid is then determined iodometrically (see page 529). This method is not recommended for adaptation to the 0.1 meq. scale because of the instability of the peracid. Mercaptans and sulfides are also oxidized and hence interfere with the determination.

4. Nonaqueous Alkalimetry. The sulfoxide function has weakly basic property. Wimer[189] demonstrated that aliphatic, aromatic, and heterocyclic sulfoxides, when dissolved in acetic anhydride can be titrated with $0.1N$ perchloric acid as shown in equation 43:

$$R—\underset{\underset{O}{\|}}{S}—R' + HClO_4 \rightarrow \left[R—\underset{\underset{OH}{\|}}{S}—R' \right]^+ ClO_4^- \qquad (43)$$

The equivalence point is determined potentiometrically. It will be recalled that the mercapto function has only acidic properties. The sulfide and sulfone functions do not exhibit basic properties in acetic anhydride solutions. Therefore, this method is unique for the sulfoxide among sulfur functions that contain no nitrogen. The procedure suited for determination on the 0.1 meq. scale is given in experiment 3.

D. Colorimetric Methods. Colorimetric methods for the determination of sulfoxides are not described in the literature. Sulfones have been reported to give a red color in the presence of di- and triaryl amines,[190] but the possibility of using this reaction for quantitative analysis has not been explored. Other reagents suggested for determining sulfones by colorimetry—such as sodium nitroprusside[191] and nitrous acid-naphthylene-

[188] H. Böhme, *Berichte*, **70**, 379 (1937).

[189] D. C. Wimer, *Anal. Chem.*, **30**, 2061 (1958).

[190] A. L. LeRosen, R. T. Movarek, and J. K. Carlton, *Anal. Chem.*, **24**, 1335 (1952).

[191] A. E. Vitolo, *Bull. Chim. Farm.*, **89**, 351 (1950).

diamine[192] mixture—are based on the carbon skeleton of the molecule and not on the presence of the sulfone function.

E. Physical Methods. In contrast to the chemical reduction of the sulfone function (see Section VI-B), polarographic investigations on sulfones indicate the suitability of this method for quantitative analysis. A two-electron transfer has been demonstrated at the dropping mercury electrode with $0.1M$ tetramethylammonium bromide as the electrolyte.[193] Levin and Sheston[194] studied the polarographic reduction of diphenylsulfone in 50% ethanol with $0.05M$ tetraethylammonium iodide background. The electrolyte shows the sulfone wave at -2.1 v and a linear relation of the wave height to concentration. The presence of sulfonic acids does not affect the results.

The polarographic behavior of the sulfoxide function awaits clarification. Stone[195] reported complete failure of sulfoxides to give anodic wave. On the other hand, Bowers and Russell[193] presented evidence of the reduction of methylphenyl and diphenyl sulfoxides.

The infrared spectrum of dimethyl sulfone,[196] and the absorption spectra of some sulfoxides[197] have been published. However, quantitative application of these studies has not been reported.

VII. The Thiocyanate and Thiourea Functions

A. General. The thiocyanate and thiourea functions are sulfur functions in which the sulfur atom is joined to nitrogen through a carbon atom. Thiocyanates (also known as rhodanins) have the general formula $R—SCN$. Thioureas are represented by the formula R_2NCNR_2. Compounds with the structure $R_2N—C{=}NR$ are called isothioureas. Both the thiocyanate and the thiourea functions are oxidizable. However, as will be shown below, the oxidation reactions of thiocyanate have not been directly applied to quantitative analysis. The reader is referred to the review by Kaufmann[198] on the chemistry of thiocyanates.

[192] F. A. Simpson, *Int. J. Leprosy,* **17,** 208 (1949).

[193] R. C. Bowers and H. D. Russell, *Anal. Chem.,* **32,** 405 (1960).

[194] E. S. Levin and A. P. Sheston, *Doklady. Akad. Nauk.,* **96,** 999 (1954).

[195] K. G. Stone, *J. Am. Chem. Soc.,* **69,** 1832 (1947).

[196] K. Fujimori, *Bull. Chem. Soc. Japan,* **32,** 1374 (1959).

[197] G. A. Leandri, A. Mangini, and R. Passerini, *J. Chem. Soc.,* **1957,** 1386.

[198] H. P. Kaufmann, *Angew. Chem.,* **54,** 168 (1941).

B. Titrimetric Methods for the Thiocyanate Function

1. Determination of Thiocyanic Acid. A macro method described by Edinger and Clemens[199] for the determination of thiocyanic acid involves the conversion of the acid to silver thiocyanate in nitric acid solution:

$$HSCN + AgNO_3 \rightarrow AgSCN + HNO_3 \tag{44}$$

The silver thiocyanate, which precipitates, is separated by filtration and transferred into a flask fitted with a ground-glass stopper. Sodium bicarbonate solution and potassium iodide are added and the flask is vigorously shaken to bring the solid into solution. A measured volume of $0.1N$ iodine solution is delivered from a buret until the reaction mixture turns decidedly brown. The flask is then closed and kept in the dark for 2 hours for completion of the reaction shown below.

$$AgSCN + 3I_2 + 4H_2O \rightarrow H_2SO_4 + HCN + AgI + 5HI \tag{45}$$

The residual iodine is determined by titration with $0.1N$ sodium thiosulfate after the solution is acidified with hydrochloric acid.

2. Determination of Thiocyanates

A. BY THE SODIUM SULFIDE REACTION. Organic thiocyanates do not precipitate silver thiocyanate on treatment with silver nitrate in nitric acid. However, these compounds react with sodium sulfide to give sodium thiocyanate:

$$2R—SCN + Na_2S \rightarrow 2NaCNS + R_2S \tag{46}$$

Panchenko and Smirnov[200] proposed a method based on this reaction. The thiocyanate (0.1–0.3 g.) is dissolved in ethanol and a saturated ethanolic solution of sodium sulfide is added. The mixture is refluxed for 15–90 minutes until a dark color appears. Sulfuric acid is introduced and the solution is boiled to expel the sulfides. After cooling, 30 ml. of $0.1N$ silver nitrate is added to precipitate silver thiocyanate, which is filtered off and washed. The excess of silver ions in the united filtrates is determined by the Volhard titration. This method has not been tested on the micro scale.

B. BY THE SODIUM PLUMBITE REACTION. Lennartz and Middeldorf[201] devised a procedure to determine thiocyanates which is based on their reaction with sodium plumbite:

$$2R—SCN + Na_2Pb(OH)_4 \rightarrow (R—S)_2Pb + 2NaOCN + 2H_2O \tag{47}$$

The sample dissolved in alcohol is treated with a known excess of sodium plumbite solution containing 0.5% lead. The reaction mixture is allowed

[199] A. Edinger and P. Clemens, *Z. Klin. Med.*, **59**, 128 (1906).

[200] A. N. Panchenko and G. S. Smirnov, *J. Gen. Chem. USSR*, **2**, 193 (1932).

[201] T. A. Lennartz and R. Middeldorf, *Süddeut.-Apoth. Z.*, **89**, 593 (1949).

to stand for 30 minutes. The lead mercaptide which precipitates is filtered off and the excess of the reagent in the united filtrates is precipitated as lead sulfate which is collected on a filter, redissolved in ammonium acetate solution, and titrated against standard ammonium molybdate solution using tannin as indicator.

C. Titrimetric Methods for the Thiourea Function

1. *Use of Silver Salts.* Volhard[202] reported the direct titration of thiourea (1–2 g.) with standard silver nitrate solution according to the following equation:

$$H_2N—\underset{\underset{S}{\|}}{C}—NH_2 + 2AgNO_3 + 2NH_3 \rightarrow Ag_2S + H_2N—CN + 2NH_4NO_3 \quad (48)$$

However, the endpoint is not sharp. Cuthill and Atkins[203] proposed a modification by using the back-titration technique. To the sample is added a known volume of $0.1N$ silver nitrate and $2N$ aqueous ammonia. The vessel containing the mixture is stoppered and shaken by hand for 2 minutes. The reaction mixture is then acidified with nitric acid. The precipitated silver sulfide is collected and discarded. The excess of silver ions in the filtrate is determined by titration with $0.1N$ ammonium thiocyanate using ferric alum as the indicator.

Williams[204] presented a method for determining thiourea using sodium silver cyanide complex as the reagent:

$$H_2NCNH_2 + 2NaAg(CN)_2 + 2NaOH \rightarrow H_2N—CN + Ag_2S + 4NaCN + 2H_2O \quad (49)$$
$$\underset{\underset{S}{\|}}{}$$

The sample (0.1 g.) dissolved in sodium carbonate solution is placed in a beaker with 30 ml. of $0.1N$ sodium silver cyanide complex. The mixture is boiled for 5 minutes. After cooling, the silver sulfide is filtered off. The amount of cyanide ions which are produced is determined by titrating the filtrate with standard silver nitrate solution.

Alpha-naphthylthiourea was determined by Prat and co-workers[205] by indirect alkalimetry. To the sample solution is added 10% silver nitrate solution. The following reaction takes place:

$$\alpha\text{-}C_{10}H_7NHCSNH_2 + 2AgNO_3 + H_2O \rightarrow 2HNO_3 + Ag_2S + \alpha\text{-}C_{10}H_7NHCONH_2 \quad (50)$$

[202] J. Volhard, *Berichte*, **7**, 100 (1874).

[203] R. Cuthill and C. S. Atkins, *J. Soc. Chem. Ind.*, **56**, 57 (1937).

[204] H. E. Williams, *J. Soc. Chem. Ind.*, **58**, 77 (1939).

[205] J. Prat, A. Colus, and H. Andre, *Phytiat-Phytopharm.*, **5**, 133 (1956).

The reaction mixture is then saturated with sodium chloride to remove the excess silver ions. The nitric acid liberated is determined by titration against standard sodium hydroxide solution.

2. Use of Mercury Compounds. Hernandez-Gutierez[206] proposed a method for determining thiourea which is based on the formation of a complex with potassium mercuric iodide (Nessler's reagent). When this complex is treated with potassium iodide, the sulfur separates as mercuric sulfide. The latter is then oxidized with a known excess amount of standard bromine solution in the presence of potassium bromide. The excess of bromine is determined iodometrically. In a later communication[207] this investigator reported difficulty in precipitating out the mercuric sulfide when working with substituted thioureas and suggested the colorimetric determination of the yellow complexes of these compounds.

Wronski[208] reported that thiourea, substituted thiourea, and thiosemicarbazide can be titrated in acidified aqueous or alcoholic solution with 0.05N tris-(acetoxymercuri)-aniline. Precision and accuracy for 2–150 mg. samples are ±1%.

3. Use of Cadmium Complex. Budesinsky and co-workers[209] suggested a method for the determination of the thiourea function which utilizes chelatometry. The sample solution is reacted with cadmium sulfate-EDTA complex. Cadmium sulfide is precipitated, liberating an equivalent amount of EDTA. The latter is titrated with 0.05M calcium chloride using methylthymol blue as the indicator. Derivatives of thiourea should be treated with hydrazine prior to the reaction with cadmium complex.

4. Use of Halogens. A number of papers have been published on the use of halogen compounds as oxidants for the determination of the thiourea function. The hypoiodide ion (iodine in alkaline solution) is recommended by most investigators:

$$H_2NCSNH_2 + 4OI^- + H_2O \rightarrow H_2NCONH_2 + H_2SO_4 + 4I^- \tag{51}$$

Skramovsky[210] used 0.1N iodine and potassium hydroxide as reagent and titrated the residual iodine by means of 0.1N sodium thiosulfate. Joshi[211] oxidized the thiourea with sodium hydroxide and potassium iodide for 30 minutes. The excess of iodine is determined by titration with standard

[206] F. Hernandez-Gutierez, *Anales real soc. espan. fis y quim.*, **51B**, 639 (1955).
[207] *Ibid.*, **53B**, 211 (1957).
[208] M. Wronski, *Z. Anal. Chem.*, **174**, 3 (1960).
[209] B. Budesinsky, E. Vanickova, and J. Körbl, *Coll. Czech. Chem. Commun.*, **25**, 456 (1960).
[210] S. Skramovsky, *Casopis Ceskoslov. Lekarnictva*, **21**, 1 (1941).
[211] M. K. Joshi, *Anal. Chim. Acta*, **14**, 509 (1956).

sodium arsenite solution. The micro procedure[212] using potassium hypoiodide as oxidant and sodium thiosulfate as titrant will be found in experiment 24.

Cihalik and Ruzicka[213] presented a method to determine thiourea by direct titration with $0.05M$ iodine monochloride in neutral to $6N$ hydrochloric acid. The endpoint is located potentiometrically. It was stated that thiourea is oxidized to $[(NH)(NH_2)CS]_2$ under this condition, whereas the reaction is not stoichiometric in alkaline solution. Deshmukh and Bapat[214] preoxidized thiourea and methyl thiourea, respectively, with iodine monochloride or monobromide in potassium hydroxide solution, followed by direct titration with standard iodate, permanganate, or ceric sulfate solution.

Bromine was employed as the oxidant by Rosenthaler[215] for determining thiourea:

$$H_2NCSNH_2 + 4Br_2 + 4H_2O \rightarrow H_2N\!-\!CN + H_2SO_4 + 8HBr \qquad (52)$$

Banerjee[216] advocated the use of potassium bromate-bromide mixture.

Chloramine-T was investigated by Afanasev[217] as a reagent for the determination of urea and thiourea, respectively. While urea can be determined in the presence of sodium bicarbonate and consumes 3 mol. of chloramine-T, thiourea requires dilute sulfuric acid solution and consumes 7 mol. of the oxidant.

5. *Use of Ferricyanide or Hydrogen Peroxide.* The thiourea function can be quantitatively converted to the urea function by oxidation in alkaline solution with hydrogen peroxide[218] or potassium ferricyanide.[219] This reaction has been tested on thiourea as well as aliphatic and aromatic substituted thioureas. The resulting urea or substituted urea is then incubated with urease and the ammonia liberated is determined (see page 316).

6. *Use of Selenious Acid.* Franchi[220] reported that the isothiourea group is oxidized by selenium dioxide according to equation 53:

[212] T. S. Ma and A. Faraone, unpublished work; see A. Faraone, *Master's Thesis*, *Brooklyn College*, 1961.

[213] J. Cihalik and J. Ruzicka, *Chem. Listy*, **49**, 1731 (1955); *Coll. Czech. Chem. Commun.*, **21**, 262 (1956).

[214] G. S. Deshmukh and M. G. Bapat, *Z. Anal. Chem.*, **156**, 276 (1957).

[215] L. Rosenthaler, *Pharm. Acta Helv.*, **30**, 332 (1955).

[216] S. N. Banerjee, *J. Indian Chem. Soc.*, **36**, 449 (1959).

[217] B. N. Afanasev, *Zavodskaya Lab.*, **15**, 1271 (1949).

[218] F. Haurowitz and S. G. Lisie, *Anal. Chim. Acta*, **4**, 43 (1950).

[219] M. K. Joshi, *Naturwissenschaften*, **44**, 537 (1957).

[220] G. Franchi, *Ann. Chim. Roma*, **42**, 701 (1952).

$$2HN{=}C{-}NH_2 + 3SeO_2 \rightarrow 2HN{=}C{-}NH_2 + 3Se + 2SO_2 \qquad (53)$$
$$\quad\;\;|\qquad\qquad\qquad\qquad\quad\;\;|$$
$$\quad\;\;SH\qquad\qquad\qquad\qquad\quad OH$$

Joshi[221] demonstrated that tetravalent selenium can be used as a quantitative oxidant for thiourea. The sample (5–10 mg.) is treated with a known volume of 0.1N selenious acid, which oxidizes thiourea:

$$3H_2NCSNH_2 + 5H_2SeO_3 \rightarrow$$
$$2HN{=}C(SO_3H)NH_2 + H_2NCONH_2 + 5Se + H_2SO_4 + 4H_2O \quad (54)$$

The excess of selenius acid is determined by iodometric titration.

D. Miscellaneous Methods for the Thiourea Function

1. Alkalimetric Methods. Thiourea has very feeble basic property; its pK_b is 14.96, which is weaker than urea with pK_b of 13.82. It was mentioned previously (see page 315) that urea can be titrated with perchloric acid when it is dissolved in acetic anhydride. Application of the same technique to thiourea gives no response. On the other hand, Alicino[222] found that, if mercuric acetate is present, microdetermination of thiourea can be accomplished in glacial acetic solution using 0.01N perchloric acid as the titrant. The detailed procedure is given in experiment 4.

The role of mercuric acetate in this method has not been elucidated. Probably the thiourea function forms a mercury complex which has stronger basic property than the original compound. It is interesting to note that the addition of mercuric acetate to urea in glacial acetic acid has no effect on the consumption of perchloric acid. Thiouracil reacts like thiourea, but the equivalence point is reached only slowly. Hence, the determination of thiouracil requires the back-titration technique. The sample is dissolved in glacial acid, mercuric acetate and a known excess of 0.01N perchloric acid is added. After 10 minutes the residual acid is titrated against standard potassium biphthalate solution.

2. Coulometric Methods. Two coulometric methods have been devised for the determination of thiourea. In one method[223] the sample is treated with excess of ammoniacal silver bromide solution, when the thiourea liberates its equivalent of bromide ions. After acidification with sulfuric acid, the bromide ions are titrated with silver ions generated by constant current electrolysis, the reaction being followed potentiometrically. In another method,[224] the thiourea sample is placed in the coulometric apparatus using mercury anode and platinum cathode. The base electrolyte

[221] M. K. Joshi, *Chem. Listy*, **50**, 1928 (1956).
[222] J. F. Alicino, *Microchem. J.*, **4**, 551 (1960).
[223] M. Nakanishi and H. Kobayashi, *Bull. Chem. Soc. Japan*, **26**, 394 (1953).
[224] H. L. Kies and G. J. van Weizel, *Z. Anal. Chem.*, **161**, 348 (1958).

comprises $0.1M$ potassium sulfate and $0.06N$ sulfuric acid. A current of 30 mv is applied between two mercury indicators. The formation of $Hg[SC(NH_2)_2]^+$ is postulated.

Both methods are suited for determination on the 0.1 meq. scale.

3. Chelatometric Method. Besides the indirect chelatometric method mentioned above (Section C-3), thiourea has been determined by chelatometric titration in the following way.[225] The sample is dissolved in nitric acid and bismuth nitrate is added to form the yellow bismuth complex. The solution is then titrated with $0.1M$ copper sulfate. The equivalence point is determined by the disappearance of the yellow color. This method is dependent on the fact that the Cu^{+2} ions form a more stable complex with thiourea than the Bi^{+3} ions.

E. Colorimetric and Physical Methods. The colorimetric methods for the determination of organic thiocyanates are based on alkaline hydrolysis of these compounds to produce alkali cyanide. The latter is then determined colorimetrically. Kemp[226] used picric acid as the reagent. Bruce and co-workers[227] converted the cyanide to cyanogen bromide, which is subsequently reacted with benzidine in pyridine to give an intense color.

Thiourea and its derivatives have been determined by the color developed with Nessler's reagent,[207] sodium nitroprusside,[228,229] or 2,6-dibromo-p-benzoquinonechlorimine.[230] DeRitis and Zaccho[231] determined thiourea in serum by oxidizing it with nitric oxide and ferric chloride to produce urea, which is then converted to ammonia and determined with Nessler's reagent. Hutchinson and Boltz[232] reacted thiourea with nitrous acid to yield thiocyanic acid. Addition of ferric sulfate produces the red ferric thiocyanate which is measured at 600 mμ.

The absorption of the thiocyanate function at the infrared range was investigated by Whiffen and co-workers.[233] A strong band appears at 1460 mμ.

The polarographic behavior of thiourea and some of its derivatives was studied by Manousek.[234] Quantitative applications have not been reported.

[225] Z. Brada, *Anal. Chim. Acta*, **3**, 53 (1949).

[226] W. E. Kemp, *Analyst*, **64**, 648 (1939).

[227] R. B. Bruce, J. W. Howard, and R. F. Hanzal, *Anal. Chem.*, **27**, 1346 (1955).

[228] I. W. Grote, *J. Biol. Chem.*, **93**, 25 (1931).

[229] R. H. Williams and J. Kay, *J. Lab. Clin. Med.*, **29**, 329 (1944).

[230] S. Kamiya, *Japan Analyst*, **8**, 596 (1959).

[231] F. DeRitis and M. Zaccho, *Arch. Sci. Med.*, **85**, 255 (1948).

[232] K. Hutchinson and D. Boltz, *Anal. Chem.*, **30**, 54 (1958).

[233] D. H. Whiffen, P. Torkington, and H. W. Thompson, *Trans. Faraday Soc.*, **41**, 200 (1945).

[234] O. Manousek, *Ceskoslov. Farm.*, **5**, 193 (1956).

VIII. The Xanthate, Thiol Acid Ester, and Dithiocarbamate Functions

A. General. The xanthate, thiol acid ester, and dithiocarbamate functions are characterized by a sulfide group attached to a carbonyl or thiocarbonyl linkage. Thiol acid esters are also called acyl mercaptans. Xanthates and dithiocarbamates may be considered derivatives of carbon disulfide as shown in the following structures:

$$
\underset{\substack{\text{(M = metal) Xanthate}}}{\text{MS—}\overset{\displaystyle S}{\underset{\displaystyle OR}{C}}}
\qquad
\underset{\substack{\text{Thiol acid ester}}}{\text{R—}\overset{\displaystyle O}{\underset{\displaystyle SR'}{C}}}
\qquad
\underset{\substack{\text{Dithiocarbamate}}}{\text{R}_2\text{N—}\overset{\displaystyle S}{\underset{\displaystyle SH}{C}}}
$$

B. Determination of the Xanthate Function

1. Methods Dependent on Oxidation. The oxidation of the xanthate function by iodine was first applied to quantitative analysis by Delachanal and Mermet[235] in 1877. The reaction is represented in equation 55:

$$
2\text{KS—}\overset{\displaystyle S}{\underset{\displaystyle OR}{C}} + I_2 \rightarrow \underset{\displaystyle RO}{\overset{\displaystyle S}{C}}\text{—S—S—}\overset{\displaystyle S}{\underset{\displaystyle OR}{C}} + 2\text{KI} \tag{55}
$$

The sample of xanthate is dissolved in dilute alcohol and acetic acid is added until the solution is just acid to phenolphthalein. The solution is then titrated with standard iodine solution. Starch can be used as the indicator for macro scale determinations,[236] while electrometric titration using the dead-stop endpoint is recommended for microanalysis.[237]

Cellulose xanthate is usually determined by boiling with phosphoric acid to liberate carbon disulfide, which is absorbed in ethanolic potassium hydroxide.[238] The potassium ethyl xanthate is then titrated iodometrically.

2. Methods Dependent on Precipitation

A. PRECIPITATION OF METAL XANTHATES. The xanthates of heavy metals can be precipitated from a solution containing alkali xanthate under suitable conditions. Makens[239] described a macro method in which silver xanthate is precipitated. The sample is dissolved in water and a slight excess of 0.1N silver nitrate is added while the solution is continuously stirred.

[235] B. Delachanal and A. Mermet, *Ann. Chim. Phys.*, **12**, 108 (1877).

[236] M. P. Matuszak, *Ind. Eng. Chem., Anal. Ed.*, **4**, 98 (1932).

[237] R. L. Bishop and E. L. Walace, *Ind. Eng. Chem., Anal. Ed.*, **17**, 563 (1945).

[238] W. H. Fock, *Kunstseide*, **17**, 117 (1935).

[239] R. F. Makens, *J. Am. Chem. Soc.*, **57**, 405 (1935).

Then the excess of silver ions is immediately titrated with standard thiocyanate solution using ferric nitrate as the indicator.

Finkelshtein[240] advocated the precipitation of the copper xanthate at pH 3.5–4.5 or mercury xanthate at pH 3.2–4.20. The turbidity is measured after 20–45 minutes.

It should be noted that the precipitant may react with the xanthate on long standing to produce metal sulfides which will vitiate the analytical result. Thus, after the precipitation of silver xanthate according to equation 56:

$$\text{KS—C}\overset{\text{S}}{\underset{\text{OR}}{\diagdown}} + \text{AgNO}_3 \rightarrow \text{AgS—C}\overset{\text{S}}{\underset{\text{OR}}{\diagdown}} + \text{KNO}_3 \qquad (56)$$

the excess silver nitrate present may react with the product as shown in equation 57:

$$\text{AgS—C}\overset{\text{S}}{\underset{\text{OR}}{\diagdown}} + 2\text{AgNO}_3 + \text{H}_2\text{O} \rightarrow \text{AgS—C}\overset{\text{O}}{\underset{\text{OR}}{\diagdown}} + \text{Ag}_2\text{S} + 2\text{HNO}_3 \qquad (57)$$

Therefore, the experimental procedure described in the original papers should be carefully followed.

B. PRECIPITATION OF XANTHYLACETDIETHYLAMIDE. Fink and coworkers[241] proposed chloroacetdiethylamide as a precipitant for the determination of cellulose xanthate:

$$\text{KS—C}\overset{\text{S}}{\underset{\text{OR}}{\diagdown}} + \text{ClCH}_2\text{—C}\overset{\text{O}}{\underset{\text{N(C}_2\text{H}_5)_2}{\diagdown}} \rightarrow \underset{(\text{C}_2\text{H}_5)_2\text{N}}{\overset{\text{O}}{\diagup}}\text{C—CH}_2\text{—C}\overset{\text{S}}{\underset{\text{OR}}{\diagdown}} + \text{KCl} \qquad (58)$$

The precipitation is carried out in dilute acetic acid solution. The gelatinous xanthylacetdiethylamide is collected on a filter, dried, and weighed. Alternately, the precipitate is transferred to a Kjeldahl flask and the nitrogen content is determined by the regular Kjeldahl procedure (see page 569).

C. Determination of Thiol Acid Esters. A colorimetric method for the determination of thiol acid esters (acyl mercaptans) was presented by Lynen[242] as follows. The ester is reacted with potassium hydroxide, which hydrolyzes the thiol acid function and liberates a mercapto group. The latter produces a red violet color when sodium nitroprusside is added. The

[240] D. N. Finkelshtein, *Zhur. Anal. Khim.*, **12**, 754 (1957).
[241] H. Fink, R. Stahn, and A. Matthes, *Angew. Chem.*, **47**, 429, 602 (1934).
[242] F. Lynen, *Ann.*, **574**, 33 (1951).

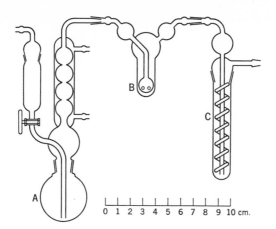

Fig. 9.3. Dithiocarbamate apparatus of Roth and Beck. Courtesy of *Mikrochimica Acta.*

color complex is stabilized by ammonium sulfate and shows an absorption band at 546 mμ. A direct proportionality exists between the extinction coefficient and the R—CO—S content.

D. Determination of the Dithiocarbamate Function. Roth and Beck[243] developed a method for the microdetermination of dithiocarbamate and thiuram disulfide groups which is dependent on the hydrolysis of these compounds to carbon disulfide. The sample is boiled with phosphoric acid and pyridine in the round bottom flask A, shown in Figure 9.3. The dithiocarbamate function is decomposed according to the following equation:

$$R_2N-\underset{SNa}{\overset{\displaystyle \overset{S}{\|}}{C}} + H_2O \rightarrow CS_2 + R_2NH + NaOH \qquad (59)$$

The carbon disulfide is purged by a slow stream of nitrogen, through the scrubber B containing cadmium acetate solution, into the absorber C containing 2N potassium hydroxide in methanol. After the reaction is complete, the potassium methyl xanthate solution in the absorber is diluted with water and neutralized with acetic acid. The xanthate is determined by titration with 0.01N methanolic iodine in the presence of potassium iodide and starch.

[243] H. Roth and W. Beck, *Mikrochim. Acta,* **1957,** 844.

10

The Unsaturated Functions

I. Introduction

Unsaturated functions in organic compounds are characterized by reactivity and particularly by addition reactions. The carbonyl, $\diagdown C{=}O$, and isothiocyanate, $-N{=}C{=}S$, functions were discussed in preceding chapters. The present chapter will deal with functions in which the unsaturation is located between contiguous carbon atoms in the alkene $\left(\diagdown C{=}C\diagup\right)$, alkyne ($-C{\equiv}C-$), alkylidene ($R_2C{=}$, such as isopropylidene ($(CH_3)_2C{=}$)), ketene ($=C{=}C{=}O$), and terminal methylene ($=CH_2$) groups.

II. The Alkene Function

A. General. The alkene function, $\diagdown C{=}C\diagup$, is commonly known as the olefinic linkage, or in the older literature as the ethylenic group. It is present in a great variety of natural products, such as fats, oils, terpenes, and many other organic compounds derived from plants. Alkenes and dienes are also produced industrially in large quantities for the manufacture of rubber and plastics. The determination of the alkene function is generally needed for the estimation of purity of ethylenic compounds. The importance of this determination is evidenced by the multitude of publications concerning the subject. Thus Polgar and Jungnickel[1] published a review on the determination of olefinic unsaturation citing 698 references. Another

---

[1] A. Polgar and J. L. Jungnickel, in *Organic Analysis*, Vol. 3, Interscience, New York, 1956, p. 203.

review by Budesinsky[2] lists 373 references. Several hundred papers have been published on the reaction of the double bond with peracids alone.[3]

All chemical methods for the determination of the alkene function are based on the addition reaction of the double bond. However, there are two points which warrant attention. First, several addition reactions commonly used in synthetic organic chemistry are not applicable to the quantitative analysis of the olefinic linkages. These reactions include the addition of hydrogen halides, sulfuric acid, and nitrosyl chloride. Second, when an addition reaction is proposed for the determination of the alkene function, different olefins may be attacked at widely different rates depending on the structure of the compound.

B. Addition of Halogens

1. Theory. According to the modern concepts of organic chemistry, addition of halogens to the alkene function proceeds by an ionic mechanism.[4] Olefins are classified as nucleophilic substances and in the reaction of bromine and ethylene, it is assumed that the first step is the addition of the bromonium ion to form a complex as shown in equation 1:

$$\text{H}_2\text{C}::\text{CH}_2 + :\ddot{\text{B}}\text{r}:\ddot{\text{B}}\text{r}: \rightarrow \left[\begin{array}{c} \text{H}_2\text{C}:\text{CH}_2 \\ :\ddot{\text{B}}\text{r}: \end{array} \right]^+ + \left[:\ddot{\text{B}}\text{r}: \right]^- \qquad (1)$$

The bromide ion then adds on to the positively charged complex transwise as depicted in equation 2:

$$\underset{:\ddot{\text{B}}\text{r}:}{\overset{+}{\text{H}_2\text{C}}}:\text{CH}_2 + :\ddot{\text{B}}\text{r}:^- \rightarrow \underset{:\ddot{\text{B}}\text{r}:}{\text{H}_2\text{C}}:\overset{:\ddot{\text{B}}\text{r}:}{\text{CH}_2} \qquad (2)$$

Substituents such as methyl or phenyl groups on the ethylene molecule which tend to increase the electron density around the alkene function will facilitate the addition reaction. On the other hand, substituents like the carboxyl, halogen, and nitrile groups, which tend to reduce the electron density around the alkene function will retard the reaction.

Comparing the reaction rate among the halogens, it has been found that

[2] B. Budesinsky, *Chem. Listy*, **53**, 997 (1959).

[3] D. Swern, *Chem. Revs.*, **45**, 1 (1949); *Organic Reactions*, Vol. 7, John Wiley and Sons, New York, 1953, p. 378.

[4] C. C. Price, *Mechanism of Reactions at Carbon-Carbon Double Bonds*, Interscience, New York, 1946.

chlorine adds the most rapidly, iodine the least, and bromine occupies an intermediate position. Chlorine is seldom used, however, for quantitative addition because of the difficulty in measuring the reagent and other complications. On the other hand, iodine monochloride, in which the iodine atom has a relative positive charge while chlorine has a relative negative one, adds readily to the alkene function as shown in equation 3:

$$
\begin{array}{c}
\underset{H_3C}{\overset{H}{\diagdown}} C = C \underset{H}{\overset{H}{\diagup}} + I^+Cl^- \rightarrow CH_3 - \underset{Cl}{\overset{H}{\underset{|}{\overset{|}{C}}}} - \underset{H}{\overset{I}{\underset{|}{\overset{|}{C}}}} - H
\end{array}
\tag{3}
$$

2. Application and Limitations of the Halogenation Methods. The halogenation methods are the most generally employed procedures for the determination of unsaturation in known compounds as well as mixtures. This is due to the fact that these methods are simple, easy to get reproducible results, and do not require special apparatus. It should be noted, however, that (a) none of the procedures described in the literature is applicable to all types of compounds containing the alkene function, and (b) a method yielding consistently reproducible results does not necessarily give the true unsaturation value of the substance under investigation.

Two inherent errors of the halogenation methods are: (a) incomplete addition and (b) substitution reactions. The latter usually can be minimized by performing the addition in the absence of light. The extent of substitution also varies with the structure of the olefin.[5-7] Olefins with branching at the alkene function were demonstrated by Petrov[7] to liberate considerably more hydrogen bromide than linear compounds of equal molecular weights.

The rate of addition is dependent on the configuration of the olefin, the reagent used, and the experimental conditions. For instance, Budesinsky and Vanickova[8] demonstrated that *cis*-α-ethoxy-β-methoxymethyl-acrylonitrile adds bromine more readily than the *trans* isomer. Cuta and Klozar[9] compared the halogenation of styrene and methyl oleate and reported that chlorine adds very fast to both, while bromine adds to the latter compound at a rate 13 times faster than to the former. The effect of temperature, pH, and excess reagent on bromination of cinnamic acid

[5] H. D. Dubois and D. A. Skoog, *Anal. Chem.*, **20**, 624 (1948).

[6] T. S. Lee, I. M. Kolthoff, and M. A. Mairs, *J. Polymer. Sci.*, **3**, 66 (1948).

[7] A. A. Petrov, *Zhur. Obekelis Khim.*, **23**, 1896 (1953).

[8] B. Budesinsky and E. Vanickova, *Ceskosl. Farm.*, **6**, 305 (1957).

[9] F. Cuta and V. Klozar, *Chem. Listy*, **52**, 1899 (1958); *Collect. Czechoslov. Chem. Commun.*, **24**, 1482 (1959).

was studied by Verma and co-workers.[10] Therefore, conflicting results reported by different workers using the same method may be due to slight variations in the experimental conditions.

Application of halogenation methods to the determination of the alkene function in conjugated double bonds, terpenes,[11] and highly branched olefins[12] is usually unsatisfactory. Difficulty in the addition reaction of unsaturated acids and esters is frequently encountered, although determination of these compounds by direct bromination has been reported.[13,14] The rate of bromine addition is greatly increased by converting the unsaturated acids and esters to the corresponding sodium salts. This principle was utilized in a macro method described by Critchfield[15] which has been adapted to the micro scale.[16] The detailed procedure is given in experiment 16.

The presence of certain groups at the alkene function sometimes affects the molar ratio of the halogenation reaction. For example, the oxymethylene group (see page 198) consumes only one halogen atom per alkene function whether the addent is bromine,[17] as shown in equation 4:

$$-\overset{|}{C}=\overset{|}{C}- \ + \ Br_2 \rightarrow -\overset{\overset{\displaystyle Br}{|}}{\underset{\underset{\displaystyle OH}{|}}{C}}---\overset{\overset{\displaystyle}{}}{\underset{\underset{\displaystyle Br}{|}}{C}}- \rightarrow -\overset{}{\underset{\underset{\displaystyle O}{\|}}{C}}-\overset{}{\underset{\underset{\displaystyle Br}{|}}{C}}\diagdown \ + \ HBr \tag{4}$$

or iodine monochloride[18] as shown in equation 5:

$$-\overset{|}{C}=\overset{\diagup}{\underset{\underset{\displaystyle OH}{|}}{C}}\diagdown \ + \ ICl \rightarrow -\overset{}{\underset{\underset{\displaystyle O}{\|}}{C}}-\overset{}{\underset{\underset{\displaystyle I}{|}}{C}}- \ + \ HCl \tag{5}$$

Whereas vinyl ketones can be determined by bromination in the usual way,[19] vinyl ethers (see page 392) add only one iodine atom when treated with standard iodine in methanol solution according to the following equation:[20]

[10] M. R. Verma, K. C. Agrawal, and S. D. Paul, *J. Sci. Ind., Res. B. India*, **16**, 213 (1957).

[11] L. Joshel, S. A. Hall, and S. Palkin, *Ind. Eng. Chem., Anal. Ed.*, **13**, 447 (1941).

[12] H. C. Johnson and R. A. Clark, *Anal. Chem.*, **19**, 869 (1947).

[13] P. Duquenois, *Bull. Soc. Chim.*, [5] **5**, 1207 (1938).

[14] K. Burger and E. Schulek, *Z. Anal. Chem.*, **172**, 98 (1960).

[15] F. E. Critchfield, *Anal. Chem.*, **31**, 1406 (1959).

[16] T. S. Ma and J. Smith, unpublished work; see J. Smith, *Master's Thesis, Brooklyn College*, 1961, p. 68.

[17] S. R. Cooper and R. P. Barnes, *Ind. Eng. Chem., Anal. Ed.*, **10**, 379 (1938).

[18] A. Gero, *J. Org. Chem.*, **19**, 469 (1954).

[19] B. Budesinsky, K. Moucek, F. Jancik, and E. Kraus, *Chem. Listy*, **51**, 1819 (1957).

[20] Z. Kapisinsky, *Chem. Prumysl.*, **7**, 66 (1957).

$$\text{ROCH}{=}\text{CH}_2 + \text{I}_2 + \text{CH}_3\text{OH} \rightarrow \underset{\underset{\displaystyle \text{OCH}_3}{|}}{\text{RO}\overset{\overset{\displaystyle \text{H}}{|}}{\text{C}}}\!\!-\!\!\overset{\overset{\displaystyle \text{I}}{|}}{\text{CH}_2} + \text{HI} \qquad (6)$$

3. Reagents for Halogenation. A large variety of reagents have been employed for analytical halogenation. A reagent may be advocated for its stability, reactivity, or convenience in preparation. Another reagent may be used simply because of an established method for routine industrial analysis. The reagents are separated into several groups as follows.

A. FREE HALOGENS. The extreme reactivity of fluorine and difficulties in handling it preclude its use as a reagent for addition to the alkene function. Chlorine is quite reactive and tends to cause substitution and side reactions. Nevertheless, chlorine mixed with cupric chloride[20] or generated by electrolysis of hydrochloric acid[9] has been used for quantitative analysis of olefins. Iodine without a catalyst is a sluggish reagent for addition to olefinic groups, though Margosches and co-workers[21] proposed standard iodine in ethanol on account of the simplicity of preparation. On the other hand, bromine has certain advantages and is the reagent of choice in the petroleum industry for determination on the macro scale. The use of bromine in aqueous solution was described by Allen[22] in 1881. Recently standard bromine in an organic solvent such as acetic acid,[23-25] chloroform,[26] or carbon tetrachloride[27,28] is generally employed. Gaseous bromine was recommended by Stieglitz and co-workers[29] for the determination of olefins since this reagent reacts quantitatively with conjugated double α,β-bonds and unsaturated acids. Electrolytically generated bromine was described by several investigators.[9,30,31]

B. BROMIDE-BROMATE MIXTURE. While standard bromine solution is a convenient and relatively stable reagent in macro scale analysis, its adaptation to the micro scale is difficult because $0.01N$ bromine deteriorates rapidly. It will be recalled (see page 292) that the combination of a measured

[21] B. M. Margosches, W. Hinner, and L. Friedman, *Angew. Chem.*, **37**, 334 (1924).
[22] A. H. Allen, *Analyst*, **6**, 177 (1881).
[23] K. Uhrig and H. Levin, *Ind. Eng. Chem., Anal. Ed.*, **13**, 90 (1941).
[24] S. A. Miller and F. H. Pearman, *Analyst*, **75**, 492 (1950).
[25] J. Dodomka, *Chem. Prumysl.*, **9**, 363 (1959).
[26] G. D. Galpern and J. V. Vinogradova, *Neftyanoe Khoz.*, **1**, 59 (1936).
[27] S. R. Olson, C. M. Hull, and W. G. France, *Ind. Eng. Chem.*, **38**, 1273 (1946).
[28] N. R. Knarth, *Oils and Oil Ind. J. (India)*, **5**, 82 (1953).
[29] E. Stieglitz, K. Andress, and T. Demedieck, *Brennstoff Chem.*, **30**, 356 (1949).
[30] J. W. Miller and D. D. DeFord, *Anal. Chem.*, **29**, 475 (1957).
[31] W. Walisch and M. R. F. Ashworth, *Mikrochim. Acta*, **1959**, 497.

volume of $0.01N$ potassium bromate with an acidified solution containing potassium bromide is the preferred method for obtaining $0.01N$ bromine *in situ*. The reaction is shown in equation 7:

$$KBrO_3 + 5KBr + 6H^+ \rightarrow 3Br_2 + 3H_2O + 6K^+ \qquad (7)$$

The bromide-bromate mixture has been used to determine olefinic unsaturation on the macro scale for a long time.[32–34] The procedure[35] for the determination of the alkene function on the 0.1 meq. scale is given in experiment 15. If precautions are taken to avoid substitution, the accuracy of this method is good.

    c. BROMINE-BROMIDE MIXTURE. Kaufmann[36] suggested a solution of bromine in methanol which is saturated with sodium bromide as the reagent for the determination of unsaturation in fats and oils. The use of bromine in aqueous solution containing an excess of potassium bromide has also been described.[1,15] These reagents are more stable than solutions containing bromine only, presumably due to the formation of a complex according to equation 8:

$$Br_2 + NaBr \rightarrow NaBr_3 \qquad (8)$$

The bromine-bromide mixture is suitable for the microdetermination of the alkene function in sodium salts of unsaturated carboxylic acids[16] (see experiment 16).

    d. HALOGEN HALIDES. Iodine monochloride is the standard reagent for the determination of the unsaturation value in fats and oils. Its use was first recommended by Hübl[37] in 1884. Later Wijs[38] proposed modification and improvements of the method. This reagent is prepared either by mixing iodine trichloride and iodine in glacial acetic acid:

$$ICl_3 + I_2 \rightarrow 3ICl \qquad (9)$$

or by passing chlorine gas into an acetic acid solution of iodine:

$$Cl_2 + I_2 \rightarrow 2ICl \qquad (10)$$

Standard iodine monochloride is also used to determine residual unsatura-

[32] M. Weger, *Chemische Industrie*, **28**, 24 (1905).

[33] W. Vaubel, *Angew. Chem.*, **23**, 2078 (1910).

[34] A. W. Francis, *Ind. Eng. Chem.*, **18**, 821 (1926).

[35] T. S. Ma and J. Smith, unpublished work; see J. Smith, *Master's Thesis, Brooklyn College*, 1961, p. 61.

[36] H. P. Kaufmann, *Z. Untersuch. Lebensm.*, **51**, 3 (1926).

[37] B. Hübl, *J. Soc. Chem. Ind.*, **3**, 641 (1884).

[38] J. J. Wijs, *Berichte*, **31**, 750 (1898).

tion in rubber materials,[39,40] and has been suggested as the reagent for microanalysis.[41,42]

Iodine monobromide was introduced by Hanus[43] in 1901. It can be prepared by adding bromine to an iodine solution in acetic acid or carbon tetrachloride. This reagent is more stable than iodine monochloride and has been recommended for the analysis of oils,[44,45] chlolesterol derivatives,[46] petroleum fractions,[47] and butadiene rubbers.[48]

Bromine monochloride was recently employed by Greger and co-workers[49] to determine the degree of unsaturation in polyesters. Like the above two reagents, it is difficult to keep a standard solution of $0.01N$ for microdeterminations.

E. CATALYSTS. The rate of halogenation can be increased by the use of a catalyst. Mercury salts are frequently recommended,[50,51] though their role has not been elucidated and reports on their effect are sometimes conflicting. Thus Ungar[52] studied the various methods for determining olefins and reported that omission of the mercuric chloride catalyst gives better results. Wood[53] stated that results 10–30% too high are obtained in the analysis of propylene and butylene polymers when mercury catalysts are added.

Hydrochloric acid is shown to have catalytic effect in bromination with the bromine-bromide mixture.[54] Pyridine sulfate[55] or acetate[56] has been used with bromine. It is postulated that the bromine molecule is attached to the heterocyclic nitrogen and acts as a reagent for addition without side reactions such as substitution and oxidation.

[39] A. R. Kemp and H. Peters, *Ind. Eng. Chem., Anal. Ed.*, **15**, 453 (1943).

[40] T. S. Lee, I. M. Kolthoff, and M. A. Mairs, *Rubber Chem. Technol.*, **21**, 835 (1948).

[41] S. Komori, *Bull. Chem. Soc. Japan, Ind. Chem. Sect.*, **51**, 120 (1948).

[42] W. M. Phillips and W. C. Wake, *Analyst*, **74**, 306 (1949).

[43] J. Hanus, *Z. Untersuch. Nahr. u. Genussm.*, **4**, 913 (1901).

[44] J. O. Ralls, *J. Am. Chem. Soc.*, **56**, 121 (1934).

[45] L. M. Yedlenayalli and J. J. Paul, *J. Sci. Ind. Research (India)*, **12**, 524 (1953).

[46] J. O. Ralls, *J. Am. Chem. Soc.*, **55**, 2083 (1933).

[47] J. C. Morrell and G. Egloff, *Ind. Eng. Chem.*, **17**, 1259 (1925).

[48] G. A. Vasil'ev, *J. Gen. Chem. USSR*, **17**, 923 (1947).

[49] K. M. Greger, I. V. Szmrecsanyi, and E. M. Bodi, *Magyar Kem. Lapja*, **15**, 72 (1960).

[50] B. Brase, *Anal. Chem.*, **21**, 1461 (1949).

[51] L. R. McNall and L. T. Eby, *Anal. Chem.*, **29**, 951 (1957).

[52] E. H. Ungar, *Anal. Chem.*, **30**, 375 (1958).

[53] J. C. S. Wood, *Anal. Chem.*, **30**, 372 (1958).

[54] R. E. Byrne and J. B. Johnson, *Anal. Chem.*, **28**, 126 (1956).

[55] K. W. Rosenmund and W. Kulnshenn, *Berichte*, **56**, 1262 (1923).

[56] A. M. Caccia-Bara, *Ateneo Parmense*, **18**, 467 (1948).

4. Halogenation Techniques. Numerous methods and procedures have appeared in the literature on the determination of olefinic unsaturation. The reader is referred to the comprehensive list compiled by Polgar and Jungnickel.[1] The simplest—and most common—procedure is to treat the sample with a measured volume of the standardized halogenation reagent, followed by the titration of the residual halogen. For determinations on the macro scale, $0.1N$ or stronger standard solution is employed and the endpoint may be located visually either by the color of the halogen (iodine or bromine) or by the starch indicator. Several investigators have used $0.1N$ reagent solution for halogenation on the micro scale. Special apparatus[42,44,57-60] were designed for such purpose in order to reduce the error in measuring the reagent and titrant. Reid[61] proposed a method using $0.01N$ bromine in acetic acid as the reagent and $0.01N$ sodium thiosulfate as the titrant. It should be noted that $0.01N$ bromine solution is very unstable. Micro procedures which utilize the bromide-bromate (see Section II-B-3-B) and the bromine-bromide (see Section II-B-3-c) techniques, respectively, will be found in the Experimental Part.

Petrova[62] suggested $0.1N$ anethole in methanol as the titrant for the residual bromine after the addition reaction. The advantage of this technique over the iodometric procedure is not known. Electrometric methods using the dead-stop endpoint have been proposed for titrations by means of potassium bromate-bromide mixture[5] or standard bromine solution.[50]

Coulometric methods for the determination of the alkene function were described in several papers.[9,30,31,63] Bromine is generated electrolytically from the reaction mixture containing bromide ions. Since electrical measurements can be made with high sensitivity, this technique is suitable for microanalysis. It should be noted, however, that this is a direct titration procedure and is limited to compounds which react with bromine instantaneously.

When bromine vapor is used as the reagent,[29,64,65] a gravimetric finish is necessary. The increase in weight of the reaction vessel after the removal of the excess bromine gives the amount of bromine added to the sample. It is difficult to obtain accurate results on the micro scale by this technique.

[57] W. Ruzicka, *Mikrochemie*, **36/37**, 924 (1951).
[58] C. Whalley, *Oil and Color Chemists Assoc. J.*, **35**, 596 (1952).
[59] B. W. Grunbaum, *Mikrochemie*, **39**, 268 (1952).
[60] A. R. Javes, *Anal. Chem.*, **30**, 1570 (1958).
[61] V. W. Reid, *Analyst*, **79**, 456 (1954).
[62] L. N. Petrova, *Zhur. Priklad. Khim.*, **22**, 122 (1949).
[63] F. A. Leisey and J. F. Grutsch, *Anal. Chem.*, **28**, 1553 (1956).
[64] O. Hechner, *Analyst*, **20**, 49 (1895).
[65] E. Rossmann, *Berichte*, **65**, 1847 (1932).

A thermometric method was proposed by Kapisinsky[20] for determining ethylene. Chlorine gas is passed into the reaction mixture containing cupric chloride as catalyst, and the heat evolved is measured through a platinum wire. Radiometric determination of the alkene function was described by Kaufmann and Budwig[66] using $I^{139}Br$ as the reagent. This technique permits determination on the μg. scale.

5. *Calculations.* The analytical results of the determination of the alkene function may be expressed in different ways. The choice is dependent on the purpose of the analysis.

A. PER CENT ALKENE FUNCTION. This expression is used to characterize a pure substance of known or unknown composition and structure. It is calculated by use of equation 11.

$$\text{Per cent } C{=}C = \frac{(\text{atom equiv. of halogen consumed})(24.02)(100)}{(2)(\text{wt. of sample})} \tag{11}$$

The atom equivalent of halogen consumed is given by the volume of standard halogen solution used multiplied by its normality. The atom equivalent of halogen is one half of its molar equivalent. Hence the factor 2 appears in the formula since each $C{=}C$ linkage consumes two halogen atoms. From the per cent alkene function and the molecular weight of the compound the number of double bonds in the substance under investigation can be estimated.

B. PER CENT PURITY, PER CENT RECOVERY AND PER CENT COMPOUND. These expressions give the purity of a sample containing a known compound. It is presumed that the impurities, if present, do not exhibit unsaturation or consume the halogenation reagent under the experimental conditions:

$$\frac{\text{Per cent}}{\text{purity}} = \frac{(\text{atom equiv. of halogen consumed})(\text{equiv. wt. of compound})(100)}{(2)(\text{wt. of sample})} \tag{12}$$

The equivalent weight of compound is calculated by its molecular weight over the number of alkene functions it contains. When an analytical procedure is tested with pure known compounds, the results are reported as "per cent recovery" which is calculated by the same formula as "per cent purity." "Per cent recovery" is also known as "per cent compound."

C. IODINE NUMBER. Fats and oils and many industrial samples that require unsaturation analysis are as a rule mixtures of indefinite composition; hence it is customary to express the result in terms of the amount of halogen consumed per unit weight of the sample. "Iodine number" is defined as the number of milligrams of iodine which are consumed by

[66] H. P. Kaufmann and J. Budwig, *Fette u. Seifen,* **52,** 390 (1951).

100 mg. of the sample, if the addition is complete. The calculation is given by equation 13:

$$\text{Iodine number} = \frac{(\text{atom equiv. of halogen consumed})(126.91)(100)}{(\text{wt. of sample})} \quad (13)$$

D. BROMINE NUMBER. The definition of "bromine number" is similar to the "iodine number," hence:

$$\text{Bromine number} = \frac{(\text{atom equiv. of halogen consumed})(79.916)(100)}{(\text{wt. of sample})} \quad (14)$$

It should be noted that standard bromine solution is seldom used and standard iodine solution is rarely used for the microdetermination of unsaturation. In reporting the "iodine number" or "bromine number" it is advisable to state which analytical procedure was employed, in view of the fact that there are discrepancies among the different procedures.

E. PER CENT OLEFIN CONTENT. If the average molecular weight of a mixture is known and the sample is assumed to contain only mono-olefinic compounds, the "per cent olefin content" is calculated by means of equation 15:

$$\text{Per cent olefin content} = \frac{(\text{atom equiv. of halogen consumed})(\text{av. mol. wt.})(100)}{(2)(\text{wt. of sample})} \quad (15)$$

C. Addition of Hydrogen

1. Principle. The alkene function upon catalytic hydrogenation adds two atoms of hydrogen to form a saturated compound:

$$\begin{array}{c} R \quad\quad R \\ \diagdown\quad\diagup \\ C{=}C \quad + \ H_2 \xrightarrow{\text{catalyst}} \\ \diagup\quad\diagdown \\ R \quad\quad R \end{array} \quad \begin{array}{c} R \ H \ H \ R \\ \diagdown\ |\ \ |\ \diagup \\ C{-}C \\ \diagup\quad\quad\diagdown \\ R \quad\quad\quad R \end{array} \quad (16)$$

It is interesting to note that olefinic hydrocarbons are seldom determined by hydrogen addition. On the other hand, hydrogenation is extensively applied to the analysis of unsaturated compounds containing functional groups besides the double bond. This method is of particular importance to the research organic chemist who is concerned with the proof of structure of new compounds. One great advantage of the hydrogenation method is the easy recovery of the reaction product, which can be subjected to further investigation, such as elemental analysis and determination of the other functional groups. The use of quantitative microhydrogenation in the study of senecio alkaloids may be cited as an example.[67] When the determination of the alkene function is associated with the elucidation of the

[67] R. Adams and M. Gianturo, *J. Am. Chem. Soc.,* **79,** 168 (1956).

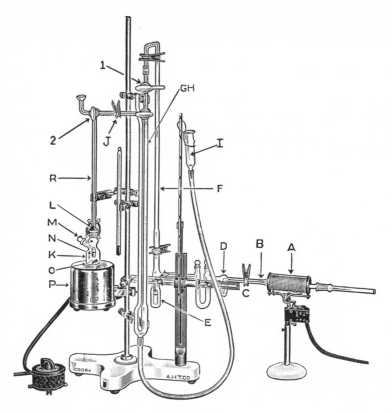

Fig. 10.1. Hydrogenation apparatus of Ogg and Cooper. Courtesy of A. H. Thomas Co.

structure of the original compound, it should be noted that molecular rearrangement may occur during the reaction of hydrogen addition. This is particularly important in the field of terpene chemistry.[68]

Quantitative hydrogenation is occasionally employed for the determination of unsaturation in fats and oils.[69] However, this method is used as a check for other methods and is not applied as a routine procedure for the analysis of industrial products.

2. *Microhydrogenation Assemblies.* Numerous designs of apparatus for quantitative hydrogenation have been published. The reader is referred to the list of references given in the review by Polgar and Jungnickel.[1] Two types of apparatus for microhydrogenation that are commercially available are shown in Figures 10.1 and 10.2. In the apparatus of Ogg and Cooper[70]

[68] Y. Naves, *Helv. Chim. Acta*, **29**, 1450 (1946).
[69] F. C. Pack and R. N. Planet, *J. Am. Oil Chemist Assoc.*, **30**, 461 (1953).
[70] C. L. Ogg and F. J. Cooper, *Anal. Chem.*, **21**, 1400 (1949).

(Fig. 10.1) the volume of hydrogen consumed is measured in the gasburet. The detailed procedure will be found in experiment 45. A modified reaction vessel is shown in Figure 10.3. The vessel allows an opening for the system to be flushed with hydrogen. Alternately, both side arms (A and B) may be provided with a plug carrying a basket. This permits the addition of a second batch of sample or catalyst. In the apparatus of Gilson and Consterdine (Fig. 10.2) two identical flasks are used; one is for the sample and the other for compensation. The amount of hydrogen consumed is calculated from the manometer readings.

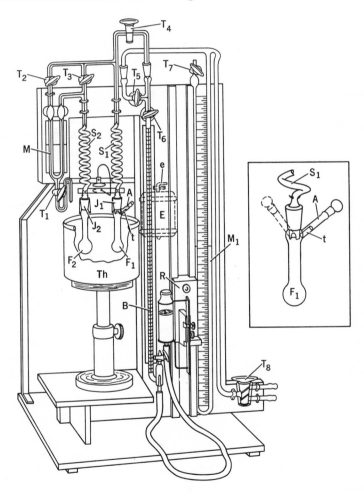

Fig. 10.2. Hydrogenation apparatus of Gilson and Consterdine. Courtesy of J. W. Towers & Co., Ltd.

The apparatus of Clauson-Kass and Limborg[71] shown in Figure 10.4 is favored by some workers. A recent modification of this design proposed by Hozumi[72] is shown in Figure 10.5. Quantitative hydrogenation apparatus for hydrogen absorption in the 1–10 meq. scale usually consists of a reaction vessel of the boat-type connected to an agitating motor.[73] These are easy to construct, but are not suitable for adaptation to microdeterminations.

3. *Microhydrogenation Techniques.* As can be seen from the apparatus described in the above section, gasometric determination of the alkene function may be accomplished volumetrically or manometrically. According

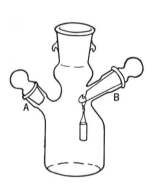

Fig. 10.3. Modified reaction vessel for microhydrogenation.

to Hozumi,[74] it is easier to construct the manometric apparatus than the volumetric apparatus. On the other hand, the operation of the volumetric procedure is less complicated. Engelbrecht[75] described a technique to analyze liquid samples using the Ogg-Cooper apparatus (Fig. 10.1). The compound to be hydrogenated is weighed in an open capillary which is covered with another tube. When the assembly is ready, the capillary is broken by means of a glass rod through the side arm. The reaction vessel shown in Figure 10.3 is recommended for this purpose.

Determination of the alkene function by the addition of hydrogen may be carried out in apparatus that were not originally designed for hydrogenation. Thus, the apparatus for determining active hydrogen by the Grignard reagent was used by several workers.[76–78] The gasometric apparatus of Ma and Scheinthal[79] (see Fig. 6.15) is suitable for microhydrogenation. When the amount of hydrogen consumed is less than 1 ml., the Warburg apparatus can be used.[80]

[71] N. Clauson-Kass and F. Limborg, *Acta Chem. Scand.*, **1**, 884 (1947).

[72] K. Hozumi, *J. Pharm. Soc. Japan*, **79**, 135 (1959).

[73] R. L. Parrette, *Anal. Chem.*, **26**, 236 (1954).

[74] K. Hozumi, *J. Pharm. Soc. Japan*, **80**, 410 (1960).

[75] R. M. Engelbrecht, *Anal. Chem.*, **29**, 1556 (1957).

[76] H. E. Zaugg and W. Lauer, *Anal. Chem.*, **20**, 1022 (1948).

[77] W. Schöniger, *Mikrochemie*, **38**, 132 (1951).

[78] M. R. Chapheker and T. S. Gore, *Mikrochim. Acta*, **1959**, 664.

[79] T. S. Ma and B. Scheinthal, unpublished work; see B. Scheinthal, *Master's Thesis, Brooklyn College*, 1961.

[80] K. Suda and S. Sakamoto, *J. Pharm. Soc. Japan*, **57**, 1032 (1937).

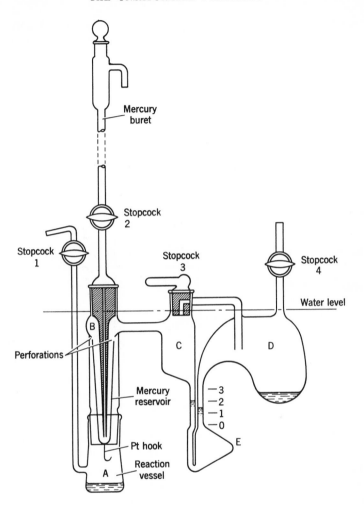

Fig. 10.4. Hydrogenation apparatus of Clauson-Kass and Limborg. Courtesy of *Acta Chemica Scandinavica*.

Coulometric methods for the determination of the alkene function by hydrogenation with hydrogen generated by electrolysis have been devised.[81,82] This depends on instantaneous quantitative hydrogenation of the compound. The general applicability of this technique has not been evaluated.

[81] H. Flaschka and M. Hochenegger, *Mikrochim. Acta*, **1957**, 586.
[82] J. W. Miller and D. D. DeFord, *Anal. Chem.*, **30**, 295 (1958).

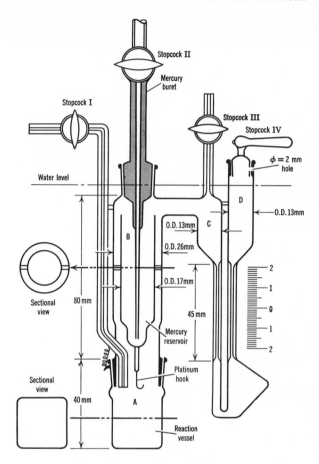

Fig. 10.5. Hydrogenation apparatus of Hozumi. Courtesy of *Journal of the Pharmaceutical Society of Japan.*

Seaman[83] proposed a titrimetric method for the determination of unsaturation by catalytic hydrogenation as follows: Standardized lithium aluminum hydride in dibutyl ether solution is introduced into a serum bottle containing the sample (1 meq.), platinum catalyst, and dry methanol under nitrogen. The excess hydrogen forms water which is determined by titration with standard Karl Fischer reagent. This procedure is not suitable for conversion to the micro scale.

4. Catalysis. The alkene function does not react with hydrogen gas

[83] W. Seaman, *Anal. Chem.*, **30**, 1840 (1958).

unless a suitable catalyst is present. Surface phenomena are involved in the activation and addition of hydrogen. Hence, the catalyst is always employed in finely divided form so as to provide the maximum surface area per unit weight of the material. In contrast to other types of catalytic reactions, considerably large amounts of catalyst are needed in micro-hydrogenation—usually more than the weight of the sample to be analyzed.

The choice of the catalyst is critical in quantitative microhydrogenation. It should be noted that the determination is performed under a gas pressure only slightly above the atmospheric pressure and the reaction is expected to be complete within a short time. Therefore, the slow catalysts containing chromium, cobalt or iron, etc., used for hydrogenation under high pressures, are not recommended for analytical hydrogenation. On the other hand, a highly active catalyst may cause hydrogenation of other functions besides the olefinic double bonds.

When the microdetermination of the alkene function by hydrogenation is made on a research compound (e.g., for the elucidation of structure of a natural product, or for the proof of identity of a new synthetic compound), it is preferable to use the same catalyst in the analytical as in the prepara-tive experiments. This will avoid discrepancies in the interpretations of results. The following catalysts are commonly used for microhydrogenation: (1) platinum black prepared from chloroplatinic acid[84] or platinum oxide;[85] platinum suspended on charcoal[86] or silica gel;[87] (2) palladium on char-coal;[70,86] (3) nickel-aluminum alloy (Raney nickel). Detailed directions for the preparation of palladium, platinum, and nickel catalysts for micro-hydrogenation at atmospheric pressure have been published by one of the authors.[88]

Precaution should be taken in storing the catalyst after it is prepared. It should be kept under a liquid or in an atmosphere of hydrogen. Exposure of the prepared catalyst to the air may lead to vigorous oxidation resulting in an explosion or fire.

Analytical hydrogenation is usually carried out at room temperature. Occasionally, reaction at elevated temperatures is recommended. Thus, Shively and co-workers[89] demonstrated that analysis with a heated catalyst takes shorter time and gives better precision. It is advisable to use an

[84] R. Willstätter and E. Waldschmidt-Leitz, *Berichte*, **54**, 113 (1921).

[85] V. Voorhees and R. Adams, *J. Am. Chem. Soc.*, **44**, 1397 (1922).

[86] W. J. C. DeKok, H. I. Waterman, and H. A. van Westen, *J. Soc. Chem. Ind.*, **55**, 225 (1936).

[87] F. A. Vandenheuvel, *Anal. Chem.*, **28**, 362 (1956).

[88] N. D. Cheronis, *Micro and Semimicro Methods*, Interscience, New York, 1954, pp. 239–241.

[89] J. H. Shively, F. Philgreen, and H. Levin, *Anal. Chem.*, **21**, 1566 (1949).

assembly provided with a heating bath so that the determination can be performed at the lower and then the higher temperature. It should also be ascertained that the catalyst does not change its characteristics at different temperatures. For instance, if the catalyst is shown to attack both the alkene function and the benzene ring at high temperatures, appropriate corrections should be made in the calculation of the olefinic content of the compound.

D. Addition of Mercuric Salts. The alkene function containing two hydrogen atoms in the *cis* position reacts with ionizable mercuric salts in the presence of methanol by addition, accompanied by the liberation of an equivalent of the corresponding acid. Mercuric acetate is the salt commonly used. The reaction is represented in equation 17:

$$
\begin{array}{c}
R \\ \diagdown \\ C=C \\ \diagup \quad \diagdown \\ H \qquad H
\end{array}
\begin{array}{c}
R' \\
\end{array}
+ \left(CH_3-C\!\!\diagup\!\!\begin{array}{c}O\\ \\ \diagdown O\end{array} \right)_2 Hg + CH_3OH \rightarrow
$$

$$
\underset{\substack{\big| \\ CH_3-C-O-Hg \\ \big\| \\ O}}{H-\overset{R}{\underset{\big|}{C}}} \;\; \underset{\substack{\big| \\ OCH_3}}{\overset{R'}{\underset{\big|}{C}}-H} + CH_3-C\!\!\diagup\!\!\begin{array}{c}O\\ \\ \diagdown OH\end{array} \qquad (17)
$$

A number of macro methods have been published for the determination of unsaturated compounds which are dependent on this reaction. In some procedures the amount of acetic acid that is liberated is titrated, after the removal of the excess of mercuric acetate in the form of mercuric halide,[90,91] potassium mercuric iodide,[92] or metallic mercury.[93] In other procedures, a measured volume of $0.1M$ mercuric acetate solution is added to the olefinic compound, and the determination is finished by the titration of the unconsumed reagent. Das[94] proposed a method by titrating the mercuric salts as bases in nonaqueous solution. It should be noted that both mercuric acetate and the methoxymercuration product are titrated, but the latter requires only one equivalent of standard acid, as shown by equations 18a and 18b:

$$
(CH_3-COO)_2Hg + 2HCl \rightarrow HgCl_2 + 2CH_3COOH \qquad (18a)
$$

[90] R. W. Martin, *Anal. Chem.*, **21**, 921 (1949).
[91] J. B. Johnson and J. P. Fletcher, *Anal. Chem.*, **31**, 1563 (1959).
[92] R. P. Marquardt and E. N. Luce, *Anal. Chem.*, **21**, 1194 (1949).
[93] R. P. Marquardt and E. N. Luce, *Anal. Chem.*, **20**, 751 (1948).
[94] M. N. Das, *Anal. Chem.*, **26**, 1086 (1954).

$$\begin{array}{ccccc} & \text{R} & \text{R} & & \text{R} \quad \text{R} \\ \text{H}-\overset{|}{\text{C}}\!\!-\!\!\overset{|}{\text{C}}\text{H} & + \text{HCl} \rightarrow \text{H}-\overset{|}{\text{C}}\!\!-\!\!\overset{|}{\text{C}}\!-\!\text{H} + \text{CH}_3\text{COOH} \quad (18b) \\ \text{CH}_3\!-\!\overset{|}{\underset{\text{O}}{\text{C}}}\!-\!\text{O}\!-\!\text{Hg} \quad \text{OCH}_3 & & \text{ClHg} \quad \text{OCH}_3 \end{array}$$

An indirect chelatometric method was proposed by Bartels and Hoyme.[95] After the methoxymercuration, a known excess of standard EDTA solution is introduced, followed by titration of the residual EDTA with $0.2M$ zinc sulfate using Erichrome Black T as the indicator. These procedures have not been adapted to the micro scale.

Mallik[96] demonstrated that a trace of perchloric acid greatly increases the rate of addition of mercuric acetate to certain olefinic compounds. Under ordinary conditions, α,β-unsaturated acids, nitriles, and esters cannot be determined by the methoxymercuration reaction. However, it was shown that quantitative addition occurs when methacrylic esters are treated with mercuric acetate-methanol mixture in the presence of perchloric acid at 45°C for 30 minutes.[97]

Two micro methods dependent on the addition of mercuric salts were proposed by Wronski for the determination of the alkene function using $0.01N$ aqueous mercuric nitrate to determine allyl alcohol.[98] The sample is reacted with an excess known amount of the standardized reagent according to equation 19:

$$\text{CH}_2\!\!=\!\!\text{CH}-\text{CH}_2\text{OH} + \text{Hg(NO}_3)_2 + \text{H}_2\text{O} \rightarrow$$
$$(^+\text{HgCH}_2\!-\!\text{CH(OH)}\!-\!\text{CH}_2\text{OH)NO}_3^- + \text{HNO}_3 \quad (19)$$

The excess of mercuric ions is then determined by back-titration with $0.01N$ thioglycolic acid (see Chapter 9, Section II-B-2) using thiofluorescein as the indicator. Styrene is determined by treatment with excess mercuric perchlorate in the presence of perchloric acid, followed by back-titration with thioglycolic acid.[99] According to Wronski, acrylonitrile and methyl acrylate do not interfere with the determination of styrene in spite of the presence of perchlorate ions.

E. Miscellaneous Methods

1. *Addition of Hypochlorous Acid.* Mukherjee[100] proposed $0.1N$ sodium hypochlorite as the reagent to determine unsaturation in fats and oils. The

[95] U. Bartels and H. Hoyme, *Faserforsch. u. Textiltech.*, **10**, 345 (1959).
[96] K. L. Mallik, *Anal. Chem.*, **32**, 1369 (1960).
[97] K. L. Mallik and M. N. Das, *Chem. & Ind. (London)*, **1959**, 162.
[98] M. Wronski, *Z. Anal. Chem.*, **171**, 177 (1959).
[99] M. Wronski, *Chemia Analityczna*, **5**, 823 (1960).
[100] S. Mukherjee, *J. Am. Oil Chem.*, **32**, 351 (1955).

sample is dissolved in glacial acetic acid and a known volume of the standardized sodium hypochlorite is added. Hypochlorous acid, which is liberated, reacts with the alkene function as shown in equation 20:

$$\diagdown C = C \diagup + HOCl \rightarrow \diagdown C - C \diagup \begin{matrix} Cl \\ | \\ \end{matrix} \qquad\qquad OH$$ (20)

The residual hypochlorite is then determined iodometrically. Other workers suggested chloramine-T in sulfuric acid[101] and t-butyl hypochlorite in an organic solvent,[102] respectively. The latter reagent gives satisfactory results only with styrene. These methods have not been tested on the micro scale.

2. *Addition of Thiocyanogen.* Thiocyanogen has been used to determine olefinic unsaturation.[103] The reaction is similar to the addition of halogens. The rate of addition, however, varies widely with different compounds and experimental conditions.[104] When this reagent is used for routine analysis of industrial samples, it is necessary to adhere strictly to the prescribed procedure.[105] Its use for the determination of the alkene function in unknown compounds is not warranted.

3. *Addition of Nitrogen Tetroxide.* Nitrogen tetroxide adds to olefinic hydrocarbons as indicated in equation 21:

$$\diagdown C = C \diagup + N_2O_4 \rightarrow -\overset{NO_2}{\underset{}{C}} - \overset{}{\underset{NO_2}{C}} -$$ (21)

The products are soluble in alcohol containing potassium hydroxide and potassium sulfide. Bond[106] described a method for the determination of the olefin content of a hydrocarbon mixture as follows. The sample is treated with a current of nitrogen tetroxide gas in a special reaction flask, until brown fumes appear for 5 minutes. Aqueous urea solution is then added to the reaction mixture to decompose the residual nitrogen tetroxide. The

[101] K. I. Brow, *Indian Soap J.*, **18**, 259 (1953).

[102] C. E. van Hall, *Anal. Chem.*, **30**, 1416 (1958).

[103] G. Gorbach, *Fette u. Seifen*, **47**, 499 (1940).

[104] A. A. Bugorkova, L. N. Petrova, and V. M. Rodinov, *Zhur. Obshchei Khim.*, **23**, 1808 (1953).

[105] *Official Method of Analysis*, 8th ed., Association of Official Agricultural Chemists, Washington, 1955, p. 465.

[106] G. R. Bond, Jr., *Ind. Eng. Chem., Anal. Ed.*, **18**, 692 (1946).

unreacted saturated hydrocarbon is measured either after steam-distillation or hydrolysis with alcoholic potassium hydroxide-sulfide mixture to separate the nitrosated product. It is apparent that this method is not suited for the microdetermination of the alkene function. It should be noted that aromatic hydrocarbons also react with nitrogen tetroxide.

4. Reaction with Perbenzoic Acid. The alkene function reacts with perbenzoic acid[3] to form an epoxide and liberate a mole of benzoic acid as indicated in equation 22:

$$\underset{/}{\overset{\backslash}{C}}=\underset{\backslash}{\overset{/}{C}} + C_6H_5CO—OOH \rightarrow —\overset{|}{\underset{\backslash}{C}}\underset{O}{\underset{/}{\quad}}\overset{|}{\underset{}{C}}— + C_6H_5—COOH \qquad (22)$$

Application of this reaction to the determination of unsaturated compounds on the macro scale has been proposed by a number of workers.[107,108] A standardized solution of $0.5N$ perbenzoic acid in chloroform or benzene is added to the sample and the unconsumed reagent is then determined (see Chapter 7, Section VI-B). This method was demonstrated to give more reliable results than halogenation methods for terpenes[109] and resin acids.[110] There is a marked difference in the rate of epoxidization between internal and external olefinic groups.[111,112] It may be utilized in the investigation of the structure of new compounds. Unfortunately, adaptation of this method to the micro scale is difficult due to the instability of the reagent and the sluggishness of the reaction between perbenzoic acid and the alkene function.

5. Addition of Ozone. Ozonolysis is used extensively in the degradative study of compounds containing the alkene function. The double bond consumes one mole of ozone. The product then forms two carbonyl compounds upon reduction. The sequence of reaction probably occurs in the following manner:

$$\underset{/}{\overset{\backslash}{C}}=\underset{\backslash}{\overset{/}{C}} + O_3 \rightarrow \underset{/}{\overset{\backslash}{C}}\overset{O}{\underset{O}{\diagup\diagdown}}\underset{\backslash}{\overset{/}{C}} \xrightarrow{[H]} \underset{/}{\overset{\backslash}{C}}=O + O=\underset{\backslash}{\overset{/}{C}} + H_2O \qquad (23)$$

[107] A. Escoruela, *Anales Fis. y. Quim.*, **40**, 1189 (1949).

[108] W. R. Kragg, *Bull. Soc. Chim.*, **1952**, 911.

[109] L. Ruzicka, H. Silberman, and M. Furter, *Helv. Chim. Acta*, **15**, 482 (1932).

[110] G. Brus and G. Martin, *Congr. Tech. Intern. L'ind. peintures et Ind. Assoc.*, 1st Congr. Paris, **1**, 317 (1947).

[111] I. M. Kolthoff and T. S. Lee, *J. Polymer Sci.*, **2**, 206 (1947).

[112] A. Saffer and B. L. Johnson, *Ind. Eng. Chem.*, **40**, 538 (1948).

Boer and Koogman[113,114] proposed a method for determining the alkene function by measuring the quantity of ozone absorbed by the sample. An electrolytic ozone generator was constructed which provides a constant stream of ozone. It was shown that the time lapse between the beginning of ozone absorption and the escaping of unreacted ozone is a quantitative measure of unsaturation. The appearance of free ozone is detected by the decolorization of a suitable dye. The results are obtained by comparing with a calibration curve. Application of this method to the microdetermination of olefinic groups is not recommended. It should be noted that ozonolysis does not take place quantitatively and instantaneously for most unsaturated compounds and some of the sample may volatilize with the stream of gases and escape. The benzenoid unsaturation also consumes ozone. Rosin acids were shown to react with ozone both by addition to the alkene function and the formation of hydroxyl groups.[115]

6. *Oxidation by Permanganate or Periodate.* The alkene function is oxidized by permanganate or periodate with the formation of a 1,2-diol (see Chapter 7, Section IV-D-1) as the first product, shown in equation 24:

$$\diagup C = C \diagdown \ + 2[OH] \rightarrow -\underset{OH}{\overset{|}{C}} - \underset{OH}{\overset{|}{C}} - \tag{24}$$

Bell and Kranty[116] described a procedure for the determination of unsaturated compounds in cyclopropane as follows. The sample is bubbled through a known excess of standardized potassium permanganate solution, which is then added in small portions to a mixture of 50 ml. of 0.01N oxalic acid with 5 ml. of concentrated sulfuric acid at 90°C. The solution is shaken until colorless after each addition of the permanganate. When all the permanganate has been added, the excess of oxalic acid is determined by titration with 0.01N potassium permanganate. This method is not recommended for the microdetermination of the alkene function because the 1,2-diol is usually further oxidized, although permanganate[117] and periodate[118] are excellent reagents for the elucidation of unsaturated structures.

7. *Reaction with Osmium Tetroxide.* Criegee and co-workers[119] reported that olefinic compounds react with osmium tetroxide in the presence of pyridine according to equation 25:

[113] H. Boer, *Rec. Trav. Chim.*, **67**, 217 (1948).

[114] H. Boer and E. Koogman, *Anal. Chim. Acta*, **5**, 550 (1951).

[115] A. Novak and N. F. Komshilov, *J. Appl. Chem.*, *USSR*, **12**, 1514 (1939).

[116] F. Bell and J. Kranty, *J. Am. Pharm. Assoc.*, **30**, 50 (1941).

[117] T. P. Hilditch and C. H. Lea, *J. Chem. Soc.*, **1927**, 3106.

[118] A. Chatterjee and S. G. Majumdar, *Anal. Chem.*, **28**, 878 (1956).

[119] R. Criegee, B. Marchand, and H. Wannowius, *Annalen*, **550**, 99 (1942).

$$\ce{>C=C< + OsO4 + 2C5H5N ->} \quad \overset{\displaystyle |}{\underset{\displaystyle O}{C}} \cdots \overset{\displaystyle |}{\underset{\displaystyle O}{C}} \quad (25)$$

Os·2C₅H₅N

$$\ce{O // \\ O}$$

Crystalline solids of this complex usually separate out in theoretical yield in a few minutes. This may provide a suitable method for the gravimetric determination of the alkene function. Water should be absent in the reaction mixture, lest the addition compounds undergo hydrolysis to form the corresponding glycols.

F. Specific Methods for Alkene Function Adjacent to a Positive Group. It will be recalled that the alkene function adjacent to a positive (electron attracting) group such as nitrile, carboxyl, ester, or amide is resistant to addition by halogens. Fortunately, there are three reagents which react with this type of alkene function preferentially and these are discussed briefly.

1. Addition of Mercapto Compounds. Mercapto compounds react with the alkene function linked to a positive group according to equation 26:

$$\ce{R-CH=CH-X + R'-SH -> R-\underset{\underset{SR'}{|}}{\overset{\overset{H}{|}}{C}}-\underset{\underset{H}{|}}{\overset{\overset{H}{|}}{C}}-X} \quad (26)$$

(X = CN, COOR, or CHO)

Belsing and co-workers[120] advocated lauryl mercaptan as the reagent and reported that the reaction goes to completion in alkaline alcoholic solution in 2–15 minutes. The excess of mercaptan is determined iodometrically or argentimetrically (see Chapter 9, Section II). Wronski[99] presented a micro method to determine acrylonitrile and methyl acrylate by reacting the sample with a known excess of thioglycolic acid in sodium hydroxide solution. The unconsumed reagent is back-titrated with standard mercuric acetate solution using thiofluorescein as the indicator. Styrene, allyl alcohol, and thiophene do not interfere with the determination.

2. Addition of Bisulfite. Unlike the reaction of the carbonyl function (see Chapter 6, Section VII) the addition of bisulfite to the olefinic double bonds, if it occurs, is irreversible (eq. 27). Two methods were published utilizing this reaction to determine α,β-unsaturated nitriles and acids on the

[120] D. W. Belsing, W. P. Tyler, D. M. Kurtz, and S. A. Harrison, *Anal. Chem.*, **21,** 1073 (1949).

macro scale. In one method[121] the sample (acrylonitrile) is treated with aqueous sodium sulfite solution for 15 hours and the sodium hydroxide formed according to equation 27 is determined by titration with $0.1N$ hydrochloric acid.

$$CH_2{=}CHCN + Na_2SO_3 + H_2O \rightarrow \underset{\underset{SO_3Na}{|}}{CH_2{-}CH_2CN} + NaOH \qquad (27)$$

In another method[122] the unsaturated compound is reacted with sodium sulfite and a measured amount of standardized sulfuric acid is added. The excess of acid is back-titrated with standard base using the alizarin yellow-R-xylene cyanole FF mixed indicator. These procedures may be adapted to the micro scale. It was reported that, whereas maleic acid (*cis* isomer) gives correct results, fumaric acid (*trans* isomer) does not react unless the latter is first isomerized.[123]

3. *Addition of Secondary Amines.* Critchfield and co-workers[124] described a macro method for determining α,β-unsaturated esters, nitriles, and amides as follows. The sample (10–23 meq.) is dissolved in acetic acid and reacted with morpholine to form the tertiary amine:

$$CH_2{=}CHC\overset{O}{\underset{NH_2}{\diagup}} + O\underset{\diagdown\diagup}{\frown}N{-}H \rightarrow O\underset{\diagdown\diagup}{\frown}N{-}CH_2{-}CH_2{-}C\overset{O}{\underset{NH_2}{\diagup}} \qquad (28)$$

After removing the excess morpholine with acetic anhydride, the tertiary amine is determined by titration with standard methanolic hydrochloric acid. The endpoint is located visually or conductometrically. A micro method was proposed by Terentev and co-workers[125] in which piperidine is used as the reagent and $0.05N$ hydrochloric acid as the titrant.

G. Specific Methods for Conjugated Alkene Linkages. The well-known Diels-Alder reaction between conjugated dienes and maleic anhydride has been applied to quantitative analysis on the macro scale.[126] The sample (3 g.) is refluxed with maleic anhydride in toluene. After the formation of the condensation product, as shown in equation 29, water and ether are added to the mixture; the unreacted maleic anhydride is hydrolyzed and remains in the aqueous layer (as maleic acid), which is

[121] A. P. Terentev and S. I. Obtemperanskaya, *Zhur. Anal. Khim.*, **11**, 638 (1956).

[122] F. E. Critchfield and J. B. Johnson, *Anal. Chem.*, **28**, 73 (1956).

[123] B. Wurtzschmitt, *Z. Anal. Chem.*, **128**, 549 (1948).

[124] F. E. Critchfield, G. L. Funk, and J. B. Johnson, *Anal. Chem.*, **28**, 76 (1956).

[125] A. P. Terentev, M. M. Buzlanova, and S. I. Obtemperanskaya, *Zhur. Anal. Khim.*, **14**, 506 (1959).

[126] American Society for Testing Materials, *Standards, Designation: D 555-54.*

separated and titrated with 1N sodium hydroxide using phenolphthalein as indicator.

$$(29)$$

This method has not been adapted to the micro scale. The rate of the condensation is dependent on the stereochemistry of the compound.[127] Cis-trans conjugated dienes do not react unless they are converted to the trans-trans isomers by a catalyst such as iodine.

Recently, it was found that the new chemical tetracyanoethylene is a specific reagent for the detection of conjugated double bonds.[128] This might provide the basis of a micro method for the determination of conjugated alkene functions.

H. Colorimetric Methods. Olefinic hydrocarbons in air were determined by MacPhee[129] using molybdate as reagent. There is a gradual change of color from yellow to green depending on the amount of unsaturated compounds present. Smits[130] proposed a colorimetric method for determining the iodine value of oils by reacting the sample (10–100 μg.) with iodine and mercuric acetate, and measuring the extinction at 375 mμ after dilution with potassium iodide in methanol. A spectrophotometric method for the determination of conjugated diolefins was proposed by Altshuller and Cohen.[131] The diene is reacted with p-nitrobenzene diazonium fluoroborate in 2-methoxyethanolphosphoric acid. Isoprene yields a colored complex which absorbs at 490 mμ. The complex from butadiene absorbs at 405 mμ.

I. Physical Methods. Many reports on the use of infrared spectra to determine known compounds containing the alkene function have been published.[132–136] cis-Double bonds exhibit a characteristic band at

[127] J. D. von Mikusch, Z. Anal. Chem., **130,** 412 (1950).

[128] K. Hafner and J. Schneider, Annalen, **624,** 37 (1959).

[129] R. D. MacPhee, Anal. Chem., **26,** 221 (1954).

[130] P. Smits, Rec. Trav. Chim., **78,** 713 (1959).

[131] A. P. Altshuller and I. R. Cohen, Anal. Chem., **32,** 1843 (1960).

[132] V. Thorton and A. E. Herald, Anal. Chem., **20,** 9 (1948).

[133] R. W. B. Johnston, W. G. Appleby, and M. O. Baker, Anal. Chem., **20,** 805 (1949).

[134] A. Delsemme, Congr. Anal. Spectrograph. Products, **12,** 69 (1949).

[135] A. Cornu, Bull. Assoc. Franc. Tech. Petrole, **87,** 33 (1951).

[136] E. L. Saier, A. Pozefsky, and N. D. Coggeshall, Anal. Chem., **26,** 1258 (1954).

2.14 μ.[137,138] Determination of olefins by measuring the ultraviolet absorption of their iodine complexes has been suggested.[139]

Polarographic methods have been applied to the determination of conjugated alkenes, allenes,[140] aromatic olefins,[141] and carotenes.[142] Ryabov and Panova[143] observed that unsaturated compounds which are not reduced at the dropping mercury electrode may be brominated by means of bromine in methanol saturated with sodium bromide and then determined polarographically.

III. The Alkyne Function

A. General. Compounds containing the alkyne function are acetylene and its homologs; hence this function is also called the acetylenic group. While the alkyne function is characterized by a triple bond and has greater unsaturation than the alkene function, reagents which will add to the latter react only slowly with the former. This has been attributed to the electrophilic (cationoid) nature of the alkyne function as against the nucleophilic alkene. Indeed, the hydrogen atom attached to the alkyne function is considered acidic, although it cannot be determined by the general methods of acidimetry (see Chapter 11, Section II). For the purpose of quantitative analysis it should be kept in mind that methods proven to give good results for alkenes may not be satisfactory for alkynes. On the other hand, there are methods which are applicable to the triple bond and not to olefinic linkages.

B. Addition of "Unsaturation" Reagents. It will be recalled that the reagents most commonly used for quantitative addition to the olefinic double bond are halogens, hydrogen and mercury acetate (see Section II). Most organic chemistry textbooks state that generally the triple bond reacts like the double bond and can form saturated carbon skeletons by addition. However, the worker who tries to apply this information to the determination of the alkyne function will be disappointed. Thus, whereas theoretically the alkyne function should consume four atoms of bromine as shown in equation 30, the reaction is not applicable for analytical purposes.

[137] R. F. Goddu, *Anal. Chem.*, **29**, 1790 (1957).

[138] A. J. Fenton, Jr. and R. O. Crisler, *J. Am. Oil Chem. Soc.*, **36**, 620 (1959).

[139] B. R. Long, *Anal. Chem.*, **27**, 1110 (1955).

[140] M. von Stackelberg and W. Stracke, *Z. Electrochem.*, **53**, 118 (1949).

[141] H. A. Laitinen and S. Wawzonek, *J. Am. Chem. Soc.*, **64**, 1765 (1942).

[142] J. Heyrovsky and H. Hasselbach, *Z. Pflazenjücht*, **25**, 443 (1943).

[143] A. V. Ryabov and G. D. Panova, *Doklady Akad. Nauk SSSR*, **99**, 547 (1954).

$$R—C\equiv C—R' + 2Br_2 \rightarrow R—\overset{\overset{\displaystyle Br}{|}}{\underset{\underset{\displaystyle Br}{|}}{C}}——\overset{\overset{\displaystyle Br}{|}}{\underset{\underset{\displaystyle Br}{|}}{C}}—R' \qquad (30)$$

Determination of the acetylenic unsaturation by bromination on the macro scale was reported by Robey[144] and Siggia.[145] The latter used potassium bromate-bromide mixture on acetylenic hydrocarbons, while the former employed bromine solution on silver acetylides. Ma and Smith[146] investigated the quantitative bromination of the alkyne function on the micro scale. It was found that when the micro procedure for the determination of the alkene function (see experiment 15) is applied to compounds containing acetylenic unsaturation, 40–50% yields were obtained. If the time of reaction is extended, more bromine will be consumed, but the amount of bromine absorbed does not exceed 70–80% after standing for several days. Hence, the addition of bromine to the alkyne function cannot be stopped at the point when a dibromo alkene group is formed unless all experimental conditions have been established for a known compound and these conditions are strictly followed in the analysis. On the other hand, the microdetermination of the alkyne function by complete saturation with bromine is not feasible.

Lindlar[147] studied the catalytic hydrogenation of alkene and alkyne functions and reported that a catalyst prepared from calcium carbonate, palladium chloride, and lead basic acetate selectively hydrogenates triple bonds in the presence of double bonds. Koulkes[148] proposed the determination of disubstituted acetylenic groups by means of mercuric acetate in ethanol. The acetic acid which is liberated from the reaction (see Section II-D) is titrated with 0.1N sodium hydroxide. These methods have not been evaluated on the 0.1 meq. scale.

C. Specific Alkyne Reagents

1. Methanol. Wagner and co-workers[149] proposed a macro method for the determination of mono and dialkyl acetylenes which is dependent on the addition of methanol to the alkyne function, using mercury oxide-boron

[144] R. F. Robey, *Anal. Chem.*, **24**, 1080 (1952).

[145] S. Siggia, *Quantitative Organic Analysis via Functional Groups*, 2nd ed., John Wiley and Sons, New York, 1954, p. 72.

[146] T. S. Ma and J. Smith, unpublished work; see J. Smith, *Master's Thesis, Brooklyn College*, 1961.

[147] H. Lindlar, *Helv. Chim. Acta*, **35**, 446 (1952).

[148] M. Koulkes, *Bull. Soc. Chim. France*, **1953**, 402.

[149] C. D. Wagner, T. G. Goldstein, and E. D. Peters, *Anal. Chem.*, **19**, 103 (1947).

trifluoride mixture as the catalyst. The reaction is represented in equation 31:

$$R—C\equiv C—R' + 2CH_3OH \xrightarrow{\text{(HgO,BF}_3\text{)}} R—\underset{\underset{OCH_3}{|}}{\overset{\overset{OCH_3}{|}}{C}}\underset{\underset{H}{|}}{\overset{\overset{H}{|}}{C}}—R' \tag{31}$$

The sample (5 meq.) is treated with 60 ml. of methanol containing 0.1 g. of mercuric oxide and 1 g. of boron trifluoride in a stoppered flask. After mixing and standing for 75 to 110 minutes at 25°C, the flask is placed in an ice bath and 200 ml. of saturated sodium bicarbonate solution are introduced to destroy the boron trifluoride. At the same time the addition product is hydrolyzed to yield a ketone as shown in equation 32:

$$R—\underset{\underset{OCH_3}{|}}{\overset{\overset{OCH_3}{|}}{C}}\underset{\underset{H}{|}}{\overset{\overset{H}{|}}{C}}—R' + H_2O \rightarrow R—\underset{\underset{O}{||}}{C}\underset{\underset{H}{|}}{\overset{\overset{H}{|}}{C}}—R' + 2CH_3OH \tag{32}$$

The contents of the reaction flask are steam-distilled until 200 ml. of the distillate has been collected in 100 ml. of 2.5% hydroxylamine hydrochloride, whereupon the ketoxime is formed according to equation 33:

$$R—\underset{\underset{O}{||}}{C}—CH_2—R' + (NH_2OH_2^+)Cl^- \rightarrow R—\underset{\underset{NOH}{||}}{C}—CH_2R' + HCl + H_2O \tag{33}$$

The amount of hydrochloric acid liberated is determined by titration with 0.1 to 0.5N sodium hydroxide using the methyl orange-xylene cyanol FF mixed indicator. A correction factor of 1.09 is applied to the result since the recovery is not quantitative.

It is apparent that the above procedure is not suitable for conversion to the 0.1 meq. scale, in view of the difficulty in the microdetermination of ketones by oximation (see Chapter 6, Section VII-B-1-A). The addition of methanol, however, might provide the basis of a micro method.

2. Water. Hydration of the alkyne function in an acidic solution using mercuric sulfate as catalyst has been applied to the determination of acetylenic compounds on the 50 to 200 meq. range.[150] The ketone formed according to equation 34 is determined either titrimetrically through oximation or gravimetrically in the form of the 2,4-dinitrophenylhydrazone (see Chapter 6, Section VII-B-1-B).

$$R—C\equiv C—R' + H_2O \xrightarrow{\text{(HgSO}_4\text{)}} R—\underset{\underset{O}{||}}{C}—CH_2—R' \tag{34}$$

This method has not been tested on the micro scale.

[150] S. Siggia, *Anal. Chem.*, **28**, 1481 (1956).

D. Determination of Alkynic Hydrogen

1. Formation of Silver Acetylide

A. SILVER NITRATE AS REAGENT.   A number of papers have been published on the macro determination of acetylenic hydrogen which is based on its reaction with silver nitrate. The hydrogen attached to the alkyne function is replaced by silver, generating an equivalent of nitric acid, as indicated in equations 35 and 36:

$$HC\equiv CH + 2AgNO_3 \rightarrow Ag—C\equiv C—Ag + 2HNO_3 \qquad (35)$$

$$RC\equiv CH + AgNO_3 \rightarrow RC\equiv C—Ag + HNO_3 \qquad (36)$$

It is generally assumed that the silver acetylide forms a complex with silver nitrate, but the molar ratio in the double salt is not definite. Upon dilution, the double salt dissociates and silver acetylide precipitates.

When the reaction is carried out in a neutral solution, the liberated nitric acid may be determined by titration with standard aqueous sodium hydroxide solution.[151–153] Miocque and Gautier[154] suggested silver nitrate in pyridine as the reagent and 0.1N sodium hydroxide in methanol as the titrant using thymolphthalein indicator. Certain acetylenic compounds, such as propargyl alcohol and 1-phenylpropynol, cannot be determined by this procedure because the reaction mixture turns brown. Barnes and Molinini[155] observed that the silver acetylide remains in solution when a concentrated aqueous silver nitrate solution was employed. On the other hand, a dilute solution resulted in precipitation, making detection of the titration endpoint difficult. These workers used 2–3 meq. samples, 0.1N sodium hydroxide and 3–4 drops of methyl purple indicator. It is stated that the amount of indicator is critical even for determination on the macro scale.

A gravimetric method which involves the determination of silver in the precipitated silver acetylide has been proposed.[156] It should be noted that metallic acetylides are dangerous, since they explode when dry. Therefore, precaution should be taken when the procedure prescribes the separation of the silver acetylide by filtration. For instance, since aldehydes interfere with the silver nitrate method for determining the acetylenic hydrogen, modification of the method by separating the silver acetylide prior to

[151] R. Chevastelon, *Compt. rend.*, **125**, 245 (1897).

[152] V. J. Altieri, *Gas Analysis and Testing of Gaseous Materials*, American Gas Association, New York, 1945, p. 330.

[153] R. E. Hyzer, *Anal. Chem.*, **24**, 1092 (1952).

[154] M. Miocque and J. A. Gautier, *Bull. Soc. Chim. France*, **1958**, 467.

[155] L. Barnes, Jr. and L. J. Molinini, *Anal. Chem.*, **27**, 1025 (1955).

[156] D. F. Novoty, *Collect. Czechoslov. Chem. Commun.*, **7**, 84 (1935).

titration has been proposed. In one procedure,[157] the excess of silver ions is removed by the addition of sodium chloride, the silver salts are filtered off, and the nitric acid in the filtrate is determined by titration with $0.1N$ sodium hydroxide. In another procedure,[158] the precipitation of silver acetylide is performed in 2% sodium acetate solution, in which medium aldehydes are only slowly oxidized by silver nitrate. After the separation of the precipitate, the filtrate containing the unconsumed silver nitrate is titrated with $0.1N$ ammonium thiocyanate using ferric alum as the indicator. The filtration process may be circumvented by using an aliquot of the supernatant solution for titration.[159]

Some of the methods mentioned above can be adapted to the micro scale. However, the micro method using silver perchlorate, discussed in the next section, is recommended because of its simplicity and accuracy.

B. USE OF SILVER PERCHLORATE OR BENZOATE. A macro method was described by Barnes[160] for the determination of acetylenic hydrogen in a nonaqueous medium using silver perchlorate in methanol as the reagent. A silver acetylide-silver perchlorate double salt was produced with the liberation of an equivalent of perchloric acid as shown in equation 37:

$$R—C≡C—H + 2AgClO_4 \rightarrow R—C≡C—Ag \cdot AgClO_4 + HClO_4 \qquad (37)$$

The increase in acidity was determined by titration with standardized tris-(hydroxymethyl)-aminomethane in methanol using the thymol blue–α-azurine mixed indicator. This method has been adapted to the 0.1 meq. scale using $0.01N$ titrant.[161] It was found that no silver acetylide precipitates when the concentration of the silver perchlorate reagent exceeds $0.25M$. Martius yellow is recommended as the indicator since the thymol blue–α-azurine mixture deteriorates on standing. The presence of halide ions or aldehydes does not interfere with the analysis—a notable advantage over the silver nitrate method. The detailed procedure is given in experiment 18.

Marszak and Koulkes[162] proposed a method for determining acetylenic hydrogen using silver benzoate as the reagent, which is prepared by precipitation from silver nitrate and sodium benzoate. The acetylenic compound is dissolved in alcohol, silver benzoate is added, and the mixture is shaken for 10 minutes. The residue is then separated by filtration and

[157] O. Frehden and I. Brincovesnu, *Rev. Chim. Bucharest*, **7**, 433 (1956).

[158] S. Siggia, *Quantitative Organic Analysis via Functional Groups*, 2nd ed., John Wiley and Sons, New York, 1954, p. 93.

[159] M. Koulkes and I. Marszak, *Bull. Chim. Soc. France*, **1952**, 556.

[160] L. Barnes, Jr., *Anal. Chem.*, **31**, 405 (1959).

[161] M. Gutterson and T. S. Ma, *Microchem. J.*, **5**, 601 (1961).

[162] I. Marszak and M. Koulkes, *Mem. Servies Chim. Etat (Paris)*, **36**, 421 (1951).

washed with water and ethanol. The combined filtrate is titrated with $0.1N$ sodium hydroxide to the phenolphthalein endpoint. This procedure is more complicate than the perchlorate method. Its precision and accuracy will be less satisfactory when applied to micro samples.

2. *Formation of Mercuric Acetylide.* Acetylenic hydrogen reacts with potassium mercuric iodide in the presence of alkali to precipitate mercuric acetylide according to equation 38:[163]

$$2R—C≡C—H + K_2HgI_4 + 2NaOH → (R—C≡C—)_2Hg + 2KI + 2NaI + H_2O \quad (38)$$

It has been demonstrated that one equivalent of sodium hydroxide is consumed for every acetylenic hydrogen atom present. This reaction was utilized by Hanna and Siggia[164] to determine acetylene and monosubstituted acetylenes as follows. The sample (10–15 meq.) is introduced into an Erlenmeyer flask containing 100 ml. of methanol and 50 ml. of the potassium mercuric iodide reagent. A measured volume of standardized $0.5N$ sodium hydroxide is added. The excess of alkali is immediately back-titrated with standard $0.5N$ sulfuric acid to the phenolphthalein endpoint. This method has not been tested on the 0.1 meq. scale.

3. *Formation of Cuprous Acetylide.* A macro method for the determination of acetylenic hydrogen through the precipitation of cuprous acetylide in pyridine solution was described by Siggia.[158] A sample containing 5 meq. of acetylenic compound is dissolved in water or pyridine and the cuprous chloride reagent in 1:1 water-pyridine solution is added. Cuprous acetylide precipitates with the simultaneous formation of an equivalent amount of pyridinium chloride:

$$2R—C≡C—H + Cu_2Cl_2 + C_5H_5N → Cu—C≡C—Cu + 2(C_5H_5NH^+)Cl^- \quad (39)$$

The determination is completed by the potentiometric titration of the pyridinium chloride by means of $0.5N$ standard sodium hydroxide. A visual endpoint cannot be obtained because the cuprous acetylide exhibits an intensely red color. This method was tested by using propargyl alcohol. It has not been evaluated on the micro scale. The cuprous chloride reagent has to be prepared fresh every day because it is extremely sensitive to air oxidation.

The rate of precipitation of cuprous acetylide varies with the nature of the alkyne function. According to Nebbia and Pagani,[165] cuprous chloride can be used to determine acetylene and diacetylene in the presence of alkyl, phenyl and vinyl acetylene, and allyne.

[163] R. J. Spahr, R. R. Vogt, and J. A. Nieuwland, *J. Am. Chem. Soc.*, **55**, 2465 (1933).
[164] J. G. Hanna and S. Siggia, *Anal. Chem.*, **21**, 1469 (1949).
[165] L. Nebbia and B. Pagani, *Chim. e Ind.*, **37**, 200 (1955).

E. Colorimetric Methods. The colorimetric methods available in the literature for the determination of the alkyne function are all concerned with acetylene. Some methods[166-168] are based on the measurement of the colloidal suspension of the red cuprous acetylide. The gaseous sample is passed through an ammoniacal solution containing cuprous chloride and gelatin or colloidion. The intensity of the resulting red reaction mixture is determined in the colorimeter. Kammori[169] employed ammoniacal silver nitrate solution as the absorbent. After the sample has bubbled through the reagent, the solution is immersed in a boiling water bath for 5 minutes and then cooled. The extinction is proportional to the concentration of acetylene in the range of 0.2–2.0 mg. of acetylene per 5 liters of the gas sample.

IV. The Alkylidene, Benzylidene, Ketene and Terminal Methylene Functions

A. General. This section comprises the organic functions which exhibit apparent unsaturation, but are not determined by the addition reactions used for the determination of the alkene and alkyne functions. Compounds containing the alkylidene function ($R_2C=$) are derived from aliphatic aldehydes or ketones. Thus the isopropylidene group is related to acetone. Similarly the benzylidene group ($C_6H_5—CH=$) is derived from benzaldehyde. When the alkylidene or benzylidene function is linked to a nitrogen (e.g., $R—CH=NR'$), the compound is known as an imine, a methine, or Schiff's base. Ketenes are characterized by the skeleton

$$\diagdown C=C=O.$$ The terminal methylene function is represented by the

structure $—CH=CH_2$ at the end of a carbon chain. Hence it is also called the "end" or "terminal" unsaturation.

B. Determination of Isopropylidene Groups.

1. When Attached to Carbon. Microdetermination of the isopropylidene function attached to carbon has been described by several investigators. The oxidative cleavage of the double bond is the basis of all these methods. Acetone, which is produced as indicated in equation 40 is separated by distillation and determined as discussed in Chapter 6, Section VII.

[166] J. Frick, *Anal. Chem.*, **19**, 919 (1947).

[167] A. S. Zhitkova and S. I. Kutin, *Zavodskaya Lab.*, **15**, 674 (1949).

[168] N. Henning, *Klinwochschr.*, **33**, 622 (1955).

[169] O. Kammori, *J. Chem. Soc. Japan*, **58**, 538 (1955).

$$\underset{CH_3}{\overset{CH_3}{\diagdown}}C=\underset{}{\overset{H}{\underset{|}{C}}}-R \xrightarrow{[O]} \underset{CH_3}{\overset{CH_3}{\diagdown}}C=O + R-C\underset{OH}{\overset{O}{\diagup}} \tag{40}$$

Kuhn and Roth[170] utilized ozonolysis to cleave the double bond (see Section II-E-5). The sample is dissolved in acetic acid and a current of ozone is passed through the solution for 2–3 hours. The resulting reaction mixture is partly neutralized with sodium hydroxide and then heated under reflux with neutral potassium permanganate to oxidize the other fragment of the sample to carboxylic groups while leaving the acetone intact. Finally the condenser is rearranged for downward distillation and the mixture is distilled, the distillate being collected in a flask kept in the ice bath. The distillate, which contains acetone and acetic acid, is made alkaline with sodium hydroxide; then 10 ml. of standardized 0.05N iodine solution are added and the reaction mixture is allowed to stand at room temperature to complete the iodoform reaction. After acidification, the excess of iodine is determined by titration with 0.05N sodium thiosulfate to the starch endpoint. A similar micro procedure was described by Szabo,[171] who recommended the treatment of the ozonolyzed products with mercuric oxide and hydrogen peroxide, and then with platinum sponge. The recovery of acetone is usually below the theoretical value, especially for the isopropylidene group present in terpenes.[172] A review of these methods was published by Lacourt.[173]

Potassium periodate in the presence of a trace of permanganate was suggested by von Rudloff[174] as the oxidant for the cleavage of the isopropylidene function attached to carbon. The yield of acetone was over 98% when the alkalinity of the reaction mixture was kept at pH 7.2–7.5. This method is more convenient than the ozonolysis technique.

It can be seen from equation 40 that two ketones will be produced if the carbon atom attached to the isopropylidene function is linked to two alkyl groups. However, the other ketone will not interfere with the determination of the acetone unless one of the alkyl groups is a methyl group.

2. When Attached to Oxygen. Isopropylidene groups attached to oxygen are synthetic products prepared from acetone and sugars or polyhydric alcohols. This grouping is easily hydrolyzed in the presence of acid to regenerate acetone as shown in equation 41:

[170] R. Kuhn and H. Roth, *Berichte*, **65**, 1285 (1932).

[171] D. Szabo, *Magyar Kem. Lapja*, **4**, 603 (1949).

[172] V. Grignard, J. Doeuvre, and R. Escorrou, *Bull. Soc. Chim. France* [4], **35**, 932 (1924).

[173] A. Lacourt, *Bull. Soc. Chim. Belg.*, **45**, 313 (1936).

[174] E. von Rudloff, *Canadian J. Chem.*, **33**, 1714 (1955).

$$\underset{\underset{CH_3}{\diagdown}}{\overset{\overset{CH_3}{\diagup}}{C}}\underset{\underset{O-C-}{\diagdown}}{\overset{\overset{O-C-}{\diagup}}{}} + 2H_2O \xrightarrow{[H^+]} \underset{\underset{CH_3}{\diagdown}}{\overset{\overset{CH_3}{\diagup}}{C}}{=}O + \underset{HO-C-}{\overset{HO-C-}{}} \qquad (41)$$

Dilute sulfuric acid is employed in the published procedures, but another acid, such as p-toluenesulfonic acid, which has no oxidizing power may be preferable. If the resulting solution does not contain interfering substances detrimental to the determination of acetone by the iodometric method described in the preceding section, it is not necessary to isolate the acetone by distillation. In the analysis of the isopropylidene function in acetonyl-glycerate and its ethers and esters, Grün and Limpächer[175,176] reported positive errors at room temperature due to the ethyl alcohol produced in the hydrolysis, but only acetone reacts at 10°C. The distillation step, however, is prescribed in the micro procedures of Kuhn and Roth,[170] Bell and Harrison,[177] and in the semimicro method of Elsner.[178] For the determination of acetone derivatives of sugars, 10% of tri- or tetramethyl-glucose may be incorporated in the reaction mixture to promote solution.[177]

C. Determination of Benzylidene Groups. Benzylidene groups attached to oxygen or nitrogen are hydrolyzed to benzaldehyde in an acid medium as shown in equations 42 and 43:

$$C_6H_5{-}\underset{\underset{O-C-}{\diagdown}}{\overset{\overset{H}{\mid}\,\overset{O-C-}{\diagup}}{C}} + H_2O \xrightarrow{[H^+]} C_6H_5{-}\overset{\overset{H}{\mid}}{C}{=}O + \underset{HO-C-}{\overset{HO-C-}{}} \qquad (42)$$

$$C_6H_5{-}\overset{\overset{H}{\mid}}{C}{=}N{-}R + H_2O + H^+ \longrightarrow C_6H_5{-}\overset{\overset{H}{\mid}}{C}{=}O + R{-}NH_3^+ \qquad (43)$$

In a micro method described by Jurecek and Obruba[179] the sample is first hydrolyzed by heating with sulfuric acid under reflux and the benzaldehyde formed is steam-distilled into 10 ml. of standardized 0.01M 2,4-dinitro-phenylhydrazine solution. After standing for 1 hour, the hydrazone is separated by filtration and washed 6 times. Hydrochloric-hydrofluoric

[175] A. Grün and R. Limpächer, *Berichte*, **59**, 695 (1926).

[176] A. Grün, *Berichte*, **63**, 473 (1929).

[177] D. J. Bell and K. Harrison, *J. Chem. Soc.*, **1939**, 350.

[178] H. Elsner, *Berichte*, **61**, 2364 (1928).

[179] M. Jurecek and K. Obruba, *Chem. Listy*, **52**, 2066 (1958); *Collect. Czechoslov. Chem. Commun.*, **24**, 3578 (1959).

acid mixture is added to the filtrate, followed by 4 ml. of 0.4N titanous chloride. The solution is boiled for 30 minutes under an atmosphere of carbon dioxide, cooled, and titrated with 0.1N ammonium ferrous sulfate using ammonium thiocyanate as indicator. The results reported for 8 test compounds all agree to within $\pm 2\%$ relative. It should be noted, however, that both the hydrazine reagent and titanous chloride solution are very unstable.

D. Determination of Ketenes. The ketene function is determined by conversion to the corresponding carboxylic acid or its derivative. Thus ketene is hydrolyzed in water according to equation 44:

$$CH_2{=}C{=}O + H_2O \rightarrow CH_3{-}C\overset{\displaystyle O}{\underset{\displaystyle OH}{\diagup}} \qquad (44)$$

The acetic acid formed is determined by titration with standard sodium hydroxide.[180] In another procedure[181] a known volume of standard sodium hydroxide is added to the sample to form the sodium carboxylate:

$$\diagup\!\!\!\diagdown C{=}C{=}O + NaOH \rightarrow H\overset{|}{\underset{|}{C}}{-}C\overset{\displaystyle O}{\underset{\displaystyle ONa}{\diagup}} \qquad (45)$$

The unconsumed base is determined by back-titration with standard hydrochloric acid.

The ketene function may be treated with aniline to form an anilide,[182] as indicated in equation 46:

$$\diagup\!\!\!\diagdown C{=}C{=}O + H_2NC_6H_5 \rightarrow C_6H_5{-}\overset{|}{\underset{H}{N}}{-}\overset{\displaystyle }{\underset{\displaystyle O}{C}}{-}CH\diagdown \qquad (46)$$

This might provide the basis for the microdetermination of ketenes. A standard solution of aniline in benzene or dioxane is prepared and the sample is treated with a known excess of aniline. After the reaction is complete, the residual aniline can be determined by nitrosation (see Chapter 8, Section III-C-1) or by titration with 0.01N perchloric acid in acetic acid (see Chapter 11, Section IV-B-2).

[180] G. Schroeter, *Berichte*, **42**, 2346 (1909).
[181] G. R. Cameron, *J. Path. Bact.*, **45**, 653 (1937).
[182] A. M. Potts, *Arch. Biochem.*, **24**, 329 (1949).

E. Determination of Terminal Methylene Groups.

1. When Attached to Carbon. When the terminal methylene function is attached to carbon, it is usually determined by oxidative cleavage to yield an equivalent for formaldehyde. Bricker and Roberts[183] described a method which involves two stages of oxidation. The sample is first treated with a slight excess of potassium permanganate to form the glycol:

$$3R—CH{=}CH_2 + 2MnO_4^- + 2H_3O^+ \rightarrow 3R—\overset{H}{\underset{OH}{C}}—\overset{H}{\underset{OH}{C}}H + 2MnO_2 \qquad (47)$$

The glycol is then split by means of periodic acid:

$$R—\overset{H}{\underset{OH}{C}}—\overset{H}{\underset{OH}{C}}—H + H_5IO_6 \rightarrow H—\overset{H}{C}{=}O + R—\overset{H}{C}{=}O + HIO_3 + 3H_2O \qquad (48)$$

The formaldehyde liberated is separated by distillation and determined by the chromotropic acid method (see Chapter 7, Section V-C).

Naves[184] decomposed the terminal methylene group by ozonolysis and determined the formaldehyde colorimetrically. Lemieux and von Rudloff[185] reported that terminal methylene groups give formaldehyde in high yield on oxidation with periodate containing a trace of permanganate at pH 7–10.

2. When Attached to Oxygen. Compounds containing the terminal methylene function attached to oxygen are vinyl ethers. This grouping upon hydrolysis in the presence of acid yields an equivalent of acetaldehyde, as shown in the following equation:

$$H_2C{=}\overset{H}{C}—O—R + H_2O \xrightarrow{[H^+]} CH_3—\overset{H}{C}{=}O + ROH \qquad (49)$$

Siggia[186] described two macro methods in which reaction 49 is utilized. In the first method the acetaldehyde is determined by sodium bisulfite addition (see Chapter 6, Section VII-B-2-A) and in the second it is estimated by oximation (see Chapter 6, Section VII-B-1-A). Satisfactory results are obtained with 10–40 meq. samples. Adaptation of these procedures to the 0.1 meq. scale has not been accomplished. Neuberg and Gottschalk[187]

[183] C. E. Bricker and K. H. Roberts, *Anal. Chem.*, **21**, 1331 (1949).

[184] Y. R. Naves, *Helv. Chim. Acta*, **32**, 1152 (1949).

[185] R. U. Lemieux and E. von Rudloff, *Canadian J. Chem.*, **33**, 1710 (1955).

[186] S. Siggia, *Quantitative Organic Analysis via Functional Groups*, 2nd ed., John Wiley and Sons, New York, 1954, p. 98.

[187] C. Neuberg and A. Gottschalk, *Biochem. Z.*, **146**, 164 (1924).

presented a method for the determination of milligram quantities of vinyl ether in blood by distillation of the acetaldehyde after hydrolysis with an accuracy of $\pm 25\%$.

Application of halogenation and methoxymercuration to the determination of the double bond in vinyl ethers requires special attention. While the addition of mercuric acetate in methanol to these compounds is quantitative,[188] according to Johnson and Fletcher[189] the addition product should be kept below $-10°C$ and the acetic acid titrated at a temperature below $15°C$. Siggia and Edsberg[190] demonstrated that iodine adds to vinyl ether in the presence of methanol as shown in equation 50:

$$R{-}O{-}CH{=}CH_2 + I_2 + CH_3OH \rightarrow RO{-}\overset{\displaystyle H}{\underset{\displaystyle OCH_3}{C}}{-}CH_2I + HI \qquad (50)$$

Note that the double bond consumes only one atom of iodine and not two as the olefinic linkage of alkenes. These methods have not been evaluated on the micro scale.

F. Colorimetric Methods. Colorimetric determination of the acetone liberated from the isopropylidene groups was suggested by von Rudloff.[174] Diggle[191] presented a colorimetric method for determining ketene in the air. The sample is absorbed in dilute sodium hydroxide, the resulting sodium acetate is converted to hydroxamic acid and the color of the ferric complex is measured (see page 61). The terminal methylene group is determined colorimetrically through the formaldehyde liberated.[183,184] The methine group in creatinine can be determined by a colorimetric method using alkaline dinitrobenzoate as the reagent.[192]

G. Physical Methods. The infrared absorption spectra of the ketene function was studied by Arendale and Fletcher.[193] Goddu[194] reported that terminal methylene groups exhibit characteristic absorption at 1.62 or 2.1 μ. The $-CH{=}NR$ group has a strong band at the 6μ region.[195]

[188] R. W. Martin, *Anal. Chem.*, **21**, 921 (1936).

[189] J. B. Johnson and J. P. Fletcher, *Anal. Chem.*, **31**, 1563 (1959).

[190] S. Siggia and R. L. Edsberg, *Anal. Chem.*, **20**, 762 (1948).

[191] W. M. Diggle, *Analyst*, **78**, 473 (1953).

[192] C. J. Julius, *Anal. Chem.*, **25**, 1859 (1953).

[193] W. F. Arendale and W. H. Fletcher, *J. Chem. Phys.*, **24**, 581 (1956); **26**, 793 (1957).

[194] R. F. Goddu, *Anal. Chem.*, **29**, 1790 (1957).

[195] E. F. Hillenbrand, Jr. and C. A. Pentz, in *Organic Analysis*, Vol. 3, Interscience, New York, 1956, p. 195.

Long[196] has investigated the ultraviolet absorption spectra of terminal methylene-iodine complexes. The maximum absorption for $RCH{=}CH_2$ occurs at 275 mμ; for $R_2C{=}CH_2$ it is 290 mμ.

The polarographic reduction of vinyl acetate has been studied by Usami[197] in the presence of mercuric acetate and methanol. An addition compound of vinyl acetate and mercury shows a reduction wave at -0.35 v which is proportional to the concentration of vinyl acetate. Polarographic determination of the imine function was described by Hall.[198]

[196] B. R. Long, *Anal. Chem.*, **27**, 1110 (1955).
[197] S. Usami, *Japan Analyst*, **5**, 499 (1956).
[198] M. E. Hall, *Anal. Chem.*, **31**, 2007 (1959).

11

Miscellaneous Functions

I. Introduction

The discussion in the present chapter includes the functional groups under the *Miscellaneous* classification; that is, functions which could not be included in the preceding chapters. Thus the acidic and basic functions cannot be easily classified as functional groups containing certain elements, as for example nitrogen, oxygen, or sulfur. Similarly, the estimation of methyl groups and other carbon skeletal structures cannot be treated under alkenes and alkynes (Chap. 10). Finally, organic compounds containing arsenic, boron, and other nonmetals or metals are not sufficiently numerous to warrant treatment under separate chapters. Therefore, for the purpose of the present discussion, the following are included in the category of *Miscellaneous Functions:*

1. Acidic functions measurable by acid-base titrimetry.
2. Acidic functions measurable by gasometric methods for active hydrogen.
3. Basic functions measurable by acid-base titrimetry.
4. Hydrocarbon functions.
5. The phenolic function.
6. Organic compounds containing arsenic.
7. Organic compounds containing boron.
8. Organic compounds containing halogens.
9. Organic compounds containing mercury.
10. Organic compounds containing phosphorus.
11. Organic compounds containing silicon.
12. Water in organic materials.

II. Acidic Functions Measurable by Acid-Base Titrimetry

A. General. As was discussed in Chapter 3, any proton donor is an acid. Since practically all organic compounds contain the element hydrogen, they are potential proton donors. However, it should be noted that hydrogen attached to a carbon atom of a saturated skeleton does not ionize. A hydrogen atom attached to the carbon carrying a double bond does not dissociate unless enolization is possible (e.g., nitro compounds, α,β-unsaturated ketones). The acetylenic hydrogen (see Chapter 10, Section III) is acidic and readily replaceable by metals, but it is not measurable by acid-base titrimetry.

Determination of a strong acid by titration with a standard alkali solution is easy and simple. However, strong acids with K_a's 10^{-1}–10^{-2}, such as p-toluenesulfonic acid and trichloroacetic acid, are rare among organic acidic functions. The largest group of organic acids are carboxylic acids and their K_a's are in the order of 10^{-5}, which is slightly larger than that of carbonic acid ($K_a = 4 \times 10^{-7}$). Therefore, generally, most organic acids can be classified as having intermediate or weak strength; that is, their K_a's are in the range of 10^{-5}–10^{-7}. It should be remembered that the presence of a basic function in the molecule drastically reduces the strength of an organic acid. For example, p-aminobenzenesulfonic acid is a weak acid with a pK_a value of 3.19. Therefore, two problems should be considered in the determination of organic acidic functions by acid-base titrimetry: (a) how to avoid the interference of carbon dioxide in the atmosphere, and (b) which solvent and titrant to use in order to obtain the equivalence points.

A review of the microdetermination of neutral equivalents for carboxylic acids was written by Steyermark.[1] Simon[1a] described a micro method to determine apparent dissociation constants of organic acids in mixed solvent containing 80% methylcellosolve and 20% water. Beckett and Tinley[2] surveyed titrations in nonaqueous solvents. The latter publication gives methods for determining organic acids and bases on the macro scale. Modification of these methods is necessary when the determination is on the micro scale using 0.1 meq. sample and $0.01N$ titrant.

B. Apparatus for Micro Acidimetry

1. The Open Flask Procedure. The conical (Erlenmeyer) flask of 50 ml. capacity is a convenient reaction vessel for the microtitration of acidic

---

[1] A. Steyermark in *Organic Analysis*, Vol. 2, Interscience, New York, 1954, p. 1.

[1a] W. Simon, *Helv. Chim. Acta*, **41**, 1835 (1958).

[2] A. H. Beckett and E. H. Tinley, *Titration in Non-Aqueous Solvents*, 3rd ed., British Drug House, Poole, 1960.

functions whose dissociation values are greater than that of carbonic acid. The application of this method is limited to carboxylic acids, acidic functions containing sulfur or phosphorus, and a few other groups. Mixing of the titrant with the sample solution is easily done by swirling the flask with the hand. No provision is made to remove carbon dioxide from the Erlenmeyer flask. Nevertheless, in the case of the determination of carboxylic acids, it is necessary to heat the flask in order to bring the sample to a boil. Carbon dioxide dissolved in the reaction mixture is thus expelled so that it does not interfere with the location of the equivalence point. The detailed procedure is given in experiment 1.

2. *Assembly for Very Weak Acids.* The titration apparatus and technique described above is not suitable for the microdetermination of organic acidic functions with dissociation constants less than 10^{-5}. Conversion of the titration assembly for determining very weak acids on the macro scale[2,3] to microdeterminations also yields erratic results. It should be noted that such a strong base as sodium methoxide absorbs carbon dioxide readily from the air. Hence, when the standard alkali solution used is in the range of $0.01N$, momentary exposure of the titrant to atmospheric carbon dioxide (as it occurs when an open buret is filled with the stock solution or when the titrant is delivered in a stream or droplets through air into the sample solution) may cause errors of sufficient magnitude to render microtitration useless. Hence, microtitrations of very weak acids should be performed in an inert atmosphere. Such an apparatus[4] is shown in Figure 11.1.

The microtitration vessel is essentially a small Florence flask with a total capacity of 50 ml. which has 5 necks, one in line with the vertical axis of the vessel and the other four equally spaced, slightly oblique and lower. The vertical neck has a ground glass joint which accommodates the tip of the microburet. Two diametrically opposed side openings are 1 cm. in diameter to allow insertion of electrodes. The other two openings permit continuous flushing with nitrogen gas. The capillary tube ends 2 to 3 mm. from the bottom of the vessel. The exit is attached with a rubber stopper (cut open in the center) that overlaps the rim of the neck.

The automatic-zero microburet is of the gravity-fed (Machlett) type. Because of the high vapor pressure and expansion coefficient of the benzene-methanol mixed solvent used in the titrant, the Pregl-microburet (see p. 90) is not recommended. Otherwise the buret might be filled by itself when standing and the solution might run into the guard tube. The

[3] J. S. Fritz, *Acid-Base Titrations in Non-Aqueous Solvents*, G. Frederick Smith Chemical Co., Columbus, 1952.

[4] R. K. Maurmeyer, M. Margosis, and T. S. Ma, *Mikrochim. Acta*, **1959**, 177; assembly available from Micro-Ware, Inc., Vineland, N.J.

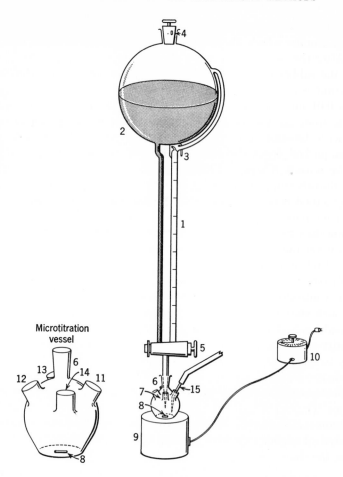

Fig. 11.1. Assembly for titration of very weak acids. 1. microburet; 2. titrant; 3. nitrogen inlet; 4. excess pressure outlet; 5. three-way Teflon stopcock; 6. ground-glass joint; 7. titration vessel; 8. stirring bar; 9. magnetic stirrer; 10. rheostat; 11, 12. electrode inlets; 13. nitrogen outlet; 14. nitrogen inlet; 15. nitrogen inlet tube. Courtesy of *Mikrochimica Acta*.

stopcock of the microburet should be made of Teflon, which is resistant to alkali and does not need any lubricant.

In addition to the use of a stream of nitrogen gas for mixing the reaction mixture during the titration, it is advisable to use a magnetic stirrer. The detailed procedure will be found in experiment 32.

3. Microtitration in a Closed Vessel.   A serum bottle of 30 to 60 ml.

capacity may be used as a closed titration vessel. It should be covered with a rubber stopper which fits down over the neck of the bottle (see Figure 11.2). After the sample, solvent, and indicator have been placed into the bottle, the rubber cap is inserted and folded over. The titrant is added by means of a syringe graduated to 0.01 ml., which draws the standard alkali solution from another serum bottle hermetically sealed with the same type of rubber stopper. Mixing is accomplished by shaking or by means of the magnetic stirrer. A blank is run to correct for the carbon dioxide trapped in the bottle.

This method is economical, but tedious. It cannot be used for potentiometric titrations. A semimicro technique in which the titrant consumed is determined by weighing the closed vessel was described by Smith, Mitchell, and Bellmeyer.[5]

Fig. 11.2. Serum bottle with rubber cap stopper. Courtesy of Fisher Scientific Co.

4. Microtitration in the "Dry Box." A chamber with a controlled atmosphere is commonly known as a "dry box." When such chamber is available, it can be used for the microtitration of very weak acids. For this purpose the atmosphere inside the chamber need not be dry since moisture does not interfere with the analysis. Nor is it necessary to replace the air with nitrogen since oxygen has no effect on the determination. It will suffice to have a beaker containing sodium hydroxide pellets placed in a corner of the chamber to absorb the carbon dioxide in the air. The chamber should have an extension to house the microburet[6] (see Figure 11.3). If the weighing device can be put inside the chamber, all analytical operations are performed through the rubber gloves without opening the chamber.

C. Solvents. The choice of the solvent for micro acidimetry depends on the dissociation constant and the solubility behavior of the compound to be titrated. The liquid or mixture of liquids used as solvent should be able to (a) keep the reactants and products in solution and (b) produce a leveling effect[7]—the phenomenon that strong and weak acids assume essentially the same strength in basic solvents—for very weak acidic functions. For instance, although it is possible to determine the neutral equivalents of carboxylic acids in aqueous solution, the insolubility of long-chain fatty acids necessitates the use of alcohol. On the other hand,

[5] D. Smith, J. Mitchell, Jr., and A. Bellmeyer, *Anal. Chem.*, **24**, 1847 (1952).

[6] T. S. Ma and R. F. Sweeney, *Mikrochim. Acta*, **1956**, 198.

[7] A. Hantzch, *Z. Physik. Chem.*, **134**, 406 (1928).

Fig. 11.3. Chamber with controlled atmosphere. Courtesy of *Mikrochimica Acta*.

it is apparent that ethanol-water mixture cannot be used for the determination of organic acids with dissociation constants less than 10^{-7}, even though the sample, as for example phenol with a K_a of 1.3×10^{-10}, and its sodium salt are readily soluble.

As discussed in Chapter 3, solvents which have been proposed for the determination of acidic functions were classified into three types:

1. *Amphiprotic (amphoteric) solvents.* Water, methanol, ethanol, iso-propanol (a common name for 2-propanol) and benzyl alcohol.

2. *Protophilic (basic) solvents.* Dimethylformamide (DMF), pyridine, *n*-butylamine, and ethylenediamine (diaminoethane);

3. *Aprotic or neutral (inert) solvents.* Benzene, chloroform, acetonitrile, acetone, methyl ethyl ketone, and methyl isobutyl ketone (4-methyl-2-pentanone).

As a general principle, as the strength of the acid function decreases, the solvent selected for its titration should be more strongly basic. Heijde and

Dahmen[8] presented an empirical acidity-potential scale of twelve solvents. A basic solvent should be chosen so that its region of acidity lies above the half-neutralization potential of the acid to be titrated. The increase of acidity of phenols in pyridine was demonstrated by Streuli and Miron.[9,10] It should be remembered that basic solvents absorb carbon dioxide readily. They are preferably stored in the "dry box."

The inert solvents are not supposed to have an effect on acidic functions. Their presence tends to sharpen the potential breaks in the titration curve, however, which is very helpful for microdeterminations. This phenomenon has not been fully elucidated. According to Mankovskaya,[11] acetone reduces the dissociation of fatty acids. The inert organic liquid is usually mixed with an amphiprotic or a protophilic solvent when it is employed in acid-base titrimetry.

D. Titrants. A number of bases in various solvents have been suggested as titrants for the determination of organic acidic functions. Some typical examples are listed in Table 11.1. The neutralization reactions of the respective types of bases are given in equations 1 to 5:

$$R\text{—}OH + NaOH \rightarrow R\text{—}ONa + H_2O \tag{1}$$

$$R\text{—}OH + NaOCH_3 \rightarrow R\text{—}ONa + CH_3OH \tag{2}$$

$$4R\text{—}OH + LiAl(NR_2)_4 \rightarrow R\text{—}OLi + (R\text{—}O)_3Al + 4R_2NH \tag{3}$$

$$R\text{—}OH + (C_6H_5)_3CNa \rightarrow R\text{—}ONa + (C_6H_5)_3CH \tag{4}$$

$$R\text{—}OH + (C_4H_9)_4NOH \rightarrow R\text{—}O\text{—}N(C_4H_9)_4 + H_2O \tag{5}$$

It should be noted that R represents the remaining portion of the organic acid, and is not necessarily a hydrocarbon group. The hydrogen atom shown in the foregoing equations may be linked to nitrogen or sulfur, in place of oxygen.

Among the titrants tabulated, sodium hydroxide, sodium ethoxide and tetrabutylammonium hydroxide have been employed in the $0.01N$ scale. The first is used for the determination of organic acids with dissociation constants larger than 10^{-5}; the other two for acidic functions weaker than this value. Theoretically, it is possible to prepare the strongest basic titrant to determine a wide range of acidic functions. This is not feasible, however, especially for microanalysis. Thus lithium aluminum hydride and sodium triphenylmethyl cannot be used as $0.01N$ standard solutions. These com-

[8] H. B. v. d. Heijde and E. A. M. F. Dahmen, *Anal. Chim. Acta,* **16,** 378, 392 (1957); E. A. M. F. Dahmen, *Chim. Anal.,* **40,** 378 (1958).

[9] C. A. Streuli and R. R. Miron, *Anal. Chem.,* **30,** 1978 (1958).

[10] C. A. Streuli, *Anal. Chem.,* **32,** 407 (1960).

[11] N. K. Mankovskaya, *Maslob. Zhir. Prom.,* **1956,** 30.

pounds are extremely sensitive to carbon dioxide, oxygen, and moisture. It is even difficult to maintain the strength of a $0.1N$ solution. Potassium methoxide is a stronger base than sodium methoxide and is more soluble in benzene. Since methanol has acidic property, proportional reduction of the relative amount of methanol with respect to benzene is desirable. On the other hand, metallic potassium is considerably more hazardous than sodium. Lithium methoxide may be a convenient reagent to use in micro-

TABLE 11.1

Titrants for Acidimetry

Type	Formula of Base	Solvent	Reference
Inorganic	NaOH	Water	1
hydroxide	NaOH	Methanol	12
	NaOH	Benzyl alcohol	13
	KOH	Isopropyl alcohol	14
	$Ba(OH)_2$	Water	15
Alkali	$NaOCH_3$	Methanol/benzene	4
alkoxide	$KOCH_3$	Methanol/benzene	16
	$LiOCH_3$	Methanol	17
	$NaOCH_2CH_2NH_2$	Ethanolamine/ethylenediamine	18
Alkali amide	$LiAl[NC_4H_9)_2]_4$	Tetrahydrofuran	19
Alkali hydride	$LiAlH_4$	Tetrahydrofuran	20
Alkali alkyl	$NaC(C_6H_5)_3$	Benzene	21
Quaternary	$(C_4H_9)_4NOH$	Methanol/benzene	14, 22–24
ammonium	$(C_2H_5)_4NOH$	Methanol/benzene	25
hydroxide	$(C_6H_5CH_2)(CH_3)_3NOH$	Pyridine	26, 27

[12] M. L. Owens, Jr. and R. L. Maute, Anal. Chem., 27, 1177 (1955).
[13] H. A. Pohl, Anal. Chem., 26, 1614 (1954).
[14] G. A. Harlow, C. M. Noble, and G. E. A. Wyld, Anal. Chem., 28, 784 (1956).
[15] D. Beranova and S. Hudecek, Chem. Listy, 49, 1723 (1955).
[16] J. S. Fritz and R. T. Keen, Anal. Chem., 25, 179 (1953).
[17] M. M. Caso and M. Cefola, Anal. Chim. Acta, 21, 205 (1959).
[18] M. Katz and R. Glenn, Anal. Chem., 24, 1157 (1952).
[19] T. Higuchi, J. Concha, and R. Kuramoto, Anal. Chem., 24, 685 (1952).
[20] T. Higuchi and D. A. Zuck, J. Am. Chem. Soc., 73, 2676 (1951).
[21] A. Corwin and R. Ellingson, J. Am. Chem. Soc., 64, 2098 (1942).
[22] V. Z. Deal and G. E. Wild, Anal. Chem., 27, 47 (1955).
[23] R. H. Cundiff and P. C. Markunas, Anal. Chem., 28, 792 (1956).
[24] M. L. Cluett, Anal. Chem., 31, 610 (1959).
[25] A. P. Kreshkov, L. N. Bykova, and N. A. Mkhitaryan, Zhur. Anal. Chem., 14, 529 (1959).
[26] A. Patchornik and S. E. Rogozinski, Anal. Chem., 31, 985 (1959).
[27] A. M. Bongiovani, W. R. Eberstein, and P. Z. Thomas, J. Clin. Endocrin. Metab., 17, 331 (1957).

determinations. One drawback in using lithium metal is that it is hard to cut at room temperature. Hence the use of lithium wire which can be cut by scissors is recommended. Sulfamic acid was advocated by Caso and Cefola[17] as the primary standard for lithium methoxide solution. Carbon dioxide does not interfere with the standardization, and the endpoint can be determined potentiometrically.

The use of quaternary ammonium hydroxide solutions as titrant is a recent innovation. According to Cundiff and Markunas,[23] tetrabutylammonium hydroxide reagent has to be prepared from the corresponding iodide and silver oxide, since the titrant prepared by ion-exchange is not suitable. This base has been used to titrate phenols, thiols, imides, and nitro compounds. Cluett[24] demonstrated that this titrant consists of a mixture of hydroxide and methoxide as shown in equation 6:

$$2(C_4H_9)_4NI + Ag_2O + CH_3OH \rightarrow (C_4H_9)_4NOH + (C_4H_9)_4NOCH_3 + 2AgI \quad (6)$$

Harlow and Wyld[28] observed that the tetrabutylammonium hydroxide titrant prepared in isopropanol is superior to titrants in ethanol, methanol, or water for the neutralization of phenols.

E. Determination of the Equivalence Point

1. By Visual Indicators. The endpoint in the titration of carboxylic or stronger acids with aqueous alkali solution is conveniently detected by means of phenolphthalein (see experiment 1). Since standard sodium hydroxide in water solution is easier to prepare and maintain than other bases in organic solvent, it is not advisable to use nonaqueous titration for the determination of carboxylic groups. However, such a change is occasionally mandatory. Thus Pohl[13] determined the carboxyl end groups in polymers that are insoluble in water-ethanol mixture by dissolving the sample in benzyl alcohol at 200°C. The solution is quickly mixed with chloroform and titrated with 0.1N sodium hydroxide in benzyl alcohol to the phenol red endpoint. Esposito and Swann[29] proposed a macro method to determine dicarboxylic acids in alkyd resins using ethylene glycol-ethanol as solvent, 0.2N potassium hydroxide in methanol as titrant, and *m*-cresol purple as the indicator.

Although amino sulfonic and amino carboxylic acids can be titrated in 90% ethanol with 0.01N sodium hydroxide using thymolphthalein as indicator,[29,30] these acidic functions are preferably determined by titration

[28] G. A. Harlow and G. E. A. Wyld, *Anal. Chem.*, **30**, 73 (1958).

[29] G. G. Esposito and M. H. Swann, *Anal. Chem.*, **32**, 49 (1960).

[30] J. Grant, *Pregl's Quantitative Organic Microanalysis*, 5th English ed., Blakiston, Philadelphia, 1951, p. 167.

in nonaqueous solvents. Thymol blue and azo violet are the recommended indicators for micro acidimetry using $0.01N$ titrants in nonaqueous media.[4]

Several papers [31-34] have been published on the selection of indicators for the determination of acidic functions. Table 11.2 lists a variety of

TABLE 11.2

Indicators for Acidimetry

Indicator	Color Change	pH Range	Reference
Thymol blue	red → yellow	1.2–2.8	4
	yellow → blue	8.0–9.6	
Quinaldine red	colorless → red	1.4–3.2	2
Phenol red	yellow → red	6.8–8.4	13
m-Cresol purple	yellow → red	7.4–9.0	29
Phenolphthalein	colorless ↠ pink	8.3–10	1
Thymolphthalein	colorless → blue	9.3–11	30
Azo violet	red → blue		4
p-Hydroxyazobenzene	orange → yellow		16
o-Nitro-aniline	yellow → red		16
4-Amino-4'-nitro-azobenzene	red → blue $(KOCH_3)$		23
β-Naphthylamino-azobenzene	for $(R_2N)_4LiAl$		19

indicators with the corresponding color change and useful pH range. Needless to say, the choice of the indicator is dependent on the dissociation constant of the acidic function to be analyzed. The weaker the organic acid, the higher pH range indicator should be used. Phenolphthalein, thymolphthalein, azo violet, and thymol blue have been evaluated for microtitrations. It should be remembered that an indicator that gives sharp endpoints with $0.1N$ titrant might be unsatisfactory for microdeterminations using $0.01N$ standard solutions. Potentiometric titration should precede or accompany visual titration for an acidic function of unknown nature, since the color change of the indicator might not occur at the equivalence point.

2. By Electrometric Methods

A. POTENTIOMETRIC METHODS. Potentiometric titrations entail expensive equipment and are more time consuming than visual titrations. However, the potentiometric method provides the absolute answer to the equivalence point and often is the mandatory technique for the determi-

[31] J. S. Fritz and N. M. Lisicki, *Anal. Chem.*, **23**, 589 (1951).
[32] K. Takiura and Y. Takino, *J. Pharm. Soc., Japan*, **74**, 971 (1954).
[33] E. Ellenbogen and E. Brand, *Anal. Chem.*, **27**, 2007 (1955).
[34] J. A. Bishop, *Anal. Chim. Acta*, **22**, 117 (1960).

nation of very weak acidic functions. The glass-calomel electrode system works well with microtitrations using $0.01N$ aqueous sodium hydroxide. On the other hand, this system gives poor response in the titration of very weak acidic functions in a protophilic solvent by means of a very strong base. Various methods have been proposed to alleviate this difficulty. A summary of electrode systems[35] used in organic acidimetry is given in Table 11.3.

TABLE 11.3

Electrode Systems for Potentiometric Determination of Acidic Functions

Electrodes	Solvent	Titrant	Reference
Glass-calomel	Water, alcohol	NaOH	
Glass-calomel	Dimethylformamide, pyridine	NaOCH₃	4
Glass-calomel	Acetonitrile, ketone	NaOCH₃	2
Glass-calomel	Dimethylformamide, ethylenediamine	R₄NOH	2
Glass-platinum	Methyl isobutyl ketone	R₄NOH	2
Glass-antimony	Butylamine	NaOCH₃	36
Pt-Pt	Ethylenediamine	R₄NOH	2, 37
Sb-Sb	Ethylenediamine	NaOCH₃	2
Al-Al	Water	NaOH	38
Pt-calomel	Ethylenediamine	NaOCH₃	39
Sb-calomel	Ethylenediamine	NaOCH₃	2

Potentiometric determination of the acidic function usually requires plotting the titration curve to obtain the endpoint. Some curves obtained by titrating approximately 0.1 meq. quantities of weak acidic functions with $0.02N$ sodium methylate are shown in Figures 11.4 and 11.5. The relationship between the indicator used (thymol blue or azo violet) and the equivalence point are also indicated.[4] Gage[40] suggested a method to transfer titration graphs to a linear form, which facilitates the location of the endpoint. Shain and Svoboda[37] applied constant-current potentiometry to nonaqueous titrations of weak acids. Two platinum indicator electrodes are polarized by a constant 1 μamp. current. The potential between the two electrodes is measured with a vacuum tube voltmeter or a pH meter. In

[35] For extensive discussion of electrode systems in nonaqueous titrimetry, see J. T. Stock and W. C. Purdy, *Chem. Reviews*, **57**, 1159 (1957); D. J. G. Ives and G. J. Janz (eds.), *Reference Electrodes*, Academic Press, New York, 1961.

[36] B. R. Warner and W. W. Haskell, *Anal. Chem.*, **26**, 770 (1954).

[37] I. Shain and G. R. Svoboda, *Anal. Chem.*, **31**, 1857 (1959).

[38] E. Scarano and S. Signoretti, *J. Electroanal. Chem.*, **1**, 218 (1960).

[39] G. Gran and B. Althin, *Acta Chem. Scand.*, **4**, 967 (1950).

[40] J. C. Gage, *Analyst*, **82**, 219 (1957).

most cases, typical peak-shaped titration curves are obtained that permit direct location of the endpoint from the meter reading.

A novel approach in locating potentiometric titration endpoints was described by Yakubik and co-workers.[41] The glass-silver electrode pair is employed in combination with certain neutral or basic solvents and alkali metal titrants. Most acids give potentiometric curves with voltage peaks. These are similar to the calculated first derivative curves from conventional

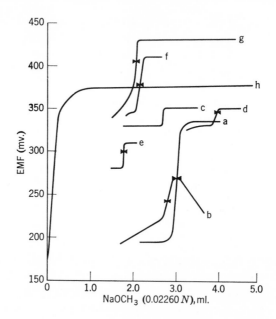

Fig. 11.4. Microtitration curves. ▶◀ = color change: a. benzoic acid in dimethylformamide; b. benzoic acid in pyridine; c. sulfanilamide in dimethylformamide; d. sulfanilamide in pyridine; e. sulfadiazine in dimethylformamide; f. barbital in dimethylformamide; g. diphenylpropanedione in dimethylformamide; h. solvent blank for dimethylformamide. Courtesy of *Mikrochimica Acta*.

potentiometric titrations. The voltage peak coincides with the equivalence point and is marked by a sudden reversal in potential.

B. CONDUCTOMETRIC, HIGH-FREQUENCY AND COULOMETRIC METHODS. Conductometric titrations of acidic functions have been reported in a number of papers. Several workers[42-44] employed quaternary ammonium

[41] M. G. Yakubik, L. W. Safranski, and J. Mitchell, Jr., *Anal. Chem.*, **30**, 1741 (1958).
[42] G. A. Harlow and D. B. Bruss, *Anal. Chem.*, **30**, 1835 (1958).
[43] N. V. Meurs, *Chem. Weekblad*, **54**, 298 (1958).
[44] N. V. Meurs and E. A. M. F. Dahmen, *Anal. Chim. Acta*, **21**, 10, 443 (1959).

hydroxide as titrant. Gaslini and Nahum[45] reported that very weak acids can be dissolved in aqueous ammonia or a weak nitrogenous base and titrated with standardized $2N$ lithium hydroxide solution. The disadvantage of conductometric titration lies in the use of concentrated titrants to minimize the dilution effect on conductance. Hence an ultramicroburet is required for microdeterminations.

High-frequency titration of weak acids was discussed in several publi-

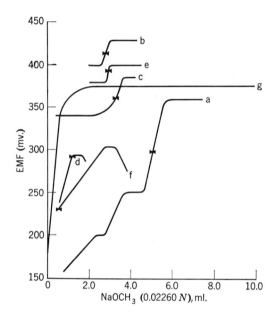

Fig. 11.5. Concurrent visual and potentiometric titration of phenolic compounds. ►◄ = color change; a. tetrachlorohydroquinone in dimethylformamide; b. sym-dimethylphenol in dimethylformamide; c. β-naphthol in dimethylformamide; d. β-naphthol in pyridine; e. thymol in dimethylformamide; f. thymol in pyridine; g. solvent blank for dimethylformamide. Courtesy of *Mikrochimica Acta*.

cations.[46–48] Constant-current coulometry was advocated by Taylor and Smith[49] for acid-base titrimetry. The latter method is precise and suited for microanalysis.

[45] F. Gaslini and L. Z. Nahum, *Anal. Chem.*, **31**, 989 (1959).
[46] R. Hara and P. W. West, *Anal. Chim. Acta*, **15**, 193 (1956).
[47] W. C. Purdy and J. T. Stock, *Drug Stds.*, **26**, 177 (1958).
[48] G. R. Jamieson, *J. Appl. Chem.*, **9**, 209 (1959).
[49] J. K. Taylor and S. W. Smith, *J. Res. Nat. Bur. Std.*, **63**, 153 (1959).

3. By Spectrophotometric Methods. Spectrophotometric methods for the determination of acidic functions are dependent on the difference of the absorption or fluorescence spectra exhibited by the free acid and its anion. For example, if phenol molecules are reacted with sodium hydroxide, as shown in equation 7, the absorption spectrum of the solution changes as the reaction proceeds, provided that the phenol molecules and phenoxide ions absorb at different wavelengths.

$$C_6H_5—OH + NaOH \rightarrow C_6H_5O^- + Na^+ + H_2O \qquad (7)$$

It has been observed that when phenols,[50,51] some aromatic amine and carbonyl compounds,[52] respectively, are dissolved in a protophilic solvent and titrated with a strong base, the organic anion shifts absorption to a longer wavelength. A suitable wavelength can be chosen, and the course of titration is followed by measuring the optical density of the reaction mixture. The equivalence point is obtained by plotting the absorbance of the solution against the volume of titrant added and locating the intersection of two straight lines. An example is given in Figure 11.6. A device for the automatic derivative spectrophotometric titration of organic acids was proposed by Malmstadt and Vassillo.[53]

[50] R. F. Goddu and D. N. Hume, *Anal. Chem.*, **26**, 1679 (1954).
[51] R. W. McKinney and C. A. Reynolds, *Talanta*, **1**, 46 (1958).
[52] E. Sawicki, T. R. Hauser, and T. W. Stanley, *Anal. Chem.*, **31**, 2063 (1959).
[53] H. V. Malmstadt and D. A. Vassillo, *Anal. Chem.*, **31**, 862 (1959).

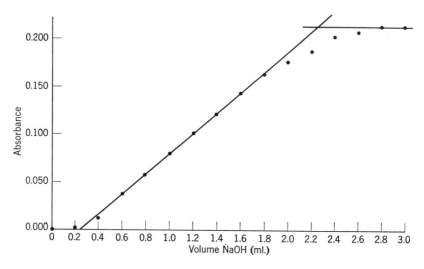

Figure 11.6. Photometric titration curve for *p*-hydroxydiphenyl. Courtesy of *Talanta*.

Fluorescence titrations of acidic functions have been described.[54,55] Since spectrophotometric measurement is very sensitive, these methods lend themselves to microdeterminations.

F. Application of Acidimetry. The application of acidimetry to the determination of the carboxyl, sulfonic, phosphonic, and similar strong acidic functions is apparent. It provides a simple and easy method for estimating these groups. The use of nonaqueous acidimetry is a recent development. However, because of its general applicability, this technique has been extensively investigated. The variety of organic functional groups that have been determined by nonaqueous titration is summarized in Table 11.4. It should be noted that most of the references cited in this table are determinations on the macro scale using $0.1N$ or more concentrated titrants.

The applicability of nonaqueous titrimetry to the microdetermination of weak acidic functions by means of sodium methoxide has been well established.[4] Phenols are titrable in dimethylformamide. Those containing one or more chlorine, hydroxyl, or carboxyl groups can be titrated to a thymol blue endpoint and those containing amino or alkyl groups to an azo violet endpoint. Sulfonamides, barbiturates, enols, imides and some hydrazides are titrable in dimethylformamide. The range extends to compounds with a pK_a of about 9 for visual titrations and 10.5 for potentiometric titrations. Pyridine may be used as a solvent for the visual titration of a weak acid with pK_a of up to about 10.5. Methyl isobutyl ketone may be used for the visual titration of acidic functions with a pK_a of about 9 and lower by using thymol blue as the indicator. Sensabough and co-workers[80] reported that 2,4-dinitrophenylhydrazones and 3,5-dinitrobenzoates[81] can be titrated with $0.01N$ tetrabutylammonium hydroxide potentiometrically.

III. Acidic Functions by Active Hydrogen Measurement

A. General. With few exceptions most organic compounds contain hydrogen. As yet, however, there is no method for the quantitative determination of hydrogen attached to a saturated alkyl group, although, under appropriate conditions, such hydrogen atoms can be substituted by halogens. On the other hand, hydrogen atoms attached to unsaturated carbon atoms, or to other elements such as oxygen, nitrogen, and sulfur, can be determined under suitable conditions and are known as *reactive*,

[54] J. de Ment, *J. Chem. Ed.*, **30**, 145 (1953).
[55] Z. Holzbecher, *Chem. Listy*, **52**, 425 (1958).

TABLE 11.4

Titration Methods for Weak Acidic Functions

Acidic Function	Titrant	Reference*
Carboxylic acid	NaOH	1
Amino acid	⎰ NaOH	30, 56, 57
	⎱ KOH	33, 58
Peracid	NaOCH$_2$CH$_2$NH$_2$	59
	⎡ NaOH	51
	⎢ KOH	60
Phenol	⎢ NaOCH$_3$	4
	⎥ KOCH$_3$	61, 62, 63
	⎢ NaOCH$_2$CH$_2$NH$_2$	64
	⎣ (C$_4$H$_9$)$_4$NOH	65, 66
Alcohol	⎰ LiAl[N(C$_4$H$_9$)$_2$]$_4$	19
	⎱ LiAlH$_4$	20
	⎡ NaOH	67, 68
	⎢ KOH	69
Barbituric acid	⎨ LiOCH$_3$	70, 71
	⎢ NaOCH$_3$	4, 72, 73
	⎣ (C$_4$H$_9$)$_4$NOH	74
Imide	NaOCH$_3$	4, 31, 75
Hydrazide	NaOCH$_3$	4
Pyrrole	NaC(C$_6$H$_5$)$_3$	21
	⎡ NaOCH$_3$	31, 76
Nitro compound	⎨ Na Colaminate	77
	⎣ R$_4$NOH	78, 79, 80, 81
Nitrate (nitroglycerine)	R$_4$NOH	79
	⎡ NaOH	82
Salt of weak base	⎨ NaOCH$_3$	3, 26
	⎣ KOCH$_3$	83
Phenate	KOCH$_3$	84
Sulfonamide	NaOCH$_3$	4, 85
Active methylene (malonic ester)	KOCH$_3$	86

[56] R. Willstätter, and E. Waldschmidt-Leitz, *Berichte*, **54**, 2988 (1921).
[57] M. Pascal, *Chim. Anal.*, **38**, 201 (1956).
[58] W. Grassman and W. Heyde, *Z. Physiol. Chem.*, **183**, 32 (1929).
[59] A. J. Martin, *Anal. Chem.*, **29**, 79 (1957).
[60] S. Wolf, *Naturwissenschaften*, **46**, 649 (1959).
[61] K. J. Karrman and G. Johansson, *Mikrochim. Acta*, **1956**, 1573.
[62] J. P. Butler and T. P. Czepiel, *Anal. Chem.*, **28**, 1468 (1956).
[63] D. H. Mathews and T. R. Welch, *J. Appl. Chem.*, **8**, 710 (1958).
[64] E. J. Greenhow and J. W. Smith, *Analyst*, **84**, 457 (1959).
[65] J. Allen and E. T. Geddes, *J. Pharmacol.*, **9**, 990 (1957).
[66] L. E. I. Hummelstedt and D. N. Hume, *Anal. Chem.*, **32**, 1792 (1960).
[67] H. Bräuniger and G. Borgwardt, *Pharm. Zentralhalle*, **93**, 266 (1954).
* (References for Table 11.4 on following page).

replaceable, or *active hydrogen*. Hydrogen functions that can be acetylated (see Chapter 7, Section IV-B and Chapter 8, Section III-B), or titrated with a base (see Section II above), or replaced by a metal (see Chapter 10, Section III-D), have been discussed in previous sections. A number of other methods will be included in this section.

The term *active hydrogen determination* was first proposed by Zerewitinoff[87] (Zerewitnov) to designate the determination of hydrogen atoms attached to oxygen, nitrogen, and other atoms which reacted with a Grignard reagent. However, since that time other organometallic reagents have been introduced for the same purpose. At present, the gasometric methods which are employed for the determination of active hydrogen use either a methyl Grignard reagent and measure the evolved methane or lithium aluminum hydride and measure the evolved hydrogen. A review which covers the literature up to 1950 has been published by Olleman.[88]

B. Use of the Grignard Reagent

1. Reaction and Method. The reaction between the active hydrogen function and the Grignard reagent is given in equation 8, using for illustration methyl magnesium iodide as the reagent and a hydrogen attached to oxygen as in an alcohol:

$$RO—H + CH_3MgI \rightarrow CH_4 + RO—MgI \tag{8}$$

[68] W. Poethke and O. Horm, *Arch. Pharm. Berlin*, **287**, 487 (1954).

[69] L. G. Chatten, *J. Pharm. Pharmacol.* **8**, 504 (1956).

[70] J. C. Ryan, L. K. Yanowski, and C. W. Pifer, *J. Am. Pharm. Assoc.*, **43**, 656 (1954).

[71] S. W. Goldstein and D. F. Dodgen, *Drug Stds.*, **26**, 113 (1958).

[72] V. Vespe and J. S. Fritz, *J. Am. Pharm. Assoc.*, **42**, 338 (1953).

[73] C. J. Schwartz and N. E. Foss, *J. Am. Pharm. Assoc.*, **44**, 217 (1955).

[74] D. E. Leavitt and J. Austian, *Drug Stds.*, **26**, 33 (1958).

[75] J. S. Fritz, *Anal. Chem.*, **24**, 674 (1952).

[76] S. M. Kaye, *Anal. Chem.*, **27**, 292 (1955).

[77] H. Brockmann and E. Meyer, *Naturwissenschaften*, **40**, 242 (1953).

[78] J. S. Fritz, A. J. Moye, and M. J. Richard, *Anal. Chem.*, **29**, 1685 (1957).

[79] R. D. Sarson, *Anal. Chem.*, **30**, 932 (1958).

[80] A. J. Sensabough, R. H. Cundiff, and P. C. Markunas, *Anal. Chem.*, **30**, 1445 (1958).

[81] W. T. Robinson, Jr., R. H. Cundiff, A. J. Sensabough, and P. C. Markunas, *Talanta*, **3**, 307 (1960).

[82] F. E. R. Sas and A. T. Torras, *Inform. Quim. Anal.*, **14**, 1 (1960).

[83] I. Gyenes and K. Szasz, *Magy. Kem. Folyoirat.*, **61**, 356 (1955).

[84] E. E. Underwood and A. L. Underwood, *Talanta*, **3**, 249 (1960).

[85] J. S. Faber, *J. Pharm. Pharmacol.*, **6**, 187 (1954).

[86] H. E. Zaugg and F. C. Garven, *Anal. Chem.*, **30**, 1444 (1958).

[87] T. Zerewitinoff, *Berichte*, **41**, 2233 (1908).

[88] E. D. Olleman, *Anal. Chem.*, **24**, 1425 (1952).

The methane gas liberated is measured. This technique is used in practically all methods described in the literature. Nevertheless, a gravimetric micro method was suggested by Evans and co-workers.[89] In the proposed method the methane is driven into a combustion train and the carbon dioxide and water produced are retained in the absorption tubes and weighed. Butyl magnesium iodide is preferable to the methyl Grignard reagent for this purpose, since the former yields more carbon dioxide and water per equivalent of active hydrogen function.

When the gasometric method is employed for the determination of active hydrogen, it should be remembered that the Grignard reagent also reacts with oxygen, water vapor, and carbon dioxide, these reactions being accompanied by the liberation or consumption of permanent gases. Therefore, if the method involves the use of a gasometric apparatus (see next section), the atmosphere inside the apparatus should be purified before the Grignard reagent is brought into contact with the sample containing the active hydrogen function. Needless to say, all apparatus and solvents used should be perfectly dry.

2. Assemblies. Many designs of active hydrogen apparatus have appeared in the literature. The micro apparatus of Roth[90] and of Soltys[91] are shown in Figures 11.7 and 11.8. Although both of these assemblies were popular at one time, they have been replaced by the development of new techniques. In the method of Roth, the reaction vessel AB is separated into two limbs. The sample is placed in limb B and the Grignard reagent in limb A. After the system has been purged with nitrogen, the reagent is caused to run into limb B by tilting the reaction vessel. Mixing is difficult with this assembly, and there is no provision to add more reagent if necessary. The Soltys apparatus was designed to measure the volume of Grignard reagent solution (in the reservoir) so that the amount consumed can be determined. Unfortunately the operation becomes rather complicated with this additional device.

The gasometric apparatus of Ma and Scheinthal[92] (see Figure 6.15), which is modified after the design of Brown and Hafliger,[93] provides a simple and convenient technique for the determination of active hydrogen function on the 0.1 meq. scale. The sample is placed in the reaction vessel F

[89] R. N. Evans, J. E. Davenport, and A. J. Revukas, *Ind. Eng. Chem., Anal. Ed.,* **12.** 301 (1940).

[90] H. Roth, *Mikrochemie,* **11,** 140 (1932).

[91] A. Soltys, *Mikrochemie,* **20,** 107 (1936).

[92] T. S. Ma and B. Scheinthal, unpublished work; see B. Scheinthal, *Master's Thesis, Brooklyn College,* 1961.

[93] H. C. Brown and O. Hafliger, *Anal. Chem.,* **26,** 757 (1954).

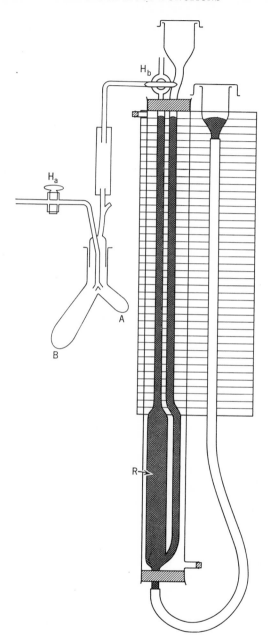

Fig. 11.7. Active hydrogen apparatus of Roth. Courtesy of *Mikrochemie*.

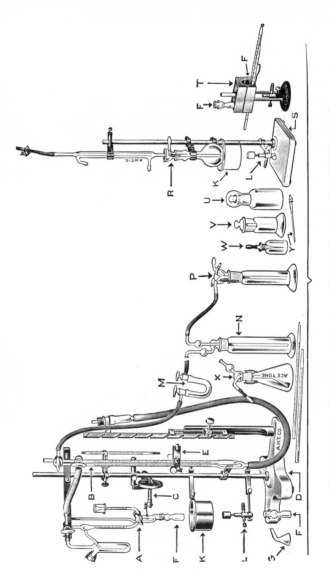

Fig. 11.8. Active hydrogen apparatus of Soltys. Courtesy of A. H. Thomas Co.

which is then connected to the gasburet I. After flushing the system with a current of purified methane gas (obtained from a cylinder), the Grignard reagent is introduced through the stopcock D by means of a syringe. Mixing is done by means of a magnetic stirrer. The reaction vessel can be immersed into a constant temperature bath (see Figure 13.2) so that the reaction occurs at a high temperature. The detailed procedure for using this apparatus is given in experiment 40.

Semimicro apparatus for determining active hydrogen functions were described by Binaghi[94] and Soucek.[95] The latter design is interesting because it eliminates the use of expensive mercury. As shown in Figure 11.9, the assembly comprises the reaction vessel R joined to the manometer $N_1 - N_2$ on one side and the buret B on the other. The apparatus is made of soft glass with a large coefficient of expansion. The manometer and buret are filled with dibutyl ether. The Grignard reagent is placed in the reaction vessel R, and the sample is kept in the basket K which hangs on the hook

[94] R. Binaghi, *Ann. Chim. Applicata*, **15**, 432 (1925).

[95] M. Soucek, *Chem. Listy*, **50**, 323 (1956); *Coll. Czechoslov. Chem. Comm.*, **23**, 554 (1958).

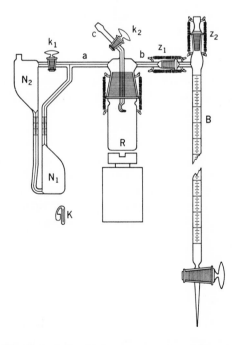

Fig. 11.9. Active hydrogen apparatus of Soucek.

of the nitrogen inlet tube C. After the apparatus has been equilibrated, the basket is brought down by means of a magnet. When the reaction is completed, the liquid in the buret is drained out until the manometer returns to the original level and the volume of methane gas produced is measured in the buret.

Lüttgens and Negelein[96] described a quartz vessel for the determination of active hydrogen in less than 1 mg. sample by a manometric procedure. Apparatus suitable for a series of determinations of active hydrogen were designed by Horner and Ehlech,[97] and Orchin and Wender.[98]

Terentev and co-workers[99,100] proposed a device in which the liberated hydrocarbon gas is collected in a micro azotometer. The reaction vessel is so designed that carbon dioxide enters under a layer of ethereal solution of the compound to be analyzed, to eliminate any initial reaction between carbon dioxide and the Grignard reagent. The stream of carbon dioxide is then stopped. The methane formed displaces carbon dioxide from the vessel and the reaction is completed in an atmosphere of methane. Dry carbon dioxide is now passed through to purge the methane into the azotometer to be measured. It is apparent that any premature contact of carbon dioxide with the Grignard reagent—before the completion of the active hydrogen reaction—will invalidate the determination.

3. *The Grignard Reagent.* The Grignard reagent for the determination of active hydrogen is best prepared from methyl iodide and pure magnesium turnings. Unlike the preparation of Grignard reagents for synthetic purposes, ethyl ether should not be used as solvent (see next section). The strength of the reagent solution should be approximately $1M$. Therefore, it is recommended to prepare a Grignard reagent more concentrated than $1M$, titrate a portion against standard acid, and dilute the solution to the suitable concentration. A procedure for preparing a small amount of Grignard reagent, sufficient for a few microdeterminations, was described by Cheronis.[101] The assembly, shown in Figure 11.10, consists of a reaction vessel with a stopcock at the bottom, so that the solution can be easily separated from the unreacted magnesium. A little turbidity has no adverse effect on the microdetermination of active hydrogen functions.[102] If it is

[96] W. Lüttgens and E. Negelein, *Biochem. Z.*, **269**, 177 (1934).

[97] L. Horner and G. Ehlech, *Agnew. Chem.*, **60**, 18 (1948).

[98] M. Orchin and J. Wender, *Anal. Chem.*, **21**, 875 (1949).

[99] A. P. Terentev and K. D. Shcherbakova, *J. Gen. Chem. USSR*, **10**, 2041 (1940).

[100] A. P. Terentev and H. I. Kireeva, *Izvest. Akad. Nauk. SSSR, Otdel. Khim. Nauk.*, **1951**, 172.

[101] N. D. Cheronis, *Micro and Semimicro Methods*, Interscience, New York, 1954, p. 347.

[102] V. Zopp and E. H. Deglorgi, *Anales Assoc. Quim. Argentina*, **18**, 214 (1930).

desirable to prepare a large amount of Grignard reagent, the methyl magnesium iodide solution should be stored in 5 to 30 ml. ampoules under nitrogen.

Several workers have proposed the use of methyl bromide[103-106] or methyl chloride[105,107] as starting material for the preparation of Grignard reagent in analysis for active hydrogen. Methyl chloride is convenient, since it is commercially available in small cylinders. However, methyl magnesium chloride is less reactive and less stable than the corresponding bromide solution.[105]

4. Solvents. The choice of solvent is critical in the determination of active hydrogen functions. Since the gasometric technique is employed, the solvent used in the preparation of Grignard reagent cannot be an ether that has a high vapor pressure. *n*-Butyl ether, *n*-amyl ether,[95] anisole,[90] and glycol ethers[107] are suitable. The liquid used to dissolve the substance to be analyzed should not cause precipitation with the Grignard reagent. Pyridine has been recommended by many investigators.[90,108,109] It was found to give more uniform results than dioxane.[108] Unfortunately, pyridine is extremely hygroscopic, and purification through its perchlorate[110,111]

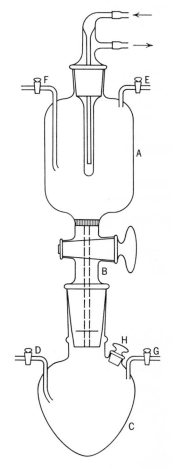

Fig. 11.10. Assembly for preparation of Grignard reagent.

[103] L. Petrova and E. E. Perrinova, *J. Appl. Chem. USSR*, **4**, 722 (1931).

[104] W. Hückel and E. Wilip, *J. Prakt. Chem.*, **156**, 95 (1940).

[105] K. D. Shcherbakova and N. V. Kremenskaya, *J. Gen. Chem., USSR*, **17**, 100 (1947).

[106] A. P. Terentev, D. G. Kadaner, and Y. K. Kopchenova, *J. Gen. Chem., USSR*, **17**, 913 (1947).

[107] G. D. Stevens, *Anal. Chem.*, **28**, 1184 (1956).

[108] M. Lieff, G. F. Wright, and H. Hubbert, *J. Am. Chem. Soc.*, **61**, 865 (1939).

[109] R. A. Lehman and H. Basch, *Ind. Eng. Chem., Anal. Ed.*, **17**, 428 (1945).

[110] F. Pregl and H. Roth, *Quantitative Organic Microanalysis*, 3rd English Ed., Blakiston, Philadelphia, 1937, p. 158.

[111] F. G. Arndt and T. Severge, *Chem. Zeitung*, **74**, 140 (1950).

involves the inherent danger of explosion. Perold and Snyman[112] proposed Kairoline (1-methyl-1,2,3,4-tetrahydroquinoline) as solvent for the microdetermination of active hydrogen in highly insoluble substances. Hydrocarbons (benzene, xylene) and chlorinated hydrocarbons (chloroform, methylene chloride) were employed by Terentev and Shcherbakova[113] in their method using the micro azotometer to collect methane.[99]

5. *Applications and Limitations.* Organic functions containing the active hydrogen function and their methane equivalents are listed in Table 11.5. It should be noted that the methane equivalent indicates the maximum yield, which is not always attainable. For instance, Zerewitinoff[87] reported that primary amines and amides liberate one equivalent of methane at room temperature, but produce two equivalents on heating. Jurecek[117] demonstrated that the reaction of the second hydrogen in

TABLE 11.5

Compounds Containing Active Hydrogen Functions

Type	Formula	Methane Equivalent	Reference
Acid	$\begin{cases} RCOOH \\ RSO_2OH \\ RPO(OH)_2 \end{cases}$	1 1 2	96
Alcohol	ROH	1	87, 114, 115, 116
Phenol	ArOH	1	87, 96
Thioalcohol	RSH	1	87
Thiophenol	ArSH	1	
Amine	RNH_2	2	114, 117
Amide	$\begin{cases} R_2NH \\ RCONH_2 \end{cases}$	1 2	87, 96 87, 118
Substituted amide	RCONHR	1	87, 118
Semicarbazone	$R_2C{=}N{-}NH{-}CO{-}NH_2$	2	87
Sulfonamide	RSO_2NH_2	2	118
Substituted sulfonamide	RSO_2NHR	1	118
Nitro compound	RNO_2	1	117
Active methylene	$={\overset{\mid}{C}}{-}CH_2$	1	87, 119
Acetylene	$R{-}C{\equiv}CH$	1	87

[112] G. W. Perold and J. M. Snyman, *Mikrochim. Acta,* **1958,** 225.

[113] A. P. Terentev and K. Shcherbakova, *J. Gen. Chem. USSR,* **16,** 855 (1946).

[114] B. Flaschträger, *Z. Physiol. Chem.,* **146,** 219 (1925).

[115] W. Fuchs, N. Ishler, and A. G. Sandhoff, *Ind. Eng. Chem., Anal. Ed.,* **12,** 507 (1940).

[116] A. P. Terentev and K. D. Shcherbakova, *J. Gen. Chem. USSR,* **15,** 86 (1945).

[117] M. Jurecek, *Chem. Listy,* **40,** 239 (1946).

[118] W. W. Becker, *Anal. Chem.,* **22,** 185 (1950).

[119] I. M. McAlpine and P. A. Ongley, *Anal. Chem.,* **27,** 55 (1955).

primary amines may not be quantitative depending on the solvent and temperature of the reaction mixture. For a diamino compound with four active hydrogen atoms, the fourth hydrogen atom does not react, and the third does not always react quantitatively.

As a rule, acids, phenols, and sulfonamides react with Grignard reagent readily and liberate methane quantitatively. Primary and secondary alcohols give correct values, but tertiary alcohols give unsatisfactory results.[116]

According to Jurecek,[117] nitroalkanes produce one equivalent of methane. On the other hand, aromatic nitro compounds do not react with Grignard reagent at room temperature and give only 0.1 to 0.3 equivalent of methane at 85°C.

McAlpine and Ongley[119] showed that the activity of the hydrogen atoms in active methylene groups varies considerably with environment. Zerewitinoff[87] stated that malonic acid has three active hydrogen atoms, whereas ethyl malonate, ethyl acetoacetate, and acetylacetone, respectively, liberate one equivalent of methane at 100°C.

If the quantity of Grignard reagent added to the reaction vessel is measured accurately, the amount of methane produced by the active hydrogen may be checked against the residual Grignard reagent. This can be done in the apparatus of Soltys[91] or Ma and Scheinthal.[92] After the volume of methane formed has been measured, an excess of hexanol, aniline,[91] or water[120] is introduced into the reaction mixture, and the additional amount of methane liberated is again determined. It should be remembered that a number of functional groups consume methyl magnesium iodide without the evolution of methane or causing any change of gas volume in the apparatus. These functional groups are listed in Table 11.6; they can be determined by means of Grignard reagent using the indirect gasometric technique described on p. 590. If the substance to be analyzed contains both types of functions, simultaneous determination of the two using one sample is possible. Thus a carboxylic acid will liberate 1 equivalent of methane and consume 2 equivalents of methyl magnesium iodide. Another example is the determination of the ratio between enol and keto forms of 1,3-diketones. The procedure for simultaneous determination of active hydrogen and carbonyl functions is given in experiment 41.

C. Use of Lithium Aluminum Hydride

1. Reaction and Method. The reaction between the active hydrogen function and lithium aluminum hydride is shown in equation 9; using alcohol as an example:

[120] E. Kohler, J. Stone, and R. Fuson, *J. Am. Chem. Soc.*, **49**, 318 (1927).

TABLE 11.6

Functional Groups Which Consume Grignard Reagent
without Producing Change in Gas Volume

Function	Structure	CH$_3$MgI Consumed, eq.	See Other Section, p.
Carbonyl	$\diagdown$C$=$O$\diagup$	1	149
Carboxylate	$-$C$\diagup$$\diagdown$ O / O$^-$	1	178
Acid halide	$-$C$\diagup$$\diagdown$ O / X	2	113
Ester	$-$C$\diagup$$\diagdown$ O / OR	2	178
Nitrile	$-$CN	1	260
Isonitrile	$-$NC	1	260

$$4RO-H + LiAlH_4 \rightarrow 4H_2 + LiOR + Al(OR)_3 \tag{9}$$

Thus one mole of hydrogen gas is liberated from each equivalent of active hydrogen. Like the determination of active hydrogen functions by means of Grignard reagent, the prevailing technique involves the measurement of the volume of hydrogen formed.

A titrimetric method was proposed by Schöniger[121] which is based on the indirect liberation of iodine through several steps as indicated below:

$$H_2 \xrightarrow{CuO} H_2O \xrightarrow{C} CO \xrightarrow{I_2O_5} I_2 \tag{10}$$

The hydrogen gas produced from the active hydrogen function is passed through a combustion tube packed with copper oxide. The water vapor formed is then reduced by carbon at 1100°C to produce carbon monoxide, which reacts with iodine pentoxide at 120°C to produce iodine:

$$5CO + I_2O_5 \rightarrow I_2 + 5CO_2 \tag{11}$$

The iodine is absorbed in acetic acid containing bromine, whereby iodic acid is formed:

$$I_2 + 5Br_2 + 6H_2O \rightarrow 2HIO_3 + 10HBr \tag{12}$$

[121] W. Schöniger, Z. Anal. Chem., **133**, 4 (1951).

After removal of excess bromine, potassium iodide is added to liberate iodine, which is then determined by titration with standard sodium thiosulfate to the starch endpoint. This method requires expensive equipment and involves various sources of error.

2. Assemblies. The various assemblies described in Section III-B-2 are suitable for the gasometric determination of active hydrogen by means of lithium aluminum hydride. The apparatus of Roth[90] (Figure 11.7) was used by two groups of investigators[122,123] and the Soltys[91] assembly (Figure 11.8) was employed by Lieb and Schöniger.[124] The micro procedure using the apparatus of Ma and Scheinthal[92] is given in experiment 40. Other assemblies were described by Colson[125] and Krynitsky and co-workers.[126]

3. Reagent and Solvents. Lithium aluminum hydride is commercially available. It is extremely sensitive to oxygen, moisture, and carbon dioxide. Exposure of the solid to air on a piece of paper might cause combustion. The material should be wrapped in aluminum foil and stored in a closed dry metal container.

The liquid usually recommended for dissolving lithium aluminum hydride is tetrahydrofuran. However, the reagent does not go into solution readily, even in this solvent. It should be noted that purified tetrahydrofuran forms explosive peroxide on standing for several days. Ulbrich and Makes[127] used a mixture of tetrahydrofuran and anisole as solvent, whereas Stefanac[128] employed *n*-butyl ether. A 0.2*M* solution is suitable for the microdetermination of active hydrogen functions.

4. Applications and Limitations. Lithium aluminum hydride reacts with all compounds listed in Table 11.5, but its application to quantitative analysis is limited to alcohols, amines, phenols, carboxylic acids, and a few other types of compounds which produce hydrogen gas without side reactions. Thus this reagent is not recommended for the analysis of nitro groups (in view of the complication due to the reduction of nitro compounds by hydrogen), although successful microdetermination of nitro compounds by means of lithium aluminum hydride has been reported.[124] Quantitative

[122] D. S. Rao, G. D. Shah, and V. S. Pansare, *Mikrochim. Acta*, **1954**, 81.

[123] K. N. Arjungi, R. S. Kulkami, and T. S. Gore, *J. Sci. Ind. Res. India B.*, **17**, 459 (1958).

[124] H. Lieb and W. Schöniger, *Mikrochemie*, **35**, 400 (1950).

[125] A. F. Colson, *Analyst*, **82**, 358 (1957).

[126] J. A. Krynitsky, J. E. Johnson, and H. W. Carhardt, *J. Am. Chem. Soc.*, **70**, 487 (1948).

[127] V. Ulbrich and J. Makes, *Chem. Prumysl*, **8**, 163 (1958).

[128] Z. Stefanac, *Croat. Chem. Acta*, **28**, 295 (1956).

studies on lithium aluminum hydride were published by Hochstein.[129] Brown and McFarlin[130] demonstrated that lithium aluminum hydride releases only 3 equivalents of its hydrogen with t-amyl or t-butyl alcohols even in an excess of alcohol.

Comparison between Grignard reagent and lithium aluminum hydride was reported in several papers.[131–133] Discrepancy of results usually appears when tautomeric changes occur. This may be attributed to the strong reducing property of lithium aluminum hydride. It might be mentioned here that this reagent is not suitable for the determination of reducible groups listed in Table 11.5. Thus, when it is desirable to determine the carbonyl group by a gasometric procedure, sodium borohydride (see experiment 33) and not lithium aluminum hydride should be used as the reagent.

D. Other Methods for Active Hydrogen

1. With Organometallic Compounds. Terentev and Shor[134] investigated the use of methyl zinc iodide for the determination of active hydrogen functions without observing any advantage. Aniline loses one hydrogen atom at room temperature and two at 70 to 80°C. Diphenylamine and p-toluidine fail to give complete reaction.

Kainz and co-workers[133] advocated lithium methyl as a reagent because of its special reactivity with certain compounds. The reaction is represented below:

$$RO—H + LiCH_3 \rightarrow CH_4 + ROLi \qquad (13)$$

Lithium alanate was employed by Budesinsky.[135]

2. With Sodium or Sodamide. Quantitative study of the reaction between alcohols and sodium amalgam, shown in equation 14, was reported by Liebhafsky[136]:

$$2RO—H + 2NaHg_x \rightarrow H_2 + 2RONa + 2xHg \qquad (14)$$

Acetonitrile was used as solvent and the reaction mixture was shaken vigorously before measuring the volume of hydrogen gas evolved. The

[129] F. A. Hochstein, *J. Am. Chem. Soc.*, **71**, 305 (1949).

[130] H. C. Brown and R. F. McFarlin, *J. Am.Chem. Soc.*, **78**, 252 (1956).

[131] J. A. Krynitsky, J. E. Johnson, and H. W. Carhardt, *J. Am. Chem. Soc.*, **70**, 486 (1948).

[132] H. E. Zaugg and B. W. Horrom, *Anal. Chem.*, **20**, 1026 (1948).

[133] G. Kainz, O. Polansky, E. Schinzel, and F. Wessely, *Mikrochim. Acta*, **1957**, 241.

[134] A. P. Terentev and N. I. Shor, *J. Gen. Chem. USSR*, **17**, 2075 (1947).

[135] B. Budesinsky, *Coll. Czech. Chem. Commun.* **24**, 2948 (1959).

[136] H. A. Liebhafsky, *J. Am. Chem. Soc.*, **65**, 1778 (1943).

results were erratic, in some cases 30% below theory. Hence, this method is not suited for the determination of active hydrogen functions.

Palfray and co-workers[137] treated primary, secondary, and tertiary alcohols, respectively, with sodamide in an atmosphere of nitrogen. Ammonia produced according to equation 15 is absorbed in water and determined by titration with standardized sulfuric acid.

$$RO—H + NaNH_2 \rightarrow NH_3 + RONa \qquad (15)$$

Positive errors are usually observed.

3. With Diazomethane. Diazomethane reacts with active hydrogen functions to produce nitrogen and methylated derivative; for example, the reaction with an alcohol gives nitrogen and the methyl ester:

$$RO—H + CH_2N_2 \rightarrow RO—CH_3 + N_2 \qquad (16)$$

Arndt[138] wrote a comprehensive review of the use of diazomethane for the determination of active hydrogen. It should be noted that this reagent is more useful for the qualitative analysis of the various active hydrogen functions than for quantitative evaluation. Thus, Schmidt and Zeiser[139] demonstrated that acids react readily, phenols less readily, alcohols slowly, and aliphatic amines do not react with diazomethane. When the methylation reaction proceeds rapidly and quantitatively, as in the case of the micropreparation of methyl esters,[140] the product can be isolated and determined (e.g., by gas chromatography).

4. With Deuterium or Tritium. Determination of active hydrogen functions by the isotopic technique has been proposed. The hydrogen atom is exchanged with deuterium or tritium, followed by measuring the change with an appropriate technique. In one method[141–144] the substance to be analyzed is treated with heavy water. The exchange reaction is shown in equation 17:

$$2RO—H + D_2O \rightarrow 2RO—D + H_2O \qquad (17)$$

The extent of exchange can be determined by measuring the density of the resulting water,[142] or by quantitative infrared spectrophotometry.[144]

In another method, the active hydrogen function is exchanged for tritium by dissolving the compound to be analyzed in an excess of tritiated

[137] L. Palfray, S. Sabetay, and E. Gordon, *Compt. rend.*, **222**, 1235 (1946).
[138] F. G. Arndt, in *Organic Analysis*, Vol. 1, Interscience, New York, 1953, p. 3.
[139] O. Schmidt and H. Zeiser, *Berichte*, **67**, 2120 (1934).
[140] R. Roper and T. S. Ma, *Microchem. J.*, **1**, 245 (1957).
[141] R. J. Williams, *J. Am. Chem. Soc.*, **58**, 1819 (1936).
[142] W. H. Hamill, *J. Am. Chem. Soc.*, **59**, 1152 (1937).
[143] M. Uchida, *J. Japan Biochem. Soc.*, **23**, 63 (1951).
[144] W. R. Harp, Jr., and R. C. Eiffert, *Anal. Chem.*, **32**, 794 (1960).

isopropyl alcohol.[145] After the exchange is complete, the solvent is removed by evaporation. The radioactivity of the tritiated sample is then measured in the Geiger counter, or other radioassay device.

IV. Basic Functions by Acid-Base Titrimetry

A. General. Organic bases are proton acceptors (or, in the old concept, form salts with acids) and hence are subject to titrimetry with acids of known molarity. Alkylamines have been determined by titration with a standard acid for a long time and the determination can be made on the micro scale using $0.01N$ hydrochloric acid with bromocresol green-methyl red mixed indicator.[146] Systematic quantitative estimation of basic functions received very little attention until the technique of nonaqueous titrimetry became popular.[147-149] At the present time, determination of organic bases by acid-base titrimetry is extensively employed in research and industry, particularly in the pharmaceutical field.

The general equation for alkalimetry is given by equation 18:

$$B + HA \rightleftharpoons BH^+ + A^- \tag{18}$$

where B stands for the organic base and HA the acid titrant. Most basic functions measurable by acid-base titrimetry contain nitrogen. Hence organic basic compounds are usually known as *nitrogen bases*. It should be noted, however, that basicity is not an exclusive property of nitrogen. For instance, the ether function can form an oxonium salt with hydrogen chloride[150] as shown in equation 19:

$$R\!-\!O\!-\!R' + HCl \rightarrow \left[\begin{matrix}H^+\\ROR'\end{matrix}\right]Cl^- \tag{19}$$

However, this reaction has not been applied to quantitative analysis. A number of sulfur functions also exhibit basic properties. Thus sulfoxides[151] are titrable as bases in acetic anhydride by means of perchloric acid in

[145] J. F. Eastham and V. F. Raaen, *Anal. Chem.*, **31**, 555 (1959).

[146] T. S. Ma and G. Zuazaga, *Ind. Eng. Chem., Anal. Ed.*, **14**, 280 (1942).

[147] M. E. Auerbach, *Drug Standards*, **19**, 127 (1951).

[148] J. S. Fritz, *Acid-Base Titrations in Nonaqueous Solvents*, G. Frederick Smith Chemical Co., Columbus, Ohio, 1952.

[149] A. H. Beckett and E. H. Tinley, *Titration in Nonaqueous Solvents*, 3rd ed., British Drug House, Poole, England, 1960.

[150] R. T. Morrison and R. N. Boyd, *Organic Chemistry*, Allyn and Bacon, Boston, 1959, p. 418.

[151] D. C. Wimer, *Anal. Chem.*, **30**, 2060 (1958).

acetic acid. With improvements in titration techniques it might be possible to determine other non-nitrogen basic functions by acid-base titrimetry.

B. Methods

1. Alkalimetry in Aqueous Solutions. Organic bases which can be determined in aqueous solutions by alkalimetry are limited to quaternary ammonium hydroxides and aliphatic amines. The former are strong bases; the latter exhibit dissociation constants slightly larger than ammonia. For example, the K_b's of a number of bases show value from 10^{-3} to 10^{-5}; $C_2H_5NH_2 = 5.65 \times 10^{-4}$; $(C_2H_5)_2NH = 1.26 \times 10^{-3}$; $(C_2H_5)_3N = 5.65 \times 10^{-4}$; $NH_3 = 1.8 \times 10^{-5}$. Basic functions whose K_b in water is greater than 10^{-5} can be titrated in aqueous solutions. The lower members of alkylamines are very soluble in water. Like ammonia, they can be separated from a reaction mixture by steam distillation,[152,153] collected in 2% boric acid, and determined on the 0.1 meq. scale by titration with 0.01N standard acid. The experimental procedure will be found on p. 571.

Amino compounds which are not readily soluble in water but which possess dissociation constants in the order of 10^{-5} may be dissolved in isopropyl alcohol or dioxane and titrated with aqueous standard acid (see experiment 2). Location of the visual endpoint in microdeterminations is not difficult, although the color change is faint compared with macro methods using 0.1N titrants. No precaution is necessary unless the room has a high concentration of ammonia in the atmosphere.

2. Alkalimetry in Nonaqueous Media. Alkalimetry in nonaqueous medium means the determination of a basic substance by titration with an acid in a system free from water and in the presence of a solvent. Inorganic nonaqueous solvents, such as liquid sulfur dioxide, have not been employed for this purpose.

Whereas acidimetry in nonaqueous solutions on the 0.1 meq. scale necessitates special reaction vessel (see Section II-B-2), micro alkalimetry can be performed with the conventional Erlenmeyer flask and microburet. Simplicity is the great attraction of nonaqueous alkalimetric methods.

A. DIRECT TITRATION METHODS. The applicability of 0.01N perchloric acid in acetic acid for the direct titration of 0.1 meq. quantities of organic bases in acetic acid or acetic anhydride has been established.[154] When acetic acid is used as solvent, basic compounds whose K_b in water is 10^{-12} or larger can be determined visually or potentiometrically. When

[152] A. E. Sobel, H. Yuska, and J. Cohen, *J. Bio. Chem.*, **118**, 443 (1937).

[153] Z. Bellen, *Chem. Anal.*, **1956**, 71.

[154] M. Gutterson and T. S. Ma, *Mikrochim. Acta*, **1960**, 1.

acetic anhydride is used as a solvent, the range of microdetermination is extended to basic functions down to K_b of 3×10^{-14}. The detailed procedure is given in experiment 3. Determination on the 0.3 to 0.5 mg. scale was described by Serrano-Berges,[155] and on the 50 μg. scale by Belcher, Berger and West,[156] using $0.01N$ titrant. The latter workers reported that some acetylation occurs in the case of aromatic amines, which invalidates the results. This difficulty does not appear in determinations on the 0.1 meq. scale. It is interesting to note that acetic acid may participate in reactions other than those involving acid-base equilibria. For instance, Hinsvark and Stone[156a] have shown that in the oxidation of oxalates by cerium (IV) in glacial acetic acid solution, the resulting carbon dioxide comes from the solvent.

B. BACK-TITRATION METHODS. Sometimes the reaction between the basic function and the acid titrant (equation 18) in organic media is not instantaneous. If the rightward reaction is slow, a known excess amount of the acid can be added and the determination is completed by back-titrating the unconsumed acid. The substance to be analyzed is dissolved in a suitable solvent in an Erlenmeyer flask, a known volume of the standardized acid titrant is added from the microburet. After standing for 5 to 10 minutes, the solution is titrated with a standardized $0.01N$ sodium acetate in acetic acid. The endpoint can be located by means of crystal violet indicator or potentiometrically (see p. 431).

C. INDIRECT METHODS. Certain basic compounds that are not titrable by the foregoing two procedures can be determined by acid-base titrimetry using indirect methods. Some examples are to be discussed.

Titration of amine hydrogen halide dissolved in acetic acid by means of standard perchloric acid solution does not exhibit sharp change on the potentiometric curve. If mercuric acetate is added before the titration, however, a sharp break occurs at the equivalence point.[157] The basis of this method is the formation of undissociable mercuric halide:

$$2RNH_3^+Cl^- + Hg(CH_3COO)_2 \rightarrow HgCl_2 + 2RNH_2 + 2CH_3COOH \qquad (20)$$

The free base then reacts with perchloric acid in acetic acid solution:

$$RNH_2 + HClO_4 \rightarrow RNH_3^+Cl^- \qquad (21)$$

Bayer and Posgay[158] demonstrated that mercaptans and compounds

[155] L. Serrano-Berges, *Inform. Quimica Analitica*, **14**, 41 (1960).

[156] R. Belcher, J. Berger, and T. S. West, *J. Chem. Soc.*, **1959**, 2882.

[156a] O. N. Hinsvark and K. G. Stone, *Anal. Chem.*, **28**, 334 (1956).

[157] C. W. Pifer and E. G. Wollish, *Anal. Chem.*, **24**, 300 (1952).

[158] I. Bayer and E. Posgay, *Naturwissenschaften*, **45**, 185 (1958); *Pharm. Zentralhalle*, **100**, 65 (1961).

containing the thiol group can be titrated as bases after the addition of mercuric acetate in acetic acid solution, the organic mercuric sulfide formed being undissociable:

$$2R—SH + Hg(CH_3COO)_2 \rightarrow R—S—Hg—S—R + 2CH_3COOH \qquad (22)$$

Alicino[159] reported the direct titration of thiourea, after the addition of mercuric acetate by means of $0.01N$ perchloric acid. On the other hand, thiouracil requires the back-titration technique after the mercuric acetate treatment.

Alkaloid salts can be exchanged with strongly basic anion exchanger (OH⁻ form) as indicated in equation 23:

$$[\text{Alkaloid—H}]^+\text{Cl}^- + \text{Resin—OH} \rightarrow \text{Alkaloid} + \text{Resin—Cl} + H_2O \qquad (23)$$

Alkaloid salt   *Alkaloid base*

The alkaloid is eluted with a suitable solvent and determined by titration with standard acid.[160]

Various methods have been suggested to convert an organic compound into a derivative which has basic properties and hence can be titrated with standard acid. Thus Nebbia and Guerrieri[161] reacted carbon disulfide with secondary amines, converted the dithiocarbamate (p. 331) into nickel complexes which are titrable as bases. Salvesen and Solli[162] proposed a method for determining Meprobamate (a carbamide) as follows. The carbamide is heated with hydrochloric acid to liberate ammonium chloride. The reaction mixture is evaporated almost to dryness and redissolved in glacial acetic acid. Mercuric acetate and dioxane are added. The ammonium acetate in the solution is then titrated with $0.1N$ perchloric acid.

C. Nonaqueous Solvents. Organic liquids which have been proposed for the nonaqueous titration of basic functions may be classified into four types:

1. *Basic or protophilic solvents.* Acetone,[163] methyl isobutyl ketone,[164] dioxane,[157] and diethyl ether.[163]

2. *Amphiprotic solvents.* Alcohols and glycols.[165]

3. *Acidic or protogenic solvents.* Acetic acid,[154,166] trifluoroacetic acid,[167]

[159] J. F. Alicino, *Microchem. J.*, **4**, 551 (1960).
[160] F. O. Gunderson, R. Heiz, and R. Klevstrand, *J. Pharm. Pharmacol.*, **5**, 608 (1953).
[161] L. Nebbia and F. Guerrieri, *Chem. e Ind.*, **35**, 896 (1953).
[162] B. Salvesen and O. Solli, *Medd. Norsk. Farmselsk.*, **21**, 85 (1959).
[163] J. S. Fritz, *Anal. Chem.*, **22**, 1028 (1950).
[164] D. B. Bruss and G. E. A. Wyld, *Anal. Chem.*, **29**, 232 (1957).
[165] S. R. Palit and V. N. Singh, *J. Indian Chem. Soc.*, **33**, 507 (1956).
[166] J. B. Conant and N. F. Hall, *J. Am. Chem. Soc.*, **49**, 3062 (1927).
[167] J. E. DeVries, S. Schiff, and E. St. C. Ganitz, *Anal. Chem.*, **27**, 1814 (1955).

propionic acid,[154,168] formic acid,[154,169] phenol,[165] nitrobenzene,[170] and nitromethane.[171]

4. *Neutral or aprotic solvents.* Acetic anhydride,[154,172] propionic anhydride,[168] acetonitrile,[173] acrylonitrile,[174] chloroform, carbon tetrachloride, methylene chloride, chlorobenzene, benzene, and petroleum ether.

As a general rule, the weaker the basic function to be titrated, the stronger should be the acidic solvent selected to produce the *leveling effect* in the neutralization reaction. For this reason glacial acetic acid (an acid of intermediate strength) is the most widely used solvent for the nonaqueous titration of organic bases. Unlike the strongly basic solvents for the nonaqueous titration of organic acids, glacial acetic acid is stable and is not affected by the atmosphere.

A mixture of two liquids is sometimes recommended to provide a suitable solvent for the substance to be analyzed and to produce a sharp endpoint. The neutral solvents are known to possess the latter characteristic. Acetic acid-acetic anhydride[154] and propylene glycol-chloroform are common mixed solvents. Another favorite mixture consists of isopropyl alcohol and ethylene glycol. For the titration of bases containing long aliphatic chains, a hydrocarbon solvent is usually mixed with the glycol. Such a mixture is known as a glycol-hydrocarbon (G-H) solvent.

The role of the solvent in the titration is complex, and occasionally unexpected phenomena are observed. Thus Streuli[171] reported that amines, amides, and ureas show diverse titration characteristics in nitromethane. In spite of being weaker bases than amines, the amides and the ureas show extremely sharp titration curves.

D. Titrants

1. *Titrants in Aqueous Medium.* Standardized 0.01N hydrochloric acid and 0.02N sulfuric acid are now commercially available.[175] These reagents are stable and can be used directly for microtitrations. If 0.1N standard acids are available, they can be diluted to the 0.01N strength with distilled water that has been boiled to expel the absorbed carbon dioxide.

[168] H. Ellert, T. Jasinski, and I. Pawelczak, *Acta Polon. Pharm.*, **16**, 235 (1959).

[169] A. M. Shkodin, N. A. Izmailov, and N. P. Dzyuba, *Zhur. Obschei Khim.*, **20**, 1999 (1950).

[170] N. V. Meurs and E. A. M. P. Dahmen, *Anal. Chim. Acta*, **21**, 193 (1959).

[171] C. A. Streuli, *Anal. Chem.*, **31**, 1652 (1959).

[172] R. Reiss, *Z. Anal. Chem.*, **167**, 16 (1959).

[173] J. S. Fritz, *Anal. Chem.*, **25**, 407 (1953).

[174] M. L. Owens, Jr. and R. L. Maute, *Anal. Chem.*, **27**, 1177 (1955).

[175] Fisher Scientific Co., New York, N.Y.

A convenient way to prepare a standard solution of $0.01N$ acid is to use potassium biniodate ($KIO_3 \cdot HIO_3$). Exactly 3.8994 g. of the pure salt are accurately weighed on the microbalance to make 1 liter of the $0.01000N$ solution. This salt is not hygroscopic, and it may be dried at room temperature under reduced pressure if necessary, but should not be subjected to evacuation at high temperatures.[176]

2. *Titrants in Nonaqueous Media*

A. PERCHLORIC ACID. Since Conant and Hall[166] first demonstrated the titration of weak organic bases by perchloric acid in acetic acid medium, perchloric acid has enjoyed a unique position in nonaqueous alkalimetry. It has been shown that perchloric acid is a strong acid in acetic acid solution, considerably stronger than sulfuric acid or hydrochloric acid.[177] Perchloric acid, $0.01N$, is easily prepared and is stable,[154] and $0.001N$ perchloric acid was reported by Keen and Fritz[178] for ultramicro titrations. The solvent generally recommended is glacial acetic acid,[154] but dioxane[179] and trifluoroacetic acid[167] have been suggested. When the base to be analyzed is dissolved in G-H solvent (see p. 428) mixture, the perchloric acid titrant should be prepared in the same medium.

It should be remembered that perchloric acid is a strong oxidizing agent and has explosive properties. Although no such danger is involved in the $0.01N$ titrant, the stock bottle of 70% perchloric acid should be carefully kept away from reducing substances and metals. When the $0.01N$ perchloric acid in glacial acetic acid is stored in the microburet, which has a reservoir, a stopcock with a needle valve control[180] is desirable. If the conventional stopcock is used and the titration flask is shaken by hand, it is important to see that the stopcock does not leak. Another precaution is to avoid temperature variation in the titrant, because acetic acid has a high coefficient of cubic expansion.[181]

Perchloric acid is usually standardized against potassium biphthalate.[154,182] Fritz[163] advocated diphenylguanidine, but the latter compound is not readily available in pure form.

B. OTHER TITRANTS. p-Toluenesulfonic acid[183,184] in chloroform and

[176] T. S. Ma, R. E. Lang, and J. D. McKinley, Jr., *Mikrochim. Acta*, **1957**, 372.

[177] R. P. Bell, *Acids and Bases*, Methuen, London, 1953, p. 33.

[178] R. T. Keen and J. S. Fritz, *Anal. Chem.*, **24**, 564 (1952).

[179] C. W. Pifer, E. G. Wollish, and M. S. Schmall, *Anal. Chem.*, **25**, 310 (1953).

[180] Micro-Ware, Inc., Vineland, N.J.

[181] W. Seaman and E. Allen, *Anal. Chem.*, **23**, 592 (1951).

[182] P. C. Markunas and J. A. Riddick, *Anal. Chem.*, **23**, 337 (1951).

[183] I. Gyenes, *Magyar Kem. Folyoirat*, **56**, 383 (1950).

[184] M. M. Davis and P. J. Schuhmann, *J. Res. Nat. Bur. Stds.*, **39**, 221 (1947).

naphthalene-2-sulfonic acid in acetone[185] have been suggested as non-aqueous titrants. These acids are difficult to purify. Davis and Hetzer[186] investigated the titration of bases with diphenylphosphate. The latter was found to be a strong acid. It cannot, however, replace perchloric acid in acetic acid.

Chloroaluminumdiisopropoxide hydrochloride, $ClAl(O-i-C_3H_7)_2HCl$, in chloroform solution was employed by Tokar and Simonyi[187] to determine basic functions whose dissociation constants in water are greater than 10^{-10}. For bases having dissociation constants above 10^{-9}, Hillenbrand and Pentz[188] recommended hydrochloric acid in methanol as the titrant on the macro scale. It should be noted that even the strength of $0.1N$ methanolic hydrochloric acid may vary from day to day. Therefore its use in microanalysis is limited.

Two papers were published on the titrimetry of weak basic functions by Lewis acids in aprotic solvents. Pyridine, quinoline and α-picoline, respectively, were titrated against boron trifluoride (equation 24) in solution of thionyl chloride, thiophosphoryl chloride, or nitrobenzene.[189]

$$C_6H_5N + BF_3 \rightarrow C_6H_5N \cdot BF_3 \tag{24}$$

The endpoint was determined conductometrically. These bases were also titrated against stannic or titanic chloride using crystal violet as the indicator.[190] The practical applications of this technique have not been explored.

E. Detection of the Equivalence Point

1. Aqueous Titrations. When it is possible to perform the alkalimetric determination of the organic base in aqueous solutions, detection of the equivalence point usually can be accomplished by means of a visual indicator. Thus phenolphthalein[191] and naphthyl red[192] have been employed for the titration of aliphatic amines using $0.1N$ standard acid. These indicators may be used for the determination of strong organic bases, such as quaternary ammonium hydroxides, on the micro scale using $0.01N$ titrant. On the other hand, they are not satisfactory in the microanalysis

[185] V. V. Udovenko and L. A. Voedenskaya, *Ukr. Khim. Zh.*, **20**, 684 (1954).

[186] M. M. Davis and H. B. Hetzer, *J. Res. Nat. Bur. Stds.*, **54**, 309 (1955).

[187] G. Tokar and I. Simonyi, *Magyar Kem. Folyoirat*, **64**, 94, 151, 379 (1958).

[188] E. F. Hillenbrand, Jr. and C. A. Pentz, in *Organic Analysis*, Vol. 3, Interscience, New York, 1956, p. 143.

[189] M. C. Henry, J. F. Hazel, and W. M. McNabb, *Anal. Chim. Acta*, **15**, 187 (1956).

[190] R. C. Paul, J. Singh, and S. S. Sandhu, *J. Indian Chem. Soc.*, **36**, 305 (1959).

[191] B. P. Fedorov and A. A. Spyskov, *Org. Chem. Ind.*, **1**, 620 (1936).

[192] K. Linderstrom-Lang, *Physiol. Chem.*, **173**, 32 (1928).

(0.1 meq.) of amino compounds having pK_b values in the order of 10^{-5}. Two reasons are apparent: (1) the extent of pH change at the equivalence point for weak bases is considerably smaller than that for strong bases (compare the potentiometric titration curves of sodium hydroxide and ammonia); (2) the concentration of the colored species of the indicator is reduced about a hundredfold as the macro procedure (1 meq. sample with $0.1N$ titrant) is converted to the micro procedure (0.1 meq. sample with $0.01N$ titrant). Therefore it becomes necessary to utilize a mixture of indicators that exhibits a neutral color at the narrow range of pH transition corresponding to the equivalence point. Such indicator mixtures are called screened indicators. For example, a mixture containing 5 parts of bromocresol green and 1 part of methyl red is recommended for the microtitration of basic functions whose equivalence points occur near pH 5. This screened indicator imparts a blue color to the basic solution. As the $0.01N$ standard acid is delivered from the microburet, the solution gradually turns green. Then it becomes gray or colorless at the equivalence point. A slight excess (0.02 ml.) of the titrant causes the appearance of a red color, which intensifies if more titrant is added.[146,176]

Detection of equivalence point by the potentiometric method, if desirable, can be performed on the micro scale using a pH meter with glass-calomel electrodes. After the transition pH range has been ascertained from the titration curve, a suitable indicator may be selected from Table 11.7.

Conductometric determination of amino acid by titration against hydrochloric acid,[193] and weak bases having dissociation constants of 10^{-8} to 10^{-12} against trichloroacetic acid[194] have been reported on the macro scale. These substances are better determined on the micro scale by nonaqueous titration.

2. Nonaqueous Titrations

A. USE OF INDICATORS

(1) *Visual endpoint.* The most widely used visual indicator for nonaqueous alkalimetry is crystal violet. It should be noted that this indicator does not exhibit a single color change during the titration. Conant and Werner[195] postulated that the crystal violet molecule, $(B^+)Cl^-$, can acquire different amounts of protons to form the various colored species as shown in the following equilibria:

$$\underset{\text{violet}}{B^+} \xrightleftharpoons{\;H^+\;} \underset{\text{green}}{BH^{+2}} \xrightleftharpoons{\;H^+\;} \underset{\text{yellow}}{BH_2^{+3}} \tag{25}$$

[193] M. Pascal, *Chim. Anal.*, **38**, 201 (1956).
[194] F. Gaslini and L. Z. Nahum, *Anal. Chem.*, **32**, 1027 (1960).
[195] J. B. Conant and T. H. Werner, *J. Am. Chem. Soc.*, **52**, 4436 (1930).

TABLE 11.7

Indicators for Alkalimetry of Basic Functions

Indicator	Color Change	pH Range	Reference
Crystal violet	purple → blue	0.0–1.8	149, 154
Malachite green	yellow → green	0.1–2.0	154
	blue → colorless	11.4–13.0	
Methyl violet	colorless → blue	0.2–1.8	149, 154
	blue → violet	2.0–3.2	
Thymol blue	yellow → red	1.2–2.8	165
	blue → yellow	8.0–9.6	
Eosin-Y	colorless → yellow	2–3.5	154
Methyl orange	yellow → red	3.1–4.4	188
Ethyl orange		3.5–4.8	187
α-Naphthyl red	yellow → red	3.7–5.0	192
Bromocresol green	blue → yellow	3.8–5.4	146
Methyl red	yellow → red	4.2–6.2	146
Neutral red	yellow → red	6.8–8.0	154
Phenolphthalein	pink → colorless	8.2–10	191
α-Naphtholbenzein	yellow → green	8.2–10.0	154
Tropaeolin-O	orange → yellow	11–13	193
Xylene cyanol FF	yellow → brown		188
Dimethyl yellow			187
Triphenylcarbinol	colorless → yellow		154
Dibenzalacetone	colorless → yellow		154
Safranin-O	pink → yellow		154
o-Nitroaniline	yellow → colorless		154
Oracet blue B	blue → pink		149
Triphenylmethane dyes			194

The reactions of Lewis acids with crystal violet in aprotic solvents were studied by Rice and co-workers.[196] Seaman and Allen[181] observed that the ionic strength of the solution has an effect on the color change of crystal violet, the endpoint color being dependent on the acid, base, as well as solvent used. A typical titration curve using $0.01N$ perchloric acid in acetic acid with the corresponding color change of crystal violet indicator[154] is shown in Figure 11.11.

Besides crystal violet, the following indicators have been studied in the titration of basic functions by means of $0.01N$ perchloric acid[154]: methyl violet, malachite green, eosin-Y, o-nitroaniline, neutral red, Safranin-O, α-naphtholbenzein, triphenylcarbinol, and dibenzalacetone. Although all these indicators exhibit color change, their characteristics are different. Thus the color of eosin-Y fades rapidly in acetic acid-acetic anhydride

[196] R. V. Rice, S. Zuffanti, and W. F. Luder, *Anal. Chem.*, **24**, 1022 (1952).

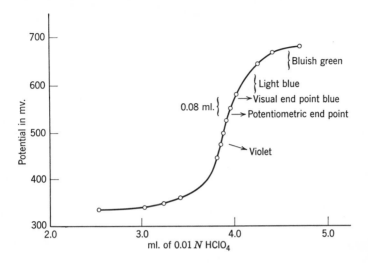

Fig. 11.11. Titration of potassium biphthalate with crystal violet indicator showing color changes. Courtesy of *Mikrochimica Acta*.

medium, and the color change of *o*-nitroaniline in the same medium is irreversible. According to Tuthill and co-workers,[197] when certain alkaloids are titrated against 0.05N perchloric acid, malachite green color change is more distinct and nearly coincidental with the potentiometric endpoint. Some indicators (e.g., Oracet blue B) which give satisfactory results in titrations using 0.02N titrant may exhibit poor endpoints in more dilute solutions. The micro procedure will be found in experiment 3.

(2) *Photometric endpoint.* Because the visual detection of the indicator endpoint in nonaqueous titrations requires some experience, spectrophotometric determination of the color change has been advocated. Tuthill and co-workers[197] reported the photometric detection of the color change of malachite green indicator in the titration of alkaloids. Ellert and co-workers[198] studied the photometric endpoints of methyl violet in acetic acid-acetic anhydride solution with 0.1N perchloric acid as titrant. Higuchi and co-workers[199,200] described a method in which a very weak basic indicator is employed such that the color change occurs after the substance to be analyzed has been overtitrated. The stoichiometric endpoint is then obtained by extrapolation of the absorbance-titration plot.

[197] S. M. Tuthill, O. W. Kolling, and K. H. Roberts, *Anal. Chem.*, **32**, 1678 (1960).
[198] H. Ellert, T. Jasinski, and K. Marcinkowska, *Acta Polon. Pharm.*, **17**, 29 (1960).
[199] C. Rehm and T. Higuchi, *Anal. Chem.*, **29**, 367 (1957).
[200] K. A. Connors and T. Higuchi, *Anal. Chem.*, **32**, 93 (1960).

B. ELECTROMETRIC METHODS

(1) *Potentiometric titrations.* In contrast to the determination of very weak acids in nonaqueous media, potentiometric titrations of weak bases in organic solvents do not require equipment different from those used for aqueous titrations. Most titrations can be performed with the glass electrode as indicator electrode and a saturated calomel half-cell of either the "sleeve" or "fiber" type as reference electrode. The micro procedure using $0.01N$ perchloric acid as titrant is given in experiment 3. Other electrode systems, such as glass-silver, silver chloride,[163] platinum,[167] and antimony,[201] respectively, have been suggested. A review of potentiometric electrode systems in nonaqueous titrimetry was prepared by Stock and Purdy.[202]

It should be noted that equilibrium in the neutralization reaction is established only slowly in nonaqueous media. Therefore the reaction mixture should be stirred vigorously after each addition of the titrant. After the potential reading is taken, the solution should be stirred again and another reading made. If the two readings agree within 2 millivolts, equilibrium may be considered established.

The potentiometric method for detecting the endpoint of a nonaqueous titration is necessary before a suitable visual indicator can be found for the determination of a particular basic function. Potentiometric titrations are usually required for the simultaneous determination of several basic substances in the solution. Kenttamaa and Heinonen[203] utilized the slope of the titration curve of a base in glacial acetic acid to calculate the ratio of dissociation constant of the base to its salt in acetic acid.

(2) *Other electrometric techniques.* Coulometric determination of basic functions was reported by several workers.[204-206] The sample to be analyzed is dissolved in acetonitrile or acetic acid-acetic anhydride mixture. The supporting electrolyte may be $0.05M$ lithium perchlorate[204] or $0.1M$ sodium perchlorate.[205] Hydrogen ions are produced by anodic oxidation of water and are detected by the glass-calomel or glass-mercury-mercurous acetate electrode system.

Conductometric titration of nitrogen bases in nitrobenzene with perchloric acid was reported by Meurs and co-workers.[170] Henry and co-workers[189] used boron trifluoride as the titrant acid. High-frequency

[201] B. R. Warner and W. W. Haskell, *Anal. Chem.*, **26**, 770 (1954).

[202] J. T. Stock and W. C. Purdy, *Chem. Reviews*, **57**, 1159 (1957).

[203] J. Kenttamaa and E. Heinonen, *Suomen. Kemistilehti B.*, **32**, 189 (1959).

[204] C. A. Streuli, *Anal. Chem.*, **28**, 130 (1956).

[205] W. B. Mather, Jr. and F. C. Anson, *Anal. Chim. Acta*, **21**, 468 (1959).

[206] J. K. Taylor and S. W. Smith, *J. Res. Nat. Bur. Stds.*, **63**, 153 (1959).

titrations of organic bases are described in several papers.[207-209] These methods are on the macro scale and have not been adapted to micro-analysis.

c. By Spectrophotometric Methods. Spectrophotometric titration of weak bases in acetic acid or acetonitrile was investigated by Hummelstedt and Hume[210] on the macro scale. The titrant employed was $0.5N$ perchloric acid. This method is most useful for differential titrations since the wavelength can be changed during the titration.

F. Applications and Limitations. As mentioned earlier, basic functions having dissociation constants to the extent of 10^{-5} can be conveniently determined by titration with standard acid in aqueous solutions. The development of nonaqueous titrimetry has greatly extended the scope of basic functions. The types of organic compounds that have been determined as bases in nonaqueous media are listed in Table 11.8. It should be noted that most of the references cited in the table are reports on determinations on the macro scale or microdeterminations using $0.1N$ titrant and ultramicroburet. However, these methods can be adapted to the micro-procedure in which $0.01N$ perchloric acid is employed for determining 0.1 meq. quantities of the basic function.[154]

It is apparent that nonaqueous alkalimetry is not specific for any types of basic functions. Nevertheless, if this technique is judiciously used, it provides a simple and convenient micro method for the determination of a great variety of organic compounds. When it is desirable to develop a procedure to determine a certain compound by nonaqueous titration, the basic characteristic of this compound should be first investigated. For instance, Phoryles and Cohen[211] demonstrated that only two of the three amino groups in Mepracrine hydrochloride and one of the two amino groups in diamino-7-ethoxyacridine lactate are titrable by $0.1N$ perchloric acid. Gutterson and Ma[154] found that caffeine gives no endpoint on titration in acetic acid medium with $0.01N$ perchloric acid, but correct results are easily obtainable in acetic anhydride solution. Ciaccio and co-workers[212] observed that 1,4-disubstituted piperazines give one endpoint when dis-

[207] W. F. Wagner and W. B. Kauffman, *Anal. Chem.*, **25**, 538 (1953).

[208] W. T. Lippencott and A. Timmick, *Anal. Chem.*, **28**, 169 (1956).

[209] C. Bertoglio-Riolo and E. Marcon, *Ann. Chim. Roma*, **46**, 528 (1956).

[210] L. E. I. Hummelstedt and D. N. Hume, U.S. Atomic Energy Comm. Rep., A.E.C. U-4561 (1959); *Anal. Chem.*, **32**, 576 (1960).

[211] L. A. Phoryles and N. Cohen, *Drug Standards*, **27**, 92 (1959).

[212] L. L. Ciaccio, S. R. Missan, W. H. McMullen, and T. C. Grenfell, *Anal. Chem.*, **29**, 1670 (1957).

TABLE 11.8

Basic Functions Titrable in Nonaqueous Media

Type of Compound	Titrant	Method	Reference
Amines	$HClO_4$	Visual	154, 213
Ketimines	$HClO_4$	Visual	214
Alkaloids	$HClO_4$	Visual	154, 215–218
N-cyclics	$HClO_4$	Visual	154, 219–224
Basic ion-exchange resins	$HClO_4$	Visual	225
Carbonamides	$HClO_4$	Potentiometric	226
Ureas	$HClO_4$	Visual	154
Hydrazides	$HClO_4$	Visual	227
Amino acids	$HClO_4$	Visual	228–230
Amine salts of weak acids	$HClO_4$	Visual	146, 231
Amine nitrates	$HClO_4$	Potentiometric	232
Amine hydrohalides	$HClO_4$	Visual	157, 233
Alkali carboxylates	$HClO_4$	Visual	154, 234
Thiols	$HClO_4$	Visual	158
Thioureas	$HClO_4$	Visual	158, 159
Sulfonamides	$HClO_4$	Visual	219
Sulfoxide	$HClO_4$	Potentiometric	151
Substituted phosphines	HCl	Potentiometric	235

[213] F. E. Critchfield and J. B. Johnson, *Anal. Chem.*, **28**, 432 (1956).

[214] P. L. Pickard and F. A. Iddings, *Anal. Chem.*, **31**, 1228 (1959).

[215] R. L. Herd, *J. Am. Pharm. Assoc.*, **31**, 9 (1942).

[216] C. H. Spengler and H. A. Kaelin, *Pharm. Acta. Helv.*, **18**, 542 (1943).

[217] J. A. Gautier and F. Pellerin, *Ann. Pharm. Franc.*, **10**, 401 (1952).

[218] L. Levi, P. M. Ostreicher and C. G. Farmilo, *Bull. Narcotics, U.N.*, **5**, 15 (1953).

[219] O. Tomicek, *Coll. Czech. Chem. Commun.*, **13**, 116 (1948).

[220] K. Dimroth and H. G. Meyer-Brunat, *Biochem. Z.*, **323**, 338 (1952).

[221] A. Poulos, *Anal. Chem.*, **24**, 1858 (1952).

[222] S. Veibel, K. Eggersen, and S. C. Linhott, *Acta Chem. Scand.*, **6**, 1066 (1952).

[223] M. Pernarowski, *Drug Standards*, **21**, 189 (1953).

[224] B. Salvesen, *Medd. Norsk. Farm. Selskap*, **19**, 199 (1957); **20**, 21 (1958).

[225] G. E. Ficken and E. S. Lane, *Anal. Chim. Acta*, **16**, 207 (1957).

[226] D. C. Wimer, *Anal. Chem.*, **30**, 77 (1958).

[227] I. Gyenes, *Magyar Kem. Folyoirat*, **62**, 26 (1956).

[228] G. F. Nadeau and L. E. Branchen, *J. Am. Chem. Soc.*, **57**, 1363 (1935).

[229] G. Toennies and T. P. Callan, *J. Biol. Chem.*, **125**, 259 (1938).

[230] P. E. Kebald, *Svensk. Farm. Tidskr.*, **57**, 185 (1953).

[231] I. Gyenes and K. Szasz, *Magyar Kem. Folyoirat*, **61**, 356 (1955).

[232] J. Minczewski and J. Mlodecka, *Chem. Anal., Warsaw*, **2**, 176 (1957).

[233] P. Ekeblad, *J. Pharm. Pharmacol.*, **4**, 636 (1952).

[234] A. H. Beckett, R. M. Camp, and H. W. Martin, *J. Pharm. Pharmacol.*, **4**, 399 (1952).

[235] C. A. Streuli, *Anal. Chem.*, **32**, 985 (1960).

solved in acetic acid and two endpoints when the solvent is either acetonitrile or nitromethane.

V. Hydrocarbon Functions

A. General. The number of hydrocarbon skeletons or groups is of course large, but the number of hydrocarbon structures for which methods have been developed for their quantitative estimation is relatively small. Of these the C-methyl function (also known as terminal methyl group), the phenyl function characterized by the benzene structure, and the active methylene group are the most important. The estimation of the C-methyl function of the type $R—CH(CH_3)CH_2R'$ is based on oxidative methods to yield acetic acid. The phenyl group together with the hydroxyl function gives rise to the aromatic hydroxyl group which is estimated by several methods owing to the great reactivity from the combined effect of these two groups. The term active methylene group has been applied both to a terminal $=CH_2$ linkage (see p. 392) and to the enolizable $—CH_2—CO—$ group (see p. 419), and also a $—CH_2—$ linkage linked to two carbon atoms which are attached to hydrogen.

B. The Active Methylene Function. As noted earlier, the term active methylene group has been applied to $—CH_2—$ groups that exhibit reactivity owing to the presence of unsaturation or neighboring groups which cause inductive effects. The estimation of $=CH_2$ unsaturated linkages and the enolizable type $—CH_2—CO—$ have been discussed in previous sections. The present brief discussion concerns $—CH_2—$ groups which exhibit activity only in certain hydrocarbons.

1. Reaction with Carbonyl Compounds. The active methylene function in a hydrocarbon reacts with an aldehyde or a ketone according to the general reaction shown in equation 26:

$$\ce{>CH2} + \ce{O=C<^{R}_{R'}} \rightarrow \ce{>C=C<^{R}_{R'}} + H_2O \qquad (26)$$

This reaction was utilized by Uhrig and co-workers[236] to determine cyclopentadiene and by Powell and co-workers[237] to determine methylcyclopentadiene, using benzaldehyde as the carbonyl reagent. The products exhibit yellow to orange color and the proposed procedures are based on

[236] K. Uhrig, E. Lynch, and H. C. Becker, *Ind. Eng. Chem., Anal. Ed.*, **18**, 550 (1946).
[237] J. S. Powell, K. C. Edson, and E. L. Fisher, *Anal. Chem.*, **20**, 213 (1948).

the measurement of the color intensity. But a titrimetric method is preferable for determination on the 0.1 meq. scale. The condensation reaction between active methylene compounds and ketones has been investigated by Ghera and Sprinzak.[238]

2. Reaction with p-Amino-N,N-diethylaniline. Ryba[239] proposed a method for determining active methylene groups which is based on their reaction with p-amino-N,N-diethylaniline:

$$\overset{\diagdown}{\underset{\diagup}{}}CH_2 + H_2NC_6H_4{-}N(C_2H_5)_2 \xrightarrow{-4\epsilon} \overset{\diagdown}{\underset{\diagup}{}}C{=}NC_6H_4N(C_2H_5)_2 + 4H^+ \qquad (27)$$

The active methylene compound is treated with 5 ml. of 0.05M solution of the reagent in alkaline solution. After the completion of the reaction, the unconsumed p-amino-N,N-diethylaniline is determined by titration with standardized 0.1N potassium ferricyanide potentiometrically.

C. The C-Methyl Function

1. Oxidation Techniques. A micro method for the determination of C-methyl groups was first described by Kuhn and Roth[240] in 1933. The sample (5 to 12 mg.) is heated with 1 ml. of concentrated sulfuric acid and 4 ml. of 5N chromic acid under reflux for 1 to 1.5 hours over a free flame. The reaction can be represented as shown in equation 28:

$$\overset{\diagdown}{\underset{\diagup}{}}C{-}CH_3 + Cr^{+6} + 5H_2O \rightarrow CH_3{-}COOH + Cr^{+3} + 3H_3O^+ \qquad (28)$$

The reaction mixture is then treated with hydrazine hydrate to remove the excess of chromic acid and partially neutralized with sodium hydroxide solution. Phosphoric acid is then added, followed by steam-distillation of the acetic acid produced by the C-methyl function. The acetic acid in the distillate is determined by titration with 0.01N sodium hydroxide to the phenolphthalein endpoint.

The use of chromic trioxide-sulfuric acid mixture has become the standard oxidizing agent for the determination of the C-methyl function. Previously, Karrer and co-workers[241] had described procedures on the macro scale using potassium permanganate in alkaline solution and chromic acid-phosphoric acid mixture, respectively. The latter reagents have not been mentioned by other investigators. The chromium trioxide should be

[238] E. Ghera and Y. Sprinzak, *J. Am. Chem. Soc.*, **80**, 5449 (1958); **82**, 4945 (1960).

[239] O. Ryba, *Coll. Czech. Chem. Commun.*, **24**, 1950 (1959).

[240] R. Kuhn and H. Roth, *Berichte*, **66**, 1274 (1933).

[241] P. Karrer, A. Heffenstein, H. Wehrli, and A. Wettstein, *Helv. Chim. Acta*, **13**, 1097 (1930).

of high purity[242,243]; Sudo and co-workers[243] specified that it must be recrystallized from 80% sulfuric acid.

The detailed procedure for determination on the 0.1 meq. scale is given in experiment 43. It will be noticed that the reaction mixture after oxidation is directly transferred to the steam-distillation apparatus and the excess chromic acid is not removed. It has been established that 0.1 meq. quantities of acetic acid can be quantitatively recovered from chromic-sulfuric acid solution by steam-distillation.[244] In this range it has been found that reduction by hydrazine hydrate and neutralization by sodium hydroxide tend to give erratic results.

2. Apparatus and Procedure. Several assemblies[240,245-248] have been proposed for the microdetermination of the C-methyl function. The apparatus of Kuhn and Roth[240] was originally designed for the estimation of acetyl groups (see Fig. 6.1). When this apparatus is used for the determination of C-methyl groups, difficulties are encountered in the final step, which involves the distillation of the acetic acid. Because of the presence of large amounts of salts, vigorous bumping usually occurs. Therefore, it is preferable to transfer the reaction mixture, after oxidation, into another vessel for steam-distillation (similar to the steam-distillation flask used in the micro-Kjeldahl procedure). The apparatus proposed by Wiesenberger[247] (Figure 11.12) includes a device to pass the vapors through hot chromic-sulfuric acid solution to destroy the oxidation products other than acetic acid. A convenient assembly in which the steam-distillation vessel can be taken apart has been presented on page 123 (see Figure 6.6).

Oxidation in an open vessel provided with a reflux condenser is not suitable for low-boiling liquids, such as ethers and the like or samples which may decompose to yield products, such as acetone, that are oxidizable to acetic acid. Hence, it is desirable to perform the oxidation reaction in a sealed tube by heating at controlled temperatures. A rocking furnace, designed by Tashinian and co-workers[248] is shown in Figure 11.13. A sand bath or metal block with a slow rotating device also may be employed.

3. Interpretation of Data

A. COMPLETE OXIDATION. The analytical data of C-methyl determination should be interpreted with discrimination. This oxidation method

[242] C. F. Garbers, H. Schmid, and P. Karrer, *Helv. Chim. Acta,* **37,** 1336 (1954).
[243] T. Sudo, D. Shimoe and T. Tsujii, *Japan Analyst,* **6,** 498 (1957).
[244] T. S. Ma and H. Lilling, unpublished work; see H. Lilling, *Master's Thesis, Brooklyn College of the City University of New York,* 1962.
[245] W. F. Barthel and F. B. LaForge, *Anal. Chem.,* **16,** 435 (1944).
[246] W. Schöniger, H. Lieb, and M. G. E. D. Ibrahim, *Mikrochim. Acta,* **1954,** 96.
[247] E. Wiesenberger, *Mikrochim. Acta,* **1954,** 127.
[248] V. H. Tashinian, M. J. Baker, and C. W. Koch, *Anal. Chem.,* **28,** 1304 (1956).

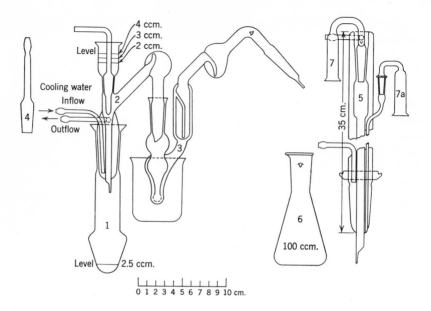

Fig. 11.12. C-Methyl apparatus of Wiesenberger. Courtesy of *Mikrochimica Acta*.

was first used to estimate the number of methyl side chains in the proof of structure of carotenoids.[240] Thus bixin yields 4 moles of acetic acid; each methyl butadiene linkage contributes 1 mole of the acid according to equation 29:

$$HOOC—CH{=}(CH—\underset{\underset{CH_3}{|}}{C}{=}CH—CH)_4{=}CH—COOCH_3 + 45[O] \rightarrow 4CH_3COOH$$

$$+ 7H_2O + 17CO_2 \qquad (29)$$

Roth[249] reported that by oxidation with chromic-sulfuric acid mixture for 60 minutes, the value of CH_3 group found was 15.13%, against the theoretical value of 15.24%. Repeated evaluation of this method seems to indicate that the results obtained generally are much lower.[244] Roth[249] also stated that the CH_3—CH= linkage gives 85 to 90% yield of acetic acid. Therefore, an error of one C-methyl group will be incurred for a compound containing six or more of such linkages (e.g., γ-carotene), if the calculation of the theoretical value is based on the quantitative conversion of the C-methyl function to acetic acid.

[249] H. Roth, *Die quantitative organische Mikroanalyse von Fritz Pregl*, 4th ed., Springer, Berlin, 1935, p. 248.

Ginger[250] extended the C-methyl determination to the study of terminal methyl groups in branched-chain fatty acids. About 75 to 80% of the calculated values were obtained. Campbell and Morton[251] reinvestigated this problem and reported that the oxidation method cannot be used to ascertain the number of methyl groups or their nature present in a molecule. Saturated aliphatic acids are known to yield mole-per-mole of acetic acid.[248,250,251] Kirsten[252] reported satisfactory results for compounds containing up to 44 carbon atoms. On the other hand, unsaturated straight-chain acids tend to give misleading values.[253]

The gem-dimethyl (isopropyl) skeleton and t-butyl groups yield little if any acetic acid on treatment with the C-methyl procedure.[249,254,255]

[250] L. G. Ginger, J. Biol. Chem., **156**, 452 (1944).

[251] A. D. Campbell and J. E. Morton, J. Chem. Soc., **1952**, 1693.

[252] W. Kirsten, Acta Chem. Scand., **6**, 82 (1952).

[253] A. D. Campbell and V. Chettleburgh, J. Chem. Soc., **1953**, 1942.

[254] E. J. Eisenbraun, J. Am. Chem. Soc., **75**, 3987 (1953).

[255] E. J. Eisenbraun, S. M. McElvain, and B. F. Aycock, J. Am. Chem. Soc., **76**, 607 (1954).

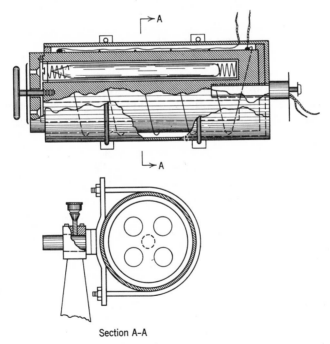

Section A-A

Fig. 11.13. Furnace for C-methyl oxidation by Tashinian, Baker, and Koch. Courtesy of *Analytical Chemistry*.

Hampton and co-workers[256] studied the mechanism of the cleavage of t-butyl-phenyl-carbinol by chromic acid. The inability of two methyl groups attached to a single carbon atom to produce acetic acid on oxidation has been ascribed to the formation of acetone.[257] However, application of gas chromatography to the investigation of the oxidation products of acetone on treatment with chromic-sulfuric acid mixture[244] proved that acetone is oxidized to give equimolar quantities of acetic acid and carbon dioxide according to equation 30:

$$H_3C-\underset{\underset{O}{\|}}{C}-CH_3 + 4[O] \rightarrow CH_3-COOH + CO_2 + H_2O \qquad (30)$$

Hence acetic acid should be formed if acetone is an intermediate product in the chromic acid oxidation of the sample.

It should be kept in mind that the C-methyl micro procedure involves the use of a strong oxidizing agent. A slight variation of the experimental conditions might lead to discrepancy in the results. Different oxidation products may be produced when the concentration of chromic acid is changed.[258] The difficulty in interpreting the data from C-methyl determinations is apparent from the statement of Petru and co-workers[259] that, except for isomerizable compounds the results are reproducible under the same conditions, but no relation can be drawn between structure and yield of acetic acid.

Methyl groups directly attached to the aromatic nucleus do not yield acetic acid on oxidation by the C-methyl micro procedure. However, a benzene carboxylic acid is conceivably produced as an intermediate in the reaction. If the latter is not further oxidized to carbon dioxide, it can be steam-distilled and titrated like acetic acid. Brandenberger and co-workers[260] have reported that n-propyl and higher alkyl side chains on the benzene ring give quantitative yields of acetic acid, whereas isopropyl, ethyl, and methyl benzenes, respectively, give negative results. This seems to indicate that cleavage starts at the second carbon atom beyond the aromatic ring and the oxidation reaction then proceeds until carbon dioxide or acetic acid results. It should be noted that acetic acid is not entirely inert to oxidation by the chromic-sulfuric acid mixture. Decomposition of

[256] H. Hampton, A. Leo, and F. H. Westheimer, J. Am. Chem. Soc., 78, 306 (1956).

[257] R. F. Milton and W. A. Waters (eds.), Methods of Quantitative Microanalysis, Edward Arnold, London, 1949, p. 111.

[258] O. Schwarzkopf and D. D. Phillips, Proceeding of the 15th International Congress of Pure and Applied Chemistry (Analytical Chemistry), Lisbon, 1956, p. 312.

[259] F. Petru, M. Jurecek, and J. Kovar, Chem. Listy, 45, 300 (1951).

[260] S. G. Brandenberger, L. W. Maas, and I. Dvoretzky, Anal. Chem., 33, 453 (1961).

acetic acid in this medium becomes noticeable upon heating in a sealed tube at 120°C for two hours.[244]

B. INCOMPLETE OXIDATION. Jurecek and co-workers[261] demonstrated that alkyl side chains in alicyclic and aromatic compounds on oxidation with chromic-sulfuric acid mixture gives a mixture of fatty acids. A method was proposed[262] to use the ratio between the titration value of the distillate and the acid value of the original sample to characterize the nature of the carboxylic acid under investigation. The ratio is less than 1 for fatty and resin acids, greater than 1 for naphthenic acids.

Barber and Clingman[263] separated the carboxylic acids produced in the chromic acid oxidation by column chromatography. It is reported that these acids are readily classified as monobasic or dibasic acids.

D. The Phenyl Function

1. Nitration. Nitration of the benzene ring has been applied to quantitative analysis.[264,265] For instance, *p*-xylene is nitrated as shown in equation 31:

$$\text{CH}_3\text{-}C_6H_4\text{-}CH_3 + HNO_3 \rightarrow \text{CH}_3\text{-}C_6H_3(NO_2)\text{-}CH_3 + H_2O \qquad (31)$$

It should be noted that the yield is not quantitative. Hence it is necessary to prepare empirical calibration curves using pure known compounds.

2. Bromination. Schulek and Burger[266] observed that bromine monochloride acts exclusively as brominating agent in substitution reaction on the phenyl function. Thus antipyrine gives the *p*-bromo product. The excess of bromine monochloride is then determined iodometrically by back-titration. This method has not been evaluated on the 0.1 meq. scale.

When the benzene skeleton carries an activating group, such as amino group, determination by bromination is possible.[267,268] Micro methods for the determination of phenols by bromination are discussed on page 448.

[261] M. Jurecek, M. Soucek, J. Churacek, and F. Renger, *Z. Anal. Chem.*, **165**, 109 (1958).

[262] M. Jurecek and P. Kozak, *Z. Anal. Chem.*, **167**, 32 (1959).

[263] H. H. Barber, Jr. and W. H. Clingman, Jr., *Anal. Chem.*, **31**, 2069 (1959).

[264] V. Sedivec, *Coll. Czech. Chem. Commun.*, **21**, 965 (1956).

[265] A. Kobayashi, S. Nagahama, and S. Akiyoshi, *J. Chem. Soc. Japan, Ind. Chem. Sect.*, **59**, 179 (1956).

[266] E. Schulek and K. Burger, *Talanta*, **1**, 147 (1958).

[267] B. Linke, H. Preissecker, and J. Stadler, *Berichte*, **65**, 1282 (1932).

[268] A. R. Day and W. T. Taggart, *Ind. Eng. Chem.*, **20**, 545 (1928).

3. Use of Tetracyanoethylene.   Aromatic hydrocarbons react with tetra-cyanoethylene to give colored products. Schenk and Ozolins[269] described a photometric titration method in which $0.1M$ tetracyanoethylene in methylene chloride is used to titrate 0.3 to 0.6 meq. of aromatic hydrocarbon. Pure aromatic hydrocarbons which are as basic as, or more basic than, naphthalene are estimated with $\pm 1\%$ accuracy.

E. Colorimetric Methods for Hydrocarbon Functions.   Colorimetric methods for the determination of active methylene groups have been reported in several papers.[236,237,270,271] All methods are dependent on the colored condensation product obtained by reacting the active methylene compound with an aldehyde or a ketone.

The benzene ring can be determined colorimetrically by nitration followed by the treatment of the nitro compound with sodium hydroxide solution.[264] The new reagent, tetracyanoethylene, has been used as a colorimetric reagent for determining aromatic skeletons.[272] Two colorimetric methods have been proposed for the determination of biphenyl. Rajzman[273] treated the sample with formaldehyde and ferric sulfate in acetic-sulfuric acid mixture. The blue color produced is measured at 610 $m\mu$. Bruce and Howard[274] determined biphenyl in biological materials by nitrating the sample to the p-nitro compound, which is then reduced to an amine, followed by coupling with N-(1-naphthyl)-ethylenediamine to produce a purple color measurable at 570 $m\mu$.

F. Physical Methods for Hydrocarbon Functions.   Since there are only a few chemical methods for the determination of the hydrocarbon functions, physical methods have been extensively employed. The infrared spectra of hydrocarbons have been published in a number of articles.[275-281] The determination of methylene groups in open-chain compounds was

[269] G. H. Schenk and M. Ozolins, *Talanta*, **8**, 109 (1961); *Anal. Chem.*, **33**, 1562 (1961).

[270] D. A. Skoog and H. D. Dubois, *Anal. Chem.*, **21**, 1528 (1949).

[271] W. Roman and M. Smith, *Analyst*, **78**, 679 (1953).

[272] R. E. Merrifield and W. D. Phillips, *J. Am. Chem. Soc.*, **80**, 2778 (1958).

[273] A. Rajzman, *Analyst*, **85**, 116 (1960).

[274] R. B. Bruce and J. W. Howard, *Anal. Chem.*, **28**, 1973 (1956).

[275] F. W. Rose, *J. Res. Natl. Bur. Stds.*, **20**, 129 (1938).

[276] R. R. Hibbard and A. P. Cleaves, *Anal. Chem.*, **21**, 486 (1949).

[277] A. Evans, R. R. Hibbard, and A. S. Powell, *Anal. Chem.*, **23**, 1604 (1951).

[278] S. H. Hastings, A. T. Watson, R. B. Williams, and J. A. Anderson, *Anal. Chem.*, **24**, 612 (1952).

[279] H. Luther and H. Oelert, *Angew. Chem.*, **69**, 262 (1957).

[280] F. F. Bentley and E. F. Wolforth, *Spectrochim. Acta*, **1959**, 165.

[281] A. Cornu, *Bull. Soc. Chim. France*, **1959**, 721.

reported by Glebovskaya and co-workers.[282] Egorov and Petrov[283] used infrared spectrometry to determine the degree of branching in paraffins. Hawkes and Neale[284] presented the infrared spectra of 42 monalkylbenzenes.

Ismailzade and co-workers[285] utilized X-ray diffraction to determine dialkylbenzenes. The hydrocarbon is oxidized to phthalic acid and the intensities of the characteristic X-ray diffraction lines are measured.

Kubota and Takamura[286] proposed the estimation of phenyl groups in methylphenylsiloxane polymers by means of proton spin resonance spectrometry. The number of each group calculated from appropriate peak areas is shown to agree with results obtained by infrared analysis.

The molecular sieve was used by Schwartz and Brasseaux[287] to analyze C_7 to C_{10} paraffins. A novel method of hydrocarbon structural group analysis was proposed by Montgomery and Boyd.[288] Three chemical and two physical properties are expressed in terms of five structural groups as equations that can be simultaneously solved by computers. The chemical properties are the carbon and hydrogen contents and the number of aromatic carbon atoms per molecule. The physical properties are molecular volume and molar refraction.

VI. The Phenolic Function

A. General. The phenolic function—also called the aromatic hydroxyl function—is characterized by the hydroxyl group attached to the benzene skeleton. The chemical reactivity of the phenolic function is attributed to a combined effect of the hydroxyl and phenyl groups, and not to these two groups separately. For instance, the micro procedure for the determination of hydroxyl groups requires modification when it is applied to phenols (see Chapter 7, Section IV). On the other hand, all methods for determining phenols that are based on the attack by the reagent on the benzene nucleus are not applicable to the determination of the phenyl function (see Section V-D above). This, plus their importance among natural and industrial

[282] E. A. Glebovskaya, E. I. Maksimov, and A. K. Petrov, *Zhur. Anal. Khim.*, **14**, 478 (1959).

[283] Y. P. Egorov and A. A. Petrov, *Zhur. Anal. Khim.*, **11**, 483 (1956).

[284] J. C. Hawkes and A. J. Neale, *Spectrochim. Acta*, **16**, 633 (1960).

[285] I. G. Ismailzade, Y. G. Mamedaliev, S. Mirazoera, and T. Zeinslova, *Zhur. Khim.*, abstract No. 12157 (1957).

[286] T. Kubota and T. Takamura, *Bull. Chem. Soc. Japan*, **33**, 70 (1960).

[287] R. D. Schwartz and D. J. Brasseaux, *Anal. Chem.*, **29**, 1022 (1957).

[288] D. S. Montgomery and M. L. Boyd, *Anal. Chem.*, **31**, 1290 (1959).

TABLE 11.9

Summary of Methods for the Determination of Phenolic Compounds

Method	Range	Reference
Titrimetric		
Halogenation	0.1 meq.	p. 446
Nonaqueous alkalimetry	0.1 meq.	p. 451
Oxidation		p. 452
Nitrosation		p. 452
Esterification		p. 453
Gravimetric	1 meq.	p. 453
Gasometric		
With Grignard reagent	0.1 meq.	p. 411
With lithium aluminum hydride	0.1 meq.	p. 419
Coupling and nitrometry	500 μg.	p. 454
Colorimetric		
With quinone chlorimine	5–100 ppb[a]	p. 454
With 4-amino-antipyrine	5–50 μg.	p. 454
With phosphomolybdic or phosphotungstic acid	25 μg./ml.	p. 454
With Hg + HNO_2 + HNO_3	4 mg.	p. 455
With xanthydrol		p. 455
With sodium cupribromide	10–50 μg./ml.	p. 455
With diazonium salt	1 ppm[b]	p. 454
With iodine		p. 455
With ferrous tartrate		p. 455
With *p*-aminodiethylaniline + oxidant	1–50 μg.	p. 454
With *p*-dimethylaminobenzaldehyde		p. 455
With nitrous acid	0.5–5 μg.	p. 455
With 1-nitroso-2-naphthol	10 μg./ml.	p. 455
Fluorometric		
With malic acid		p. 456
With NaOH in ethanol	1–10 μg./ml.	p. 456
Spectrophotometric		
Infrared absorption	0.2–1 mg.	p. 456
Ultraviolet absorption	25–100 μg./ml.	p. 456

[a] ppb. = parts per billion.
[b] ppm. = parts per million.

products, accounts for the separate treatment of the phenolic function. A large variety of procedures has been proposed for the determination of organic compounds containing the phenolic function. Methods applicable to industrial products were reviewed by Goupil and Mangency.[289] Table 11.9 gives a more comprehensive summary of all available methods and

[289] R. Goupil and G. Mangency, *Chim. Anal.*, **41**, 18 (1959).

provides choices open to the investigator for the quantitative estimation of phenols. It should be noted, however, that most methods are for the analysis of known compounds and cannot be used to determine the phenolic function in a substance of unknown structure.

B. Halogenation Methods

1. Halogenating Reagents. Since the presence of hydroxyl group facilitates rapid substitution on the benzene nucleus, a number of methods have been proposed to determine phenolic compounds by halogenation. The basic principle is to treat the phenolic function with a known excess of the halogenating agent and then determine the unconsumed reagent after the completion of the substitution reaction. For example, β-naphthol is expected to react with one mole of halogen according to equation 32:

$$\text{(naphthol)}-\text{OH} + X_2 \rightarrow \text{(X-naphthol)}-\text{OH} + HX \qquad (32)$$

The reagents for halogenation which were suggested by various workers may be classified into the following categories:

1. *Pure halogen.* Iodine.[290,291]
2. *Halogen halides.* Iodine trichloride,[292] iodine monochloride,[293,294] iodine monobromide,[295,296] bromine monochloride.[297]
3. *Alkali halide—oxidant mixtures.* Potassium iodide-potassium iodate,[297,298] potassium bromide-potassium bromate,[297,299–301] potassium bromide-chloramine-B.[302]

Schulek and Burger[296] observed that bromine monochloride acts exclusively as brominating agent in substitution reaction, with no chlorophenols

[290] Y. A. Fialkov and A. I. Gengrinovich, *Zapiski Inst. Khim. Akad. Nauk. USSR*, **7**, 125 (1940).
[291] H. H. Willard and A. L. Wooten, *Anal. Chem.*, **22**, 670 (1950).
[292] F. E. Kagan, *Kain. Khim. Zhur.*, **22**, 94 (1956).
[293] A. I. Gengrinovich, *Farmatsiya*, **11**, 23 (1947).
[294] J. Cihalik and D. Vavrejnova, *Chem. Listy*, **49**, 1176 (1955).
[295] B. Singh and M. Singh, *Research Bull. Panjab Univ.*, **1955**, 73.
[296] E. Schulek and K. Burger, *Talanta*, **1**, 147 (1958).
[297] M. François and L. Seguin, *Bull. Soc. Chim.*, **53**, 711 (1933).
[298] A. I. Gengrinovich, *Pharm. J.*, **14**, 19 (1941).
[299] M. Beukema-Goudsmit, *Pharm. Weekblad*, **71**, 380 (1934).
[300] W. L. Spliethoff and H. Hart, *Anal. Chem.*, **27**, 1492 (1955).
[301] T. S. Ma and R. Burstein, unpublished work; see R. Burstein, *Master's Thesis, Brooklyn College*, 1959.
[302] A. Singh, *J. Indian Chem. Soc.*, **31**, 605 (1954).

being formed. On the other hand, iodine monobromide gives both iodo and bromo derivatives. Because it is very difficult to prepare and store standard $0.01M$ solutions of halogens or halogen halides, however, these reagents are not recommended for the determination of the phenolic function on the 0.1 meq. scale. For the latter purpose, a mixture of potassium bromide and standardized $0.02M$ potassium bromate is generally used as discussed in the following section.

2. *Use of Bromide-Bromate Mixture.*   The determination of phenolic compounds on the 0.1 meq. scale by means of bromide-bromate mixture followed by iodometry has been critically evaluated.[301] The detailed procedure will be found in experiment 14. The sample containing phenolic groups is dissolved in an aqueous medium and treated with a calculated excess of acidified potassium bromide-$0.02M$ potassium bromate mixture. After the bromination reaction is completed, potassium iodide is added to liberate iodine, which is determined by titration with standardized sodium thiosulfate to the starch endpoint. The sequence of reactions are expressed in equations 33 to 37, using phenol as the sample subjected to analysis.

Generation of bromine:

$$5KBr + KBrO_3 + 6HCl \rightarrow 3Br_2 + 3H_2O + 6KCl \tag{33}$$

Bromination of phenol:

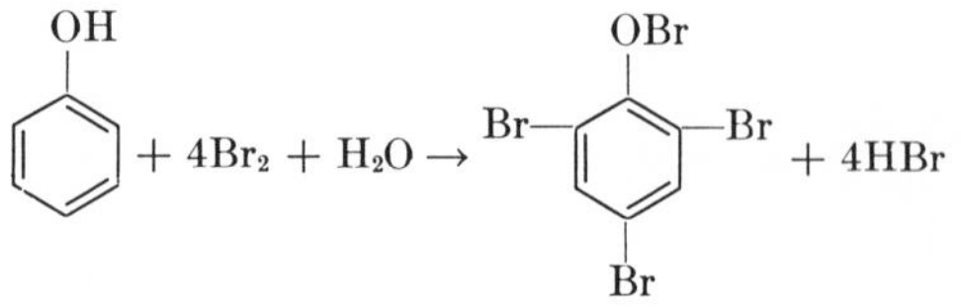

$$\tag{34}$$

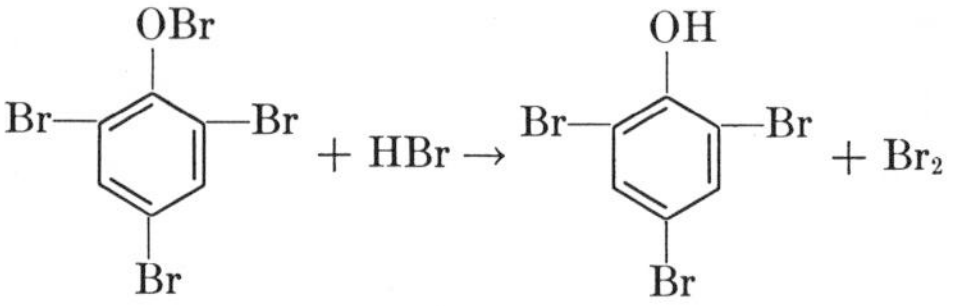

$$\tag{35}$$

Determination of unconsumed bromine:

$$Br_2 + 2KI \rightarrow I_2 + 2KBr \tag{36}$$

$$I_2 + 2Na_2S_2O_3 \rightarrow 2NaI + Na_2S_4O_6 \tag{37}$$

It should be recognized that this method is dependent on electrophilic substitution of the hydrogen atoms on the phenyl group by bromine atoms, and not on the reaction of the hydroxyl group. The bromate ions (eq. 33) determine the quantity of bromine available for the bromination reaction. Potassium bromide is added in large excess to insure complete reduction of the bromate ions and also to keep the bromine in solution (bromine being slightly soluble in water, but very soluble in a bromide solution).

The reaction mixture for bromination must be acidic, since bromine is converted to hypobromite and bromide in alkali solutions, as shown in equations 38 and 39:

$$Br_2 + 2OH^- \rightarrow BrO^- + Br^- + H_2O \tag{38}$$

$$3BrO^- \rightarrow BrO_3^- + 2Br^- \tag{39}$$

The quantitative bromination of phenol must be performed in the absence of sunlight, since in the presence of acid, sunlight catalyzes the oxidation of bromide to bromine:

$$4Br^- + 4H^+ + O_2 \rightarrow 2Br_2 + 2H_2O \tag{40}$$

It is necessary to carry out prior study of the number of equivalents of bromine required by the phenolic compound in question, and also the conditions for quantitative bromination. Ma and Burstein[301] investigated the bromination of various types of phenolic compounds with respect to temperature, amount of excess reagent, and length of reaction time. A summary of the results is given in Table 11.10.

It is shown that for the purpose of identification, the determination of the phenolic function may be performed under a wide range of experimental conditions. On the other hand, only a narrow limit of variations can be tolerated if the analysis is intended for quality control or for testing the purity of the sample. For the latter purpose the optimum conditions should be established for the particular phenolic compound to be determined. For instance, Mlodecka[303] specified a procedure for the bromometric determination of phenol and cresol isomers as follows. The sample containing 5 to 50 mg. of phenol in 20 ml. solution is treated with 5 ml. of concentrated hydrochloric acid and $0.1N$ potassium bromate-potassium bromide mixture is added from a buret until the solution is yellow. Then 20 to 25% excess is added, and the flask is closed. After exactly 2 minutes, 2 g. of potassium iodide are introduced and the reaction mixture is set aside for 5 minutes. The iodine liberated is determined by titration with $0.02N$ sodium thiosulfate using starch as indicator.

The presence of carbonyl groups does not interfere with the determination.[301,304] On the other hand, decarboxylation and oxidation to quinone occur in certain cases (see Table 11.10). Johnson and co-workers[305] reported the displacement of the nitro group during the determination of nitrophenols.

[303] J. Mlodecka, Rec. Chim. Bucharest, **10**, 343 (1959).
[304] V. V. Ramanujam, J. Sc. Ind. Res. B. (India), **14**, 564 (1955).
[305] L. D. Johnson, W. M. McNabb, and E. C. Wagner, Anal. Chem., **27**, 1494 (1955).

TABLE 11.10

Microdetermination of Phenolic Compounds

Phenolic Compound	Bromine (eq./mole) Calcd.	Found	Temp. °C	Reagent Excess %	Time Range Minutes	No. of Determinations	Deviation OH Group %
Phenol	3	3.0	20	8–250	2–20	4	0.54
Resorcinol	3	3.0	20	115–150	2–20	4	0.59
Phloroglucinol	3	3.0	20	40–75	10–60	3	0.75
p-Hydroxybenzoic acid	3	3.0[a]	20	10–260	1–40	7	0.30
Benzyl-p-hydroxy-benzoate	2	2.3	20	180–570	5–60	2	0.01
		2.2	0	55–615	5	3	0.68
p-Hydroxybenz-aldehyde	2	2.0	20	320	20	1	—
		2.0	0	80–320	1–20	4	0.19
5-Bromo-2-hydroxy-benzaldehyde	1	1.0	20	366–1120	5–25	2	0.33
			0	350–1200	20–25	2	0.62
2-Nitrophenol	2	2.0	20	285–385	5–50	7	0.13
4-Nitrophenol	2	2.0	20	315–525	5–40	7	0.45
			0	335–830	20–40	4	0.24
2,4-Dinitrophenol	1	1.0	20	730–1000	5–60	4	0.46
Acetyl-o-aminophenol	3	2.9	20	10–255	10–30	4	0.98
Acetyl-p-aminophenol	3	2.9	20	30–45	10–60	2	0.31
			0	15–110	10–30	3	0.81
3,4-Dimethylphenol	2	2.0	20	30–270	5–40	6	0.75
3,5-Dimethylphenol	3	2.9	20	100–330	10–40	2	0.33
2,6-Dimethylphenol	1	1.9[b]	20	70–310	1–20	3	0.37
4-t-amylphenol	2	2.0	20	45–165	5–40	3	0.24
Thymol	2	2.1	20	145–190	10–60	2	0.33
1-Naphthol	3	2.9	20	45–75	30–60	2	0.13
	2	2.0	0	20–280	15–25	3	0.70
2-Naphthol	1	1.0	0	200–430	1–15	4	0.71
Naphthoresorcinol	2	2.0	20	290	15	1	—
		2.0	0	80–210	30–60	3	0.74

[a] Decarboxylation occurs simultaneously with formation of 2,4,6-tribromophenol.

[b] The second equivalent of bromine is used in the formation of the orthoquinone.

3. Other Bromination Procedures. Although back-titration with standardized sodium thiosulfate after bromination of the phenolic function is the most convenient and generally recommended procedure, other methods have been advocated. Berka and Zyka[306] titrated the unconsumed bromine from $0.1N$ potassium bromide-potassium bromate mixture with $0.05M$

[306] A. Berka and J. Zyka, *Ceskol. Farm.*, **8**, 17 (1959).

hydrazine sulfate solution. The endpoint is located potentiometrically. Van Zyl and Murray[307] determined phenols by direct potentiometric titration with bromide-bromate mixture. Vorobjov[308] described an amperometric titration procedure using 0.1N potassium bromate in the presence of potassium bromide and hydrochloric acid. Coulometric methods were proposed by several investigators.[309-311] Cuta and Kucera[311] employed bromine electrolytically generated from hydrobromic acid in the solution and reported that the degree of bromination is dependent on the pH of the solution. Thus o-cresol gives the monobromo product in 0.1N hydrobromic acid solution and the tribromo compound at pH 7. Quinol is oxidized to p-benzoquinone in the determination.

Schulek and Burger[312] devised a micro method to determine phenol in the presence of reducing agents based on the consumption of four bromine atoms per molecule of phenol as shown in equation 34. The sample containing phenol is brominated by means of bromine water and, after the removal of the excess of bromine, the reaction mixture is titrated iodometrically.

C. Nonaqueous Acidimetry. As a rule the phenolic function cannot be determined by acidimetry in aqueous medium, but it can be titrated as an acid in nonaqueous solutions without difficulty. Schryver[313] determined phenol by means of sodamide in 1899. This alkali reagent is difficult to handle. Standardized 0.02N sodium methoxide[314] is recommended for microdeterminations (for procedure, see p. 561). Potassium methoxide,[315] quaternary ammonium hydroxide,[316-318] alcoholic potassium hydroxide,[316] barium hydroxide,[319] lithium aluminum hydride,[320] and lithium aluminum piperidide[321] have been proposed as titrants for the determination of phenols. The last two reagents are not suitable for use in the micro range.

[307] C. N. Van Zyl and K. A. Murray, *South African Ind. Chemist*, **8**, 222 (1954).

[308] V. Vorobjov, *Chem. Prumysl*, **9**, 834 (1959).

[309] C. N. Van Zyl and K. A. Murray, *South African Ind. Chemist*, **8**, 243 (1954).

[310] K. Sykut, *Ann. Univ. M. Curie Sklodowska A.A.*, **10**, 25 (1955).

[311] F. Cuta and Z. Kucera, *Chem. Listy*, **52**, 595 (1958).

[312] E. Schulek and K. Burger, *Z. Anal. Chem.*, **161**, 184 (1958).

[313] S. B. Schryver, *J. Soc. Chem. Ind.*, **18**, 533 (1899).

[314] R. K. Maurmeyer, M. Margosis, and T. S. Ma, *Mikrochim. Acta*, **1959**, 177.

[315] J. Minczewski, *Roczn. Chem.*, **29**, 948 (1955).

[316] V. Z. Deal and G. E. A. Wyld, *Anal. Chem.*, **27**, 47 (1955).

[317] R. H. Cundiff and P. C. Markunas, *Anal. Chem.*, **28**, 792 (1956).

[318] J. S. Fritz and S. S. Yamamura, *Anal. Chem.*, **29**, 1079 (1956).

[319] D. Beranova and S. Hudecek, *Chem. Listy*, **49**, 1723 (1955).

[320] C. J. Lintner, R. H. Schleif, and T. Higuchi, *Anal. Chem.*, **22**, 534 (1950).

[321] T. Higuchi, J. Concha, and R. Kuramoto, *Anal. Chem.*, **24**, 685 (1952).

Takiura and Takino[322] recommended 4-amino-4'-nitro-azobenzene as a special indicator for the titration of phenols.

Conductometric,[323] high-frequency,[324-326] and amperometric[327] titration of phenolic compounds were described by several workers. The difference in the absorption spectra of the phenolic function and its phenoxide can be utilized to locate the endpoint in photometric titration of phenols.[328,329]

D. Oxidimetry. Oxidation methods have been proposed for the determination of the phenolic function containing two or more hydroxyl groups. Mikhkelson[330] proposed a micro procedure to determine p-dihydroxy benzene using ferricyanide as the oxidant. The phenolic compound is treated with zinc sulfate and sodium acetate solution. A known volume of $0.1N$ potassium ferricyanide in sodium carbonate solution is added. After the solution has been stirred for 5 minutes, potassium iodide and sulfuric acid are introduced and the iodine liberated is titrated with $0.05N$ sodium thiosulfate. Rao and Sastri[331] presented a method to determine hydroquinone and Metol, respectively, by titration with $0.05N$ sodium vanadate in the presence of sulfuric acid and oxalic acid, using diphenylbenzidine as an indicator. These workers stated that benzoquinone and vanadyl salts retarded the reaction between the titrant and the indicator, whereas oxalic acid accelerated it. Several investigators[332] employed ceric sulfate to determine phenols on the macro scale. Smit and co-workers[333] described a procedure to titrate tannins with standard potassium permanganate solution. It should be noted that the stoichiometry must be established before an oxidation method can be applied.

E. Nitrosation. Matrka[334] suggested the volumetric determination of α-naphthol by nitrosation as shown in equation 41:

[322] K. Takiura and Y. Takino, *J. Pharm. Soc. Japan*, **74**, 991 (1954).
[323] K. Sarkanen and C. Schuerch, *Anal. Chem.*, **27**, 1245 (1955).
[324] E. S. Lane, *Analyst*, **80**, 675 (1955).
[325] E. T. Lippman, *Zh. Analit. Khim. SSSR*, **10**, 169 (1955).
[326] K. J. Karrman and G. Johansson, *Mikrochim. Acta*, **11**, 1573 (1956).
[327] N. Konopik, *Öst. Chem. Ztg.*, **55**, 127 (1954).
[328] R. F. Goddu and D. N. Hume, *Anal. Chem.*, **26**, 1679 (1954).
[329] R. W. McKinney and C. A. Reynolds, *Talanta*, **1**, 46 (1958).
[330] V. Y. Mikhkelson, *Trudy Tallin Politekh Inst.*, **1955**, A, 127.
[331] G. G. Rao and T. P. Sastri, *Z. Anal. Chem.*, **151**, 415 (1956).
[332] K. Kimoto, *Repts. Inst. Ind. Sci., Tokyo Univ.*, **3**, 20 (1952); T. Takahashi, *J. Chem. Soc. Japan*, **56**, 491 (1953); W. R. Spencer and F. R. Duke, *Anal. Chem.*, **26**, 919 (1954).
[333] C. J. B. Smit, M. A. Joslyn, and A. Lukton, *Anal. Chem.*, **27**, 1159 (1955).
[334] M. Matrka, *Coll. Czech. Chem. Commun.*, **25**, 964 (1960).

$$HO-\langle\!\!\!\langle\bigcirc\rangle\!\!\!\rangle + HNO_2 \rightarrow HO-\langle\!\!\!\langle\bigcirc\rangle\!\!\!\rangle -NO + H_2O \qquad (41)$$

The sample is dissolved in a solution containing sodium m-xylenesulfonate and hydrochloric acid, and titrated potentiometrically with $0.1N$ sodium nitrite solution.

F. Esterification. As was mentioned in the section on acylation of hydroxyl groups (Chapter 7, Section IV-B), the esterification of phenols does not take place as rapidly as that of alcohols. Schenk and Fritz [335] devised a macro method to determine phenols by acetylation using perchloric acid as the catalyst. This method has been adapted to the micro scale (see Chapter 12, page 496). It should be noted that the reagent for micro-determinations has to be prepared fresh daily.

G. Gravimetric Methods. The phenol function can be quantitatively converted to the insoluble 2,4-dinitrophenylether by means of 2,4-dinitrofluorobenzene:

$$\langle\!\!\!\bigcirc\!\!\!\rangle-OH + F-\langle\!\!\!\bigcirc\!\!\!\rangle-NO_2 + NaHCO_3 \rightarrow \langle\!\!\!\bigcirc\!\!\!\rangle-O-\langle\!\!\!\bigcirc\!\!\!\rangle-NO_2$$

$$+ NaF + H_2O + CO_2 \qquad (42)$$

A gravimetric method based on this reaction was described by Zahn and Würz[336] using 1 millimole of the phenolic compound. This method can be adapted to determinations on the 0.1 meq. scale[337] employing the inverted filtration technique (see p. 98).

François and Seguin[297] determined phenols by separating and weighing the iodination product. It was reported that the iodo derivative does not always give the expected composition, although a definite relationship exists between the weight of the precipitate and the original weight of phenol.

H. Gasometric Methods. The phenolic function can be determined as active hydrogen by the gasometric methods given in Section III (p. 409). An indirect gasometric determination was suggested by Yamagishi and

[335] G. H. Schenk and J. S. Fritz, *Anal. Chem.*, **32**, 987 (1960).
[336] H. Zahn and A. Würz, *Z. Anal. Chem.*, **134**, 183 (1951).
[337] T. S. Ma and A. Becker, unpublished work.

co-workers.[338] The phenolic compound is treated with a known amount of diazobenzenesulfonic acid at pH 9 and, after the coupling reaction is complete, the excess of diazo compound is determined by decomposition to liberate nitrogen which is measured in the nitrometer.

I. Colorimetric Methods.   Colorimetric methods are recommended for the determination of phenolic compounds on or below the μeq. scale. The most sensitive method[339-345] for the colorimetric estimation of the phenolic function is based on its reaction with 2,6-dichloro- or 2,6-dibromo-quinone-chlorimine in alkaline solution as shown in equation 43:

$$\text{HO}-\!\!\left\langle\bigcirc\right\rangle + \text{Cl}-\text{N}=\!\!\left\langle\bigcirc\right\rangle=\!\text{O} + 2\text{NaOH} \rightarrow \text{NaO}-\!\!\left\langle\bigcirc\right\rangle-\text{N}=\!\!\left\langle\bigcirc\right\rangle=\!\text{O}$$

$$+ \text{NaCl} + 2\text{H}_2\text{O} \qquad (43)$$

This method was used by Boreham and Cunningham[345] to determine phenol spots on a paper chromatogram. Gorbach and co-workers[340] reported determination of 0.01 μg. of phenol in 1 ml. solution with an accuracy of 2.5%.

Coupling with diazonium salts,[346-349] formation of indophenols,[350,351] and development of color with phosphomolybdate[333,352-355] or 4-amino-anti-

[338] M. Yamagishi, M. Yokoo, and S. Inoue, J. Pharm. Soc. Japan, 77, 1234 (1957).

[339] H. D. Gibbs, J. Biol. Chem., 72, 649 (1927).

[340] G. Gorbach, O. G. Koch, and G. Dedic, Mikrochim. Acta, 1955, 882.

[341] G. Wildbrett, Fette u Seifen, 59, 245 (1955).

[342] T. D. Johnson, Anal. Chem., 27, 1494 (1955).

[343] E. A. Bozhevolnov, Tr. Vses. Nauchn. Inst. Khim. Reaktivov, 21, 38 (1956).

[344] P. S. Jones and D. Thigpen, J. Am. Pharm. Assoc., 45, 268 (1956).

[345] G. R. Boreham and J. A. P. Cunningham, Fuel, London, 38, 489 (1959).

[346] M. T. Hanke and K. K. Koessler, J. Biol. Chem., 50, 235 (1922).

[347] R. H. DeMeio, Science, 108, 391 (1948).

[348] T. Takeuchi, M. Furusawa, and Y. Takayama, Japan Analyst, 4, 568 (1955).

[349] E. K. Rud and S. Y. Skochilova, Zavodskaya Lab., 22, 919 (1956).

[350] C. U. Houghton and R. G. Petty, Analyst, 62, 117 (1937).

[351] B. Camber, Nature, 175, 1085 (1955).

[352] O. Folin and V. Ciocalteu, J. Biol. Chem., 73, 627 (1927).

[353] H. Wachsmuth, J. Pharm. Belge, 10, 300 (1955)

[354] L. Viognoli and B. Cristau, Bull. Soc. Pharm. France, 9, 43 (1952).

[355] J. Halmekoski, Suomen Kemistilehti, 32, 274 (1959).

pyrine[356-362] are frequently used for the quantitative analysis of phenols. A number of other reagents also have been suggested, such as α-nitro-β-naphthol,[363,364] p-dimethylaminobenzaldehyde,[365] xanthydrol,[366] nitrous acid,[367] mercury with nitrous and nitric acid,[368] sodium cupric bromide,[369] and ferrous tartrate.[370] One disadvantage of the colorimetric methods is the instability of the reagents. In most cases it is necessary to adhere strictly to the prescribed conditions. For example, the color produced by 4-amino-antipyrine with phenols is seriously affected by the pH and ionic strength of the reaction mixture.[361]

Willard and Wooten[371] described procedures for the colorimetric determination of o-substituted phenols and o- and m-dihydroxy benzenes which are based on iodination of the phenyl group. o-Substituted phenols are titrated with $0.1N$ iodine solution in a sodium carbonate buffer for 1 minute. The excess iodine is destroyed by means of $0.1N$ sodium thiosulfate, using starch as indicator. Toluene is added to extract the colored product and an aliquot is passed through a filter paper into a colorimeter tube. The intensity of the color is determined in the spectrophotometer, the wavelength used being varied with the compound. It should be noted that the reaction is not stoichiometric. For the determination of o-dihydroxybenzene, the sample is mixed with a fixed amount of the m-isomer and then iodinated in a sodium acetate buffer. After removal of the excess iodine, acetone is added to dissolve the precipitate. The intensity of the color is measured at 725 mμ. Identical procedure is used for the determination of m-dihydroxybenzene, except that a fixed amount of the o-isomer is added. Separate standardization curves are necessary, however, even though the colored product is the same in both cases.

[356] R. W. Martin, *Anal. Chem.*, **21**, 1419 (1949).
[357] M. B. Ettinger, C. C. Richhoft, and R. J. Lishka, *Anal. Chem.*, **23**, 1783 (1951).
[358] P. Kind and E. J. King, *J. Clin. Pathol.*, **7**, 322 (1954).
[359] E. F. Mohler and L. N. Jacob, *Anal. Chem.*, **29**, 1369 (1957).
[360] R. Drabek, *Chem. Tech. Berlin*, **9**, 77 (1957).
[361] R. J. Lacoste, S. H. Venable, and J. C. Stone, *Anal. Chem.*, **31**, 1246 (1959).
[362] H. G. Peer, *Rec. Trav. Chim. Pays. Bas*, **78**, 631 (1959).
[363] L. Nicolas and R. Burel, *Chim. Anal.*, **38**, 316 (1956).
[364] J. Mlodecka, *Chem. Anal. Warsaw*, **4**, 45 (1959).
[365] J. Meyer and G. Hintz, *Bull. Assoc. Diplomes, Microbiol. Fac. Pharm. Nancy*, **56**, 18 (1954).
[366] N. P. Yavorskii, *Zhur. Anal. Khim.*, **13**, 255 (1958).
[367] S. Y. Shnaiderman, *Ukran. Khim. Zhur.*, **21**, 99 (1955).
[368] M. T. Kohs, *Pharm. Weekblad.*, **68**, 557 (1931).
[369] S. Sass, J. J. Kaufman, and J. Kiernan, *Anal. Chem.*, **29**, 143 (1957).
[370] A. L. Kursanov and M. N. Zaprometov, *Biokhimiya*, **14**, 467 (1949).
[371] H. H. Willard and A. L. Wooten, *Anal. Chem.*, **22**, 423, 670 (1950).

A color reaction which is specific for a particular substance to be analyzed would be very desirable. Mlodecka[364] reported the determination of p-cresol by the red color produced with α-nitroso-β-naphthol in nitric-acetic acid mixture. It is claimed that the presence of phenol or o- and m-cresols does not interfere with the results. Colorimetric methods for the identification of the respective o-, m-, and p-dihydroxybenzenes in presence of one another have been developed.[372] In dilute acetic acid solution resorcinol gives a brown color with mercurous nitrate; hydroquinone forms a green product with sodium cyanide; pyrocatechol exhibits a brown color with potassium dichromate. These reactions probably can be utilized for quantitative analysis.

Fluorometric determination of the phenolic function has been suggested. Hercules and Rogers[373] measured the fluorescence of naphthols dissolved in ethanolic sodium hydroxide. Leininger and Katz[374] employed malic acid as the reagent to form the fluorescent product with 2-naphthol in sulfuric acid solution. Another approach being explored by Cheronis and co-workers is the reaction of phenolic compounds with fluorescent reagents to yield compounds which have different fluorescent peaks. This method appears applicable to microgram samples.

J. Physical Methods.   Many papers[375–381] have appeared that utilize the absorption bands of the hydroxyl group in the infrared region to determine phenolic compounds. It should be recognized that the strong absorption exhibited by these compounds in the vicinity of 2.75 to 3.00 μ and at about 9.5 μ is a general characteristic of the hydroxyl group and not limited to phenols. On the other hand, the phenolic function is also measurable by ultraviolet absorption spectrometry[382,383] because of its resonating structure, although the hydroxyl group does not absorb in the ultraviolet region.

[372] T. S. Ma and A. Hirsch, *Chemist-Analyst*, **50**, 12 (1961).

[373] D. Hercules and L. B. Rogers, *Anal. Chem.*, **30**, 96 (1958).

[374] E. Leininger and S. Katz, *Anal. Chem.*, **21**, 1375 (1949).

[375] W. W. Robertson, N. Ginsburg, and F. A. Matsen, *Ind. Eng. Chem., Anal. Ed.*, **18**, 746 (1946).

[376] M. J. Murray, *Anal. Chem.*, **21**, 941 (1949).

[377] R. A. Friedel, L. Pierce, and J. J. McGovern, *Anal. Chem.*, **22**, 418 (1950).

[378] O. E. Knapp, H. S. Moe, and R. H. Bernstein, *Anal. Chem.*, **22**, 418 (1950).

[379] R. G. Simard, I. Hasegawa, W. Bandarvek, and C. E. Headington, *Anal. Chem.*, **23**, 1384 (1951).

[380] R. J. Stone and H. W. Thompson, *Spectrochim. Acta*, **10**, 17 (1957).

[381] R. Goddu, *Anal. Chem.*, **30**, 2009 (1958).

[382] C. F. Smullin and F. Wetterau, *Anal. Chem.*, **27**, 136 (1955).

[383] B. T. Commins and A. J. Lindsey, *Anal. Chim. Acta*, **15**, 446 (1956).

VII. Organic Functions Containing Arsenic

A. Determinations by Conversion to Arsenate. There is very little information available in the literature on the determination of organic compounds of arsenic. The general practice is to oxidize the compound to yield arsenate ions. In one method the sample is treated with nitric-sulfuric acid mixture in a micro-Kjeldahl digestion flask. The resulting arsenic acid is determined gravimetrically as magnesium pyroarsenate.[384]

$$\text{Org. arsenic compound} \xrightarrow[\text{HNO}_3]{\text{H}_2\text{SO}_4} \text{H}_3\text{AsO}_4 \xrightarrow{\text{Mg(OH)}_2} \text{Mg}_3(\text{AsO}_4)_2 \xrightarrow{\text{heat}} \text{Mg}_2\text{As}_2\text{O}_7 \quad (44)$$

It should be noted that this is a method for the determination of arsenic in organic compounds, and does not differentiate the various organic functions containing arsenic, such as arsonic acids, arsines, arseno and arsonium groups.

Another method involves oxidation with nitric acid in a Carius combustion tube, followed by iodometric determination of arsenic acid.[385]

$$\text{H}_3\text{AsO}_4 + 2\text{HI} \rightarrow \text{H}_3\text{AsO}_3 + \text{I}_2 + \text{H}_2\text{O} \quad (45)$$

B. Precipitation of Metal Salts of Arsonic Acids. Pietsch[386] reported that many metal ions are precipitated quantitatively by o-, m-, and p-aminophenylarsonic acids and also the corresponding nitro arsonic acids. This may serve as the basis of a microgravimetric method for determining arsonic acids.

C. Colorimetric Determination of Arsonium Salts. Coursier and co-workers[387] observed that fluoroboric acids react with tetraphenylarsonic chloride to form tetraphenylarsonium fluoroborate. The product is colored and can be extracted with chloroform: then absorbance is measured at 540 mμ. This may be a general property of arylarsonium salts.

VIII. Organic Functions Containing Boron

A. Determination of Alkyl and Aryl Boron Compounds. Alkyl boron compounds can be dealkylated in the presence of carboxylic acids, as indicated in equation 46:

[384] H. Roth, *Quantitative Organic Microanalysis of Fritz Pregl*, 3rd English ed., Blakiston, Philadelphia, 1937, p. 133.

[385] A. Steyermark, *Quantitative Organic Microanalysis*, Blakiston, Philadelphia, 1951, p. 199; O. Wintersteiner, *Mikrochemie*, **4**, 155 (1926).

[386] R. Pietsch, *Mikrochim. Acta*, **1955**, 954, 1019.

[387] J. Coursier, J. Huré, and R. Plitzer, *Anal. Chim. Acta*, **13**, 379 (1955).

$$R_3B + 2R'COOH \rightarrow 2RH + (R'COO)_2BR \tag{46}$$

Crighton and co-workers[388] heated the sample with anhydrous propionic, acetic, and trifluoroacetic acid, respectively, in a sealed tube at 130°C and then determined the alkane produced. Experiments with trimethyl and tributylboron gave recovery from 95 to 100%.

Heyrovsky[389] proposed a method to determine aromatic boron compounds by titration with mercuric ions. The sample is dissolved in $0.1N$ sodium acetate solution and the solution is then titrated with standardized mercuric nitrate or mercuric perchlorate. The endpoint is located either potentiometrically using the mercury-coated platinum electrode against calomel, or amperometrically with the dropping mercury electrode. Sodium tetraphenylboron, triphenylboron, diphenyl hydrogen borate, and phenyl dihydrogen borate were successfully analyzed by this method.

B. Determination of Alkylboroxines and Alkylhydroxyboranes. The Karl Fischer reagent (see page 472) has been utilized to determine the boron oxide function as well as the hydroxyl group in boranes. According to Mattraw, Erickson, and Laubengayer,[390] alkyldihydroxyboranes react with methanol to liberate 2 equivalents of water:

$$RB(OH)_2 + 2CH_3OH \rightarrow RB(OCH_3)_2 + 2H_2O \tag{47}$$

Trialkylboroxines liberate three equivalents of water as shown in equation 48:

$$R-B \overset{\displaystyle \overset{R}{\underset{|}{B}}}{\underset{O}{\underset{\diagup \diagdown}{}}} B-R + 6CH_3OH \rightarrow 3RB(OCH_3)_2 + 3H_2O \tag{48}$$

Both reactions proceed to completion when the boron compounds are titrated with standardized Karl Fischer reagent, which reacts with water as soon as the latter is liberated. Satisfactory results were obtained on the macro scale, which involves the titration of several millimoles of water with Karl Fischer reagent having a strength of 2.5 to 5 mg. of water per ml. The presence of boron compounds containing B—C and B—O—C groups

[388] J. Crighton, A. K. Holliday, A. G. Massey, and N. R. Thompson, *Chem. & Ind.*, **1960**, 347.

[389] A. Heyrovsky, *Z. Anal. Chem.*, **173**, 301 (1960).

[390] H. C. Mattraw, C. E. Erickson, and A. W. Laubengayer, *J. Am. Chem. Soc.*, **78**, 4901 (1956).

does not interfere with the determination.[391] This method can be adapted to the 0.1 meq. scale (see p. 613).

C. Determination of Boron Tribromide Addition Compounds. Schuele and co-workers[392] described a procedure to determine boron tribromide addition compounds. The sample (3 meq.) is dissolved in water and warmed gently if necessary, then hydrolyzed:

$$Organic\ base \cdot BBr_3 + 3H_2O \rightarrow Organic\ base + H_3BO_3 + 3HBr \qquad (49)$$

The solution is then passed through cationic exchange resin Amberlite IR-100 (H form) packed in a Jones reductor tube. The effluent containing the combined boric and hydrobromic acids are determined by titration with standard sodium hydroxide in two steps. After the first endpoint, which measures the amount of hydrobromic acid, has been taken, mannitol is added and the titration is then continued to determine the amount of boric acid present in the solution.[393] It should be noted that boric acid is a very weak acid, not titrable by aqueous alkali solution. However, boric acid forms a diol complex with polyhydroxy compounds to liberate one equivalent of hydronium ions.[394,395]

$$H_3BO_3 + 2 \quad \begin{array}{c} -C-OH \\ | \\ -C-OH \end{array} \rightarrow \left[\begin{array}{c} -C-O \qquad O-C- \\ | \qquad B \qquad | \\ -C-O \qquad O-C- \end{array} \right]^{-} + H_3O^+ + 2H_2O \qquad (50)$$

Therefore, each mole of boric acid consumes one mole of alkali after treatment with mannitol.

IX. Organic Halogen Functions

A. Ionizable Halogens. Ionizable halogen in organic compounds, such as acid chlorides and quaternary ammonium iodides, can be determined by the conventional methods for halide ions. These compounds are usually soluble in water or dilute ethanol. Direct determination of the

[391] C. E. Erickson, private communication.

[392] W. J. Schuele, J. F. Hazel, and W. M. McNabb, *Anal. Chem.*, **28**, 505 (1956).

[393] I. M. Kolthoff and E. B. Sandell, *Textbook of Quantitative Inorganic Analysis*, 3rd ed., Macmillan, New York, 1952, p. 534.

[394] J. Boerseken, N. Vermaas, and A. T. Kuchlin, *Rec. Trav. Chim. Pays-Bas*, **49**, 711 (1930).

[395] H. Schafer, *Z. Anorg. Chem.*, **247**, 96 (1941).

halogen on the micro scale is feasible, either by gravimetric methods[396] or by titrimetric methods.[397] Unless the carbon skeleton interferes with the analysis, it is not advisable to decompose the organic fragment of the molecule by combustion. It should be recognized that determination of halogens in organic compounds by the micro combustion method is not discriminative.

B. Halogen on the α-Carbon Atom. A halogen atom attached to carbon with an adjacent electron-withdrawing group is reactive. Generally, α-halogen acids (such as chloroacetic, α-bromopropionic acid and the like) undergo hydrolysis readily when they are heated with dilute sodium hydroxide. The halogen is then estimated by titrimetry (Volhard method). When the α-carbon atom adjacent to the carboxyl group is attached also to an alkyl group besides the halogen, the reactivity of the halogen is tremendously increased. Thus, α-bromo-α-methyl-hexanoic acid is hydrolyzed rapidly in contact with water at 25°C to yield nearly equal amounts of the corresponding hydroxy and unsaturated acid.[398]

A method was proposed by Woidich and co-workers[399] for the determination of bromoacetic acid by conversion to the corresponding amino acid by ammonolysis followed by the determination of the resulting glycine:

$$BrCH_2COOH + 2NH_3 \rightarrow H_2NCH_2COOH + NH_4Br \qquad (51)$$

This method is open to objections. It is doubtful whether even for bromoacetic acid the yield of α-aminoacetic acid is quantitative, since the amount of primary amino compound produced in the ammonolysis of α-halogen acids is dependent on the molar ratio of halogen acid to ammonia and, even with a ratio of 1:60, the yield is not over 75%.[400,401] In all reactions of α-halogen acids with ammonia there are formed, besides the primary amino compound, appreciable quantities of secondary and tertiary amino carboxylic acids. Hence in each case the equilibrium yield of amino must be determined. In addition, it should be noted that in the case of the α-halogen acids with alkyl groups on the same carbon atom as the halogen, appreciable amounts of unsaturated acids are produced.[398]

[396] F. Hecht, in *Handbuch der mikrochemischen Methoden*, Vol. 1, part 2, Springer, Vienna, 1959.

[397] J. Mika, *Die Methoden der Mikromassanalyze*, 2nd ed., Enke, Stuttgart, 1958.

[398] N. D. Cheronis and P. Kraft, unpublished work; see P. Kraft, *Master's Thesis*, Brooklyn College, 1957.

[399] K. Woidich, L. Schmid, T. Langer, H. Gnauer, and H. Woidich, *Z. Lebensmitt. Untersuch*, **109**, 329 (1959).

[400] G. R. Robertson, *J. Am. Chem. Soc.*, **49**, 2889 (1927).

[401] N. D. Cheronis and K. Spitzmueller, *J. Org. Chem.*, **6**, 349 (1941).

The β-halogen acids, besides halogen ions, yield almost quantitatively unsaturated acids, if proper conditions are chosen. The γ-halogen acids yield halogen ions and γ-hydroxy acids on hydrolysis, which readily form lactones.

Kalinowski[402] proposed a coulometric method for the microdetermination of α-bromoisovalerylurea and α-bromodiethylacetylurea. Electrically generated silver ions are employed to react with the bromine. It is stated that this method is superior to that in which the external addition of silver ions is used.

C. Vinyl Halides. The halogen linked to the vinyl group is unreactive and cannot be determined by direct titration or precipitation of the silver halide. Kryszewski and Mazur[403] proposed a method for determining vinyl chloride and vinyl bromide which is based on their decomposition by heating with potassium methoxide at 40 to 50°C.

$$CH_2{=}CHCl + KOCH_3 \rightarrow CH_2{=}CHOCH_3 + KCl \qquad (52)$$

The reaction time is about 20 minutes. The potassium halide formed is then determined in the usual manner.

D. Positive Halogens. The halogen of N-halogenated compounds (e.g., bromosuccinimide, chloramine-T) possesses a relatively positive oxidation state and, hence, exhibits oxidizing properties. Freedman[404] described a macro method for the determination of positive halogen by the indirect application of the Karl Fischer reaction (see p. 472). The sample (3 meq.) to be analyzed is dissolved in water or methanol and treated with potassium iodide in acetic acid solution. The reaction is shown in equation 53:

$$\text{\Large$\diagdown$}NCl + 2KI + CH_3COOH \rightarrow I_2 + \text{\Large$\diagdown$}NH + KCl + CH_3COOK \qquad (53)$$

The quantity of iodine liberated is then determined by titration with standardized $0.5N$ solution of sulfur dioxide in pyridine-methanol mixture, according to equation 54:

$$I_2 + 2C_5H_5N + SO_2 \cdot C_5H_5N + H_2O + CH_3OH \rightarrow 2C_5H_5N \cdot HI$$
$$+ C_5H_5N(H)SO_4CH_3 \qquad (54)$$

The endpoint is observed by the disappearance of the yellow color or determined electrometrically. This method has not been adapted to the 0.1 meq. scale.

[402] K. Kalinowski, *Acta Polon. Pharm.*, **16**, 225 (1959).
[403] M. Kryszewski and L. Mazur, *Roczn. Chem.*, **31**, 287 (1957).
[404] R. W. Freedman, *Anal. Chem.*, **28**, 247 (1956).

E. Gas Chromatography of Organic Halides. Because of the inertness of organic halides and their ready volatility, gas chromatography provides an ideal tool for the determination of these compounds. Numerous papers have been published on the application of gas chromatography to the determination of fluorides,[405-408] chlorides,[406,409-413] bromides,[406] and iodides.[414] It should be noted that this method is limited to the determination of known halogenated compounds. It also necessitates the preparation of calibration curves using pure samples.

F. Colorimetric Methods for Carbon Tetrachloride. Two colorimetric methods for the determination of carbon tetrachloride have been suggested. In one method the sample containing 0.1 to 1 mg. of the chloride is treated with 0.1N sodium hydroxide in pyridine solution. The color developed on warming the reaction mixture is measured. This is a general reaction for chlorinated hydrocarbons. The color intensity is affected by the concentration of sodium hydroxide, temperature, and heating time.[415] A specific color reaction for the determination of carbon tetrachloride was reported by Blanc and co-workers.[416] The sample is dissolved in ethanol and heated under reflux for 5 minutes with a reagent containing thymol and copper sulfate in dilute ethanolic sodium hydroxide solution. After rapid cooling, two phases separate. The alcoholic layer develops a rose-red coloration, the intensity of which depends on the concentration of carbon tetrachloride in the original sample. The presence of acids, even in the atmosphere, causes interference.

X. Organomercury Functions

A. Gravimetric Estimation of Mercury. Organic mercury compounds are easily decomposed on heating in the presence of air to yield metallic mercury. Micro methods based on weighing the amount of mercury

[405] W. C. Percival, *Anal. Chem.*, **29**, 20 (1957).
[406] F. H. Pollard and C. J. Hardy, *Anal. Chim. Acta*, **16**, 135 (1957).
[407] M. J. Root and M. Maury, *Soap Chem. Specialties*, **33**, 75, 101 (1957).
[408] T. M. Reed, *Anal. Chem.*, **30**, 221 (1958).
[409] J. D. Griffiths, H. James, and C. S. G. Phillips, *Analyst*, **77**, 897 (1952).
[410] D. H. James and C. S. G. Phillips, *J. Chem. Soc.*, **1953**, 1600.
[411] A. T. James and A. J. P. Martin, *Brit. Med. Bull.*, **10**, No. 3, 170 (1954).
[412] R. R. Barefoot and J. E. Currah, *Chem. Can.*, **7**, 45 (1955).
[413] N. H. Ray, *Analyst*, **80**, 853 (1955).
[414] A. T. James, *Research*, **8**, 8 (1955).
[415] T. E. Burke and H. K. Southern, *Analyst*, **83**, 316 (1958).
[416] P. Blanc, O. Godfrain, and R. Lescure, *Chim. Anal.*, **41**, 54 (1959).

formed were described by Meixner and Kröcker[417] and Boetius.[418] The sample to be analyzed is placed in a porcelain microboat and inserted into a combustion tube which is packed with calcium oxide[417] or lead chromate.[418] The tip of the combustion tube is jacketed with a previously weighed small glass tubing containing fine gold wire. A current of air is passed through the combustion tube during the decomposition of the organic compound. As the mercury vaporizes and travels along the combustion tube, it is conducted (by heating the tip of the combustion tube with a small flame) into the glass tubing, where it is retained in the form of solid amalgam. The increase in weight of the glass tubing corresponds to the amount of mercury present in the original sample. A simple and convenient assembly has been described by Ma.[419]

B. Titrimetric Estimation of Mercuric Ions. Roth and Beck[420] proposed a microtitrimetric method for the determination of mercury in organic compounds as follows. The sample is oxidized by heating at 250°C with nitric acid in a micro-Carius tube for 5 hours. After cooling, the contents are diluted with water and quantitatively transferred into a 250 ml. Erlenmeyer flask fitted with a ground-glass stopper. The solution is neutralized by the addition of ammonium hydroxide and buffered with tartaric acid. The mercuric ions are then determined by titration with standardized $0.01N$ sodium diethyldithiocarbamate according to the procedure of Wickbold:[421]

$$\text{Organic mercury compound} \xrightarrow{\text{HNO}_3} \text{Hg(NO}_3)_2 \tag{55}$$

$$\text{Hg(NO}_3)_2 + 2(\text{C}_2\text{H}_5)_2\overset{\overset{\text{S}}{\|}}{\text{N}}\text{C—SNa} \rightarrow (\text{C}_2\text{H}_5)_2\text{N}—\overset{\overset{\text{S}}{\|}}{\text{C}}—\text{S}—\text{Hg}—\text{S}—\overset{\overset{\text{S}}{\|}}{\text{C}}—\text{N(C}_2\text{H}_5)_2 \\ + 2\text{NaNO}_3 \tag{56}$$

Cupric acetate and chloroform are used as the indicator. The mercuric diethyldithiocarbamate which precipitates as a white solid in the aqueous phase redissolves in chloroform on vigorous stirring. After all mercuric ions have been removed from the aqueous solution, the copper diethyldithiocarbamate precipitates and goes into solution in chloroform to give a yellowish to brown color. It should be recognized that this is a two-phase

[417] A. Meixner and F. Kröcker, *Mikrochemie*, **5**, 131 (1927).

[418] M. Boetius, *J. Prakt. Chem.*, **151**, 279 (1938).

[419] T. S. Ma, in F. J. Welcher (ed.), *Standard Methods of Chemical Analysis*, 6th edition, Vol. 2, Van Nostrand, Princeton, 1963, p. 403.

[420] H. Roth and W. Beck, in *Pregl-Roth: Quantitative organische Mikroanalyse*, 7th ed., Springer, Wien, 1958, p. 184.

[421] R. Wickbold, *Z. Anal. Chem.*, **152**, 261 (1956).

titration, being more difficult to perform than the conventional titration in aqueous solutions.

Chambers and co-workers[422] determined mercury in organic mercurials by reduction with zinc in methanol. The zinc amalgam is dissolved in nitric acid, and the mercuric ions are determined by titration with standardized potassium thiocyanate solution using ferric alum as indicator.[423]

C. Titrimetric Estimation of Alkyl and Aryl Mercury Functions. Hetnarski and Hetnarska[424] suggested a micro method for the determination of certain alkyl and aryl mercury functions that is based on the precipitation of the 2-mercaptobenzothiazole derivatives:

$$=N\text{—HgR} + \underset{S}{\overset{N}{\bigcirc\!\!\bigcirc}}\!\!C\text{—SH} \rightarrow \underset{S}{\overset{N}{\bigcirc\!\!\bigcirc}}\!\!C\text{—S—HgR} + =NH \quad (57)$$

The sample to be analyzed is reacted with a known excess volume of $0.01N$ 2-mercaptobenzothiazole solution. After the precipitation is complete, the solution is filtered and the excess of the reagent in the filtrate is determined by titration with $0.01N$ iodine solution.[425] This method was tested with N-organomercury compounds. It may be extended to other organic functions containing mercury.

XI. Organophosphorus Functions

A. General. The importance of both natural and synthetic organophosphorus compounds has been steadily increasing during the last decade.[426,427] Both DNA and RNA are composed of nucleotides, which are, in turn, phosphoric esters of nucleosides (composed of a purine or pyrimidine base condensed with a pentose). Generally, organic phosphates are esters of phosphoric acid in which the organic radical is linked to the phosphorus atom by means of oxygen. The synthetic phosphorus compounds, besides the phosphates, with a direct C—P linkage are shown in the following types in which R represents an alkyl or aryl radical:

[422] V. H. Chambers, F. R. Cropper, and H. Crossley, *J. Sci. Food Agr.*, **7**, 17 (1956).

[423] I. M. Kolthoff and E. B. Sandell, *Textbook of Quantitative Inorganic Analysis*, 3rd ed., Macmillan, New York, 1952, p. 547.

[424] B. Hetnarski and K. Hetnarska, *Bull. Acad. Polonaise*, **7**, 645 (1959).

[425] G. Blockinger, *Chem. Zvesti*, **6**, 340 (1957).

[426] G. M. Kosolapoff, *Organo Phosphorus Compounds*, John Wiley, New York, 1950.

[427] P. C. Crafts, *Quart. Rev., Chem. Soc.*, **12**, 341 (1958).

R_3P	R_2PX	R_4PX
		Quaternary phosphonium
Phosphine	*Phosphine halide*	*salt*

$$R{-}\overset{\displaystyle O}{\overset{\|}{P}}{-}OH$$
$\diagdown$
OH

$$R_2\overset{\displaystyle O}{\overset{\|}{P}}{-}OH$$

$$R_3P{=}O$$

Phosphoric acid   *Phosphinic acid*   *Phosphine oxide*

$C_6H_5{-}P{=}P{-}C_6H_5$ $R{-}P{=}N{-}N{=}CR_2$ $R_3P{=}S$

Phosphobenzene   *Phosphazine*   *Phosphine sulfide·*

Methods for the determination of the various phosphorus functions are gradually being developed. Nevertheless, it is still a general practice to determine the total phosphorus in organic compounds. The recommended procedure[428] for determination on the 0.1 meq. scale involves oxidation by sulfuric-nitric acid mixture, followed by the colorimetric determination of the phosphovanadomolybdate. The other methods that have been described in the literature for the quantitative analysis of organic phosphorus compounds will be briefly surveyed in the following sections.

B. Titrimetric Methods

1. Iodimetric Determination of Phosphites. Yarden and Eger[429] proposed a method to determine alkyl phosphites in the presence of other organic phosphorus compounds as follows. The sample (50 to 150 mg.) is treated with 10 ml. of standardized $0.2N$ iodine in pyridine in a tightly stoppered flask in the dark for 30 minutes. Then 20 ml. of peroxide-free dioxane and 24 ml. of $5N$ hydrochloric acid are added, and the reaction mixture is titrated with $0.1N$ sodium thiosulfate until the color changes to yellow, when 75 ml. of water is introduced, followed by 5 ml. of 1% starch solution. The titration is then continued to the disappearance of the blue color. The results are reproducible, but not stoichiometric. Therefore, a reference curve must be prepared.

It is interesting to note that dialkyl phosphites react at a much slower rate toward iodine than trialkyl phosphites. Saunders and Stark[430] reported that a rough estimation of trialkyl phosphites can be obtained by titration against standardized iodine solution under conditions in which the dialkyl esters do not react appreciably.

2. Iodometric Determination of Phosphorus Halidates and Pyroesters. Sass and co-workers[431] described semimicro methods for the determination

---

[428] T. S. Ma and J. D. McKinley, Jr., *Mikrochim. Acta*, **1953**, 4.

[429] A. Yarden and C. Eger, *Bull. Res. Council, Israel*, **7**, 81 (1958).

[430] B. C. Saunders and B. P. Stark, *Tetrahedron*, **4**, 198 (1958).

[431] S. Sass, I. Master, P. M. Davis, and N. Beitsch, *Anal. Chem.*, **32**, 285 (1960).

of organophosphorus fluoridate, chloridate, and pyroester compounds using a peroxide reagent in an alkaline medium. The method is dependent on the formation of a perphosphorus halidate or pyroester and the subsequent determination of excess peroxide:

$$R-\overset{\displaystyle O}{\underset{\displaystyle OR'}{\overset{\|}{P}}}-X \xrightarrow{[OOH^-]} R-\overset{\displaystyle O}{\underset{\displaystyle OR'}{\overset{\|}{P}}}-OOH \xrightarrow{[OOH^-]} R-\overset{\displaystyle O}{\underset{\displaystyle OR'}{\overset{\|}{P}}}-O^- + O_2 + H_2O \qquad (58)$$

(R = alkyl or alkoxyl; R' = alkyl; X = Cl, F or the phosphorus group as in pyrophosphates and pyrophosphonates.)

The sample (80 to 240 mg.) is added to a measured volume of standardized sodium pyrophosphate peroxide solution buffered to pH 10 with sodium borate-sodium hydroxide. After a few minutes, the solution is acidified with sulfuric acid; potassium iodide is added, and the liberated iodine is titrated with 0.1N sodium thiosulfate.

3. Hydrolysis of Alkyl Phosphites. According to Bernhart and Rattenbury,[432] dialkyl phosphites can be determined by reacting the sample dissolved in ethanol with a known volume of standard sodium hydroxide solution:

$$(RO)_2 \!\!=\!\! \overset{\displaystyle O}{\overset{\uparrow}{P}}-H + NaOH \rightarrow RO-\underset{\displaystyle ONa}{\overset{\displaystyle O}{\overset{\uparrow}{P}}}-H + ROH \qquad (59)$$

The unconsumed alkali is then back-titrated with standard acid to the phenolphthalein endpoint.

Trialkyl phosphites react with alkali only slowly. However, these compounds can be hydrolyzed with a known amount of standard acid:

$$(RO)_3 \!\!\equiv\!\! P + H_2O \rightarrow (RO)_2 \!\!=\!\! \overset{\displaystyle O}{\overset{\uparrow}{P}}-H + ROH \qquad (60)$$

The dialkyl phosphite formed is then determined by the method described earlier. These methods were tested on the macro scale using 2 to 3 meq. samples; they have not been adapted to the micro range.

4. Acid-Base Titrations. Acidimetric titration of the phosphonic and phosphinic acid functions can be performed in aqueous solutions. On the other hand, nonaqueous titrimetry is necessary for the phosphorus bases. Streuli[433] determined the basicity of organic phosphines by titrating the samples dissolved in nitromethane with 0.1N hydrochloric acid in meth-

---

[432] D. N. Bernhart and K. H. Rattenbury, *Anal. Chem.*, **28**, 1765 (1956).
[433] C. A. Streuli, *Anal. Chem.*, **32**, 985 (1960).

anol. The endpoint is located potentiometrically. Tertiary alkyl phosphines are shown to be the stronger bases whereas aryl and negatively substituted compounds decrease in basic strength.

Phosphoranes $(R_3\equiv P=CH—CO—CH_3)$ were determined on the 0.1 meq. scale by Ross and Denney[434] by titration with $0.02N$ perchloric acid in acetic acid (see p. 429). Phosphonium halides can be titrated as bases after addition of mercuric acetate (see p. 426).

C. Gravimetric Methods. A gravimetric method for the determination of the tetramethylphosphonium function was suggested by Anderson and Keeler.[435] The method is based on the insolubility of tetramethylphosphonium chloroplatinate in ethanol. The sample in the chloride form is reacted with chloroplatinic acid and the solution is evaporated to small bulk. The residue is extracted with ethanol, filtered, and weighed after washing and drying. This method has not been tested on the micro scale. The presence of ammonium or alkali metal ions interferes with the analysis, but moderate amounts of calcium, strontium, and magnesium ions can be tolerated.

Banks and Davis[436] observed that benzenephosphonic acid is quantitatively precipitated by means of thorium ions in form of $Th(C_6H_5PO_3)_2 \cdot 3H_2O$. This may be used as the basis for gravimetric determination of aryl phosphonic acids.

D. Miscellaneous Methods

1. Colorimetric Methods. When the organic phosphorus compound is easily hydrolyzed to yield phosphate ions, the most sensitive colorimetric method for its determination is the "molybdenum blue" exhibited by the phosphomolybdenum complexes.[437-439] Tri-n-butyl phosphate has been determined colorimetrically using vanadium and aluminum nitrite as the reagent[440] or by the molybdovanadophosphate color.[441] Colorimetric reagents for the determination of alkyl phosphites include 1,3,5-trinitrobenzene,[442] 3,5-dinitrobenzoic acid,[443] diisonitrosoacetone,[444] and cacothe-

[434] S. T. Ross and D. B. Denney, *Anal. Chem.*, **32**, 1896 (1960).
[435] C. J. Anderson and R. A. Keeler, *Anal. Chem.*, **26**, 213 (1954).
[436] C. V. Banks and R. J. Davis, *Anal. Chim. Acta*, **12**, 418 (1955).
[437] B. L. Horecker, T. S. Ma, and E. Haas, *J. Biol. Chem.*, **136**, 775 (1940).
[438] L. Macho, *Chem. Zvesti*, **11**, 175 (1957).
[439] J. Kolmerten and J. Epstein, *Anal. Chem.*, **30**, 1536 (1958).
[440] R. J. Allen and M. A. DeSesa, *Nucleonics*, **15**, 88 (1957).
[441] A. J. Fudge and G. C. Hutton, A.E.R.E. Rept. C/R 2384, p. 18 (1957).
[442] S. Sass and J. Cassidy, *Anal. Chem.*, **28**, 1968 (1956).
[443] B. C. Saunders and B. P. Stark, *Tetrahedron*, **4**, 197 (1958).
[444] S. Sass, W. D. Ludemann, B. Witten, V. Fische, A. J. Sisti, and J. I. Miller, *Anal. Chem.*, **29**, 1346 (1957).

line.[445] Phenyl phosphites were determined by alkaline hydrolysis and coupling of the phenol.[446]

Phosphonates have been determined by reduction to phosphine which is measured colorimetrically with silver nitrate.[447] Gehauf and co-workers[448] determined phosphorus halidates using sodium perborate and benzidine. Thiophosphonic acid and derivatives have been determined by their nickel salts[449] or by means of sodium cyanide.[450] Determination of organic phosphorus compounds by fluorescence[451] or chemiluminescence[452] have been reported.

2. Physical Methods. Allen and DeSesa[453] applied ultraviolet spectrophotometry to determine tri-*n*-butyl phosphate. Whiffen and co-workers[454] determined alkyl and aryl phosphonates by their absorption band in the infrared region. Polarographic determination of quaternary phosphonium salts was reported by Colichman.[455] These compounds are reduced at a potential higher than quaternary ammonium or sulfonium salts.

3. Enzymatic Methods. Because of the bioactivity of certain organic phosphorus compounds, enzymatic methods have been applied to the quantitative analysis of these compounds. Choline esterase is used as the enzyme system. The reader is referred to the original literature[456-458] for detailed discussions.

XII. Organosilicon Functions

A. General. Organosilicon compounds have received considerable attention in the last two decades because of extensive applications of organic polysiloxanes and other silicon containing polymers. The common method for the analysis of silicon compounds is to oxidize the sample and

[445] T. D. Smith, *Anal. Chim. Acta*, **22**, 249 (1960).

[446] A. C. Nawakowski, *Anal. Chem.*, **30**, 1868 (1958).

[447] F. T. Eggertsen and F. T. Weiss, *Anal. Chem.*, **29**, 453 (1957).

[448] B. Gehauf, J. Epstein, G. B. Wilson, B. Witten, S. Sass, V. E. Bauer, and W. H. C. Rueggeborg, *Anal. Chem.*, **29**, 278 (1957).

[449] M. Masoero and M. Perini, *Chim. Ind.*, **37**, 945 (1955).

[450] B. Soville, *Chem. Ind.*, **1956**, 660.

[451] B. Gehauf and J. Goldenson, *Anal. Chem.*, **29**, 276 (1957).

[452] J. Goldenson, *Anal. Chem.*, **29**, 877 (1957).

[453] R. J. Allen and M. A. DeSesa, A.E.C. Rept. WIN-52 (1956).

[454] D. H. Whiffen, P. Tarkington, and H. W. Thompson, *Trans. Faraday Soc.*, **41**, 197 (1945).

[455] E. L. Colichman, *Anal. Chem.*, **26**, 1204 (1954).

[456] H. O. Fallscher and J. W. Cook, *J. Assoc. Offic. Agr. Chemists*, **39**, 691 (1956).

[457] J. Janik and R. Kemka, *Chem. Zvesti*, **10**, 177 (1956).

[458] J. Epstein, M. Demek and V. C. Wolff, Jr., *Anal. Chem.*, **29**, 1050 (1957).

weigh the residue as silicon dioxide, then treat the residue with hydrofluoric acid and volatilize the silica as SiF_4. However, several investigators have reported on the determination of some functions containing silicon which are not based on elemental combustion procedures.

B. Alkoxyl Groups Attached to Silicon. Bondarevskaya and co-workers[459] described a method for the determination of ethoxyl groups in organosilicon compounds as follows. The sample (120 to 150 mg.) is heated with a known quantity of potassium dichromate in dilute sulfuric acid solution. Ethanol, which is liberated, is oxidized by the dichromate. After the reaction is completed, the unconsumed dichromate is determined by the addition of potassium iodide and titration of the liberated iodine with $0.1N$ sodium thiosulfate.

C. Organochlorosilanes. Most organochlorosilanes undergo hydrolysis readily when treated with water to give polysiloxanes and halide ions:

$$nR_2SiCl_2 + nH_2O \rightarrow (R_2SiO)_n + 2nHCl \qquad (61)$$

It is often possible to choose conditions for stoichiometric hydrolysis followed by argentimetric titration of the halide ions. In some instances, however, the hydrolysis may be incomplete, and some halide may be retained in the polymer.

Two methods were proposed by Takiguchi for the determination of methylchloro- and phenylchlorosilanes. In one method[460] the sample is dissolved in anhydrous ether and reacted with aniline in the same solvent. Aniline hydrochloride, which is formed, is then determined. In another method[461] the compound (100 mg.) dissolved in anhydrous ether is titrated with standardized $0.1M$ solution of potassium or ammonium thiocyanate in acetone. Potassium and ammonium chlorides, respectively, precipitate during the titration. The endpoint is determined by using ferric chloride dissolved in ether as indicator.

Electrometric titration of alkylchlorosilanes was suggested by Kreshkov and co-workers. Mono-, di-, and trimethylchlorosilanes can be quantitatively converted into the respective methylthiocyanto derivatives by the action of ammonium thiocyanate. The methylthiocyanates are then titrated conductometrically in acetonitrile-ethyl ether solution with $0.1M$ amidopyrine in benzene.[462]

[459] E. A. Bondarevskaya, S. V. Syavtsillo, and R. N. Potsepkina, *Zhur. Anal. Khim.*, **14**, 501 (1959).

[460] T. Takiguchi, *J. Chem. Soc. Japan*, **61**, 1236 (1958).

[461] T. Takiguchi, *Analyst*, **83**, 482 (1958); *J. Chem. Soc. Japan*, **61**, 587 (1958).

[462] A. P. Kreshkov and V. A. Drozdov, *Dokl. Akad. Nauk. SSSR*, **131**, 1345 (1960).

D. Nonaqueous Titration of Organosilicon Compounds. According to Kreshkov, Drozdov, and Vlasova,[463] alkylchlorosilanes can be titrated as acids in acetonitrile solution by means of $0.05N$ Phenazone or Nitron in acetonitrile, or standardized aminopyrine in benzene. Visual and potentiometric methods were employed. The indicators used were crystal violet, dimethylazobenzene, bromocresol purple, methyl orange, bromophenol blue, and gallo sea blue. The addition of benzene, chlorobenzene, or carbon tetrachloride does not affect the results.

Organosilicon compounds containing nitrogen attached directly to silicon and those with nitrogen in an organic radical have been titrated with standard perchloric acid in acetonitrile, methyl nitrite, benzene, or dioxane. The endpoint can be determined visually or potentiometrically. The potential jumps when titrating in methyl nitrite are 10 mv. larger than those in acetonitrile.[464]

E. Physical Methods. Tanaka[465] studied the infrared absorption spectra of methoxy, methyl-methoxy and methoxy end-blocked dimethyl polysiloxanes. It was observed that the Si—O—CH$_3$ function has a characteristic absorption band near 1190 cm^{-1}. This band is not shown by C—O—C groups and, hence, can be used for the quantitative analysis of methoxysilanes.

XIII. Determination of Water in Organic Analysis

A. General. Water is not an organic compound, but its determination is frequently needed in organic analysis for several reasons: (1) water is a common contaminant in organic samples; (2) a number of organic compounds possess water of crystallization [e.g., oxalic acid dihydrate, $(COOH)_2 \cdot 2H_2O$]; (3) some organic compounds release water at elevated temperatures (e.g., chloral hydrate, $Cl_3CCHO \cdot H_2O$); (4) many organic reactions occur with the liberation or consumption of a mole of water. Determination of water is also known as *aquametry*. A comprehensive survey of the literature on aquametry has been published by Mitchell and Smith.[466] Hence only recent publications will be cited as references in the following sections.

If the organic compound to be analyzed is known not to possess oxygen in

[463] A. P. Kreshkov, V. A. Drozdov, and E. G. Vlasova, *Izv. Vyssh. Uchebn. Zavedenii, Khim. i. Khim. Tekhnol.*, **3**, 85 (1960).

[464] *Ibid.*, **3**, 80.

[465] T. Tanaka, *Bull. Chem. Soc. Japan*, **31**, 762 (1958).

[466] J. Mitchell, Jr., and D. M. Smith, *Aquametry*, Interscience, New York, 1948.

its molecule, determination of oxygen by the direct combustion method[467] (not by difference) usually indicates the amount of water present as impurity. It is more convenient, however, to determine water in the sample by the methods given later.

The most sensitive reagent for the detection of water[468] is tetraisopropyl titanate; about 0.01 to 0.05 ml. (one drop or less) of the reagent is added to a drop of the liquid or a solution of the solid in anhydrous methanol. Water hydrolyzes the reagent to produce hydrated titanium oxides, which precipitate as chalky solids. The amount of precipitate is a measure of the amount of water in the sample.

Another test is to add a drop of the liquid or solution to a few crystals of aluminum ethoxide or isopropoxide; the presence of water is indicated by the appearance of gelatinous aluminum hydroxide. The disadvantage of aluminum alkoxides is that once the bottle is opened, it is difficult to keep the moisture in air from attacking the reagent.

B. Vaporization

1. Methods Dependent on Drying. For organic solids with a melting point above 100°C, it is a common practice to heat a weighed sample to constant weight in an oven kept at 105°C and ascribe the loss in weight upon drying as due to water originally present. An improved drying device which permits heating under reduced pressure at closely controlled temperatures was described by Schenck and Ma[469] (see Figure 5.28, p. 101). By performing the experiment at different temperatures, it is possible to differentiate surface moisture and water of crystallization. An absorption tube filled with indicator-silica gel and connected to the exhaust will serve as a check on the amount of water released from the organic sample.

2. Methods Dependent on Distillation. A method generally used on the macro scale for the determination of water in organic solutions is based on azeotropic distillation. A large volume of toluene or xylene is added to the sample placed in a distilling vessel. The flask is connected to a condenser and a receiving tube which is graduated. Various types of apparatus have been proposed.[466,470] Water co-distils with toluene or xylene and settles at

[467] J. Unterzaucher, *Berichte*, **73**, 391 (1940); V. A. Aluise, R. T. Hall, F. C. Staats, and W. W. Becker, *Anal. Chem.*, **19**, 347 (1947).

[468] N. D. Cheronis and J. B. Entrikin, *Semimicro Qualitative Organic Analysis*, 2nd ed., Interscience, New York, 1957, p. 161.

[469] R. T. E. Schenck and T. S. Ma, *Mikrochemie*, **40**, 236 (1953); apparatus available from Micro-Ware, Inc., Vineland, N.J.

[470] L. Hubschen, *Z. Lebensm. Untersuch.*, **111**, 371 (1960).

the bottom of the graduated receiver. The volume of water is measured when the lower liquid layer in the receiver shows no increase, indicating the complete removal of water from the sample in the distilling vessel. This method requires the presence of about 2 to 3 ml. of water and is not suitable for microdeterminations.

C. Use of Karl Fischer Reagent

1. Principle. A chemical method for the determination of water was proposed by Fischer[471] in 1935 which is based on the reaction between iodine and sulfur dioxide in the presence of water as shown in equation 62:

$$H_2O + I_2 + SO_2 \rightarrow SO_3 + 2HI \tag{62}$$

Fischer observed that a methanol-pyridine mixture serves as a suitable solvent for the reaction and recommended this reagent for the determination of water in organic liquids. Investigations by Smith, Bryant, and Mitchell[472] established the participation of the solvent in the reaction which proceeds in two steps: (1) formation of pyridinium iodide and pyridine-sulfur trioxide complex:

$$H_2O + I_2 + SO_2 + 3C_5H_5N \rightarrow 2(C_5H_5NH^+)I^- + C_5H_5N \cdot SO_3 \tag{63}$$

and (2) conversion of the complex to pyridinium methyl sulfate:

$$C_5H_5N \cdot SO_3 + CH_3OH \rightarrow C_5H_5N \cdot HSO_3OCH_3 \tag{64}$$

Recent studies have shown that pyridine is indispensable whereas methanol can be replaced by other organic liquids, such as methyl cellosolve,[473] dioxane,[474,475] and glacial acetic acid.[476] Attempts were made by Belcher and West[477] to replace iodine with bromine or cupric chloride:

$$2H_2O + 2CuCl_2 + SO_2 \rightarrow H_2SO_4 + Cu_2Cl_2 + 2HCl \tag{65}$$

The results are not satisfactory. The cupric chloride reagent is efficient when freshly prepared, but becomes useless after 5 days.

[471] K. Fischer, *Angew. Chem.*, **48**, 394 (1935).

[472] D. M. Smith, W. M. D. Bryant, and J. Mitchell, Jr., *J. Am. Chem. Soc.*, **61**, 2407 (1939).

[473] E. D. Peters and J. L. Jungnickel, *Anal. Chem.*, **27**, 450 (1955).

[474] E. Bonauguri and G. Seniga, *Ann. Chim. Roma*, **45**, 9 (1955).

[475] V. G. Jensen, *Danak Tidssker*, **29**, 77 (1955).

[476] L. Barnes, Jr., and M. S. Pawlak, *Anal. Chem.*, **31**, 1875 (1959).

[477] R. Belcher and T. S. West, *J. Chem. Soc.*, **1953**, 1772.

2. Assemblies and Reagents. Various apparatus[478-483] have been proposed for titration using the Karl Fischer reagent. The essential feature of all assemblies is to protect the reagent from deterioration or exposure to moisture. The apparatus recommended for determination on the micro scale is the Wiberley microburet[484] (Figure 5.16) which is commercially available.[485]

The Karl Fischer reagent may be prepared in several ways. Originally, iodine, sulfur dioxide, pyridine, and methanol were mixed together as one reagent solution. Later it was found that a more stable reagent could be obtained by dissolving iodine in methanol and sulfur dioxide in pyridine separately and then combining the two solutions when needed.[486] This technique is not suitable for microdeterminations, however, because of the difficulty in mixing two solutions without contamination by atmospheric moisture. Eberius and Bohnes[487] advocated the addition of liquid bromine to the methanol-pyridine solution of iodine and sulfur dioxide. Meyer and Boyd[488] described a method in which the iodine in the Karl Fischer reagent is coulometrically generated, thus permitting the determination of microgram quantities of water.

The Karl Fischer reagent may be standardized by titration against known amounts of water dissolved in methanol. However, this procedure is not recommended for the determination of 0.1 millimole of water. A solid standard such as disodium tartrate dihydrate[489] should be used.

3. Location of the Endpoint. Determination of water by Karl Fischer titration may be performed on the macro scale using the brown color of iodine in the reagent as the visual indicator. This technique, however, cannot be used in microdeterminations because the color becomes indistinguishable in dilute solutions. Therefore the electrometric endpoint location is generally recommended. Potentiometric,[490] "dead-stop" polar-

[478] H. Sieber, *Faserforsch. Textiltech.*, **6**, 421 (1955).

[479] W. Bohm, *Z. Anal. Chem.*, **147**, 415 (1955).

[480] J. F. Brown and W. F. Volume, *Analyst*, **81**, 308 (1956).

[481] E. P. Bahari, *Birmingham Univ. Chem. Engr.*, **7**, 70 (1956).

[482] M. Vasta, *Chem. Listy*, **52**, 763 (1958).

[483] F. B. Waddington, *Lab. Practice*, **8**, 275 (1959).

[484] J. S. Wiberley, *Anal. Chem.*, **23**, 656 (1951).

[485] Metro Scientific, Inc., Carle Place, L.I., N.Y.

[486] W. Seaman, W. H. McComas, and G. A. Allen, *Anal. Chem.*, **21**, 510 (1949).

[487] E. Eberius and H. Bohnes, *Z. Anal. Chem.*, **168**, 330 (1959).

[488] A. S. Meyer, Jr., and C. M. Boyd, *Anal. Chem.*, **31**, 215 (1959).

[489] J. D. Neuss, M. G. O'Brien, and H. A. Frediani, *Anal. Chem.*, **23**, 1332 (1951).

[490] F. L. J. Van Lamoen and W. Borsten, *Anal. Chem.*, **27**, 1638 (1955).

ization,[466,491–493] amperometric,[494] and coulometric[488] determinations have been reported. Connors and Higuchi[495] proposed the spectrophotometric detection of the endpoint by utilizing the absorption at 525 mμ for water in methanol. Fischer[496] suggested methylene blue in absolute alcohol or pyridine as the visual indicator. The last two methods have not been tested on the micro scale.

4. *Applications and Limitations.* At present, the Karl Fischer reagent is the most popular chemical method for determining water. It has been extensively applied to the determination of water as impurity in organic samples, and also for functional group analysis based on reactions that involve consumption or liberation of water. Adaptation of these determinations to the micro scale has been investigated.[497] The experimental procedure will be found in experiment 48.

It should be recognized that the Karl Fischer method is dependent on the redox reaction of iodine. Hence any substance that can be oxidized by iodine or reduced by iodide ions will interfere with the analysis. Furthermore, methanol cannot be used as the solvent to determine water in vinyl ethers since the vinyl group reacts with iodine in the presence of methanol:

$$\text{RO—CH=CH}_2 + \text{I}_2 + \text{CH}_3\text{OH} \rightarrow \text{RO—CH—CH}_2\text{I} + \text{HI} \qquad (66)$$
$$\underset{\text{OCH}_3}{|}$$

Barnes and Pawlak[476] reported that correct values of water are obtained by replacing methanol in the reagent with glacial acetic acid. Carbonyl compounds interfere with water determination in the presence of methanol due to the formation of acetal or ketal by the catalytic effect of hydrogen iodide:

$$\begin{array}{c}\diagdown\\ \diagup\end{array}\!\!\text{C=O} + 2\text{CH}_3\text{OH} \rightarrow \begin{array}{c}\diagdown\\ \diagup\end{array}\!\!\text{C}\begin{array}{c}\diagup \text{OCH}_3\\ \diagdown \text{OCH}_3\end{array} + \text{H}_2\text{O} \qquad (67)$$

Johansson[498] reported that the Karl Fischer method can be used to determine water in oxidants, reductants, and amines by using the two-

[491] K. G. Stone and H. G. Scholten, *Anal. Chem.*, **24**, 671 (1952).

[492] J. G. Van Pelt and H. Keuker, *Chem. Weekblad.*, **51**, 97 (1955).

[493] F. Oehme, *Chem. Tech. Berlin*, **9**, 340 (1957).

[494] E. L. Bastin, H. Siegel, and A. B. Bullock, *Anal. Chem.*, **31**, 467 (1959).

[495] K. A. Connors and T. Higuchi, *Chemist-Analyst*, **48**, 91 (1959).

[496] E. Fischer, *Angew. Chem.*, **64**, 592 (1952).

[497] T. S. Ma and B. L. Hensle, unpublished work; see B. L. Hensle, *Master's Thesis, New York University*, 1957.

[498] A. Johansson, *Anal. Chem.*, **28**, 1166 (1956).

solution modification. Matsudaira and Muroi[499] proposed to determine water in samples containing substances that react with Karl Fischer reagent in the following manner. The sample to be analyzed is distilled with toluene or xylene. The distillate is then determined for water by Karl Fischer titration.

Determination of water in drugs by the Karl Fischer method was shown to give better results than by the oven-drying method.[500] Hoffmann[501] compared the results of water determination in sugars by Karl Fischer titration with those obtained by oven drying. The titration method gives high values, but the discrepancy is eliminated by standardizing the Karl Fischer reagent against the test sugar.

D. Hydrolytic Methods

1. Use of Acetic Anhydride. Barltrop and Morgan[502] proposed acetic anhydride as the reagent to determine water. The method is based on the hydrolytic reaction of water on the anhydride in the presence of perchloric acid:

$$H_2O + (CH_3CO)_2O \rightarrow 2CH_3COOH \tag{68}$$

The reaction rate is rapid enough for the application of a titrimetric procedure. The endpoint is located externally by means of hydroxylamine hydrochloride and ferric chloride in ethanol to give the violet ferric hydroxamate color for acid anhydride (see Chapter 6, Section III-F). This method was employed to determine water in acetic acid, acetonitrile, ethylacetate, acetone, benzene, carbon tetrachloride, and alcohols. It is not applicable to amines, owing to the formation of salts with perchloric acid. The necessity of using an outside indicator makes it undesirable for adaptation to the micro scale.

2. Use of Dimethyl Oxalate. The hydrolysis of dimethyl oxalate by water in sodium methylate solution was used as the basis for determining water in alcohols by Koskikallio:[503]

$$2H_2O + (COOCH_3)_2 + 2NaOCH_3 \rightarrow (COONa)_2 + 4CH_3OH \tag{69}$$

The sample is treated with a measured excess volume of standardized methanolic solution containing dimethyl oxalate and sodium methoxide, each of 0.2M concentration. The reaction is completed in 10 minutes at room temperature. The unconsumed alkali is then back-titrated with 0.2M benzoic acid in anhydrous benzene to the cresol red endpoint. This method

[499] J. Matsudaira and K. Muroi, *Japan Analyst*, **8**, 429 (1959).
[500] G. J. Mulder and J. A. C. Van Pinxteren, *Pharm. Weekblad*, **91**, 33 (1956).
[501] R. Hoffmann, *Zucker*, **12**, 247 (1959).
[502] J. A. Barltrop and R. J. Morgan, *Anal. Chim. Acta*, **16**, 520 (1957).
[503] J. Koskikallio, *Suomen Kemistilehti.*, B, **30**, 108 (1957).

has not been tested on the 0.1 meq. scale. It cannot be used to determine water in ketones because of the condensation reaction of carbonyl compound in the presence of strong alkali. Dimethyl oxalate cannot be replaced by other esters such as diethyl oxalate, since the rate of hydrolysis of the latter is 10^4 times slower than that of the former.

3. Use of Acid Chlorides.   Belcher and co-workers[504,505] investigated the use of acid chlorides as hydrolytic reagents for the determination of water according to the following reaction:

$$H_2O + R—COCl \rightarrow HCl + RCOOH \tag{70}$$

The hydrogen chloride formed is purged from the reaction mixture and determined titrimetrically. The most promising reagent was shown to be β,β-diethyl-glutaryl chloride. This method is not recommended for determination on the micro scale since acid chlorides invariably have appreciable vapor pressure or decompose on prolonged heating.[506]

E. Miscellaneous Methods

1. Precipitation of Lithium Bromide Monohydrate.   Aubry and Monnier[507] determined water in ether by adding a saturated solution of lithium bromide. Lithium bromide monohydrate is quantitatively precipitated. It is then filtered off in a water-free atmosphere, dissolved in water, and the bromide ion is determined by titration with $0.1N$ silver nitrate. For the determination of water in other organic liquids, anhydrous ether is first added before the introduction of saturated lithium bromide solution. It is difficult to convert this method to the micro scale.

2. Gasometric Methods.   Water in organic samples can be determined by gasometric methods for active hydrogen (see p. 409), provided that the organic compounds do not possess active hydrogen groups.

Sirotenko[508] proposed a micro method for determining water in hydrates as follows. The water is extracted with anhydrous pyridine. The pyridine solution is allowed to react with calcium hydride, and the hydrogen gas liberated is measured in the gasometer:

$$2H_2O + CaH_2 \rightarrow 2H_2 + Ca(OH)_2 \tag{71}$$

[504] R. Belcher, J. H. Thompson, and T. S. West, *Anal. Chim. Acta*, **19**, 148 (1958).

[505] R. Belcher, L. Ottendorfer, and T. S. West, *Talanta*, **4**, 116 (1960).

[506] T. S. Ma and D. G. Shaheen, unpublished work; see D. G. Shaheen, *Masters' Thesis, New York University*, 1957.

[507] J. Aubry and G. Monnier, *Compt. rend.*, **235**, 1037 (1952).

[508] A. A. Sirotenko, *Mikrochim. Acta*, **1955**, 917.

3. Colorimetric Methods. A colorimetric method for the determination of water in ketones, esters, and ethers was proposed by Jackwerth and Specker.[509] The sample is treated with cupric perchlorate and lithium chloride in dry acetone, and the extinction of the orange-red $LiCuCl_3$ formed is measured at 366 mμ. Alternately, the sample can be treated with lithium chloride in acetone and titrated photometrically with $0.001M$ cupric perchlorate in acetone until the maximum response is reached. The change in extinction is linear for water contents of 0.1 to 5%.

4. Physical Methods. Water exhibits strong absorption bands in the infrared region owing to the OH stretching and hydrogen bonding. Therefore, infrared spectrometry offers a sensitive method for the determination of traces of water in organic samples that do not contain hydroxyl groups.

Several electrometric methods have been suggested for the determination of water. Keidel[510] described a method to determine water by direct amperometric measurement, which is based on the quantitative electrolysis of water in a specially designed electrolytic cell. Cole and co-workers[511] determined water in organic liquids by means of a continuous coulometric titration system. Water is removed from the sample stream by stripping with counter-current nitrogen gas and is passed through a coulometric cell, consisting of an anhydrous phosphorus pentoxide matrix between platinum electrodes. Accurate analysis was reported at a level as low as 1 ppm. Determination of water in organic samples by measurement of dielectric constant was advocated by two groups of investigators.[512,513] The sample is extracted with anhydrous dioxane. The dielectric constant of the dioxane solution is shown to vary linearly with its water content. Needless to say, this method is limited to the determination of water in nonpolar compounds such as sucrose and the like.

Elvidge and Proctor[514] utilized gas chromatography to determine water in pharmaceutical preparations. The peak height on the recorder was reported to be linearly related to the concentration of water in the sample. The phase rule was employed to determine small traces of water in acetone by Jordan and Fischer,[515] who described a method in which a mixture of

[509] E. Jackwerth and H. Specker, *Z. Anal. Chem.*, **171**, 270 (1959).

[510] F. A. Keidel, *Anal. Chem.*, **31**, 2043 (1959).

[511] L. G. Cole, M. Czuha, R. W. Mosley, and D. T. Sawyer, *Anal. Chem.*, **31**, 2048 (1959).

[512] L. Cavallaro and L. Filloni, *Ind. Saccar. Ital.*, **52**, 57 (1959).

[513] G. Leonardi, E. Mariani, and B. Rumi, *Ind. Saccar. Ital.*, **52**, 68 (1959).

[514] D. A. Elvidge and K. A. Proctor, *Analyst*, **84**, 461 (1959).

[515] K. Jordan and W. R. Fischer, *Z. Anal. Chem.*, **168**, 182 (1959).

the sample (20 ml.) and light petroleum (20 ml.) becomes homogeneous. The water content is obtained from a calibration curve.

Critchfield and Bishop[516] recently proposed an indirect physical method for determining water, which is based on its reaction with 2,2-dimethoxypropane to form acetone. The yield is quantitative, using methanesulfonic acid as a catalyst. The amount of acetone formed is then measured at 5.87 μ.

[516] F. E. Critchfield and E. T. Bishop, *Anal. Chem.*, **33**, 1034 (1961).

PART THREE
Experimental Procedures

12

Microdetermination of Functional Groups with Ordinary Equipment

---

I. Introduction

This chapter deals with the description of experimental procedures for the determination of functional groups on the 0.1 meq. scale that employ conventional glassware and equipment—flasks of various types, pipets, 10-ml. microburets and so on. Since electroanalytical apparatus such as the pH meter and spectrophotometers have become general equipment in the analytical laboratory, experimental methods which entail the use of these devices are also included. However, unless the determination of a particular function cannot be accomplished without using complex or special assemblies and expensive equipment, the procedure that requires simple and inexpensive equipment will be cited as the method of choice. A list of suggested experiments for a laboratory course in organic functional group analysis is given in Appendix B.

Table 12.1 gives a summary of the experimental procedures described in this chapter. The procedures that involve the use of special apparatus and assemblies are described in Chapter 13.

II. Experimental Procedures

Experiment 1: Microdetermination of the Acidic Function by Aqueous Titration

1. Principle. As discussed in Chapter 11, Section II, acidic functions may be determined by titrimetry with a base. Many organic acids are strong enough to be determined by an aqueous titration. For example, benzoic acid is titrable using sodium hydroxide as the titrant:

$$C_6H_5COOH + OH^- \rightleftharpoons C_6H_5COO^- + H_2O \tag{1}$$

TABLE 12.1

Summary of Laboratory Procedures Using Ordinary Equipment

Experiment	Function	Method	Page
1	Acidic	Acidimetry by aqueous titration	481
2	Basic	Alkalimetry by aqueous titration	486
3	Basic	Alkalimetry by nonaqueous titration	487
4	Salts and some sulfur compounds	Perchloric acid titration	490
5	Hydroxyl	Acetylation	493
6	Carbonyl	Oximation	497
7	Carbonyl	Hydrazone formation	500
8	Carbonyl in RCHO and CH_3COR	Addition of sodium bisulfite	502
9	Carbonyl in formaldehyde	Chromotropic acid reaction	504
10	Methylene dioxy	Decomposition with strong acid to H_2CO	506
11	1,2-Diols and carbohydrates	Periodate oxidation	507
12	Ester	Saponification equivalent	510
13	Acyl	Hydrolysis and ion-exchange	513
14	Phenol	Bromination	517
15	Unsaturation (olefinic)	Bromine addition	519
16	Unsaturation (α,β-unsaturated acids)	Bromine addition	522
17	Unsaturation (olefinic)	Addition of mercuric acetate	525
18	Acetylenic	Nonaqueous titration	527
19	Peroxide	Iodometric	529
20	Acid anhydride	Anilide formation	532
21	Acid anhydride	Indirect bromination	534
22	Thiol	Iodimetric	536
23	Sulfide and disulfide	Bromine oxidation	538
24	Thiourea and thio-semicarbazide	Hypoiodite oxidation	541
25	Heterocyclic bases (alkaloids)	Gravimetric	543
26	Quaternary ammonium salts	Gravimetric	544
27	Quaternary ammonium salts	Titrimetric	545
28	Isocyanate and isothiocyanate	Reaction with butylamine	547
29	Alkali sulfonates and sulfoxylates	Gravimetric	549
30	Phosphorus functions	Colorimetric	551

For greater solubility of the acid and to minimize the leftward reaction in equation 1, alcohol is often used as solvent. The presence of carbon dioxide produces a serious error in microdeterminations. This can be eliminated by boiling the solution during titration and especially near the endpoint.

2. Apparatus

A. MICROBURETS. Two automatic zero microburets, capacity 10-ml., graduated to 0.02 or 0.05 ml. are recommended. The reservoir has a capacity of 500 to 1000 ml. One microburet is for the 0.01N sodium hydroxide, another for the 0.01N hydrochloric acid. The buret should be fitted with a guard tube to prevent the entry of carbon dioxide and moisture.

3. Reagents

A. SODIUM HYDROXIDE SOLUTION, 0.01N ($= 0.01M$). Use the commercial $N/100$ standardized sodium hydroxide if available. Pour the contents of a bottle of this reagent into the reservoir of the microburet and replace the guard tube. Check the normality after standing overnight.

If necessary, prepare an approximately 0.01N carbon dioxide-free reagent from sodium hydroxide pellets as follows. Place 25 grams of reagent grade sodium hydroxide pellets and 25 ml. of distilled water in a polyethylene or alkali-resistant glass bottle. Close the bottle with a rubber stopper, wrap it in a towel, and shake it slowly until the sodium hydroxide dissolves. Care should be taken since considerable heat is evolved. Let the solution stand for several days so that any sodium carbonate present will settle to the bottom, leaving a clear supernatant liquid (Note 1). Pipet 0.6 ml. of this stock solution into a 1-liter volumetric flask and fill to the mark with freshly boiled distilled water. Close the flask with a rubber stopper, mix the solution, and let it stand overnight. Then transfer the solution rapidly through a funnel into the reservoir of the microburet.

Standardization. Weigh accurately 15 to 20 mg. of reference standard potassium acid phthalate into a 50-ml. Pyrex conical flask by means of the weighing tube (see Chapter 5, Section V). Add 5 ml. of distilled water and 2 drops (0.05 ml., Note 2) of phenolphthalein indicator. Bring the solution to a boil and while hot, titrate with the approximately 0.01N sodium hydroxide solution to a faint pink color which persists for 30 seconds. Alternately, the standardization can be performed using pure benzoic acid (N.B.S. acidimetric standard) according to the procedure given below for test compounds.

B. PHENOLPHTHALEIN INDICATOR SOLUTION, 1%. Dissolve 100 mg. of the pure indicator in 10 ml. of 95% ethanol.

c. NEUTRAL ETHANOL.   Add 4 to 5 drops of phenolphthalein indicator to 200 ml. of 95% ethanol. Bring the solution to a boil on the water bath and boil 30 seconds. Titrate while hot with $0.01N$ sodium hydroxide to a faint pink color which persists for 30 seconds. Store in a ground-glass stoppered bottle and neutralize with additional $0.01N$ sodium hydroxide if needed during use. Prepare 50% ethanol by mixing equal volumes of neutral ethanol and distilled water.

d. DISTILLED WATER.   Boil the distilled water several minutes and titrate 10 ml. while hot with $0.01N$ sodium hydroxide using 2 drops of phenolphthalein indicator. If more than 1 drop of the base is needed, neutralize as described for the neutral ethanol.

e. HYDROCHLORIC ACID, $0.01N$ ($= 0.01M$).   Use the commercial standard $N/100$ hydrochloric acid if available. Alternately, prepare approximately $0.01N$ hydrochloric acid by combining 0.9 ml. of concentrated hydrochloric acid (reagent grade, 35 to 37% HCl) with 1 liter of recently boiled distilled water. Transfer the $0.01N$ solution to the reservoir of the microburet. Standardize against the standard $0.01N$ sodium hydroxide using phenolphthalein as indicator.

f. TEST COMPOUNDS.   Benzoic acid, m.p. 122.5°C; salicylic acid, m.p. 158.5°C.

4. Procedure.   Using the weighing tube or micro weighing cup (see Chapter 5, Section V), weigh accurately a sample containing 0.05 to 0.1 meq. of acidic function and transfer it into a 50-ml. conical Pyrex flask. Add 5 ml. of neutralized 50% ethanol (Note 3) and 2 drops of phenolphthalein indicator solution. Bring to a boil over a small flame. Titrate while hot with the standardized $0.01N$ sodium hydroxide solution. Boil again at or near the endpoint and complete the titration until the faint pink color of the indicator persists for 30 seconds. If the solution has been overtitrated, add 0.5 to 1 ml. of standardized $0.01N$ hydrochloric acid and back-titrate with the sodium hydroxide solution to the faint pink color which persists for 30 seconds (Note 4).

5. Calculations

A. STANDARDIZATION OF THE NaOH SOLUTION

$$\text{Normality of NaOH} = \frac{\text{mg. of KC}_8\text{H}_5\text{O}_4}{204.22 \times \text{ml. of NaOH}}$$

B. NEUTRALIZATION EQUIVALENT (N.E.).   This is defined as the number of grams of substance required to neutralize 1 liter of normal alkali.

$$\text{N.E.} = \frac{\text{wt. of sample in mg.} \times 100}{\text{ml. of } 0.01N \text{ alkali used}}$$

c. Per Cent Carboxyl Group

$$\% \text{ COOH} = \frac{\text{ml. of } 0.01N \text{ NaOH} \times 0.4502 \times 100}{\text{wt. of sample in mg.}}$$

d. Per Cent Compound

$$\% \text{ Compound} = \frac{\text{ml. of titrant} \times \text{normality} \times \text{meq. wt. of compound in mg.} \times 100}{\text{wt. of sample in mg.}}$$

6. Notes

Note 1. If the concentrated sodium hydroxide is needed before it becomes clarified, attach a filterstick to the end of the pipet as shown in Figure 12.1. The lower end of the filterstick below the constriction C is fitted with a piece of filter paper P, which is rolled up and protrudes 1 to 2 mm. beyond the glass rim. While the solution is sucked up into the pipet, solid particles are retained by the filter paper. The pipet is then removed from the stock bottle, the roll of filter paper is taken out by means of a pair of forceps, and the required amount of sodium hydroxide is delivered into the volumetric flask.

Note 2. The volume of a drop depends on the size of the nozzle and also on the liquid. It is advisable to draw out the tip of the ordinary dropper so that each drop delivers 0.02 to 0.03 ml. of the indicator solution.

Note 3. Neutralized 95% ethanol and ethanol mixed with chloroform or dioxane, respectively, may be employed for samples that do not dissolve readily in 50% ethanol. In that case, the solution should be heated over the steam bath instead of the free flame.

Note 4. It is not feasible to titrate the excess alkali directly with standard 0.01N hydrochloric acid because of the difficulty in observing the disappearance of the pink color.

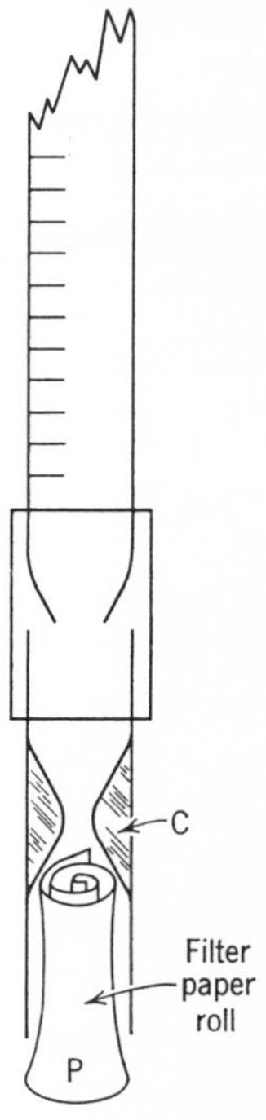

Fig. 12.1. Filterstick attached to pipet.

7. Comments.

This procedure is applicable to organic acids which have K_a values greater than 10^{-6}. Needless to say, any inorganic acid or base present in the sample constitutes an interference. It is not easy to observe the color change of phenolphthalein using 0.01N titrant, since the pink color fades rapidly. But correct results can be obtained after a little practice. This experiment serves as a good introduction to microchemical techniques. It indicates to the beginner the difference between observation on the micro scale and that on the macro scale with which he has had experience. It also demonstrates a simple method to eliminate the interference of carbon dioxide without the use of an elaborate apparatus.

Experiment 2: Microdetermination of the Basic Function by Aqueous Titration

1. Principle. As discussed in Chapter 11, Section IV, quaternary ammonium hydroxide and alkyl amines are sufficiently basic to be titrated in aqueous media with standard hydrochloric or sulfuric acid. Equations 2 and 3 show typical reactions for such titrations:

$$(C_2H_5)_4NOH + HCl \rightarrow (C_2H_5)_4NCl + H_2O \tag{2}$$

$$C_4H_9NH_2 + HCl \rightarrow C_4H_9NH_3^+Cl^- \tag{3}$$

Long-chained alkyl amines insoluble in water may be dissolved in isopropyl alcohol or dioxane prior to titration.

2. Apparatus. Same as in experiment 1.

3. Reagents

A. STANDARD HYDROCHLORIC ACID $(0.01N = M/100)$. See experiment 1.

B. NEUTRAL ISOPROPYL ALCOHOL. Neutralize the commercial isopropyl alcohol with the standard $0.01N$ hydrochloric acid, if necessary, using methyl red as the indicator.

C. METHYL RED INDICATOR SOLUTION (0.1%). Dissolve 0.1 g. of methyl red in 100 ml. of 95% ethanol.

D. TEST COMPOUNDS. *n*-Butylamine, b.p. 78°C; tetraethylammonium hydroxide hexahydrate, m.p. 55°C (usually dispensed as 10% aqueous solution).

4. Procedure. Weigh or measure accurately about 0.1 meq. of the sample and transfer it into a 50-ml. Erlenmeyer flask. Add 5 ml. of distilled water or neutral isopropyl alcohol and 2 drops (0.05 ml.) of methyl red indicator. Titrate the solution with the standard $0.01N$ hydrochloric acid to a definitely pink endpoint.

5. Calculations

A. FOR NEUTRALIZATION EQUIVALENT

$$\text{N.E.} = \frac{\text{wt. of sample in mg.} \times 100}{\text{ml. of } 0.01N \text{ acid used}}$$

B. FOR PER CENT COMPOUND.   See experiment 1.

6. Comments. If methyl red indicator is not available, it is possible to use phenolphthalein as indicator. In this case, the solution containing the sample should be treated with a slight excess of the standard $0.01N$ hydrochloric acid until the pink color disappears, heated over a small flame to a boil, and back-titrated with standard $0.01N$ sodium hydroxide to the pink endpoint (see experiment 1).

Experiment 3: Microdetermination of the Basic Function by Nonaqueous Titration

1. Principle. The reader is referred to Chapter 3, Section II-C and Chapter 11, Section IV for discussion of alkalimetry in nonaqueous media. Briefly stated, when a weak base, such as aniline, is dissolved in a weakly acid medium, such as acetic acid (HAc), the following equilibrium occurs:

$$C_6H_5NH_2 + HAc \rightleftharpoons C_6H_5NH_3^+ + Ac^- \tag{4}$$

The equilibrium is shifted to the right because of the excess of acetic acid. Therefore, when the solution is titrated with a strong acid, such as acetous perchloric acid, the acetate ions act as proton acceptors:

$$Ac^- + H^+ \rightarrow HAc \tag{5}$$

The use of acetic acid in conjunction with nonpolar solvents, such as chloroform or benzene, sharpens the endpoint and hence is generally recommended. Some very weakly basic compounds that do not give satisfactory results in acetic acid alone can be titrated in a medium containing acetic anhydride and acetic acid. For this situation, the titration should be performed at low temperatures to prevent acetylation.

2. Apparatus

A. MICROBURET.   Any suitable microburet can be used (Note 1). A 10-ml. automatic-zero microburet, graduated in 0.02 or 0.05 ml. is preferable.

B. pH METER.   The Beckman model G pH meter with the ordinary $2\frac{1}{2}$-inch glass electrode and fiber-type $2\frac{1}{2}$-inch calomel electrode is satisfactory.

C. MAGNETIC STIRRER

3. Reagents

A. STANDARD ACETOUS PERCHLORIC ACID, $0.01N$ ($= M/100$).   Use the commercial standard $M/100$ perchloric acid in glacial acetic acid when available (Note 2). If necessary, prepare this solution by dissolving 0.85 ml. of 72% perchloric acid in glacial acetic acid and diluting to 1 liter.

B. STANDARD PERCHLORIC ACID IN DIOXANE, $0.01N$ $(= M/100)$. Dissolve 0.85 ml. of 72% perchloric acid in dioxane and dilute to 1 liter with the same solvent.

Standardization. Determine the exact concentration of the $0.01N$ perchloric acid by means of potassium acid phthalate (analytical standard). Use the same microburet (Note 3) and procedure (acetic acid as solvent) as in the determination of the basic compound.

C. INDICATOR SOLUTIONS. 0.1% crystal violet in acetic acid; 0.1% neutral red in acetic acid; 1% dibenzalacetone in acetic acid.

D. SOLVENTS. Reagent grade acetic acid, chloroform, dioxane, and acetic anhydride.

E. TEST COMPOUNDS. Glycine, dec. 233°C, brucine, m.p. 178°C, and diethylaniline, b.p. 215°C for titrations in acetic acid; caffeine, m.p. 238°C, and urea, m.p. 133°C, for titrations in acetic anhydride.

4. Procedures

A. ACETIC ACID AS SOLVENT

Potentiometric titration. Weigh accurately about 0.1 meq. of the sample into a 100-ml. beaker. Add 10 ml. of glacial acetic acid to dissolve the sample. Warm, if necessary, on the hot plate to effect solution. After cooling to room temperature, add 20 ml. of chloroform. Put in the stirring bar and place the beaker on top of the magnetic stirrer. Insert the electrodes into the solution and start the titration with $0.01N$ perchloric acid in dioxane. Deliver the titrant in large increments at first, recording the potential *vs.* the volume of standard acid introduced (Note 4). Add the titrant in 0.02 to 0.05 ml. increments near the equivalence point. Continue the titration until the equivalence point is well passed, adding large amounts of titrant at this stage. Plot potential *vs.* volume of titrant and determine the equivalence point graphically.

Run a blank by using exactly the same procedure, omitting the sample.

Visual titration. Weigh accurately about 0.1 meq. of the sample into a 125-ml. Erlenmeyer flask. Dissolve the sample in 10 ml. of glacial acetic acid as previously described. Add 30 ml. of chloroform and 2 drops (0.1 ml.) of crystal violet indicator solution. Titrate with the standardized $0.01N$ perchloric acid in dioxane until the solution changes from violet to blue. Run a blank similarly.

B. ACETIC ANHYDRIDE AS SOLVENT

Potentiometric titration. Weigh accurately about 0.1 meq. of the sample into a 100-ml. beaker and dissolve it in 5 ml. of acetic anhydride, heating if necessary. After cooling, add 30 ml. of acetic anhydride and titrate the solution with the 0.01N acetous perchloric acid, using the techniques described for acetic acid as solvent.

Use the following modified procedure for basic compounds that might react with acetic anhydride by acetylation (e.g., urea). After dissolving the sample in 5 ml. of acetic acid, cool the solution in an ice bath. Cool 30 ml. of acetic anhydride separately in an ice-salt bath. Add the cooled acetic anhydride to the cold acetic acid solution containing the sample. Perform the titration with the beaker remaining in the ice bath.

Run a blank in a similar manner.

Visual titration.   Weigh accurately about 0.1 meq. of the sample and transfer it into a 125-ml. Erlenmeyer flask. Dissolve the sample in 5 ml. of glacial acetic acid and add 30 ml. of acetic anhydride as described in potentiometric titration. Titrate the solution with 0.01N acetous perchloric acid after adding 0.2 ml. (4 drops) of the proper indicator solution. For caffeine use neutral red which changes from pink to blue at the endpoint, whereas for urea, use dibenzalacetone which changes from colorless to yellow. Run a blank similarly.

5. *Calculations*

A. For Neutralization Equivalent

$$\text{N.E.} = \frac{\text{wt. of sample in mg.} \times 100}{\text{ml. of } 0.01N \text{ acid required}}$$

B. For Per Cent Compound

$$\% \text{ Compound} = \frac{(\text{ml. of titrant for sample} - \text{blank})(\text{normality})(\text{meq. wt. in mg.}) \times 100}{\text{wt. of sample in mg.}}$$

6. *Notes*

Note 1.   A precision-ground or Teflon stopcock should be used. Acetic acid dissolves stopcock grease. If acetic acid leaks through the stopcock and gets onto the hand, it will cause painful irritation. Should this happen, wash the area immediately with water and follow with application of 5% sodium bicarbonate solution.

Note 2.   Since it takes only 0.85 ml. of 72% perchloric acid to make 1 liter of 0.01N solution, it is not advisable to purchase a pound of 72% perchloric acid just to prepare the 0.01N solution. Concentrated perchloric acid is corrosive and an explosive hazard.

Note 3. Since all commercial microburets and pipets are calibrated for work with aqueous solutions, the same measuring device should be used for the standardization as for determinations. In this way errors in measurement are eliminated by compensation.

Note 4. The attainment of a steady potential in nonaqueous titration is sometimes difficult. Therefore, after a potential reading has been taken, the solution is stirred again, and another reading is made. If the two readings agree within 2 mv., it is considered that equilibrium has been reached. If the pH meter acts erratically after a series of titrations, the solution in the calomel electrode should be replaced with fresh saturated potassium chloride solution after a thorough rinsing of the electrode with this solution, and the pH meter should be checked against a standard buffer solution.

7. Comments. The beginner learns the technique of nonaqueous potentiometric titration in this experiment, which, it should be noted, is more involved than potentiometric determination in an aqueous solution.

The procedures described in this experiment are applicable to most amines, alkaloids, and heterocyclic nitrogen compounds. Organic bases with equilibrium constants greater than 10^{-12} can be titrated in acetic acid; those with constants between 10^{-12} and 10^{-14} require acetic anhydride as solvent.

Water has a harmful effect on acid-base titrations in nonaqueous solvents. This can be demonstrated by titrating potassium acid phthalate (analytical standard) in acetic anhydride with the addition of varying amounts of water. With 1% water, the endpoint is still sharp, but occurs somewhat too early. With 2 to 5% water, fair endpoints are still obtainable, but their sharpness is reduced so that they are difficult to locate; in addition, the endpoints occur too early so that 2% less compound is found. If the acetic anhydride containing the added water is allowed to stand for a few days, the sharpness of the endpoint is restored. Allowing a solution of 5% water in acetic anhydride to stand for only 2 hours does not give a beneficial effect. These facts should be kept in mind when a solution is submitted for microtitration, and the possibility is open that the organic solvent may contain water.

Experiment 4: Microdetermination of Salts and Some Sulfur Compounds by Titration with Perchloric Acid

1. Principle. Determination of salts by nonaqueous titration with perchloric acid is discussed in Chapter 7, Section VIII-D and Chapter 8, Section VIII-B-2B. Thus potassium acid phthalate reacts with one mole of perchloric acid:

$$\text{(benzene ring)}\begin{matrix}-\text{COOH}\\-\text{COOK}\end{matrix} + \text{HClO}_4 \rightarrow \text{(benzene ring)}\begin{matrix}-\text{COOH}\\-\text{COOH}\end{matrix} + \text{KClO}_4 \qquad (6)$$

Amine sulfates give an endpoint when the sulfate has been neutralized to the bisulfate:

$$(RNH_3^+)_2SO_4^- + HClO_4 \rightarrow 2(RNH_3^+) + ClO_4^- + HSO_4^- \tag{7}$$

Amine halides require the addition of mercuric acetate (HgAc₂) before titration. The non-ionized mercury halide is formed, and the titration actually involves the neutralization of the liberated acetate ion:

$$2(RNH_3)^+Cl^- + HgAc_2 \rightarrow HgCl_2 + 2RNH_3^+ + 2Ac^- \tag{8}$$

$$Ac^- + HClO_4 \rightarrow HAc + ClO_4^- \tag{9}$$

Certain sulfur compounds, such as thiourea and thiouracil, which do not give observable endpoints on reacting with perchloric acid, also can be titrated after the addition of mercuric acetate. The mechanism has not been elucidated.

2. Apparatus.   See experiment 3.

3. Reagents

A. STANDARD ACETOUS PERCHLORIC ACID, $0.01N$ ($= M/100$).   See experiment 3.

B. STANDARD PERCHLORIC ACID IN DIOXANE, $0.01N$ ($= M/100$).   See experiment 3.

C. STANDARD POTASSIUM ACID PHTHALATE SOLUTION, $0.01N$ ($= M/100$). Dissolve 204.20 mg. of potassium acid phthalate (analytical standard) in hot glacial acetic acid in a 100-ml. volumetric flask. After cooling to room temperature, dilute the solution exactly to the mark.

D. MERCURIC ACETATE SOLUTION, 3%.   Dissolve 3 g. of mercuric acetate in 100 ml. of glacial acetic acid.

E. INDICATOR SOLUTIONS.   0.1% crystal violet in acetic acid; 0.1% quinaldine red in acetic acid.

F. SOLVENTS.   Reagent grade glacial acetic acid, chloroform, dioxane, chlorobenzene, benzene.

G. TEST COMPOUNDS.   Potassium acid phthalate; amphetamine sulfate $[C_6H_5CH_2CH(NH_2)CH_3]_2H_2SO_4$, m.p. $> 300°C$; thiamine hydrochloride, $C_{12}H_{17}ClN_4OS \cdot HCl$, dec. 248°C; thiourea, m.p. 178°C; 2-thiouracil, $C_4H_4N_2OS$, no definite m.p.

4. Procedures

A. DETERMINATION OF ALKALI CARBOXYLATES.   Weigh accurately about 0.1 meq. of the salt by means of the weighing tube (see Chapter 5, Section V-B) and transfer the sample into a 50-ml. Erlenmeyer flask. Dissolve the sample in 5 ml. of glacial acetic acid or the other solvents given previously, warming, if necessary. After cooling to room temperature, add 2 drops (0.1 ml.) of the crystal violet indicator solution. Titrate with the standard 0.01N perchloric acid until the purple color changes to blue.

B. DETERMINATION OF AMINE NITRATES OR SULFATES. Use the foregoing procedure if the sample dissolves readily. For less soluble compounds, use the indirect titration technique as follows. Accurately weigh less than 0.1 meq. of the compound into a 125-ml. Erlenmeyer flask. Add 10 ml. of glacial acetic acid. Introduce exactly 10.00 ml. of 0.01N perchloric acid. Attach a reflux condenser to the flask and heat the solution on a hot plate until the sample disappears. Cool the solution to room temperature. Add 2 drops of crystal violet indicator and note the color. Now deliver into the flask from a pipet or microburet an accurately measured volume (2 to 5 ml.) of the standardized 0.01N potassium acid phthalate solution (Note 1). The color should change to decidedly purple. Then titrate the contents of the flask with the 0.01N perchloric acid.

C. DETERMINATION OF AMINE HALIDES. Weigh accurately about 0.1 meq. of the amine salt into a 50-ml. Erlenmeyer flask. Add 5 ml. of glacial acetic acid and 1 ml. of 3% mercuric acetate solution. After the sample has completely dissolved, add 2 drops of crystal violet indicator and titrate the mixture with 0.01N perchloric acid in dioxane.

D. DETERMINATION OF THIOUREA. Weigh to the μg. 4 to 7 mg. of thiourea into a 50-ml. Erlenmeyer flask. Add 5 ml. of glacial acetic acid and 1 ml. of 3% mercuric acetate solution. Warm to dissolve the solid. After cooling, add 2 drops of quinaldine red indicator. Titrate the solution with 0.01N acetous perchloric acid until the color turns from pink to colorless (Note 2).

E. DETERMINATION OF THIOURACIL. Weigh accurately about 10 mg. of 2-thiouracil into a 50-ml. Erlenmeyer flask. Dissolve the sample in 5 ml. of glacial acetic acid. Add 1 ml. of 3% mercuric acetate solution and mix. Now add exactly 10.00 ml. of 0.01N acetous perchloric acid. Mix again and let the solution stand for 10 minutes. Add 2 drops of quinaldine red indicator. Titrate the solution with the 0.01N potassium acid phthalate until a permanent pink color appears.

5. Calculations. See experiment 3.

6. Notes

Note 1. If standardized 0.01N potassium acid phthalate is not available, weigh accurately 5 to 10 mg. of the primary standard reagent by means of the weighing tube and introduce into the flask. Warm on the hot plate, if necessary, to effect solution.

Note 2. Crystal violet indicator may be used. In that case the endpoint is reached when the purple color turns to green.

7. Comments. The beginner learns the back-titration technique in this experiment. This technique is also recommended for the titration of amino acids which are not readily soluble in acetic acid or neutral solvents.

Potentiometric titration becomes necessary when a colored solution is encountered. However, a yellow solution sometimes can be titrated by means of a visual indicator. For example, amine picrates can be titrated with acetous perchloric acid using Oracet blue B as indicator. The yellow color of the picrate ion combines with the blue color of the indicator and imparts a green color to the solution. This gives place to the true blue color of the indicator shortly before the endpoint, which is indicated by the change to a pink color.

Experiment 5: Microdetermination of the Hydroxyl Function by Acetylation

1. Principle. The most common method for the microdetermination of hydroxyl groups (see Chapter 7, Section IV) is by acetylation with a known excess of acetic anhydride. Equation 10 illustrates the reaction using 1-butanol as an example:

$$C_4H_9OH + (CH_3CO)_2O \rightarrow CH_3COOC_4H_9 + CH_3COOH \qquad (10)$$

When pyridine is used in conjunction with acetic anhydride, the reaction proceeds quantitatively and more rapidly and smoothly as the acetic acid formed in the reaction (eq. 10) combines with pyridine.

After the esterification is completed, the residual acetic anhydride is hydrolyzed by the addition of water:

$$(CH_3CO)_2O + H_2O \rightarrow 2CH_3COOH \qquad (11)$$

The total amount of acetic acid in the resulting mixture is determined by titration with standardized sodium hydroxide solution.

$$CH_3COOH + NaOH \rightarrow CH_3COONa + H_2O \qquad (12)$$

An alternate procedure based on acid-catalyzed acetylation of hydroxyl groups at room temperature is briefly described in Note 5.

2. Apparatus
A. MICROBURET. 10-ml. capacity, graduated in 0.02 or 0.05 ml.
B. REACTION TUBES. Prepare reaction tubes as follows. Cut a piece of 6-mm. soft glass tubing about 140 mm. long. Heat the center part until the glass becomes very soft and then draw the two ends apart as far as

possible. Discard the middle section which is a fine capillary. Use the ampoule cutter to cut off the section where the 6 mm. tubing has narrowed to about 2 mm. Heat this end in the flame to close it and form a round bottom. Thus two reaction tubes, each about 60 mm. long, are made from a length of glass tubing. Use one tube for the sample and the other for the blank.

c. CAPILLARY PIPETS. Draw out medicine droppers to give capillary tips. Alternately, prepare capillary pipets from soft glass tubing and affix a rubber bulb at the wide end.

3. Reagents

A. ACETYLATING REAGENT. Add 10 ml. of reagent grade acetic anhydride to 30 ml. of reagent grade pyridine and mix. Store the mixture in a screw-capped amber bottle (Note 1).

B. STANDARD ALCOHOLIC SODIUM HYDROXIDE, $0.05N$ ($= 5M/100$). Mix 2.8 ml. of saturated aqueous sodium hydroxide (see experiment 1) with 95% ethanol to prepare 1 liter of approximately $0.05N$ alcoholic sodium hydroxide. Determine the exact concentration by titrating 1.00 ml. of this solution against standardized $0.01N$ hydrochloric acid.

C. STANDARD SODIUM HYDROXIDE, $0.01N$ ($= M/100$). See experiment 1.

D. MIXED INDICATOR SOLUTION. Prepare 0.1% neutralized aqueous cresol red solution by adding 26 ml. of $0.01N$ aqueous sodium hydroxide to 100 mg. of the indicator and diluting to 100 ml. Similarly, prepare 0.1% thymol blue solution by adding 22 ml. of $0.01N$ aqueous sodium hydroxide to 100 mg. of the indicator and making up to 100 ml. Prepare the mixed indicator solution by mixing 10 ml. of 0.1% cresol red with 30 ml. of thymol blue. Check the neutrality of the mixture by means of $0.01N$ sodium hydroxide and $0.01N$ hydrochloric acid.

E. TEST COMPOUNDS. 1-Butanol, b.p. 117°C; cyclohexanol, b.p. 161°C (distilled over anhydrous calcium oxide or use Eastman cyclohexanol grade X-703 which does not require any purification); phenol, m.p. 41°C.

4. Procedure

A. PREPARATION OF THE SAMPLE. Place the reaction tube in a small beaker or preferably in the cavity of a small stand (see Figure 5.8b) and weigh to ±0.01 mg. Introduce the solid sample (about 0.1 meq.) by the plunger technique (see Chapter 5, Section V-C, Figure 5.7), or add liquid sample by means of the capillary pipet. Make sure that the sample is placed at the bottom of the reaction tube and no sample touches the upper part of the tube. Weigh the tube containing the sample accurately. Now add the acetylating reagent, by means of another capillary pipet, in 100 to 200 mole-per cent excess (about 75 mg., Note 2). Again weigh to ±0.01 mg.

Quickly seal the reaction tube containing the sample and acetylating reagent by means of a sharp flame (see Chapter 5, Section VII-C, Figure 5.20).

Prepare a blank in another reaction tube which contains about the same quantity of acetylating reagent (accurately weighed) but no sample. Seal the blank tube as described earlier.

B. ACETYLATION. Turn the sealed tubes upside down several times to effect intimate mixing of the contents. Place the tubes in a beaker of water and boil for 1 hour. Then remove the tubes from the water bath and allow them to cool to room temperature.

C. TITRATION. Scratch a line on the upper part of the sealed tube by means of a glass cutter. Touch the line with a hot glass bead to crack the tube. Drop the upper portion into a 50-ml. Erlenmeyer flask containing 5 ml. of distilled water. Carefully empty the contents of the tube into the flask. Wash the tube with 1 ml. of distilled water and empty the washing into the flask. Now scratch a line near the bottom of the tube and crack it with a hot glass bead. Drop the end and center portion of the tube into the flask.

Swirl the Erlenmeyer flask to ensure complete hydrolysis of acetic anhydride. Add 2 drops (0.08 ml.) of the mixed indicator solution (Note 3) and titrate with the standardized 0.05N alcoholic sodium hydroxide until the color changes from yellow to blue (Note 4).

5. *Calculations*

A. FOR PER CENT HYDROXYL GROUP

$$\% \text{ OH} = \frac{(17.01)(a - b)(\text{normality of titrant}) \times 100}{\text{sample wt. in mg.}}$$

where $a = \dfrac{\text{ml. titrant for blank}}{\text{mg. acetyl. reagent for blank}} \times \text{mg. acetyl. reagent for sample}$

b = ml. titrant for sample

B. FOR PER CENT COMPOUND

$$\% \text{ Compound} = \frac{(a - b)(\text{normality})(\text{meq. wt. of compound in mg.}) \times 100}{\text{wt. of sample in mg.}}$$

6. Notes

Note 1. The rate of acetylation is greatly increased by adding a small amount of perchloric acid in the acetylating reagent (see Note 5). The reagent then becomes rather unstable, however, and it is difficult to obtain reproducible results.

Note 2. For multiple determinations in routine analysis, it is more convenient to measure the acetylating reagent accurately by volume using a micro syringe.

Note 3. Phenolphthalein may be used as the indicator (see experiment 1).

Note 4. To obtain high precision, it is advisable to deliver an exact volume (say 8.00 ml.) of the 0.05N alcoholic sodium hydroxide to neutralize about 90% of the acetic acid, and then finish the titration with the standardized 0.01N sodium hydroxide. The 0.05N titrant must be used in the beginning, since the blank contains 0.2 to 0.3 millimoles of acetic anhydride which is equivalent to 40 to 60 ml. of 0.01N sodium hydroxide.

Note 5. The acid-catalyzed acetylation of hydroxyl groups at room temperature [G. H. Schenck and M. Santiago, *Microchem. J.*, **6**, 77 (1962)] employs 0.06M acetic anhydride in anhydrous ethyl acetate and a small amount of perchloric acid as a catalyst. About 0.05 to 0.1 meq. of the hydroxyl group is accurately weighed and added into a 50- or 125-ml. ground-glass stoppered flask. To the sample is added 5 ml. of 0.06M acetic anhydride prepared by addition of 0.40 ml. of acetic anhydride to 50 ml. of perfectly dry (over K_2CO_3 or P_2O_5) ethyl acetate followed by addition of 0.03 ml. of 72% perchloric acid. This solution should be prepared fresh daily. The reaction mixture is shaken for a few seconds and allowed to stand for 20 minutes when 0.5 ml. of water and 4.5 ml. of pyridine are added and allowed to stand for 10 minutes. The reaction mixture is then titrated with 0.05N sodium hydroxide after adding 4 drops of the mixed indicator solution. A reagent blank is run under identical conditions omitting the hydroxyl sample.

7. Comments. This method is suitable for the determination of aliphatic alcohols and phenols, except tertiary alcohols and 2,4,6-tri-substituted phenols which do not react quantitatively. Primary and secondary amines interfere. Low molecular weight aldehydes, if present, may vitiate the results.

The beginner learns in this experiment the technique of performing a quantitative reaction in a sealed tube and the use of the screened indicator.

Soft glass may contain ingredients which react with acetic anhydride. By using the same piece of glass tubing to prepare the sample and blank tubes, this error is eliminated by compensation.

Experiment 6. Semimicro Determination of the Carbonyl Function by Oximation

1. Principle. A titrimetric procedure for determining aldehydes and ketones (see Chapter 6, Section VII-B-1-A) is based on the addition of hydroxylamine, either as the free amine or its hydrochloride, to form an oxime (oximation). The reaction between benzaldehyde and hydroxylamine hydrochloride is given in equation 13:

$$\overset{H}{\underset{|}{C_6H_5C}}{=}O + H_2NOH \cdot HCl \rightleftharpoons C_6H_5{-}\overset{H}{\underset{|}{C}}{=}NOH + H_2O + HCl \qquad (13)$$

A. REACTION IN AQUEOUS MEDIUM. The oximation reaction in equation 13 proceeds at a much faster rate if free hydroxylamine is used. This reagent is very unstable, however. To circumvent this difficulty, one technique is to half-neutralize the hydroxylamine hydrochloride with a strong base producing the free amine as shown in equation 14:

$$H_2NOH \cdot HCl + NaOH \rightarrow H_2NOH + H_2O + NaCl \qquad (14)$$

The resulting solution, although not quite stable, is more so than if the free amine had been used. The oximation reaction now proceeds through the free hydroxylamine. The decrease in alkalinity of the resulting solution is then determined by titration with standard acid. (See also Note 1.)

B. REACTION IN NONAQUEOUS MEDIA. As shown in equation 13, the oximation reaction is favored by removal of the water produced in the reaction. Hence it is advantageous to use an organic amine to half-neutralize the hydroxylamine hydrochloride and carry out the oximation reaction in a nonaqueous medium. The amine chosen should be: (1) strong enough to cause the reaction in equation 15 to proceed rightwards; (2) a tertiary amine in order to prevent side reactions; (3) one whose hydrochloride is soluble in the organic solvent used. Diethylaminoethanol meets all these requirements.

$$H_2NOH \cdot HCl + (C_2H_5)_2NCH_2CH_2OH \rightarrow H_2NOH$$
$$+ [(C_2H_5)_2(CH_2CH_2OH)NH^+] + Cl^- \qquad (15)$$

The oximation proceeds again via the free hydroxylamine. The change in basicity of the reaction is then determined by titration with perchloric acid in a nonaqueous medium.

2. Apparatus
A. MICROBURETS. 10-ml. capacity, graduated in 0.02 or 0.05 ml.

3. Reagents

a. For Aqueous Procedure

A. ALCOHOLIC SODIUM HYDROXIDE, 0.75M.   Dissolve 42.0 g. of a 50% (w/w) sodium hydroxide solution in 688 ml. of 95% ethanol.

B. HYDROXYLAMINE REAGENT.   Dissolve 40.0 g. of hydroxylamine hydrochloride ($H_2NOH \cdot HCl$) in 80 ml. of water; then dilute to 1 liter with 95% ethanol. To this add 400 ml. of the 0.75M alcoholic sodium hydroxide solution and 10 ml. of bromophenol blue indicator solution.

C. STANDARD HYDROCHLORIC ACID, 0.1N (= 0.1M).   Use the commercial standard $M/10$ hydrochloric acid. Alternately, prepare approximately 0.1N solution by diluting 8.5 ml. of reagent grade concentrated hydrochloric acid to 1 liter with distilled water. Determine the exact concentration by titrating 1.00 ml. against standard 0.01N sodium hydroxide.

D. BROMOPHENOL BLUE INDICATOR SOLUTION, 0.4%.   Dissolve 200 mg. of the indicator in 50 ml. of 95% ethanol.

b. For Nonaqueous Procedure

A. SOLVENTS.   Reagent grade isopropyl alcohol, methyl cellosolve, and methanol.

B. TRIS-(HYDROXYMETHYL)-AMINOMETHANE.   Primary standard grade.

C. HYDROXYLAMINE HYDROCHLORIDE SOLUTION, 0.2M.   Dissolve 13.9 g. of the pure salt in 300 ml. of anhydrous methanol and dilute to 1 liter with isopropyl alcohol.

D. DIETHYLAMINOETHANOL SOLUTION, 0.1M.   Dissolve 11.7 g. of the reagent in isopropyl alcohol and make up to 1 liter.

E. STANDARD PERCHLORIC ACID, 0.1N (= $M/10$).   Measure 8.5 ml. of 70% perchloric acid into a 1 liter volumetric flask and dilute to the mark with methyl cellosolve. Standardize against tris-(hydroxymethyl)-aminomethane as follows: Weigh to ±0.01 mg. about 100 mg. of the primary standard reagent into a 125-ml. Erlenmeyer flask and dissolve it in 20 ml. of methanol. Add 2 drops (0.08 to 0.1 ml.) of martius yellow indicator solution and titrate with the perchloric acid solution until the solution turns from yellow to bluish-gray.

F. MARTIUS YELLOW INDICATOR SOLUTION.   Dissolve 66 mg. of martius yellow and 4 mg. of methyl violet in 95% ethanol and dilute to 50 ml.

G. TEST COMPOUNDS.   Vanillin, m.p. 81°C; p-nitrobenzaldehyde, m.p. 106°C; methyl butyl ketone, b.p. 127°C; benzaldehyde, b.p. 179°C.

4. Procedures

A. AQUEOUS PROCEDURE.   Weigh accurately about 0.5 meq. of the carbonyl compound into a 50-ml. Erlenmeyer flask. Pipet 10.00 ml. of the hydroxylamine reagent solution into the flask and mix to dissolve the sample. Allow to stand for 30 minutes (Note 2). Prepare a blank and treat in the same manner.

After the oximation, titrate the reaction mixture and the blank solution, respectively, with the standardized 0.1N hydrochloric acid. The endpoint is from blue to a distinct yellow color.

B. NONAQUEOUS PROCEDURE. Accurately weigh about 0.5 meq. of the sample into a 125 ml. Erlenmeyer flask. Pipet 10.00 ml. of the diethyl-aminoethane solution and 10.00 ml. of the hydroxylamine hydrochloride solution (in that order) into the flask. Mix thoroughly and allow to stand for 30 minutes (Note 2). Add 2 drops of martius yellow indicator solution and titrate with the standardized 0.1N perchloric acid in cellosolve. The endpoint is reached when the yellow solution turns to bluish-gray. Prepare and treat a blank in the exact same manner.

5. Calculations
A. FOR NORMALITY OF THE STANDARD PERCHLORIC ACID

$$N = \frac{\text{mg. of tris-(hydroxymethyl)-aminomethane}}{\text{ml. of HClO' used} \times 121.14}$$

B. FOR PER CENT CARBONYL GROUP

$$\% \ C{=}O = \frac{(28.01)(a - b)(\text{normality of titrant}) \times 100}{\text{wt. of sample in mg.}}$$

where a = ml. of titrant used for blank solution, and b = ml. of titrant used for sample.

C. FOR PER CENT CARBONYL COMPOUND

$$\% \ \text{Compound} = \frac{(a - b)(\text{normality of titrant})(\text{meq. wt. in mg.}) \times 100}{\text{wt. of sample in mg.}}$$

6. Notes
Note 1. Direct titration of the liberated hydrochloric acid by incorporating pyridine in the reagent can be performed on the macro scale using 5 to 10 meq. of the carbonyl compound. Unsatisfactory results are obtained, however, when the sample size is reduced below 1 meq.

Note 2. If the oximation is not quantitative at room temperature, place the flasks in a water bath at 70°C for 1 hour. Then cool to room temperature and titrate.

7. Comments.
This experiment illustrates the difficulty in converting certain macro procedure into a micro method. The semimicro procedure using 0.5 meq. carbonyl group is the lower limit that is possible by the

oximation method. Erratic results will be obtained when 0.1 meq. sample and 0.01N titrant are employed.

Experiment 7: Microdetermination of the Carbonyl Function by Hydrazone Formation

1. Principle. Most carbonyl compounds form insoluble 2,4-dinitrophenylhydrazones under suitable conditions (see Chapter 6, Section VII-B-1-B). The reaction is generally acid catalyzed. A strongly acidic solution is not favorable to hydrazone formation, however, and hydrazones may undergo hydrolysis in an acidic medium. Therefore a moderately strong acid (oxalic acid) is chosen to provide the desired acid strength for the reaction between 2,4-dinitrophenylhydrazine and the carbonyl function. The stoichiometry is illustrated by the formation of benzophenone 2,4-dinitrophenylhydrazone:

$$(C_6H_5)_2C{=}O + (NO_2)_2C_6H_3NHNH_2 \rightarrow (C_6H_5)_2C{=}N{-}NH{-}C_6H_3(NO_2)_2 \downarrow + H_2O \quad (16)$$

The precipitated hydrazone is then separated by filtration, washed, dried, and weighed.

2. Apparatus

A. REACTION TUBE. Use a test tube of 23-mm. inside diameter, 100-mm. length, and 35-ml. capacity.

B. FILTERSTICK. Prepare the filterstick (see Figure 5.23) of 120-mm. length from 4-mm. glass tubing (I.D., 2 mm.) by making a capillary constriction about 10 mm. from the bottom. Fill the bottom of the filterstick with a tiny roll of filter paper and allow the latter to protrude 1 mm. beyond the filterstick.

C. BEAKER, 30-ml. Place the prepared filterstick and reaction tube inside a clean 30-ml. beaker. Always weigh these pieces together.

3. Reagents

A. 2,4-DINITROPHENYLHYDRAZINE REAGENT SOLUTION. Weigh 0.1 g. of oxalic acid, C.P., and 0.02 g. of 2,4-dinitrophenylhydrazine, C.P., into a 100-ml. volumetric flask (Note 1). Add methanol to the mark, stopper the flask, and shake the contents vigorously. Let the insoluble solids settle on standing. Pipet the clear supernatant liquid for analysis; filtration is unnecessary.

B. SOLVENT. Reagent grade methanol.

C. TEST COMPOUNDS. Benzophenone, m.p. 48°C; vanillin, m.p. 81°C; progesterone, m.p. 127°C.

4. Procedure

A. WEIGHING THE SAMPLE. Place the clean, dry reaction tube, filterstick, and beaker on the left pan of the semimicro balance. Place a second 30-ml. beaker and test tube on the right pan to serve as the counterpoise, and add lead shots to the counterpoise until the two sides are balanced with the rider sitting between 0 and 5 mg. on the beam (Note 2). If the sample is a solid, introduce it directly into the reaction tube by means of the microspatula. If the sample is a semi-solid or an oil, use a microboat (see Figure 5.5) which is preweighed with the beaker. Insert the microboat containing the sample into the reaction tube after weighing. If the sample is a low-boiling liquid, use the microweighing bottle (see Figure 5.10) with ground-glass stopper. Carefully slide the microweighing bottle containing the sample into the reaction tube after the weight has been taken. Record the weight to ±0.01 mg.

B. PRECIPITATION. Remove the beaker containing the filterstick and reaction tube with the sample from the balance. Add 4 ml. of methanol into the reaction tube. If the sample is weighed in the microweighing bottle, use a wire hook to disengage the stopper. Pipet a 20-ml. aliquot of the 2,4-dinitrophenylhydrazine reagent solution into the reaction tube. Mix the contents thoroughly by swirling the tube with a finger. Fifteen minutes after the appearance of the precipitate, remove the reaction tube from the beaker and place it in an ice-water bath for 1 hour, or until the precipitate settles to the bottom.

C. FILTRATION, DRYING, AND REWEIGHING. Wipe the outside of the reaction tube and replace it in the beaker. Connect the filterstick through a rubber tubing to the siphon which leads to the filtrate receiver (see Figure 5.23). Immerse the filterstick in the solution in such position that the filter mat is just above the precipitate and draw off the supernatant liquid. Use small amounts of 1:1 methanol-water mixture to wash the precipitate free of the 2,4-dinitrophenylhydrazine reagent. The washing is complete when the liquid passing through the siphon becomes colorless. Then disconnect the filterstick and wipe its tip which has been attached to the rubber tubing.

Dry the precipitate, filterstick, reaction tube and beaker at 75°C. Weigh to ±0.01 mg.

5. Calculations

A. FOR PER CENT CARBONYL GROUP (NOTE 3).

$$\% \text{ C=O} = \frac{\text{wt. ppt.}}{\text{wt. sample}} \times \frac{28.01}{\text{mol. wt. of hydrazone}} \times 100$$

B. For Per Cent Compound

$$\% \text{ Compound} = \frac{\text{wt. ppt.}}{\text{wt. sample}} \times \frac{\text{mol. wt. of compound}}{\text{mol. wt. of hydrazone}} \times 100$$

6. Notes

Note 1. It is not advisable to prepare a large volume of stock solution because the reagent deteriorates on long standing and exposure to air.

Note 2. No counterpoise is used with the single-pan balance. In this case the total weight should be recorded to ±0.01 mg.

Note 3. The formula given requires the molecular weight of the 2,4-dinitrophenylhydrazone and hence is applicable to known carbonyl compounds only. If the empirical formula of the sample is not known, the precipitate after weighing can be analyzed for total nitrogen (see experiment 35) or nitro groups (see experiment 37). The percentage of carbonyl group is then calculated from the number of equivalents of 2,4-dinitrophenylhydrazine consumed.

7. Comments. This experiment demonstrates gravimetric microanalysis. Advantage is taken of the large gravimetric factor of 2,4-dinitrophenylhydrazones. Hence, an accurate determination of 0.1 meq. of the carbonyl group can be performed on a semimicro balance sensitive to ±0.01 mg.

By using the inverted filtration technique, only three weighings are needed. This is more convenient and expedient than the method of four weighings commonly practiced in gravimetric analysis on the macro scale.

Experiment 8: Semimicro Determination of Aldehydes and Methyl Ketones by Sodium Bisulfite Addition

1. Principle. Aldehydes and methyl ketones form addition products with sodium bisulfite (see Chapter 6, Section VII-B-2-A). Thus benzaldehyde reacts according to equation 17:

$$\underset{\text{H}}{C_6H_5\overset{\displaystyle|}{C}{=}O} + NaHSO_3 \rightleftharpoons C_6H_5 \overset{\displaystyle\overset{\text{H}}{|}}{\underset{\displaystyle\underset{SO_3Na}{|}}{C}} {-}OH \qquad (17)$$

Besides the nature of the carbonyl compound, the distribution of this reversible reaction at equilibrium depends on the pH of the reaction mixture, the temperature, the concentration of the solution, and the excess of bisulfite. If the conditions are found such that the reaction proceeds nearly to completion, the excess of bisulfite ions in the solution can be determined by iodimetry, either by direct titration with standardized iodine solution (eq. 18) or by adding a known volume of iodine solution and back-titrating the excess of iodine with $0.05N$ sodium thiosulfate as shown in equation 19:

$$HSO_3^- + I_2 + H_2O \rightarrow 2HI + HSO_4^- \qquad (18)$$

$$I_2 + 2Na_2S_2O_3 \rightarrow 2NaI + Na_2S_4O_6 \qquad (19)$$

2. Apparatus

A. MICROBURETS. 10-ml. capacity, graduated in 0.02 or 0.05 ml. (Note 1).

B. IODINE FLASK. 125 ml. capacity.

3. Reagents

A. SODIUM BISULFITE REAGENT SOLUTION (APPROXIMATELY $0.3M$). Dissolve 3.1 g. of reagent grade sodium bisulfite in 100 ml. of distilled water (Note 2).

B. STANDARD IODINE SOLUTION, $0.1N$ ($= M/20$). Use the commercial standardized $N/10$ iodine if available. Alternately, prepare this solution as follows: weigh 12.691 g. of resublimed iodine into a 1-liter volumetric flask; add 40 g. of potassium iodide and a small amount of water until the iodine dissolves; then make up to the mark with distilled water. Standardize against $0.1N$ sodium thiosulfate or arsenous acid (As_2O_3, primary standard).

C. STANDARD SODIUM THIOSULFATE SOLUTION, $0.1N$ ($= M/10$). Use the commercially available $N/10$ standard sodium thiosulfate. Alternately, prepare this solution by dissolving 24.819 g. of $Na_2S_2O_3 \cdot 5H_2O$ in water and dilute to 1 liter.

D. STARCH INDICATOR SOLUTION, 0.5%. Dissolve 0.5 g. of soluble starch in boiling water. Cool to room temperature before use.

E. TEST COMPOUNDS. Benzaldehyde, b.p. 179°C; formaldehyde (aqueous solution); acetoacetanilide, m.p. 85°C.

4. Procedures

A. DIRECT TITRATION PROCEDURE. Weigh accurately a sample containing 0.3 to 0.5 meq. of the carbonyl group (Note 3) into the 125-ml. iodine flask. Add 5.00 ml. of the sodium bisulfite reagent solution followed by 5.00 ml. of distilled water. Prepare a blank in the exact same manner, without the sample. Stopper the flasks, mix the contents, and allow them to stand for 1 hour. Add 0.5 ml. of the starch indicator solution. Titrate both sample and blank as rapidly as possible with the standardized $0.1N$ iodine to the blue endpoint.

B. BACK-TITRATION PROCEDURE. Prepare the blank and sample as described in Procedure A. After letting it stand for 1 hour, introduce the standardized $0.1N$ iodine from the microburet until the solution becomes pale yellow, swirling the flask constantly. Then add about 1 ml. more so that the level of the $0.1N$ iodine in the microburet reaches an even mark. Close the flask and swirl for 1 minute. Now titrate the excess of iodine in the reaction mixture with the standardized $0.1N$ sodium thiosulfate. Add 1 ml. of starch indicator solution when the solution becomes very faintly yellow, and continue titration until the blue color disappears.

5. Calculations

A. FOR PER CENT CARBONYL GROUP

$$\% \; C{=}O = \frac{(28.01)(\text{ml. of I}_2 \text{ soln. consumed})(\text{normality}) \times 100}{2 \times \text{wt. of sample in mg.}}$$

B. FOR PER CENT COMPOUND

$$\% \; \text{Compound} = \frac{(\text{ml. of I}_2 \text{ soln. consumed})(\text{normality})(\text{meq. wt. in mg.}) \times 100}{2 \times \text{wt. of sample in mg.}}$$

6. Notes

Note 1.   More than 10 ml. of standard iodine solution will be required for each determination. However, since the determination is dependent on the difference between the sample and the blank, the 10-ml. microburet gives better precision than the conventional 50-ml. buret.

Note 2.   It is not advisable to prepare a large quantity of sodium bisulfite solution because the reagent is not stable.

Note 3.   One meq. of the carbonyl group means the weight in mg. of the compound containing one $C{=}O$ group, and not the weight of the compound which consumes 10 ml. of $0.1N$ iodine solution. In the present case, 1 meq. of the carbonyl group consumes 20 ml. of $0.1N$ iodine solution. Hence the factor "2" appears in the denominator in the formula for the calculation of per cent carbonyl or per cent compound.

7. Comments.   It is important to run the blank and sample in an identical manner, since a slight variation may cause big errors.

Rapid titration is necessary since aldehydes are susceptible to oxidation by iodine.

This experiment can be converted to the micro scale. In view of the aforementioned difficulties, however, inexperienced workers may not obtain satisfactory results with 0.1 meq. samples.

Experiment 9: Colorimetric Determination of Formaldehyde by the Chromotropic Acid Method

1. Principle.   Formaldehyde develops a purple color on treatment with chromotropic acid in the presence of concentrated sulfuric acid (see Chapter 6, Section VII-C). Although the chemistry involved is not known, this method provides a specific procedure for the determination of formaldehyde.

2. Apparatus

A. REACTION TUBE. Use 22-mm. × 175-mm. test tube fitted with ground-glass stopper.

B. SPECTROPHOTOMETER. Beckman model D or spectrophotometer of other type for the visual range (Note 1).

3. Reagents

A. CHROMOTROPIC ACID REAGENT SOLUTION, 10%. Dissolve 2 g. of chromotropic salt (Eastman Organic Chemicals No. 230: 4,5-dihydroxy-2,7-naphthalenedisulfonic acid disodium salt) in 20 ml. of distilled water.

B. SULFURIC ACID. Concentrated, C.P.

C. TEST COMPOUND. Formaldehyde (aqueous solution).

4. Procedure

A. PREPARATION OF THE CALIBRATION CURVE. Prepare an aqueous solution containing 100 μg. of formaldehyde per ml. Measure 1.00, 1.20, 1.40, 1.60, 1.80, and 2.00 ml., respectively, into six reaction tubes. Add 1.00 ml. of the chromotropic acid reagent solution into each tube and mix. Then carefully introduce 10 ml. of concentrated sulfuric acid along the wall of the reaction tube. Stopper the tube and mix the solution by swirling. Place the six reaction tubes in a boiling water bath for 30 minutes. Remove the tubes from the bath and allow to cool to room temperature. Quantitatively transfer the contents into six 100-ml. volumetric flasks and dilute to the mark with distilled water.

Measure the transmittance of the resulting solutions at 570 mμ. Plot the transmittance against the concentration of formaldehyde. A straight line should be obtained, which may or may not pass through the origin.

B. ANALYSIS OF THE SAMPLE. Measure accurately an aliquot of the sample in water solution such that the amount of formaldehyde present is between 100 and 200 μg., whereas the volume is between 1 and 2 ml. Deliver the aliquot into a reaction tube and proceed exactly as in the preparation of the calibration curve described in Step A. Take the transmittance of the resulting solution using the same spectrophotometer. Determine the amount of formaldehyde from the calibration curve (Note 2).

5. Calculations

A. FOR PER CENT FORMALDEHYDE

$$\% \text{ HCHO} = \frac{\text{wt. of HCHO found}}{\text{vol. of aliquot}} \times \frac{\text{total vol. of sample soln.}}{\text{wt. of sample}} \times 100$$

6. Notes

Note 1. A colorimeter may be used if a spectrophotometer is not available, but the result will be less accurate. In this case, a calibration curve is not prepared, but the sample is compared with one or more standard solutions processed in the exact same manner.

Note 2. Since the chromotropic acid reagent solution is not very stable, the intensity of color developed may vary with the age of the reagent. However, it is not necessary to prepare a new calibration curve for each set of determinations. The equation of the original calibration curve (a straight line) can be derived from its slope and intercept. By running a formaldehyde solution of known concentration with each set of determinations, the displacement of the curve is discovered and the proper correction can be made.

7. Comments. This experiment demonstrates the use of colorimetric. methods for the determination of known compounds. The pure compound (or a sample of known purity) is required in the procedure.

Colorimetric methods can seldom be applied directly to determinations on the 0.1 meq. scale. For instance, if the amount of formaldehyde present is 0.1 meq. (= 3.0 mg.), it is necessary to dilute the sample solution to 25.00 ml. and take 1.00 ml. aliquot for the development of the purple color.

Experiment 10: Microdetermination of the Methylene Dioxy Function by Decomposition with Strong Acid

1. Principle. As was discussed in Chapter 7, Section V, the methylene dioxy function is decomposed by strong acids to liberate a mole of formaldehyde. For example, the bis-methylenedioxy derivative of cortisone produces on heating with sulfuric acid two equivalents of formaldehyde, which is determined colorimetrically with chromotropic acid.

2. Apparatus
A. SPECTROPHOTOMETER

3. Reagents
A. CHROMOTROPIC ACID REAGENT SOLUTION, 2%. Dissolve 2 g. of chromotropic salt in 100 ml. of distilled water.
B. SULFURIC ACID. Concentrated, C.P.
C. TEST COMPOUND. Cortisone BMD.

4. Procedure. Weigh accurately about 4 mg. of the test compound into a 100-ml. volumetric flask. Dissolve the sample in 20 ml. of 95% ethanol and dilute the solution with distilled water to the mark.

Transfer a 1.00-ml. aliquot to each of three 10-ml. volumetric flasks.

Place the flasks in the ice-water bath. Add 5 drops of 2% chromotropic acid reagent solution, followed by 4 ml. of concentrated sulfuric acid. Now heat the solutions in a water bath at 65°C for 5, 20, and 120 minutes, respectively (Note 1). At the end of the heating period, replace the flasks in the ice-water bath and dilute the solution to the mark with distilled water. Measure the transmittance of the respective solutions at 570 mμ. against a blank run in the same manner. Determine the amount of formaldehyde in each flask by comparing to the calibration curve which has been prepared by measuring various quantities of formaldehyde (see experiment 9). If two of the three values agree, the liberation of formaldehyde is considered complete. Otherwise, repeat the experiment by heating for longer periods.

5. Calculations

A. FOR PER CENT METHYLENE DIOXY GROUP

$$\% \ CH_2O_2{<} = \frac{(46.03)}{(30.03)} \times \frac{\text{mg. of } H_2CO \text{ found}}{\text{mg. of sample}} \times 100$$

B. FOR PER CENT COMPOUND

$$\% \ \text{Compound} = \frac{(\text{mg. of } H_2CO \text{ found})(\text{meq. wt. of compound in mg.}) \times 100}{(30.03) \qquad\qquad (\text{wt. of sample in mg.})}$$

6. Note

Note 1. Owing to the variation of the rate of hydrolysis of different compounds, it is advisable to perform the reaction at varying lengths of time. Some steroids require a 2-hour heating period for the complete hydrolysis of the methylene dioxy group.

Experiment 11: Microdetermination of 1,2-Glycols and Carbohydrates by Periodate Oxidation

1. Principle. The use of periodic acid in organic analysis was discussed in Chapter 6, Section VIII-B-1 and Chapter 7, Section IV-C-1. As shown in equations 20 to 22, 1,2-glycol consumes 1 molar equivalent of periodic acid; glucose requires 5 moles of the reagent, whereas fructose requires 4 moles:

$$CH_2OH{-}CH_2OH + HIO_4 \rightarrow 2H_2CO + HIO_3 + H_2O \qquad (20)$$

$$CH_2OH{-}(CHOH)_4{-}CHO + 5HIO_4 \rightarrow H_2CO + 5HIO_3 + 5HCOOH \qquad (21)$$

$$CH_2OH{-}(CHOH)_3{-}CO{-}CH_2OH + 4HIO_4 \rightarrow H_2CO + 4HIO_3 + 3HCOOH$$
$$+ CH_2OH{-}COOH \qquad (22)$$

The method described in this experiment involves (1) treatment of the sample with a measured amount of periodic acid; (2) partial neutralization of the solution after the oxidation has been completed; (3) introduction of a known volume of $0.06N$ sodium arsenite (eq. 23); and (4) titration of the excess of arsenite by means of $0.025N$ iodine to the starch endpoint (eq. 24).

$$HIO_4 + Na_3AsO_3 + NaHCO_3 \rightarrow NaIO_3 + Na_3AsO_4 + H_2CO_3 \qquad (23)$$

$$I_2 + Na_3AsO_3 + 2NaHCO_3 + H_2O \rightarrow 2NaI + Na_3AsO_4 + 2H_2CO_3 \qquad (24)$$

2. Apparatus

A. MICROBURET.   10-ml. capacity, graduated in 0.02 or 0.05 ml., Koch type (see Chapter 5, Section VI-A).

B. REACTION FLASKS.   Use 75-ml. Erlenmeyer flasks with ground-glass stoppers, or 125-ml. iodine flasks.

C. MAGNETIC STIRRER

3. Reagents

A. PERIODIC ACID REAGENT SOLUTION, $0.1N$ ($= 0.05M$).   Weigh 11.501 g. of potassium metaperiodate (KIO_4) into an 800-ml. beaker. Add 400 ml. of distilled water and 100 ml. of $1N$ sulfuric acid. Stir and heat, if necessary, until all solid particles dissolve. Transfer to a 1-liter volumetric flask. After cooling to room temperature, dilute to the mark.

B. STANDARD SODIUM ARSENITE SOLUTION, $0.06N$ ($= 0.03M$).   Accurately weigh 2.9673 g. of arsenic trioxide (primary standard grade) into a 250-ml. Erlenmeyer flask. Add 60 ml. of $1N$ sodium hydroxide and heat until the solid dissolves. Now add 100 ml. of distilled water and 2 drops of phenolphthalein indicator. Acidify the solution by adding $3N$ hydrochloric acid and then add 2 drops of acid in excess. Quantitatively transfer the solution into a 1-liter volumetric flask. Dilute to the mark after the solution has been equilibrated to room temperature.

C. STANDARD IODINE SOLUTION, $0.025N$ ($= M/80$).   Weigh accurately 3.1728 g. of iodine (resublimed grade) into a 1-liter volumetric flask. Rinse the neck of the flask with 25 ml. of distilled water containing 8.3 g. of potassium iodide. Add water and shake the flask until all the iodine dissolves. Then dilute to the mark and transfer to the microburet when needed (Note 1).

Standardize the iodine solution in the following manner. Deliver exactly 4.00 ml. of the standard $0.06N$ sodium arsenite solution into a 50-ml. Erlenmeyer flask. Add 2 ml. of saturated sodium bicarbonate solution and 0.2 ml. of the starch indicator solution. Introduce the stirring bar (Note 2) and place the flask on the magnetic stirrer. Titrate the solution with the iodine solution from a 10-ml. microburet (Note 3).

D. POTASSIUM IODIDE SOLUTION, 20%. Dissolve 20 g. of potassium iodide (reagent grade) in 80 ml. of distilled water. Store in an amber bottle.

E. STARCH INDICATOR SOLUTION, 0.5%. Grind 1 g. of soluble starch with 10 mg. of mercuric iodide to a smooth paste in 5 ml. of cold water. Pour the paste into 200 ml. of boiling water and boil for 5 min.

F. SODIUM BICARBONATE SOLUTION, SATURATED. Add 12 g. of sodium bicarbonate to 100 ml. of distilled water and shake until a saturated solution is obtained.

G. SODIUM BICARBONATE. Anhydrous, reagent grade.

H. TEST COMPOUNDS. Ethylene glycol, b.p. 197°C; D-glucose, dec. 147°C; D-fructose, dec. 103°C; D-sorbitol, m.p. 110°C.

4. *Procedure.* Pipet 5.00 ml. of the periodic acid reagent solution into each of two reaction flasks. Weigh accurately a sample containing about 0.1 meq. of 1,2-diol function (Note 4) into one of the two flasks, the other being used for blank determination. Stopper both flasks and shake the contents occasionally. After the oxidation reaction is completed (30 minutes for simple glycols, 60 minutes for monosaccharides, 90 minutes for complex glycols), add the stirring bar and then 5 ml. of saturated sodium bicarbonate solution by means of a pipet while stirring the solution vigorously. Now introduce exactly 10.00 ml. of the standard $0.06N$ sodium arsenite. Add 0.5 ml. of 20% potassium iodide solution and then 2 g. of anhydrous sodium bicarbonate. Allow both the sample and blank to stand for 15 minutes with occasional agitation. Then add 0.2 ml. of starch indicator solution and titrate the contents in each flask with the standardized $0.025N$ iodine while the solution is stirred magnetically. The endpoint is the appearance of a faint blue color.

5. *Calculations*

A. FOR PER CENT COMPOUND

$$\% \text{ Compound} = \frac{(s - b)(N)(M) \times 100}{2(W)(E)}$$

where s = ml. of sodium arsenite equivalent consumed by sample, b = ml. of sodium arsenite equivalent consumed by blank, N = normality of sodium arsenite, M = molecular weight of compound, W = weight of sample in mg., and E = moles of periodate reacting per mole of compound.

B. FOR PER CENT DIOL GROUP (NOTE 5)

$$\% \text{ (OH)}_2 = \frac{(s - b)(N)(17.01) \times 100}{W}$$

6. Notes

Note 1. Because iodine solution is sensitive to light, it is not advisable to store the standard solution in the microburet with 1-liter reservoir.

Note 2. Magnetic stirring is desirable in this experiment. However, the determination can be performed by swirling the titration flask.

Note 3. For best results, the 0.025N iodine solution should be standardized daily.

Note 4. One-tenth meq. of 1,2-diol function is the amount of sample which will react with 0.1 millimole of periodic acid.

Note 5. This formula can only be used for simple 1,2-glycols.

7. Comments. Periodic acid oxidation may be employed to determine several types of functional groups. Besides 1,2-glycols and carbohydrates, any adjacent hydroxyl, carbonyl adjacent to an hydroxyl, adjacent carbonyl groups which hydrate, and adjacent amino-hydroxyl linkages in which the amino group is not tertiary are quantitatively oxidized under the conditions described in this experiment. The following classes of compounds react with periodic acid nonstoichiometrically. Hence they constitute interferences: 1,2-diketones which do not hydrate, 1,2-diamines, α-keto acids, phenols, thiols, sulfinic acids, disulfides, compounds containing active methylene groups, and compounds like oximes and hydrazones which can be cleaved under the experimental conditions to form products which react with periodic acid.

0.1N Periodic acid and 0.06N sodium arsenite are used so that the former solution may be delivered with a 5 ml. pipet and the latter with a 10 ml. pipet to allow 20% excess.

Experiment 12: Semimicro Determination of the Saponification Equivalent or Saponification Number

1. Principle. The saponification equivalent discussed in Chapter 7, Section III-B-1, is a method to determine the molecular weight of a pure ester. For instance, 1 mole of ethyl benzoate consumes 1 mole of potassium hydroxide upon complete hydrolysis:

$$C_6H_5COOC_2H_5 + KOH \rightarrow C_6H_5COOK + C_2H_5OH \tag{25}$$

Similarly, triacetin requires 3 moles of potassium hydroxide:

$$(CH_3COO)_3C_3H_5 + 3KOH \rightarrow 3CH_3COOK + CH_2OHCHOHCH_2OH \tag{26}$$

In practice, the ester is treated with a known amount of potassium hydroxide and heated to complete the hydrolytic reaction. The residual alkali is then determined by back-titration with standard acid. If the sample is pure and the nature of its parent acid (mono- or diprotic) and alcohol (mono- or polyhydroxy) is known, the molecular weight of the ester can be calculated. On the other hand, if the sample consists of a mixture, which is very common for ester analysis, or is a compound of unknown nature, the analytical result can only be expressed in terms of the quantity of potassium hydroxide consumed, either as the saponification equivalent or saponification number. The former value indicates the weight of sample in milligrams which reacts with 1 meq. of alkali. The latter number gives the weight in mg. of potassium hydroxide (Note 1) which will be consumed by 1000 mg. of the sample.

Since esters in general are insoluble in water, and their hydrolytic cleavage does not take place instantaneously, an aqueous solution of potassium hydroxide cannot be used for quantitative saponification. Therefore an organic solvent and elevated temperatures are necessary. The sealed-tube technique is recommended for micro and semimicro determinations, because it provides a means to heat the reaction mixture without the danger of losing the sample through volatilization.

2. Apparatus

A. REACTION TUBE.   See experiment 5 for instruction to make the tube, but use an 8-mm. Pyrex tubing if an oxygen torch is available (Note 2).

B. MICROBURET.   10-ml. capacity, graduated in 0.02 or 0.05 ml.

C. HEATING DEVICE.   Use a metal heating block or a sand bath.

3. Reagents

A. POTASSIUM HYDROXIDE REAGENT SOLUTION, $1N$ ($= 1M$).   Dissolve 64 g. (Note 3) of potassium hydroxide pellets (reagent grade) in diethylene glycol (Note 4) and dilute to 1 liter with the same solvent. Determine the titer of this solution by pipetting 1.00 ml. into a 50-ml. Erlenmeyer flask, adding 10 ml. of distilled water, and titrating with the standard $0.1N$ hydrochloric acid to the phenolphthalein endpoint. Store this reagent in a polyethylene bottle.

B. STANDARD HYDROCHLORIC ACID, $0.1N$.   See experiment 6.

C. PHENOLPHTHALEIN INDICATOR SOLUTION, 1%.   See experiment 1.

D. TEST COMPOUNDS.   Ethyl benzoate, b.p. 211°C; dimethyl phthalate, b.p. 284°C; triacetin, b.p. 258°C.

4. Procedure.   Place the reaction tube in a beaker and weigh to ±0.05 mg. Introduce to the bottom of the reaction tube by means of a capillary pipet (or plunger for solids) a sample which will consume about 0.3 meq. of potassium hydroxide and reweigh to ±0.05 mg. Quickly add 1.00 ml. of the potassium hydroxide reagent solution and seal the reaction tube in the oxygen flame. Using the same pipet, add 1.00 ml. of the same reagent to a blank tube made of the same glass, then seal the blank tube. Heat both tubes in the metal heating block or sand bath at 150°C for 1 to 3 hours. After cooling to room temperature, open the tubes separately, transfer the contents into 75-ml. Erlenmeyer flasks (see experiment 5) using 15 ml. of distilled water. Add 4 drops (0.2 ml.) of phenolphthalein indicator solution and titrate with the standardized 0.1N hydrochloric acid until the solution is just colorless.

5. Calculations

A. FOR SAPONIFICATION EQUIVALENT

$$\text{Sap. Equiv.} = \frac{\text{wt. of sample in mg.}}{(b - s)(\text{normality of HCl})}$$

where b = ml. HCl for titration of blank, and s = ml. HCl for titration of sample.

B. FOR SAPONIFICATION NUMBER

$$\text{Sap. No.} = \frac{(b - s)(1000)(56.10)(\text{normality of HCl})}{\text{wt. of sample in mg.}}$$

C. FOR PER CENT COMPOUND

$$\% \text{ Compound} = \frac{(b - s)(\text{normality of HCl})(\text{meq. wt. of ester in mg.}) \times 100}{\text{wt. of sample in mg.}}$$

6. Notes

Note 1. The same formula for the calculation of saponification number is used, whether sodium or potassium hydroxide is employed as hydrolytic reagent.

Note 2. Pyrex glass is more resistant to alkali than soft glass and, hence, gives reproducible results more easily. Soft glass may be used, however, if an oxygen flame is not available. In case the blank indicates considerable variation from the original titer of the 1N potassium hydroxide reagent solution, both blank and sample determinations should be run in duplicate.

Note 3. The exact amount is not given here because pure potassium hydroxide (mol. wt., 56.10) is not commercially available. The reagent grade pellets contain about 85% KOH.

Note 4. Potassium hydroxide is preferable to sodium hydroxide because sodium salts might produce an emulsion on titration. Methanol or *n*-amyl alcohol may be used as the solvent, but the former has low boiling point and the latter is not completely miscible with water.

7. Comments.
This experiment can be reduced to the micro (0.1 meq.)

scale by using $0.5N$ potassium hydroxide reagent solution and standardized $0.05N$ hydrochloric acid, respectively. More caution is needed, however, to obtain the same precision and accuracy as in the semimicro method. Determination of the endpoint by potentiometric titration is recommended for microdetermination.

Amides can be determined by the same procedure except that the heating time should be extended and the resulting solution should be boiled to remove the ammonia or alkyl amine before titration. Anilides are even more resistant to saponification. Hence it is advisable to heat two reaction tubes containing the same sample for different lengths of time and compare the results.

Obviously any free acid present in the original sample constitutes an interference. This can be corrected, however, by titration of a sample for acid in the original sample (see experiment 1). On the other hand, if tertiary aldehydes are present and the Cannizaro reaction occurs, it is difficult to correct for the amount of alkali consumed by the side reactions.

Experiment 13: Microdetermination of the Acyl Function by Hydrolysis and Ion-Exchange

1. Principle. The acyl function (see Chapter 6, Section V) in esters, amides and anilides can be determined by: (1) hydrolysis in the presence of sodium hydroxide to form the corresponding sodium salt; (2) liberation of the free carboxylic acid through ion-exchange, and (3) titration of the free acid. The equations for the determination of methyl laurate are given below.

$$CH_3(CH_2)_{10}COOCH_3 + NaOH \rightarrow CH_3(CH_2)_{10}COONa + CH_3OH \quad (27)$$

$$CH_3(CH_2)_{10}COONa + (R-SO_3)H \rightarrow CH_3(CH_2)_{10}COOH + (R-SO_3)Na \quad (28)$$

$$CH_3(CH_2)_{10}COOH + NaOH \rightarrow CH_3(CH_2)_{10}COONa + H_2O \quad (29)$$

A strongly acidic ion-exchange resin is required to quantitatively displace the carboxylic acid. Since long-chain fatty acids are insoluble in water, the elution is carried out in an alcohol-water mixture.

2. Apparatus

A. REACTION TUBE. Use 10×75-mm. soft glass test tube without flange (see Chapter 5, Figure 5.20).

B. ION-EXCHANGE COLUMN. Use a 10-ml. ordinary buret, graduated in 0.1 ml. (Note 1).

C. MICROBURET. 10-ml. capacity, graduated in 0.02 or 0.05 ml. (see experiment 1).

D. HEATING DEVICE. Use the metal heating block or sand bath.

3. Reagents

A. SODIUM HYDROXIDE SAPONIFYING REAGENT, $3N$ ($= 3M$). Add 36 g. of sodium hydroxide pellets (reagent grade) into an Erlenmeyer flask containing 300 ml. of n-amyl alcohol. Allow the flask to stand at room temperature for 2 hours, shaking occasionally to prevent formation of a solid cake. Then heat the flask on a water bath at 70°C, also with occasional shaking until the solid dissolves (Note 2).

B. STANDARD SODIUM HYDROXIDE SOLUTION, $0.02N$ ($= 0.02M$). Introduce 100.00 ml. of standardized $0.1N$ sodium hydroxide solution into a 500-ml. volumetric flask and dilute to the mark with distilled water. After thorough mixing, determine the exact normality by titrating a 2.00-ml. aliquot with standardized $0.01N$ hydrochloric acid to the phenolphthalein endpoint.

C. ION-EXCHANGE RESIN—AMBERLITE IR-120. Sodium form (Rohm and Haas—Note 3).

D. DILUTE ISOPROPYL ALCOHOL, 40%. Add 40 g. of isopropyl alcohol (reagent grade) to 60 g. of distilled water and mix.

E. DILUTE HYDROCHLORIC ACID. Mix 1 volume of C.P. concentrated hydrochloric acid with 9 volumes of distilled water.

F. PHENOLPHTHALEIN INDICATOR SOLUTION, 1%. (See experiment 1.)

G. MIXED INDICATOR SOLUTION. Mix 1 part of 0.1% aqueous cresol red with 3 parts of 0.1% aqueous thymol blue.

H. TEST COMPOUNDS. Methyl laurate, m.p. 5°C; phenyl salicylate, m.p. 41°C; acetanilide, m.p. 113°C; benzanilide, m.p. 163°C.

4. Procedure

A. PREPARATION OF THE ION-EXCHANGE COLUMN. Convert the ion-exchange resin Amberlite IR-120, sodium form, to the hydrogen form in the following manner. Suspend 1 g. of the resin in 20 ml. of the dilute hydrochloric acid in a beaker for 20 minutes. Decant the acid and repeat the process three times.

Pack the bottom of the ion-exchange column with a layer (3 mm.) of glass wool. Transfer the foregoing converted resin into the column. Tap lightly, but do not pack it tight. The length of the resin column will be about 80 mm. Cover the resin with a second layer (3 mm.) of glass wool. Wash the column with distilled water until the eluate is free from chloride ions as shown by the silver nitrate test. Always cover the resin with liquid and close the top of the buret with a rubber stopper when the column is not in use (Note 4).

B. HYDROLYSIS OF THE SAMPLE. Accurately weigh about 0.1 meq. of the sample into the reaction tube. Cover the sample with 1 ml. of n-amyl alcohol. Add 0.10 ml. of the sodium hydroxide saponifying reagent by means of a pipet. Seal the tube (see Figure 5.20) as follows. Heat the rim of the glass reaction tube with an air-gas torch to a red glow. Simultaneously heat a 3 mm. soft glass rod and join it to the tube. Then heat the reaction tube approximately 10 mm. below the joint. When the glass has reached the molten stage and has thickened, draw it out to a capillary. Place the capillary end in the flame again and fuse the opening.

Place the reaction tube in the metal heating block or sand bath adjusted to 150°C and heat for 1 to 2 hours. After cooling the tube to room temperature, heat the narrow tip with a flame. When the tip melts, the expansion of gas inside the reaction tube will force an opening. Now scratch the tube with a glass cutter at the position shown in Figure 5.20. Place a drop of water on the scratch. Apply a preheated glass rod to the water drop—the top of the tube will snap off—then proceed according to Section c.

c. LIBERATION OF THE CARBOXYLIC ACID. Add 3 ml. of the 40% isopropyl alcohol to the reaction tube and mix the contents by swirling. With the stopcock of the ion-exchange column closed, transfer quantitatively the contents of the reaction tube into the column. Rinse the reaction tube three times with 2-ml. portions of the 40% isopropyl alcohol. Now place a 125-ml. Erlenmeyer flask under the ion-exchange column and open the stopcock so that the eluate runs into the flask at the rate of 1 to 2 ml. per minute (Note 5). When the liquid level in the column approaches the resin, introduce 5 ml. of 40% isopropyl alcohol into the column. Repeat this process 3 times. Then close the stopcock.

d. TITRATION OF THE CARBOXYLIC ACID. Add 4 drops (0.2 ml.) of phenolphthalein indicator to the colorless eluate (about 25 ml.) and titrate with the standardized 0.02N sodium hydroxide until a faint pink color appears which persists for 30 seconds. If the eluate acquires a yellowish tint, add 4 drops of the mixed indicator solution in place of phenolphthalein and titrate with the standard alkali until the yellow color of the mixed indicator turns violet. It is not necessary to boil the solution (see experiment 1), if the eluate is titrated immediately after collection from the ion-exchange column.

5. Calculations

A. FOR PER CENT ACYL COMPOUND

$$\% \text{ Compound} = \frac{(\text{ml. NaOH})(\text{normality})(\text{meq. wt. of sample in mg.})(100)}{\text{wt. of sample in mg.}}$$

6. Notes

Note 1. The ordinary 10-ml. buret (Micro-Ware, Inc., catalog No. 5050) serves well for this purpose because it has a capacity of about 15 ml. and a funnel top to facilitate filling. A more elaborate ion-exchange column is shown in Figure 12.2. The resin is packed in the left tube A only. This permits a slow rate of flow and therefore a more complete exchange. However, it takes a longer time to drain the liberated carboxylic acid into the titration flask.

Note 2. A saturated solution of sodium hydroxide in *n*-amyl alcohol is about 3*M*.

Note 3. Other types of cation-exchange resin containing sulfonic groups also may be used.

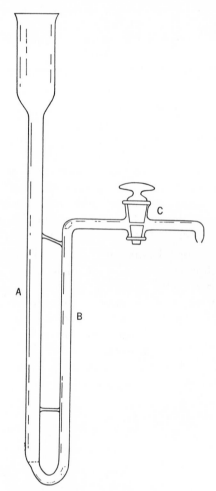

Fig. 12.2. Ion-exchange column.

Note 4. The capacity of Amberlite IR-120 reported by the manufacturer is 4.25 meq. per g. of dry resin. This figure should not be used for quantitative analytical work, however. If the resin in the column is kept under the dilute hydrochloric acid between determinations, the column may be used for about twenty samples before it is replaced.

Note 5. If the rate of flow from the column exceeds 2 ml. per minute, proper exchange will not take place.

7. Comments. This experiment illustrates the application of the ion-exchange technique in quantitàtive microanalysis.

The procedure given here for the determination of esters, amides, and anilides is more time consuming than the estimation of saponification equivalent, but it is a direct method and is more accurate.

Experiment 14: Microdetermination of Phenols by Bromination

1. Principle. A convenient method for the determination of phenols on the 0.1 meq. scale is by bromination. This was discussed in detail in Chapter 11, Section VI. Thus phenol reacts with 3 molar equivalents of bromine:

$$C_6H_5OH + 3Br_2 \rightarrow C_6H_2Br_3(OH) + 3HBr \tag{30}$$

Since a standard solution of bromine is unstable and not suitable for microanalysis, bromine is generated, when needed, from a mixture of potassium bromate and potassium bromide by acidification:

$$KBrO_3 + 5KBr + 6HCl \rightarrow 3Br_2 + 6KCl + 3H_2O \tag{31}$$

For reasons given in Note 1, potassium bromate is selected as the limiting factor in the preparation of the reagent for bromination. After the bromination of the phenolic compound is completed, the residual bromine in the reaction mixture is determined by (1) the addition of potassium iodide (eq. 32),

$$Br_2 + 2KI \rightarrow I_2 + 2KBr \tag{32}$$

followed by (2) the titration of the liberated iodine with standardized sodium thiosulfate solution using starch as the indicator (eq. 33).

$$I_2 + 2Na_2S_2O_3 \rightarrow 2NaI + Na_2S_4O_6 \tag{33}$$

2. Apparatus

A. IODINE FLASKS. 125-ml.

B. MICROBURET. 10-ml. capacity, graduated in 0.02 or 0.05 ml.

3. Reagents

A. POTASSIUM BROMATE–POTASSIUM BROMIDE MIXTURE. Introduce 3.3402 g. (0.02 moles) of potassium bromate (reagent grade) and 200 g. (1.68 moles) of potassium bromide (reagent grade) into a 1-liter volumetric flask. Add distilled water to dissolve the solids. Then dilute to the mark (Note 1).

B. DILUTE HYDROCHLORIC ACID, 1:1. Mix concentrated C.P. hydrochloric acid with equal volume of distilled water.

C. POTASSIUM IODIDE, 20%. Dissolve 5 g. of potassium iodide (reagent grade) in 20 ml. of distilled water. Prepare this solution fresh daily.

D. SODIUM HYDROXIDE SOLUTION, 2%. Dissolve 2 g. of sodium hydroxide pellets in 98 ml. of distilled water.

E. STANDARD SODIUM THIOSULFATE, $0.1N$ ($= M/10$). See experiment 8; use the commercial standard $M/10$ sodium thiosulfate (Note 2).

F. STARCH INDICATOR SOLUTION, 1%. See experiment 11.

G. TEST COMPOUNDS. Phenol, m.p. 41°C; p-hydroxybenzaldehyde, m.p. 116°C; salicylic acid, m.p. 157°C.

4. Procedure. Accurately weigh a sample estimated to consume about 0.1 millimole of bromine and introduce the sample into a 125 ml. iodine flask. Add 5 ml. of distilled water, if the sample is water soluble; otherwise, dissolve the compound in 5 ml. of 2% sodium hydroxide solution. Introduce exactly 5.00 ml. of the potassium bromate–potassium bromide mixture, followed by 5 ml. of distilled water. Wrap the flask with aluminum foil. Prepare a blank in the same manner.

Swirl the flasks to mix the contents. Quickly introduce 2 ml. of 1:1 hydrochloric acid using a pipet (fast flowing). Stopper the flasks and shake each flask vigorously for 20 seconds (Note 3). Then let the flasks stand for 10 to 60 minutes in the dark (Note 4). If it is desirable to perform the bromination at 0 to 2°C, place the flasks, after vigorous shaking, in an ice-water bath for 15 minutes before adding the hydrochloric acid, and keep the flasks in the cold bath for the duration of the bromination.

After the appropriate time has passed, remove the aluminum foil. Introduce 10 ml. of the potassium iodide solution to the well of the iodine flask. Remove the stopper gently to let the solution run down the sides of the flask. Add 3 ml. of distilled water. Replace the stopper and shake the flask vigorously for 30 seconds. Add 2 to 3 ml. of distilled water to the well. Remove the stopper and titrate the liberated iodine with the standardized $0.1N$ sodium thiosulfate. When the solution becomes faintly yellow, add 1 ml. of the starch indicator solution and complete the titration until the blue color disappears.

5. Calculations

A. FOR PER CENT HYDROXYL GROUP

$$\% \text{ OH} = \frac{(b - s)(\text{normality of Na}_2\text{S}_2\text{O}_3)(17.01)(100)}{(\text{wt. of sample in mg.})(2)(f)}$$

where b = ml. of $Na_2S_2O_3$ for the blank, s = ml. of $Na_2S_2O_3$ for the sample, and f = number of bromine atoms substituting in the compound.

B. FOR PER CENT COMPOUND

$$\% \text{ Compound} = \frac{(b - s)(\text{normality of } Na_2S_2O_3)(\text{mol. wt. of cmpd. in mg.})(100)}{(\text{wt. of sample in mg.})(2)(f)}$$

6. Notes

Note 1. A very large excess of potassium bromide is used to insure complete reduction of the bromate and also to keep the free bromine in solution. Bromine is slightly soluble in water, but very soluble in bromide solution owing to the formation of the complex ion Br_3^-.

Note 2. $0.05N$ Sodium thiosulfate may be used to increase the precision. However, the blank will require more than 10 ml. for titration.

Note 3. The reaction mixture must be acidic, since bromine reacts with alkali to form hypobromite and bromide:

$$Br_2 + 2OH^- \rightarrow BrO^- + Br^- + H_2O \tag{34}$$

Note 4. The bromination reaction is carried out in the dark to prevent the oxidation of bromide ions in acid solution, which is catalyzed by sunlight.

$$4Br^- + 4H^+ + O_2 \rightarrow 2Br_2 + 2H_2O \tag{35}$$

Bromine substitution of the alkyl side chain is also minimized in the absence of light.

7. Comments. The method described in this experiment is applicable only to phenols which have been previously investigated, since a knowledge of the bromination factor is necessary before the analytical result can be calculated.

Experiment 15: Microdetermination of Olefinic Unsaturation by the Bromate-Bromide Method

1. Principle. Among the various reagents which have been used to determine olefins by halogenation (see Chapter 10, Section II-B) the potassium bromate–potassium bromide mixture is recommended for determinations on the micro scale. The equations for the generation of bromine, and the addition of bromine to the double bond (using styrene as example) are shown in equations 36 and 37:

$$KBrO_3 + 5KBr + 6HCl \rightarrow 3Br_2 + 6KCl + 3H_2O \tag{36}$$
$$C_6H_5-CH=CH_2 + Br_2 \rightarrow C_6H_5CHBrCH_2Br \tag{37}$$

The endpoint of the determination is shown by the appearance of the yellow color of bromine in the special solvent system employed.

2. Apparatus

A. REACTION FLASK.   Use a 50-ml. Erlenmeyer flask fitted with ground glass stopper.

B. MICROBURET.   10-ml. capacity, graduated in 0.02 or 0.05 ml., Koch type (Note 1).

C. MICROPIPET.   Prepare this by drawing out a 2-mm. capillary tube to a tip of 0.2 mm. Cut the pipet to a length of 80 mm. with the tip 5 mm. long. Select a plastic tubing to fit the pipet.

3. Reagents

A. BROMATE-BROMIDE REAGENT SOLUTION CONTAINING 0.05N ($= 0.025M$) BROMINE.   Dissolve 1.392 g. of potassium bromate (reagent grade) in 200 ml. of distilled water in a 1-liter volumetric flask. Then make up to the mark and mix. After it has stood overnight, determine the strength of this reagent solution in the following manner.

Pipet 10 ml. of glacial acetic acid and 1 ml. of concentrated hydrochloric acid into a 125-ml. iodine flask (see experiment 14) and chill the mixture in an ice-water bath for 5 minutes. Introduce 5.00 ml. of the bromate-bromide reagent. Quickly close the flask and swirl. Replace the flask in the ice bath for 5 minutes. Quickly add 5 ml. of 5% potassium iodide solution. Close the flask and swirl again for 1 minute. Then put the flask in the dark for 5 minutes to allow the iodine to be completely liberated.

Replace the flask in the ice bath for 5 minutes. Add 20 ml. of distilled water. Titrate the contents of the flask with the standardized 0.05N sodium thiosulfate. Run in the titrant at a fairly rapid rate until the solution turns light yellow. Now add 0.25 ml. of 1% starch indicator solution and continue the titration slowly until the blue color disappears.

B. STANDARD SODIUM THIOSULFATE SOLUTION, 0.05N ($= 0.05M$).   Dissolve 12.410 g. of reagent grade $Na_2S_2O_3 \cdot 5H_2O$ in 200 ml. of freshly boiled distilled water in a 1-liter volumetric flask. Add 1 g. of reagent grade sodium carbonate as preservative. Dilute the solution to the mark with distilled water (Note 2).

Standardize the foregoing solution as follows. Accurately weigh about 20 mg. of potassium dichromate (reagent grade, fine crystals, previously dried at 130°C for 2 hours) into the 50-ml. reaction flask containing 10 ml. of distilled water. Add 0.5 ml. of concentrated hydrochloric acid and then 100 mg. of sodium bicarbonate. Loosely cover the flask with the ground-glass stopper and swirl the flask gently until the evolution of carbon dioxide subsides. Now add 3 ml. of 5% potassium iodide solution, quickly stopper the flask and swirl for 30 seconds. Place the flask in a dark cabinet for 5 minutes. Then cool the contents in an ice-water bath for 5 minutes. Add 20 ml. of distilled water. Titrate the solution with the approximately 0.05N

sodium thiosulfate until the color becomes light yellow. Then add 0.25 ml. of 1% starch indicator solution and complete the titration until the solution becomes colorless.

c. SOLVENT MIXTURE. Prepare 1 liter of solvent mixture by combining the following liquids: 714 ml. of glacial acetic acid, 134 ml. of carbon tetrachloride, 116 ml. of methanol, 18 ml. of dilute sulfuric acid (1:5 v/v), and 18 ml. of 10% solution of mercuric chloride in methanol.

d. STARCH INDICATOR SOLUTION, 1%. Use the commercially available 1% starch indicator solution stabilized with acetic acid.

e. TEST COMPOUNDS. Styrene, b.p. 146°C; 1-octene, b.p. 121°C; allyl alcohol, b.p. 97°C.

4. *Procedure.* Introduce 10 ml. of the solvent mixture to the 50-ml. reaction flask. Stopper the flask and place it near the microbalance.

Accurately weigh the empty micropipet (Note 3). Dip the tip of the micropipet into the sample (liquid) to be analyzed, which is kept in a small vial. Allow the liquid to enter the micropipet by capillary action. A sample containing 0.1 meq. of the olefinic function (10 to 25 mg.) usually can be taken in this manner by keeping the micropipet at an angle of 45°. (If necessary, attach the plastic tubing to the micropipet and apply gentle suction to draw up the liquid sample.) Remove the micropipet from the vial and turn the pipet to a nearly horizontal position to let the liquid go beyond the tip. Wipe the tip with a tissue or filter paper. Weigh the micropipet and sample accurately. If too much sample has been drawn into the micropipet, remove the excess sample by tilting the pipet and touch the tip with a tissue paper. After the proper amount of sample is weighed, bring the micropipet containing the sample to the reaction flask. Let the micropipet tip just touch the surface of the solvent mixture in the flask. Attach the plastic tubing and gently blow the sample into the solution. Then draw up some solvent to rinse the micropipet. Rinse the micropipet twice more by drawing up anhydrous methanol from a small vial and expelling the rinsings into the reaction flask.

Cool the reaction flask containing the sample in the ice-water bath for 5 minutes. Add 0.25 ml. of concentrated hydrochloric acid, and then titrate the contents of the flask with the standardized $0.05N$ potassium bromate-potassium bromide mixture. The endpoint is the appearance of a yellowish tinge which persists on swirling for 30 seconds.

Run a blank along with the sample and titrate in exactly the same way.

5. *Calculations*

A. FOR PER CENT OLEFINIC GROUP

$$\% \ C{=}C = \frac{(\text{ml. KBrO}_3 - \text{KBr consumed})(\text{normality})(24.02)(100)}{(\text{mg. sample})(2)}$$

B. For Per Cent Compound

$$\% \text{ Compound} = \frac{(\text{ml. } KBrO_3\text{—}KBr \text{ consumed})(\text{normality})(\text{meq. wt. cmpd. in mg.})(100)}{(\text{wt. of sample in mg.})(2)}$$

6. *Notes*

Note 1.   The standardized potassium bromate-potassium bromide solution should not be stored in a microburet with a 1-liter reservoir.

Note 2.   The 0.05N sodium thiosulfate also can be made from the commercial standard 0.1N sodium thiosulfate by dilution. The solution thus prepared, however, should be restandardized.

Note 3.   The micro weighing tube (Figure 5.6) is used for solid samples. The micro weighing pipet (Figure 5.11) also can be used for liquids in this experiment. The tip and air chamber are broken off and dropped into the reaction flask with the liquid chamber. The latter is then crushed with a glass rod under the solvent mixture.

7. *Comments.*   The addition of bromine to the olefinic group is carried out in a cooled solution to minimize side reaction due to substitution. Mercuric chloride is added as a catalyst. A standardized bromate-bromide solution containing $0.025M$ bromine is used because it gives a titration volume of 4 ml. for 0.1 meq. of the double bond and a discernible endpoint by the yellow color of bromine.

The procedure described in this experiment is not applicable to the determination of olefinic groups adjacent to the carboxyl group or its derivatives (see experiment 16).

Experiment 16:   Microdetermination of α-β-Unsaturated Acids and Their Derivatives by the Bromine-Sodium Bromide Method

1. *Principle.*   Whereas α-β-unsaturated acids, esters, and amides brominate at a very slow rate (see Chapter 10, Section II-B), sodium salts of unsaturated carboxylic acids brominate at a vastly greater speed than the parent acid. By neutralizing the acid with sodium hydroxide, the resulting mixture reacts quantitatively with bromine dissolved in sodium bromide. By using crotonic acid as example, equations 38 to 41 show the reactions:

$$CH_3CH\text{=}CH\text{—}COOH + NaOH \rightarrow CH_3CH\text{=}CH\text{—}COONa + H_2O \qquad (38)$$

$$CH_3CH\text{=}CH\text{—}COONa + NaBr_3 \rightarrow CH_3CHBrCHBrCOONa + NaBr \qquad (39)$$

The residual bromine-sodium bromide mixture is then determined iodometrically.

$$NaBr_3 + 2KI \rightarrow I_2 + NaBr + 2KBr \qquad (40)$$

$$I_2 + 2Na_2S_2O_3 \rightarrow 2NaI + Na_2S_4O_6 \qquad (41)$$

Esters and amides can be saponified by means of potassium hydroxide, converted to the free carboxylic acid with hydrochloric acid, which is then neutralized with sodium hydroxide and brominated.

2. Apparatus

A. REACTION FLASKS.   Use 50-ml. Erlenmeyer flasks fitted with ground-glass stoppers.

B. MICROBURETS.   10-ml. capacity, graduated in 0.02 or 0.05 ml.

3. Reagents

A. BROMINE-SODIUM BROMIDE REAGENT, CONTAINING 0.075N (= 0.0375M) OF BROMINE.   Dissolve 10.0 g. of sodium bromide (reagent grade) in 100 ml. of anhydrous methanol in a 250-ml. volumetric flask. Add 0.5 ml. of bromine (reagent grade). Mix and then dilute to the mark with methanol. Transfer to an amber bottle with a screw cap for storage.

Determine the exact normality of bromine in the foregoing bromine-sodium bromide solution as follows. Pipet 5.00 ml. of the solution into the 50-ml. reaction flask. Stopper the flask and place it in the ice-water bath for 10 minutes. Add 5 ml. of the 3% potassium iodide solution, quickly restopper the flask, mix the contents, and then keep the flask in a dark place for 5 minutes to allow complete liberation of iodine. Now add 10 ml. of distilled water and titrate the contents of the flask with the standardized 0.05N sodium thiosulfate to a light yellow color. Add 0.25 ml. of the starch indicator solution and continue titration to the colorless endpoint.

B. STANDARD SODIUM THIOSULFATE, 0.05N (= 0.05M).   See experiment 15.

C. SODIUM HYDROXIDE SOLUTION, 0.05N.   Mix 0.1N sodium hydroxide with an equal volume of distilled water.

D. POTASSIUM HYDROXIDE, 0.1N.   Dissolve 580 mg. of potassium hydroxide pellets in 100 ml. of distilled water.

E. HYDROCHLORIC ACID, 0.05N.   Dilute 0.1N hydrochloric acid with an equal volume of distilled water.

F. POTASSIUM IODIDE, 3%.   Dissolve 3 g. of reagent grade potassium iodide in 97 ml. of distilled water.

G. SODIUM BROMIDE SOLUTION, SATURATED.   Add 25.0 g. of sodium bromide (reagent grade) in a 250-ml. volumetric flask. Fill to the mark with anhydrous methanol. Stopper and shake mechanically for 8 hours. Filter before use.

H. SODIUM BROMIDE.   Solid, reagent grade.

I. PHENOLPHTHALEIN INDICATOR SOLUTION, 1%.   Dissolve 100 mg. of phenolphthalein in 10 ml. of methanol.

J. STARCH INDICATOR SOLUTION, 1%.   See experiment 15.

к. TEST COMPOUNDS. Crotonic acid, m.p. 71°C; acrylamide, m.p. 84°C; maleic anhydride, m.p. 196°C.

4. Procedures

A. FOR α-β-UNSATURATED ACIDS AND ACID ANHYDRIDES. Weigh accurately a sample that will consume about 0.1 millimole of bromine into the 50-ml. reaction flask. Cover the sample with 5 ml. of distilled water. Add 3 drops of 1% methanolic phenolphthalein indicator and introduce 0.05N sodium hydroxide solution dropwise until the contents of the flask turn pink. Add 10 ml. of distilled water, stopper the flask and swirl to mix the contents (Note 1). Run a blank in another flask.

Add 5 ml. of the saturated methanolic sodium bromide solution into each flask, followed by 200 mg. of solid sodium bromide. Stopper the flask and swirl to mix its contents thoroughly. Place the flask in the ice-water bath. Introduce 5.00 ml. of the standardized 0.075N bromine-sodium bromide reagent. Quickly stopper the flask and allow it to stand in a dark place for 1 hour.

After 1 hour, again cool the blank and sample in the ice-water bath. Add 10 ml. of methanol and 5 ml. of the 3% potassium iodide solution into each flask. Let the flasks stand in a dark place for 10 minutes to allow complete liberation of iodine. Then titrate the blank and sample, respectively, with the standardized 0.05N sodium thiosulfate solution. Add the starch indicator (5 drops or 0.25 ml.) when the contents of the flask become light yellow, and complete the titration until the blue color disappears.

B. FOR α-β-UNSATURATED ESTERS AND AMIDES. Accurately weigh about 0.1 meq. sample (Note 2) into the 50-ml. reaction flask. Add 3 ml. of 0.1N potassium hydroxide and 1 ml. of acetone. Stopper the flask and place it on a laboratory shaker for 1 hour (Note 3). Prepare a blank in the same manner.

Now add 3 drops of 1% phenolphthalein indicator and introduce 0.05N hydrochloric acid dropwise until the contents of the flask change from pink to colorless. Then add 0.05N sodium hydroxide until the pink color reappears. Add 10 ml. of distilled water (Note 1). Finish the determination as described in Procedure A.

5. Calculations

A. FOR PER CENT OLEFINIC LINKAGE

$$\% \ C{=}C = \frac{(b - s)(\text{normality of Na}_2\text{S}_2\text{O}_3)(24.02)(100)}{(\text{wt. of sample in mg.})(2)}$$

where b = ml. of Na$_2$S$_2$O$_3$ for blank, and s = ml. of Na$_2$S$_2$O$_3$ for sample.

B. FOR PER CENT COMPOUND

$$\% \text{ Compound} = \frac{(b-s)(\text{normality of Na}_2\text{S}_2\text{O}_3)(\text{meq. wt. of cmpd. in mg.})(100)}{(\text{wt. of sample in mg.})(2)}$$

6. Notes

Note 1. If the pink color disappears at this point or at any subsequent point before the addition of bromide-sodium bromide reagent, more $0.05N$ sodium hydroxide should be added dropwise to restore the pink color.

Note 2. A 0.1 meq. sample is equivalent to 0.1 millimole of bromine since each double bond reacts with 2 atoms of bromine.

Note 3. If a shaker is not available, heat the reaction mixture on the steam bath using a finger condenser in place of the ground-glass stopper.

7. Comments. This experiment illustrates a modification of the halogenation method for determining unsaturation. Without this modification, α-β-unsaturated acids, anhydrides, esters and amides cannot be analyzed by bromine addition.

Experiment 17. Microdetermination of Olefinic Unsaturation by the Mercuric Acetate Method

1. Principle. Olefinic unsaturation can be determined by the addition of mercuric acetate (see Chapter 10, Section II-D). Since the reaction takes place in methanol, the solvent participates in the reaction (known as methoxymercuration), in which 1 mole of methanol and 1 mole of mercuric acetate are consumed by each double bond. At the same time, a mole of acetic acid is liberated for every equivalent of olefinic linkage which becomes saturated. For example, the equation for the addition of mercuric acetate to styrene may be written as:

$$C_6H_5CH{=}CH_2 + Hg(CH_3COO)_2 + CH_3OH \rightarrow CH_3COOH$$
$$+ C_6H_5CH(OCH_3)CH_2Hg(CH_3COO) \qquad (42)$$

After the reaction is completed, sodium bromide is added to convert the excess mercuric acetate to the slightly ionized mercuric bromide. The amount of acetic acid in the reaction mixture is then determined by titration with standardized hydroxide in methanol.

2. Apparatus

A. REACTION FLASK. Use a 50-ml. Erlenmeyer flask fitted with ground-glass stopper.

B. MICROBURET. 10-ml. capacity, graduated in 0.02 or 0.05 ml. for storing alkali solution.

C. MICROPIPET AND PLASTIC TUBING. See experiment 15.

3. Reagents

A. MERCURIC ACETATE REAGENT SOLUTION (APPROX. $0.03M$). Add 2.5 g. of mercuric acetate (reagent grade) and 150 ml. of anhydrous methanol into a 250-ml. volumetric flask. Shake the contents until all solid dissolves. Then add 3 drops of glacial acetic acid as a stabilizing agent (Note 1). Dilute to the mark with methanol and mix.

B. STANDARD POTASSIUM HYDROXIDE SOLUTION, $0.05N$ ($= 0.05M$). Add 3.0 g. of potassium hydroxide pellets (reagent grade, approx. 85% KOH) into a 1-liter volumetric flask containing 500 ml. of anhydrous methanol. Shake the flask to dissolve the pellets. Then dilute to the mark with anhydrous methanol. Mix and let the solution stand overnight before transferring into the microburet (Note 2).

Standardize the preceding methanolic potassium hydroxide solution in the following manner. Deliver 5.00 ml. of this solution into the 50-ml. reaction flask. Stopper the flask and place it in the ice-water bath for 5 minutes. Then remove the flask from the cooling mixture, add 4 drops of 1% methanolic phenolphthalein indicator, and titrate the contents of the flask with standardized $0.05N$ aqueous hydrochloric acid until the pink color disappears.

C. PHENOLPHTHALEIN INDICATOR SOLUTION, 1%. Dissolve 100 mg. of phenolphthalein in 10 ml. of anhydrous methanol.

D. TEST COMPOUNDS. Styrene, b.p. 146°C; allyl alcohol, b.p. 97°C; α-pinene, b.p. 155°C.

4. Procedure.

Introduce 10.00 ml. of the mercuric acetate reagent solution into the 50-ml. reaction flask. Weigh accurately about 0.1 meq. sample and add it into the flask. Use the micro weighing tube (Figure 5.6) for solids and the technique described in experiment 15 for liquids. Stopper the flask, swirl to mix the contents, and let stand at room temperature for 15 minutes (Note 3). Now add 0.5 g. of sodium bromide (reagent grade), replace the stopper, and swirl the flask gently until the sodium bromide dissolves.

Place the flask in an ice-water bath for 5 minutes. Then remove it, add 5 drops (0.2 ml.) of 1% methanolic phenolphthalein indicator, and titrate the contents of the flask with the standardized $0.05N$ methanolic potassium hydroxide. The endpoint is the appearance of pink color which persists for 30 seconds.

Run a blank in exactly the same way, without the sample.

5. *Calculations*

A. FOR PER CENT OLEFINIC UNSATURATION

$$\% \ C{=}C = \frac{(s - b)(\text{normality})(24.02)(100)}{\text{wt. of sample in mg.}}$$

where s = ml. of KOH for sample, and b = ml. of KOH for blank.

B. FOR PER CENT COMPOUND

$$\% \ \text{Compound} = \frac{(s - b)(\text{normality})(\text{meq. wt. of compound in mg.})(100)}{\text{wt. of sample in mg.}}$$

6. *Notes*

Note 1. The mercuric acetate reagent solution cannot be kept for more than a few days. It should be discarded when a yellow precipitate appears in the flask. Addition of acetic acid in the solution necessitates the blank titration.

Note 2. Standardized 0.02N methanolic potassium hydroxide may be used to give more accurate measurement of the volume of titrant consumed.

Note 3. If the result of the determination is lower than the expected value, repeat the analysis with the reaction mixture cooled in the ice-water bath for 15 minutes before adding the sodium bromide.

7. *Comments.* A completely nonaqueous medium is employed in this experiment. This is advantageous, since most olefinic compounds are insoluble in water.

Experiment 18: Microdetermination of Acetylenic Compounds by Nonaqueous Titration

1. Principle. The analysis of acetylenic compounds was discussed in Chapter 10, Section III. The hydrogen attached to the triple bond may be displaced by a number of metallic ions on treatment with the metallic salt, liberating 1 mole of the corresponding inorganic acid. For example, 1 mole of 1-decyne reacts with silver perchlorate to yield one mole of perchloric acid:

$$CH_3(CH_2)_7C{\equiv}CH + AgClO_4 \rightarrow HClO_4 + CH_3(CH_2)_7C{\equiv}CAg \qquad (43)$$

The quantity of acid produced is determined by titration with tris-(hydroxymethyl)-aminomethane in nonaqueous medium:

$$HClO_4 + (HOCH_2)_3CNH_2 \rightarrow (HOCH_2)_3CNH_3ClO_4 \qquad (44)$$

2. Apparatus

A. MICROBURETS. 10-ml. capacity graduated in 0.02 or 0.05 ml.

B. REACTION FLASK. Use the 50-ml. Erlenmeyer flask.

3. Reagents

A. SILVER PERCHLORATE SOLUTION, 0.25N (= $M/4$). Dissolve 26.0 g. of anhydrous silver perchlorate in anhydrous methanol in a 500-ml. volumetric flask and dilute to the mark (Note 1). Store this reagent in a polyethylene bottle.

B. STANDARD TRIS-(HYDROXYMETHYL)-AMINOMETHANE (THAM), 0.01N. Dissolve 1.2114 g. of tris-(hydroxymethyl)-aminomethane (primary standard grade) in absolute methanol in a 1-liter volumetric flask and make up to the mark. To standardize, titrate against 0.01N perchloric acid in methanol using the Martius yellow-methyl violet mixed indicator.

C. STANDARD PERCHLORIC ACID, 0.01N (= 0.01M). Dissolve 0.85 ml. of 72% perchloric acid in absolute methanol in a 1-liter volumetric flask and dilute to the mark. Standardize this solution with standard 0.01N sodium hydroxide using phenolphthalein as indicator.

D. MIXED INDICATOR SOLUTION. Dissolve 67 mg. of Martius yellow and 4 mg. of methyl violet in 50 ml. of absolute ethanol.

E. TEST COMPOUNDS. 1-Decyne, b.p. 80°C (30 mm.); phenyl acetylene, b.p. 143°C; propargyl alcohol, b.p. 110–113°C; ethynylbenzene, b.p. 141–144°C.

4. Procedure.

Weigh accurately about 0.1 meq. of the sample into a 50-ml. Erlenmeyer flask containing 10 ml. of methanol. Add 2 drops (0.05 ml.) of the mixed indicator solution. If the solution turns blue, titrate to a faint yellow color with the 0.01N THAM. If the presence of a strong base is suspected, titrate the contents of the flask with the 0.01N perchloric acid until the yellow color just disappears.

To a separate flask add 10 ml. of the 0.25M silver perchlorate solution. Neutralize the solution with 0.1N THAM until the blue color begins to change, and then add the titrant slowly until a faint yellow color appears.

Add the neutralized 0.25M silver perchlorate to the sample solution. Swirl to mix thoroughly. Then titrate the contents of the flask with the standardized 0.01N THAM. The endpoint is the appearance of a faint yellow color (Note 2).

5. Calculations

A. FOR PER CENT ACETYLENIC HYDROGEN

$$\% \text{ H} = \frac{(\text{ml. of THAM})(\text{normality})(1.008)(100)}{\text{wt. of sample in mg.}}$$

B. FOR PER CENT ACETYLENIC GROUP

$$\% \text{ C} \equiv \text{C} = \frac{(\text{ml. of THAM})(\text{normality})(24.02)(100)}{\text{wt. of sample in mg.}}$$

C. FOR PER CENT COMPOUND

$$\% \text{ Cmpd.} = \frac{(\text{ml. of THAM})(\text{normality})(\text{meq. wt. of cmpd. in mg.})(100)}{\text{wt. of sample in mg.}}$$

6. Notes

Note 1. The concentration of the silver perchlorate should not be less than $0.25M$, otherwise silver acetylide precipitates and the observation of the endpoint becomes difficult.

Note 2. The solution changes from blue to a grayish color near the endpoint, and finally to pale yellow at the equivalence point.

7. Comments.
This experiment illustrates the requirement of a non-aqueous condition in certain cases of organic analysis. If the methanol contains 3% or more of water, the results obtained will be definitely lower than theoretical values.

Experiment 19: Microdetermination of Organic Peroxides by Iodometric Method

1. Principle. Organic peroxides (Chapter 7, Section VI) can oxidize iodide ions in acetic acid solution to yield iodine. Representative reactions are given below for perbenzoic acid and benzoyl peroxide respectively:

$$C_6H_5CO \cdot O_2H + 2NaI + CH_3COOH \rightarrow I_2 + C_6H_5COONa + CH_3COONa + H_2O \quad (45)$$

$$C_6H_5CO \cdot O_2 \cdot OCC_6H_5 + 2NaI + 3CH_3COOH \rightarrow I_2 + 2C_6H_5COONa + 2CH_3COONa \quad (46)$$

The reaction is slow and nonstoichiometric under ordinary conditions. In the presence of a trace of ferric ion, however, the liberation of iodine becomes rapid and is quantitative. The amount of iodine produced then can be determined by titration with standard sodium thiosulfate:

$$I_2 + 2Na_2S_2O_3 \rightarrow 2NaI + Na_2S_4O_6 \quad (47)$$

2. Apparatus
A. MICROBURET. 10-ml. capacity, graduated in 0.02 or 0.05 ml.
B. REACTION FLASK. Use the 125-ml. iodine flask (Note 1).
C. MAGNETIC STIRRER. Any model.

3. Reagents
A. STANDARD SODIUM THIOSULFATE, $0.02N$ ($= 0.02M$). Boil 600 ml. of distilled water in a 1-liter Erlenmeyer flask to remove all traces of dissolved oxygen and then cool it under a stream of nitrogen gas. Weigh accurately

4.9639 g. of sodium thiosulfate pentahydrate (reagent grade) and dissolve it in 100 ml. of the distilled water. Transfer the solution into a 500-ml. volumetric flask. Add about 300 ml. of distilled water, then 0.25 g. of anhydrous sodium carbonate to inhibit the growth of microorganisms. Finally, dilute to the mark and mix thoroughly (Note 2).

Standardize this solution against 0.02N potassium iodate as follows. Introduce 5.00 ml. of the standard 0.02N potassium iodate solution into a 50-ml. Erlenmeyer flask fitted with a ground-glass stopper and containing a clean magnetic stirring bar. Add 5 ml. of distilled water and 500 mg. of potassium iodide (reagent grade). When all the iodide has dissolved, add 1 ml. of 6N sulfuric acid. While the solution is being stirred, titrate the iodine liberated by means of the sodium thiosulfate solution. Add 1 ml. of 1% starch indicator solution when the titration approaches the endpoint, as indicated by the change of the color of the solution to pale yellow. Now add the titrant dropwise until the solution becomes colorless.

Run a blank on the reagents by substituting 5 ml. of distilled water for the 0.02N potassium iodate solution. If any iodate impurity is present in the potassium iodide, an iodine color will appear. Titrate the iodine in the same manner and subtract the volume of sodium thiosulfate solution used in the blank from the volume used in the standardization titration.

B. STANDARD POTASSIUM IODATE SOLUTION, 0.02N ($= M/300$). Dry the potassium iodate (reagent grade) at 105°C for 2 hours before using. Weigh accurately 357.33 mg. of the crystalline solid in a 150-ml. beaker. Dissolve it in distilled water. Quantitatively transfer the solution into a 500-ml. volumetric flask with the aid of a stirring rod. Rinse the beaker 5 times with distilled water. Finally, make up the volume to the mark.

C. FERRIC CHLORIDE REAGENT SOLUTION. Dissolve 20 ± 1 mg. of ferric chloride hexahydrate in 1 liter of glacial acetic acid. Store this solution in a glass-stoppered bottle.

D. SODIUM IODIDE SOLUTION, SATURATED. Dissolve 184 g. of sodium iodide (reagent grade) in 100 ml. of distilled water. Store the solution in an amber colored bottle provided with a medicine dropper graduated in 0.1 ml., fitted with a screw cap.

E. STARCH INDICATOR SOLUTION, 1%. Suspend 2 g. of soluble starch powder in 20 ml. of cold distilled water. Add this suspension slowly into 180 ml. of boiling water with stirring. Cool the solution; add 5 ml. of chloroform to inhibit growth of molds. If any sediment settles out overnight, decant the solution and add 2 ml. more of chloroform.

F. SULFURIC ACID, 6N. Add 100 ml. of C.P. concentrated sulfuric acid slowly, with stirring, to 500 ml. of distilled water. After cooling, transfer to a glass-stoppered reagent bottle.

G. HYDRIODIC ACID, 57%. Analytical reagent, not stabilized.

H. TEST COMPOUNDS. Benzoyl peroxide, m.p., 103°C; perbenzoic acid, m.p., 41°C; dicumyl peroxide, crystalline solid; di-*tert*-butyl peroxide, b.p., 110°C. (Caution! All peroxy compounds are unstable and may decompose with explosive force!)

4. Procedures

A. SODIUM IODIDE AS THE REAGENT—FOR ACYL PEROXIDES, PEROXY-ESTERS, ALKYL HYDROPEROXIDES AND DIALKYL PEROXIDES WITH ACTI-VATING ADJACENT GROUPS. Weigh to the microgram no less than 3 mg. and no more than 15 mg. of sample (containing about 1 mg. of active oxygen) into an iodine flask. Add 3 ml. of chloroform to dissolve the sample, followed by 3 ml. of the ferric chloride reagent in glacial acetic acid. Flush the flask with nitrogen as its contents are swirled. Then place the stopper in position. Carefully raise the stopper after 1 minute. Add 0.2 ml. of the saturated sodium iodide solution by means of the medicine dropper. Replace the stopper and again swirl the contents of the flask for complete mixing. Let the flask stand in the dark for exactly 5 minutes. Now add 10 ml. of distilled water and a clean magnetic stirring bar into the flask. Place the flask in the magnetic stirrer and titrate the contents of the flask with the standardized 0.02N sodium thiosulfate until the iodine color fades to a pale yellow. Increase the speed of the magnetic stirrer at this point, so that the iodine dissolved in the chloroform phase will be more readily transferred to aqueous phase. Add 0.5 ml. of the starch indicator and complete the titration to the colorless endpoint.

Run a blank determination following the foregoing procedure exactly, but without the sample.

B. HYDRIODIC ACID AS THE REAGENT—FOR DIALKYL PEROXIDES. Accurately weigh a sample containing about 1 mg. of active oxygen into an iodine flask. Dissolve the sample in 3 ml. of glacial acetic acid while a current of nitrogen is passed through the flask, and then replace the stopper. Raise the stopper sufficiently to introduce 3.0 ml. of the 57% hydriodic acid (Note 3) from a pipet. Now stopper the flask and place it in a shallow water bath of 15-mm. depth, maintained at 60°C, and away from sunlight. Remove the flask from the water bath after 15 minutes and allow the flask to stand at room temperature for 1 minute. Add 15 ml. of distilled water and a magnetic stirring bar. Titrate the contents of the flask with the standardized 0.02N sodium thiosulfate as described in Procedure A.

Run a blank using the same quantities of reagents and heating for the same length of time in the water bath.

5. *Calculations*

A. For Per Cent Active Oxygen

$$\% \text{ Active O} = \frac{(\text{ml. Na}_2\text{S}_2\text{O}_3 - \text{blank})(\text{normality})(16.00)(100)}{(\text{wt. of sample in mg.})(2)}$$

B. For Per Cent Compound

$$\% \text{ Cmpd.} = \frac{(\text{ml. Na}_2\text{S}_2\text{O}_3 - \text{blank})(\text{normality})(\text{meq. wt. of cmpd. in mg.})(100)}{(\text{wt. of sample in mg.})(2)}$$

6. *Notes*

Note 1. Iodine flasks of 50 ml. or 75 ml. are more suitable, but the smallest iodine flask available commercially has 125-ml. capacity.

Note 2. The normality of $0.02N$ sodium thiosulfate prepared in this way remains constant for several months.

Note 3. The hydriodic acid should not contain any stabilizer.

7. *Comments.* Detailed directions are given in this experiment to demonstrate how to obtain accurate results using very dilute standard solutions ($0.02M$ sodium thiosulfate and $0.003M$ potassium iodate).

The differences among various peroxy groups are shown in the applicability of the two procedures. Thus di-*tert*-butyl peroxide cannot be reduced by Procedure A. On the other hand, it is not advisable to use Procedure B for easily reducible peroxy compounds because of the high blanks given by 57% hydriodic acid.

Experiment 20: Microdetermination of Acid Anhydride by Anilide Formation

1. *Principle.* Acid anhydrides (see Chapter 6, Section III) react with aniline to form the corresponding anilides. The reaction for acetic anhydride may be written thus:

$$(\text{CH}_3\text{CO})_2\text{O} + \text{C}_6\text{H}_5\text{NH}_2 \rightarrow \text{CH}_3\text{COHNC}_6\text{H}_5 + \text{CH}_3\text{COOH} \qquad (48)$$

With liquid anhydrides the reaction usually is complete at room temperature, but solid anhydrides generally require heat for a quantitative yield of the anilide.

Since aniline and anilide differ significantly in basicity (see Chapter 11, Section IV), the amount of aniline consumed can be determined by titration with perchloric acid in nonaqueous medium:

$$\text{C}_6\text{H}_5\text{NH}_2 + \text{HClO}_4 \rightarrow \text{C}_6\text{H}_5\text{NH}_3\text{ClO}_4 \qquad (49)$$

2. *Apparatus*

A. Reaction Tubes. Prepare reaction tubes from 4-mm. or 6-mm. soft glass tubing (see experiment 5).

B. MICROBURET.   10-ml. capacity, graduated in 0.02 or 0.05 ml.

C. pH METER.   See experiment 3 (Note 1).

D. MAGNETIC STIRRER

3. Reagents

A. STANDARD PERCHLORIC ACID IN DIOXANE, $0.05N$ ($= 0.05M$).   Dissolve 4.2 ml. of 72% perchloric acid in dioxane and dilute to 1 liter. Determine the exact normality as described in experiment 3 (Note 2).

B. ANILINE.   Reagent grade, freshly distilled before use (Note 3).

C. TITRATION SOLVENT.   1,4-Dioxane, purified grade, or a mixture containing equal volumes of ethylene glycol and isopropyl alcohol.

D. TEST COMPOUNDS.   Acetic anhydride, b.p. 139°C; phthalic anhydride, m.p. 131°C.

4. Procedure.   Accurately weigh 0.1 to 0.2 meq. of the acid anhydride into a reaction tube using the capillary pipet for liquid and the plunger technique for solid, respectively, as described in experiment 5. Then introduce to near the bottom of the reaction tube, 30 to 40 mg. of aniline and reweigh accurately. Seal the reaction tube.

Accurately weigh 20 to 30 mg. from the same lot of aniline into another reaction tube which contains no sample. Seal this tube, which will be the blank.

Place both the sample and blank reaction tubes in a beaker of water (Note 4) and boil for 15 minutes. Remove the tubes, wipe them dry, and allow them to cool to room temperature.

Open the blank tube first, as described in experiment 5. Place the tube and its contents in a 100-ml. beaker, add 10 ml. of titration solvent, and titrate with the standardized $0.05N$ perchloric acid potentiometrically.

Similarly, open the sample tube, place it in another beaker, add 10 ml. of the same titration solvent, and titrate the solution potentiometrically.

5. Calculations

A. FOR PER CENT ACID ANHYDRIDE FUNCTION

$$\% \ (CO)_2O = \frac{(a - b)(\text{normality of } HClO_4)(72.02)(100)}{\text{mg. sample}}$$

where $a = \dfrac{(\text{ml. } HClO_4 \text{ for blank})(\text{mg. aniline in sample tube})}{(\text{mg. aniline in blank tube})}$

$b = \text{ml. } HClO_4 \text{ for sample}$

B. FOR PER CENT COMPOUND

$$\% \ Cmpd. = \frac{(a - b)(\text{normality of } HClO_4)(\text{mol. wt. of cmpd. in mg.})(100)}{\text{wt. of sample in mg.}}$$

6. Notes

Note 1. If a pH meter is not available, a visual indicator may be employed (see experiment 3). However, potentiometric titration may show two inflections for the sample tube and only one for the blank containing aniline.

Note 2. If high precision is desired, $0.02N$ perchloric acid may be used, but the volume of titrant for the blank will be over 10 ml.

Note 3. Since less than 1 ml. of purified aniline is needed, the distilling tube shown in Figure 5.26 serves well for this purpose. It is not necessary to measure the boiling point of the distillate. *p*-Chloroaniline may be used in place of aniline.

Note 4. Use the heating stage (Figure 5.19) if available.

7. Comments. This experiment illustrates a method of differential determination. As acid anhydride is usually contaminated with the parent free carboxylic acid, determination of the acid anhydride by titration with standard alkali is not satisfactory. Therefore, a procedure specifically for acid anhydride, which can be used for its determination in the presence of carboxylic acids, is very desirable.

Obviously acid chloride, if present in the sample, constitutes an interference, since it also reacts with aniline to form the anilide. Indeed, the procedure described in this experiment can be used to determine acid chlorides with slight modification. After the reaction mixture is transferred into the 100-ml. beaker and 10 ml. of titration solvent is added, 1 ml. of 3% mercuric acetate solution is introduced (see experiment 4), and the titration is then carried out in the usual manner.

Experiment 21: Microdetermination of Acid Anhydride by Indirect Bromination

1. Principle. As was shown in experiment 20, an acid anhydride reacts quantitatively with aniline to form the corresponding anilide. In the method to be described, 2,4-dichloroaniline is used as the reagent. Equation 50 shows the reaction for phthalic anhydride:

$$(50)$$

Because of the absence of the activating amino group, the dichloroanilide is brominated much more slowly than 2,4-dichloroaniline. Hence by comparing the amount of brominating reagent consumed by the blank containing the reagent only, as shown in equation 51, and that by the sample, the quantity of 2,4-dichloroaniline used in the formation of the substituted anilide can be calculated.

$$+ Br_2 \rightarrow \qquad + HBr \qquad (51)$$

The brominating reagent consists of a mixture of potassium bromate and potassium bromide. The excess of bromine is titrated iodometrically (see experiment 14).

2. Apparatus
A. Reaction Flasks. Use 125-ml. iodine flasks.
B. Microburet. 10-ml. capacity, graduated in 0.02 or 0.05 ml.

3. Reagents
A. 2,4-Dichloroaniline in Acetic Acid, 1%. Weigh 1.00 g. of 2,4-dichloroaniline (reagent grade) into a 100-ml. volumetric flask. Add glacial acetic acid to dissolve the solid and make up to the mark.

B. Standard Potassium Bromate-Potassium Bromide Solution, $0.02N$ ($= 0.01M$) in Bromine. Weigh 556.72 mg. of potassium bromate (reagent grade) and 4.0 g. of potassium bromide in a 1-liter volumetric flask. Dissolve the solids in distilled water and dilute to the mark.

C. Standard Sodium Thiosulfate Solution, $0.02N$ ($= 0.02M$). See experiment 19.

D. Potassium Iodide, 20%. See experiment 14.

E. Hydrochloric Acid, $2N$ ($= 2M$). Mix 20 ml. of concentrated C.P. hydrochloric acid with 80 ml. of distilled water.

F. Glacial Acetic Acid. Reagent grade.

G. Starch Indicator Solution, 1%. See experiment 19.

H. Test Compounds. See experiment 20.

4. Procedure.
Accurately weigh about 0.1 meq. of the acid anhydride into the reaction flask. Dissolve the sample in 5.0 ml. of glacial acetic acid. Introduce exactly 5.00 ml. of the 2,4-dichloroaniline reagent solution by means of a pipet. Stopper the flask and swirl to mix the contents. Add the same amounts of the reagents into another reaction flask which serves as blank. Let both flasks stand in a dark place for 2 hours. Now add into each flask 20 ml. of glacial acetic acid, 20 ml. of distilled water, and 5 ml. of

dilute hydrochloric acid. After mixing the solution, introduce exactly 15.00 ml. of the standardized 0.02N potassium bromate-potassium bromide solution. Stopper the flasks and shake for 2 minutes. Then let the flasks stand in a dark place for 10 minutes (Note 1). Now add 2 ml. of the potassium iodide solution. Stopper and shake for 2 minutes. Titrate with the standardized 0.02N sodium thiosulfate until the contents of the flask turn pale yellow (Note 2). Add 0.5 ml. of the starch indicator and continue the titration until the solution becomes colorless.

5. Calculations

A. FOR PER CENT ACID ANHYDRIDE

$$\% \ (CO)_2O = \frac{(b - s)(\text{normality of } Na_2S_2O_3)(72.02)(100)}{(2)(\text{wt. of sample in mg.})}$$

where b = ml. of $Na_2S_2O_3$ for blank, and s = ml. of $Na_2S_2O_3$ for sample.

B. FOR PER CENT COMPOUND

$$\% \ \text{Cmpd.} = \frac{(b - s)(\text{normality of } Na_2S_2O_3)(\text{meq. wt. of cmpd. in mg.})(100)}{(2)(\text{wt. of sample in mg.})}$$

6. Notes

Note 1. See experiment 14 about the precautions in the bromination of the benzene nucleus.

Note 2. Since the blank will require more than 10 ml. of the 0.02N thiosulfate, this amount can be added rapidly.

7. Comments. This experiment illustrates the application of the rate of reaction in quantitative analysis. It should be recognized that the substituted anilide is also susceptible to bromination. Therefore, the blank and the sample should be treated under identical conditions.

Analytical bromination of an aromatic amine is demonstrated in this experiment. This is similar to the bromometric determination of phenols (see experiment 14). However, microdetermination of aniline and related compounds by bromination is not commonly used, because of the difficulty in controlling the reaction.

Experiment 22: Microdetermination of the Thiol Function by Iodimetric Method

1. Principle. The thiol function is quantitatively oxidized by iodine in acid solution to disulfide (see Chapter 9, Section II-C). Using thiosalicylic acid as an example, the stoichiometry is given by equation 52:

$$2(HOOC)C_6H_4(SH) + I_2 \rightarrow (HOOC)C_6H_4\text{—}S\text{—}S\text{—}C_6H_4(COOH) + 2HI \quad (52)$$

A standard iodine solution is too unstable for microdeterminations. To circumvent this difficulty, the thiol compound is mixed with potassium iodide in glacial acetic acid. The solution is then titrated with standardized $0.03N$ potassium iodate. Iodine is generated *in situ* according to equation 53:

$$KIO_3 + 5KI + 6CH_3COOH \rightarrow 3I_2 + 6CH_3COOK + 3H_2O \qquad (53)$$

The endpoint is indicated by the appearance of free iodine.

2. Apparatus
A. REACTION FLASK.   Use a 50-ml. Erlenmeyer flask.
B. MICROBURET.   10-ml. capacity, graduated in 0.02 or 0.05 ml.

3. Reagents
A. STANDARD POTASSIUM IODATE SOLUTION, $0.03N$ ($= 0.005M$).   Prepare 500 ml. of this solution by weighing exactly 536.00 mg. of reagent grade potassium iodate according to the directions given in experiment 19. Alternately, prepare the $0.03N$ solution by diluting 150 ml. of the $0.1N$ potassium iodate solution to 500 ml. in a volumetric flask. Mix thoroughly and determine the exact strength as follows. Pipet 5.00 ml. of the solution into a 125 ml. iodine flask. Add 20 ml. of glacial acetic acid. Swirl the contents and allow the mixture to stand for 5 minutes. Now add 2 ml. of 15% potassium iodide solution into the well of the iodine flask. Gently lift the stopper. Then add 10 ml. of distilled water in the same manner. Shake the flask for 2 minutes. Quickly titrate the liberated iodine with the standardized $0.03N$ sodium thiosulfate until the brown color of iodine begins to fade. Add 1 ml. of 1% starch indicator at this point and continue the titration until the blue color is completely discharged.
B. POTASSIUM IODIDE.   Reagent grade.
C. GLACIAL ACETIC ACID.   Reagent grade.
D. METHANOL.   Reagent grade.
E. TEST COMPOUNDS.   Thiosalicylic acid, m.p., 164°C; cysteine hydrochloride, m.p., 175°C.

4. Procedure.   Accurately weigh a sample containing about 0.1 meq. of thiol group (Note 1) into a 50-ml. Erlenmeyer flask. Add 5 ml. of methanol to dissolve the sample, followed by 1 ml. of glacial acetic acid, 400 mg. of potassium iodide, and 1 ml. of distilled water. Swirl the flask until all solids have dissolved. Then titrate the contents of the flask with the standardized $0.03N$ potassium iodate. The endpoint is the appearance of the yellow color of free iodine, which persists for 30 seconds.

5. *Calculations*

A. FOR PER CENT THIOL GROUP

$$\% \text{ -SH} = \frac{(\text{ml. of KIO}_3)(\text{normality})(33.074)(100)}{\text{wt. of sample in mg.}}$$

B. FOR PER CENT COMPOUND

$$\% \text{ Compound} = \frac{(\text{ml. of KIO}_3)(\text{normality})(\text{meq. wt. of cmpd. in mg.})(100)}{\text{wt. of sample in mg.}}$$

6. *Note*

Note 1. One-tenth milliequivalent of thiol group reacts with 0.1 mg. atom of iodine and hence, consumes about 3.3 ml. of $0.03N$ potassium iodate.

7. *Comments.* This experiment illustrates a micro procedure employing the direct iodimetric method. Direct titration with standard potassium iodate solution is possible in the present case because (1) the oxidation of the thiol function is very rapid, and (2) the color of one drop excess of $0.03N$ iodine is discernible in the acetic acid-methanol-water mixed solvent.

Experiment 23: Microdetermination of the Sulfide and Disulfide Functions by Bromine Oxidation

1. Principle. Both the sulfide and disulfide functions (see Chapter 9, Section III) can be quantitatively oxidized by bromine. However, as will be shown in the procedures below, the experimental conditions depend on the type of compounds to be determined. The stoichiometry also varies. Thus *n*-butyl sulfide consumes one molar equivalent of bromine:

$$(C_4H_9)_2S + Br_2 + H_2O \rightarrow (B_4H_9)_2SO + 2HBr \qquad (54)$$

whereas phenyl disulfide requires 5 molar equivalents:

$$C_6H_5\text{—}S\text{—}S\text{—}C_6H_5 + 5Br_2 + 4H_2O \rightarrow 2C_6H_5SO_2Br + 8HBr \qquad (55)$$

Since it is not feasible to use a standard bromine solution for microanalysis, the oxidizing agent is obtained *in situ* by mixing a standardized solution of potassium bromate with an excess amount of potassium bromide.

$$KBrO_3 + 5KBr + 6HCl \rightarrow 3Br_2 + 6KCl + 3H_2O \qquad (56)$$

The large ratio between bromine and disulfide (eq. 55) permits the use of $0.2N$ potassium bromate solution so that the endpoint can be easily detected by the color of bromine.

2. Apparatus

A. MICROBURET. 10-ml. capacity, graduated in 0.02 or 0.05 ml.

B. REACTION FLASK. Use 125-ml. iodine flask, or 75-ml. Erlenmeyer flask fitted with ground-glass stopper.

3. Reagents

A. STANDARD POTASSIUM BROMATE SOLUTION, $0.2N$ ($= M/30$). Accurately weigh 5.567 g. of reagent grade potassium bromate into a 1-liter volumetric flask. Dissolve the solid in distilled water and dilute to the mark. Standardize this solution in the following manner. Transfer exactly 5.00 ml. of the solution into a 125-ml. iodine flask. Add 25 ml. of glacial acetic acid, followed by 400 mg. of potassium bromide (reagent grade) and stopper the flask. Swirl to mix and let the solution stand for 5 minutes. Then add 5 ml. of 15% potassium iodide solution and 50 ml. of distilled water. Stopper and shake the contents of the flask for 2 minutes. Titrate with standardized $0.1N$ sodium thiosulfate until the brown color of iodine begins to fade. Add 1 ml. of 1% starch indicator and complete the titration until the solution becomes colorless.

B. STANDARD POTASSIUM BROMATE SOLUTION, $0.1N$ ($= M/60$). Prepare this solution using 2.7835 g. of potassium bromate, or by mixing the $0.2N$ potassium bromate solution with an equal volume of distilled water.

C. STANDARD POTASSIUM BROMATE SOLUTION, $0.03N$ ($= M/200$). Dilute a $0.2N$ or $0.1N$ solution with the proper volume of distilled water. Determine the exact strength by the direction given in reagent A, using standardized $0.02N$ sodium thiosulfate as the titrant.

D. POTASSIUM IODIDE SOLUTION, 15%. Dissolve 15 g. of potassium iodide in 85 ml. of distilled water.

E. STANDARD SODIUM THIOSULFATE, $0.1N$ ($= M/10$). Use the commercial standard $M/10$ sodium thiosulfate.

F. STARCH INDICATOR SOLUTION, 1%. See experiment 19.

G. TEST COMPOUNDS. n-Butyl sulfide, b.p. 182°C; benzyl sulfide, m.p. 49°C; phenyl sulfide, b.p. 296°C; benzyl disulfide, m.p. 71°C; L-cystine, m.p. 258°C; phenyl disulfide, m.p. 61°C.

4. Procedures

A. FOR ALIPHATIC DISULFIDES. Weigh accurately about 0.1 meq. of the sample into the reaction flask and dissolve it in 10 ml. of glacial acetic acid. Add into the flask 1 ml. of distilled water, 1.0 g. of potassium bromide (reagent grade), and 2 ml. of concentrated hydrochloric acid. Stopper the flask and shake the mixture for one minute. Then titrate the contents with the standardized $0.2N$ potassium bromate until the appearance of bromine color which persists for 30 seconds.

B. For Aromatic Disulfides. Accurately weigh about 0.1 meq. of the sample into the reaction flask. Add 20 ml. of 95% ethanol to dissolve the sample, followed by 2 ml. of concentrated hydrochloric acid and 800 mg. of potassium bromide. Stopper the flask and shake the contents for 1 minute. Titrate the solution with the standardized $0.2N$ potassium bromate until the appearance of free bromine (Note 1). Replace the stopper on the reaction flask and place it in the dark for one hour. The bromine color will have disappeared. Now finish the determination with the same titrant until the bromine color appears and persists for 30 seconds.

C. For Aliphatic Sulfides. Accurately weigh about 0.1 meq. of the sulfide into the reaction flask and dissolve the sample in 5 to 10 ml. of glacial acetic acid. Add 1 ml. of concentrated hydrochloric acid and 400 mg. of potassium bromide into the flask. Stopper and shake for one minute. Then titrate the contents of the flask with the standardized $0.03N$ potassium bromate solution. The endpoint is the appearance of bromine color which persists for 30 seconds.

D. For Aromatic Sulfides. Weigh accurately about 0.1 meq. of the sample into the reaction flask and add 10 ml. of glacial acetic acid together with 5 ml. of 95% ethanol. After the sample has dissolved, deliver into the reaction flask exactly 5.00 ml. of standardized $0.1N$ potassium bromate solution. Add 500 mg. of potassium bromide and 2 ml. of concentrated hydrochloric acid. Stopper the flask and swirl to mix the contents. Place the flask in a water bath at 60°C for 5 minutes. Then cool the contents of the flask to room temperature and add 2 ml. of the 15% potassium iodide solution. Replace the stopper, shake for 1 minute, and titrate the iodine with the standard $0.1N$ sodium thiosulfate to the starch endpoint.

Run a blank using exactly the same amounts of reagents and the identical conditions.

5. *Calculations*

A. For Per Cent Disulfide Group

$$\% \text{ —S—S— } = \frac{(\text{ml. of KBrO}_3)(\text{normality of KBrO}_3)(64.12)(100)}{(\text{wt. of sample in mg.})(10)}$$

B. For Per Cent Purity (= Per Cent Compound) of Disulfide

$$\% \text{ Purity } = \frac{(\text{ml. of KBrO}_3)(\text{normality of KBrO}_3)(\text{meq. wt. of cmpd. in mg.})(100)}{(\text{wt. of sample in mg.})(10)}$$

C. For Per Cent Aliphatic Sulfide Group

$$\% \text{ —S— } = \frac{(\text{ml. of KBrO}_3)(\text{normality of KBrO}_3)(32.06)(100)}{(\text{wt. of sample in mg.})(2)}$$

D. FOR PER CENT PURITY OF ALIPHATIC SULFIDE

$$\% \text{ Purity} = \frac{(\text{ml. of } KBrO_3)(\text{normality of } KBrO_3)(\text{meq. wt. of cmpd. in mg.})(100)}{(\text{wt. of sample in mg.})(2)}$$

E. FOR PER CENT AROMATIC SULFIDE GROUP

$$\% -S- = \frac{(b - s)(\text{normality of } Na_2S_2O_3)(32.06)(100)}{(\text{wt. of sample in mg.})(2)}$$

where b = ml. of $Na_2S_2O_3$ for blank, and s = ml. of $Na_2S_2O_3$ for sample.

F. FOR PER CENT PURITY OF AROMATIC SULFIDES

$$\% \text{ Purity} = \frac{(b - s)(\text{normality of } Na_2S_2O_3)(\text{meq. wt. of cmpd. in mg.})(100)}{(\text{wt. of sample in mg.})(2)}$$

6. Note

Note 1. At this point about 70% of the aromatic disulfide has been oxidized. For reasons unknown, the remaining portion cannot be oxidized instantaneously.

7. Comments. This experiment illustrates the importance of choosing the proper method and conditions in the microdetermination of certain functional groups.

Experiment 24: Microdetermination of Thiourea and Thiosemicarbazide by Hypoiodite Oxidation

1. Principle. Thiourea and thiosemicarbazide are readily oxidized by hypoiodite (see Chapter 9, Section VII-C-4). Thiourea is converted to urea on treatment with hypoiodite:

$$CS(NH_2)_2 + 4KOI + H_2O \rightarrow CO(NH_2)_2 + 4KI + H_2SO_4 \qquad (57)$$

The reagent is prepared by mixing solutions of iodine and potassium hydroxide. If thiosemicarbazide is treated under similar conditions, nitrogen gas and cyanate ions are produced instead of urea, as shown in equation 58:

$$H_2NCS(NHNH_2) + 6I_2 + 5H_2O \rightarrow N_2 + HCNO + 12HI + H_2SO_4 \qquad (58)$$

The reactions shown in equations 57 and 58 are the basis of the iodimetric method for determining thiourea, thiosemicarbazide, and thiosemicarbazones (Note 1). Since a standard iodine in alkaline solution does not maintain its strength, standardized potassium iodate is employed. In alkaline solution and in the presence of excess amounts of potassium iodide, potassium iodate may be considered to liberate hypoiodite and iodine according to equation 59:

$$KIO_3 + 4KI + 2H_2O \rightarrow KOI + 2I_2 + 4KOH \qquad (59)$$

From the foregoing equations, it becomes apparent that the molar equivalence between potassium iodate and thiourea and thiosemicarbazide, respectively, is very favorable. Therefore a standard $0.1N$ solution of potassium iodate may be used for the determination of thiourea and thiosemicarbazide on the 0.1 meq. scale. The unconsumed potassium iodate is then back-titrated by means of $0.1N$ sodium thiosulfate after the reaction mixture is acidified:

$$KIO_3 + 5KI + 6HCl \rightarrow 3I_2 + 6KCl + 3H_2O \tag{60}$$

$$I_2 + 2Na_2S_2O_3 \rightarrow 2NaI + Na_2S_4O_6 \tag{61}$$

2. Apparatus

A. REACTION FLASK. Use a 125-ml. iodine flask or a 75-ml. Erlenmeyer flask fitted with ground-glass stopper.

B. MICROBURET. 10-ml. capacity, graduated in 0.02 or 0.05 ml.

3. Reagents

A. STANDARD POTASSIUM IODATE SOLUTION, $0.1N$ $(= M/60)$. Use the commercial standard $0.1N$ potassium iodate solution.

B. STANDARD SODIUM THIOSULFATE SOLUTION, $0.1N$ $(= 0.1M)$. Use the commercial standard $0.1N$ sodium thiosulfate solution.

C. POTASSIUM HYDROXIDE SOLUTION, 15%. Dissolve 15 g. of potassium hydroxide pellets (reagent grade) in 85 ml. of distilled water.

D. POTASSIUM IODIDE. Reagent grade.

E. HYDROCHLORIC ACID, C.P.

F. STARCH INDICATOR SOLUTION, 1%. See experiment 19.

G. TEST COMPOUNDS. Thiourea, m.p. 182°C; thiosemicarbazide, m.p. 181°C.

4. Procedure. Weigh accurately 0.1 millimole of thiourea (or 0.05 millimole of thiosemicarbazide) into the reaction flask. Dissolve the sample in 10 ml. of 15% potassium hydroxide solution. Add exactly 10.00 ml. of standard $0.1N$ potassium iodate solution, followed by 500 mg. of potassium iodide. Stopper the flask and shake the contents for 1 minute. Let the flask stand in a dark place for 30 to 60 minutes. Add 5.0 ml. of concentrated hydrochloric acid. Shake the flask to liberate the iodine. Then titrate with standard $0.1N$ sodium thiosulfate using starch as indicator (see experiment 23).

Run a blank in the same manner.

5. Calculations. The stoichiometry of thiourea and thiosemicarbazide oxidation cannot be exactly expressed by equations 57 and 58 respectively. Therefore it is necessary to establish the molar-equivalence of the standard potassium iodate solution used in the experiment by analyzing a pure sample of thiourea (thiosemicarbazide as the case may be), and then apply the factor to calculate the value of the unknown sample.

6. Note

Note 1. Thiosemicarbazones can be hydrolyzed in acid or strong alkaline solutions to the parent carbonyl compound and thiosemicarbazide.

7. Comments. This experiment illustrates iodimetry in alkaline solution and the need of a pure reference sample (or a sample of known composition) in certain methods of analysis. An unknown thiosemicarbazone can be determined, however, by standardizing the procedure with pure thiosemicarbazide.

Experiment 25: Microdetermination of Heterocyclic Bases (Alkaloids) by Gravimetric Method

1. Principle. As was stated in Chapter 8, Section VIII-E, many alkaloids form salts or complexes which are only slightly soluble in water. A reagent commonly used for precipitating alkaloids is picrolonic acid [3-methyl-4-nitro-1-(*p*-nitrophenyl)-5-pyrazolone]:

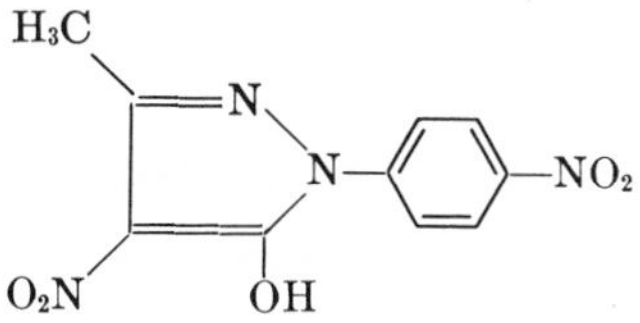

Thus codeine precipitates codeine picronolate according to equation 63.

$$C_{18}H_{21}NO_3 + C_{10}H_8N_4O_5 \rightarrow C_{18}H_{21}NO_3 \cdot C_{10}H_8N_4O_5 \qquad (63)$$
codeine   picrolonic acid

2. Apparatus

A. REACTION TUBE.   See experiment 7.

B. FILTRATION DEVICE.   See experiment 7.

3. Reagents

A. PICROLONIC ACID SOLUTION, 0.1*M*.   Dissolve 2.6 g. of picrolonic acid (highest purity grade) in 100 ml. of 95% ethanol.

B. TEST COMPOUNDS.   Codeine citrate; quinine gluconate.

4. Procedure.   Accurately weigh about 0.1 meq. of the alkaloid into the reaction tube. Add 5 to 10 ml. of distilled water to dissolve the sample.

Deliver 5.0 ml. of the picrolonic acid solution into the reaction tube by means of a pipet. Swirl to mix the solution. Then let the reaction tube stay in the beaker overnight (Note 1).

Filter off the supernatant liquid according to the directions given in experiment 7. Wash twice with 5-ml. portions of water. Dry the container and the precipitate at 105°C and reweigh.

5. Calculations

A. FOR PER CENT PURITY (= PER CENT COMPOUND)

$$\% \text{ Purity} = \frac{(\text{mg. precipitate})(\text{gravimetric factor})(100)}{\text{mg. sample}}$$

6. Note

Note 1.   If a refrigerator is available, place the reaction tube and beaker in the refrigerator, but not in the very cold section.

7. Comments.   This method may be used for all nitrogen bases known to form insoluble picrolonates. If the compound is an unknown, the precipitate, after weighing, may be redissolved in glacial acetic acid (or other suitable solvent) and titrated as a base by means of $0.01N$ perchloric acid (see experiment 4). The milliequivalent weight of the free base can then be calculated.

Picrolonic acid has the molecular weight of 264.09, hence it offers a favorable gravimetric factor.

Experiment 26:   Microdetermination of Quaternary Ammonium Salts by Gravimetric Method

1. Principle.   Quaternary ammonium salts (see Chapter 8, Section IV-E) in general form tetraphenylboron derivatives which are insoluble in water. The equation for cetyldimethylbenzylammonium chloride is shown in equation 64:

$$(C_{16}H_{33})(CH_3)_2(C_6H_5CH_2)NCl + (C_6H_5)_4BNa \rightarrow (C_{16}H_{33})(CH_3)_2(C_6H_5CH_2)NB(C_6H_5)_4$$
$$+ NaCl \quad (64)$$

2. Apparatus

A. REACTION TUBE.   Use a large test tube 40-mm. × 150-mm.

B. FILTRATION DEVICE.   Use the sintered glass filter tube (see Figure 5.22, p. 97) with medium porosity.

3. Reagents

A. SODIUM TETRAPHENYLBORON REAGENT SOLUTION, $0.1M$.   Dissolve 3.4 g. of sodium tetraphenylboron (highest purity) in 100 ml. of distilled water.

B. TEST COMPOUNDS.   Cetyldimethylbenzylammonium chloride; Phemerol chloride tincture (Note 1).

4. Procedure.   Accurately weigh about 0.1 meq. of the sample into the reaction tube. (In the case of the tincture solution, measure 25 ml. with a pipet.) Dissolve the solid sample in 25 ml. of water. Swirl the solution. Then add 10 ml. of the sodium tetraphenylboron reagent solution by means of a pipet so that the reagent falls into the center of the sample. Continue swirling for 2 minutes. Let the precipitate stand overnight at room temperature.

Place a piece of filter paper (cut to fit the sintered glass plate) in the filter tube. Weigh the tube accurately. Then assemble the filtration device as shown in Figure 5.22. Siphon off the supernatant liquid first. Now raise the reaction tube so that the siphon tube nearly touches the precipitate. Cover the precipitate with a few milliliters of distilled water and siphon the precipitate into the filter tube. Do not let the precipitate dry in the reaction tube. If solid adheres to the walls, loosen it with a feather (Note 2) or rubber policeman.

Add 5 ml. of distilled water into the reaction tube to rinse the tube and siphon. Remove the siphon. Take the filter tube off the adapter. Dry the tube and precipitate at 105°C for 1 hour. Cool to room temperature and reweigh.

5. Calculations

A. FOR PER CENT COMPOUND

$$\% \text{ Compound} = \frac{(\text{mg. precipitate})(\text{gravimetric factor})(100)}{\text{mg. sample}}$$

6. Notes

Note 1.   The Phemerol chloride tincture contains a red dye and, hence, cannot be determined by the titrimetric method given in experiment 27.

Note 2.   A snipe feather cemented into a glass handle, available from A. H. Thomas Co., Philadelphia, Penn.

7. Comments.   This experiment demonstrates the use of a gravimetric procedure and use of the sintered glass filter tube.

Experiment 27:   Microdetermination of Quaternary Ammonium Salts by Titrimetric Method

1. Principle.   Quaternary ammonium salts, $[R_1R_2R_3R_4N^+]X^-$, where R_1, R_2, and R_3 are methyl or longer chained alkyls, and R_4 is benzyl, butyl or longer chained aryl-alkyl, will form salts with bromophenol blue (a sulfonphthalein) which can be extracted from alkaline solution. The reaction is represented in equation 65:

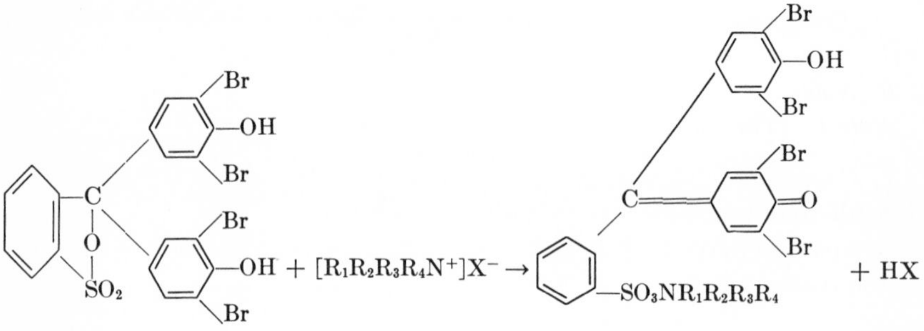

$$\text{(65)}$$

To apply this reaction to the determination of quaternary ammonium salt, the blue color is discharged by the conversion of this salt into the insoluble tetraphenylboron derivative (see experiment 26).

2. *Apparatus*

A. MICROBURET.   10-ml. capacity, graduated in 0.02 or 0.05 ml.

B. MAGNETIC STIRRER

3. *Reagents*

A. STANDARD SODIUM TETRAPHENYLBORON SOLUTION, $0.02N$ ($= M/50$). Dissolve 3.4224 g. of sodium tetraphenylboron (highest purity grade) in distilled water in a 500 ml. volumetric flask and dilute the solution to the mark.

B. BROMOPHENOL BLUE REAGENT SOLUTION, 0.05%.   Dissolve 50 mg. of bromophenol blue indicator in 3.0 ml. of $0.1N$ sodium hydroxide and add 97 ml. of distilled water.

C. CHLOROFORM.   Reagent grade.

D. TEST COMPOUNDS.   Cetyldimethylbenzylammonium chloride; Phemerol chloride crystals.

4. *Procedure.*   Weigh accurately about 0.1 millimole of the quaternary ammonium salt into a 100-ml. Erlenmeyer flask. Dissolve the sample in 15 ml. of distilled water. Add 0.5 ml. of the bromophenol blue reagent solution, 10 ml. of chloroform, and 10 ml. of $0.1N$ sodium hydroxide. Swirl to mix. Add the clean magnetic stirring bar into the flask. Titrate the contents of the flask while it is being stirred (Note 1). Observe the gradual fading of the blue color from the chloroform layer. Add the last portions of the titrant drop by drop until the chloroform layer becomes colorless.

5. Calculations

A. FOR PER CENT COMPOUND

$$\% \text{ Compound} = \frac{[\text{ml. Na}(C_6H_5)_4B](\text{normality})(\text{meq. wt. of cmpd. in mg.})(100)}{\text{wt. of sample in mg.}}$$

6. Note

Note 1. The stirring should not be too rapid.

7. Comments. This method is an example of two-phase titration. It is difficult to obtain high precision by this technique.

A separatory funnel or a flask with a ground-glass stopper may be used as the reaction flask, but it requires shaking and is tedious.

Experiment 28: Microdetermination of the Isocyanate and Isothiocyanate Functions by Reaction with Butylamine

1. Principle. As was discussed in Chapter 8, Section X-B, a useful method for determining the isocyanate function is by its reaction with an amine. Thus phenylisocyanate reacts with butylamine according to equation 66 to form a symmetrical substituted urea:

$$C_6H_5NCO + C_4H_9NH_2 \rightarrow C_6H_5NH(CO)NHC_4H_9 \qquad (66)$$

Phenylisothiocyanate reacts in an analogous manner to form a substituted thiourea:

$$C_6H_5NCS + C_4H_9NH_2 \rightarrow C_6H_5NH(CS)NHC_4H_9 \qquad (67)$$

In practice a measured amount of n-butylamine dissolved in dioxane is added to the sample. The unconsumed amine is then determined by back-titration with standardized hydrochloric acid.

2. Apparatus

A. MICROBURET. 10-ml. capacity, graduated in 0.02 or 0.05 ml.

B. REACTION FLASK. Use a 125-ml. iodine flask.

C. MAGNETIC STIRRER AND STIRRING BAR

3. Reagents

A. STANDARD HYDROCHLORIC ACID, $0.05N$ ($= M/20$). See experiment 1 (Note 1).

B. n-BUTYLAMINE REAGENT SOLUTION, 0.2%. Weigh 2.00 g. of n-butylamine (reagent grade) into a 1-liter volumetric flask. Add p-dioxane (see D. below) and make up to the mark. Transfer the solution to a screw-capped amber bottle for storage.

C. METHYL RED INDICATOR SOLUTION, 0.1%. Dissolve 100 mg. of methyl red indicator in 100 ml. of 95% ethanol.

D. *p*-DIOXANE. Use the reagent grade solvent, if available. Alternately, purify the dioxane by adding some potassium hydroxide pellets to 100 ml. of dioxane. Change the pellets when they turn brown. The *p*-dioxane is ready for use when the color change no longer occurs after the solution has stood for 2 days.

E. TEST COMPOUNDS. Phenylisocyanate, b.p. 55°C/13 mm.; 2,4-tolyene diisocyanate, m.p. 19–20°C; phenyl isothiocyanate, b.p. 100°C/15 mm.

4. Procedure. Place a clean stirring bar in the reaction flask. Add exactly 10.00 ml. of the 0.2% *n*-butylamine and stopper the flask. Accurately weigh about 0.1 meq. of the sample (Note 2) using the micro weighing bottle shown in Figure 5.10 (p. 85). Carefully drop the weighing bottle and the sample into the reaction flask and quickly replace the stopper. Place the reaction flask on the magnetic stirrer. The stirring of the contents is usually sufficient to open the weighing bottle. If necessary, use a glass hook to catch the eye on the weighing bottle stopper to disengage the latter. Break off the lower part of the glass hook with an ampoule cutter and leave it in the reaction flask.

After stirring the solution for 1 minute, allow the reaction mixture to stand for 15 minutes for aromatic isocyanates or isothiocyanates and 45 minutes for aliphatic compounds. Then add 20 ml. of distilled water into the well of the reaction flask and open the stopper. Add 2 drops (0.08 ml.) of methyl red indicator and titrate the contents of the flask with the standardized 0.05*N* hydrochloric acid to a distinct pink endpoint.

Run a blank on 10.00 ml. of the *n*-butylamine reagent solution under identical conditions but without the sample.

5. Calculations

A. FOR PER CENT ISOCYANATE FUNCTION

$$\% \text{ NCO} = \frac{(b - s)(\text{normality of HCl})(42.02)(100)}{\text{wt. of sample in mg.}}$$

where b = ml. HCl for blank, and s = ml. HCl for sample.

B. FOR PER CENT ISOTHIOCYANATE FUNCTION

$$\% \text{ NCS} = \frac{(b - s)(\text{normality of HCl})(58,08)(100)}{\text{wt. of sample in mg.}}$$

C. FOR PER CENT COMPOUND

$$\% \text{ Compound} = \frac{(b - s)(\text{normality of HCl})(\text{meq. wt. of compound in mg.})(100)}{\text{wt. of sample in mg.}}$$

6. Notes

Note 1. Standardized 0.02N hydrochloric acid may be used for better precision.

Note 2. The milliequivalent weight of a diisocyanate is one-half its molecular weight. If one millimole of 2,4-tolylene diisocyanate has been weighed by mistake, add 20.00 ml. of the *n*-butylamine reagent solution into the reaction flask.

7. Comments. The technique of handling volatile liquid samples and volatile standard reagent solution is demonstrated in this experiment.

Experiment 29: Microdetermination of Alkali Sulfonates and Sulfoxylates by the Ashing Method

1. Principle. Because sulfonic acids are strong acids, alkali sulfonates cannot be determined by acid-base titrimetry as can the alkali carboxylates. If the sample is free from other metallic salts, a convenient method for determining alkali sulfonate consists of simply igniting it to yield the corresponding alkali sulfate (see Chapter 9, Section IV-E-1). Thus sodium benzenesulfonate reacts as follows:

$$2C_6H_5SO_3Na + 15O_2 \rightarrow Na_2SO_4 + 12CO_2 + 5H_2O + SO_3 \qquad (68)$$

After the removal of carbon dioxide, sulfur trioxide, and water vapor, the residue is weighed in form of sodium sulfate.

The previously mentioned procedure is also applicable to the determination of alkali sulfoxylates (bisulfite addition products of carbonyl compounds). For example, after the isolation of acetaldehyde sodium bisulfite addition product (see Chapter 6, Section VII-B-2), it may be analyzed by ignition to yield an equivalent quantity of sodium sulfate.

$$2CH_3-\overset{\overset{\displaystyle H}{|}}{\underset{\underset{\displaystyle OH}{|}}{C}}-SO_3Na + 8O_2 \rightarrow Na_2SO_4 + 4CO_2 + 5H_2O + SO_3 \qquad (69)$$

2. Apparatus

A. PLATINUM MICROCRUCIBLE (NOTE 1). 1.5-ml. capacity, with cover.

3. Reagents

A. DILUTE SULFURIC ACID. Add 1 part of reagent grade concentrated sulfuric acid to 4 parts of distilled water.

B. TEST COMPOUNDS. Benzenesulfonic acid sodium salt; 3-amino-2,7-naphthalenedisulfonic acid monosodium salt; 4,5-dihydroxy-3-(*p*-sulfophenylazo)-2,7-naphthalenedisulfonic acid trisodium salt. Acetaldehyde sodium bisulfite addition compound; ethyl methyl ketone sodium bisulfite addition compound.

4. Procedure

A. WEIGHING THE SAMPLE. Thoroughly clean the microcrucible and cover, using nitric acid and distilled water; then place them on an ordinary (macro) platinum crucible lid which rests on a triangle. Heat with Bunsen burner for 2 minutes, cool for 2 minutes, and transfer the microcrucible and cover to the metal block in the microdesiccator. Allow 10 min. to equilibrate the temperature of the platinum ware and that of the microbalance. Now place the microcrucible and cover on the balance pan; weigh accurately to ±5 μg. Introduce 10 to 20 mg. of the sample into the microcrucible by means of the weighing tube (Chapter 5, Section V-B). Again weigh to ±5 μg., to obtain the exact weight of the sample taken.

B. THE FIRST COMBUSTION. Replace the microcrucible on the ordinary platinum lid and place the cover beside the microcrucible. Carefully apply a small oxidizing flame to the outer surface of the microcrucible, starting from the upper edge. (If there is indication of spattering of the sample, place the cover over the microcrucible; otherwise leave the microcrucible open to get the maximum amount of oxygen for combustion.) After the flame has reached the bottom of the microcrucible, put the cover on and raise the flame so that the lower portion of the microcrucible is heated to dull red. Then move the flame to under the ordinary platinum lid and continue heating for 5 minutes. Cool and reweigh (Note 2) as described in the last paragraph.

C. THE SECOND COMBUSTION. Again place the microcrucible containing the ash on the ordinary platinum lid. Using a capillary pipet, carefully add a drop of dilute sulfuric acid along the walls of the microcrucible so that the ash is barely moistened. Replace the cover loosely and apply a small flame on the side of the microcrucible. Remove the flame momentarily when fumes evolve. Finish the combustion as mentioned earlier; weigh the microcrucible containing the alkali sulfate, together with the cover, when it has cooled.

5. Calculations

$$\% \text{ Compound} = \frac{\text{mg. residue} \times \text{gravimetric factor} \times 100}{\text{mg. sample}}$$

6. Notes

Note 1. Porcelain crucibles may be used. It should be noted, however, that porcelain ware may chip on ignition. Because of poor heat conductivity, the porcelain crucible should be allowed to stand in the micro-desiccator for 30 min. before weighing.

Note 2. This weighing may be omitted. However, the nature of the ash can better be scrutinized by taking a weighing after the first combustion. If there is no change between this and the next weighing, it can be assumed that no alkali carbonate was formed.

7. Comments. This experiment illustrates the microtechnique of ashing, which is a useful method for determining single metallic elements in organic compounds. When it is employed to determine sulfonates and sulfoxylates, prior knowledge should be established that the sample does not contain other metals or other alkali salts.

Experiment 30: Microdetermination of Organophosphorus Functions by Colorimetric Method

1. Principle. The reader is referred to Chapter 11, Section XI for the discussion of organophosphorus functions. It will be noted that there are very few methods that may be used to determine specifically certain functional groups containing phosphorus. Hence the general practice in the analysis of an organic phosphorus compound is to determine its total phosphorus content. The colorimetric method described in this experiment is dependent on the conversion of organically bound phosphorus to the phosphate ion, followed by the formation of the yellow heteropoly compound. This colored complex, known as ammonium phosphovanado-molybdate or molybdivanadophosphoric acid, is recommended for the determination of phosphorus functions on the 0.1 meq. scale for several reasons: (1) it is very stable—the color intensity of the solution does not change after standing for several weeks; (2) it is not sensitive to redox agents or slight temperature variations; (3) Beer's law is obeyed over a wide range—from 0 to 5 mg. of phosphorus in 100 ml. of solution; (4) the presence of other ions does not interfere with the determination.

Using triphenylphosphine as example, the chemistry involved in the determination may be depicted in the following sequence.

$$(C_6H_5)_3P \xrightarrow{HNO_3 + H_2SO_4} H_3PO_4 \xrightarrow{NH_4VO_3 + (NH_4)_6Mo_7O_{24}} \text{yellow heteropoly cmpd.} \qquad (70)$$

A balanced equation cannot be written for the last reaction because the composition of the colored complex has not been established.

2. Apparatus

A. MICRO-KJELDAHL DIGESTION FLASKS. 10-ml. capacity.

B. VOLUMETRIC FLASKS. 100-ml. capacity.

c. MICROBURET.   10-ml. capacity, graduated in 0.05 ml.

d. SPECTROPHOTOMETER.   For visual range.

3. Reagents

A. STANDARD PHOSPHATE SOLUTION.   Prepare a standard phosphate solution containing 0.500 mg. of phosphorus per ml. by dissolving 2.1315 g. of pure diammonium hydrogen phosphate (or 2.196 g. of pure potassium dihydrogen phosphate) in a 1-liter volumetric flask and diluting to the mark.

B. AMMONIUM VANADATE SOLUTION CONTAINING 0.20% VANADATE. Cautiously add 2.35 g. of ammonium metavanadate, NH_4VO_3, into 500 ml. of boiling distilled water, followed by 100 ml. of dilute sulfuric acid (1:12). After cooling, add distilled water to make 1 liter of solution.

c. AMMONIUM MOLYBDATE SOLUTION CONTAINING 10% MoO_3.   Dissolve 122 g. of ammonium molybdate, $(NH_4)_6Mo_7O_{24}\cdot4H_2O$, reagent grade, in 800 ml. of distilled water.

D. CONCENTRATED SULFURIC ACID.   Reagent grade.

E. CONCENTRATED NITRIC ACID.   Reagent grade.

F. TEST COMPOUNDS.   Triphenylphosphine, m.p. 78°C; phenylphosphoric acid, disodium salt.

4. Procedure

A. PREPARATION OF THE STANDARD CURVE.   Accurately measure ten aliquots of the standard phosphate solution, covering the range from 0.50 to 3.50 mg. phosphorus, into 100-ml. volumetric flasks. Keep another 100-ml. flask for the reagent blank. Add 60 ml. of distilled water to each flask, followed by 1.4 ml. of concentrated sulfuric acid. While swirling the flask continuously, deliver slowly into it 15 ml. of the vanadate solution and 15 ml. of the molybdate solution. Then dilute the solution to the mark with distilled water and let it stand for 30 minutes (Note 1).

Now measure the intensities of the yellow solutions at 410 mμ against the reagent blank (Note 2). Plot absorbance ($A = -\log T$) against mg. of phosphorus in 100 ml. of solution. The straight line obtained is the standard curve. An equation of the form

$$w = \alpha A + \beta$$

can be derived from the standard curve, where w gives the weight of phosphorus in the sample, A is the observed absorbance of the solution, and α and β are constants.

B. ANALYSIS OF THE SAMPLE.   Using the weighing tube with long handle (Chapter 5, Section V-B) accurately weigh 10 to 20 mg. of the sample (corresponding to about 2 mg. phosphorus) into the micro-Kjeldahl digestion flask. Add 2 ml. of concentrated sulfuric acid and 6 drops (0.3 ml.) of concentrated nitric acid. Gently heat the flask on the digestion rack until the reaction subsides. After cooling, add 4 more drops of concentrated nitric acid and again heat the flask with a medium flame until the solution is clear and sulfur trioxide fumes appear. Allow the reaction mixture to cool and carefully add 10 ml. of distilled water into the digestion flask. Then transfer the solution, with several rinsings, into the 100-ml. volumetric flask. Deliver the vanadate and the molybdate solutions, respectively, into the flask according to the direction given in the foregoing section and measure the absorbance of the unknown solution against the reagent blank in the same manner.

5. *Calculations.* From the observed absorbance of the unknown solution, obtain the weight of phosphorus in the sample by means of the standard curve or the equation derived from it (Note 3). Calculate per cent function and per cent compound, respectively, by the following formulas.

A. FOR PER CENT PHOSPHORUS FUNCTION

$$\% \text{ P function} = \frac{\text{mg. P} \times \text{(meq. wt. of function in mg.)} \times 100}{30.98 \times \text{mg. sample}}$$

B. FOR PER CENT PHOSPHORUS COMPOUND

$$\% \text{ Compound} = \frac{\text{mg. P} \times \text{(mol. wt. of compound in mg.)} \times 100}{30.98 \times \text{mg. sample}}$$

6. *Notes*

Note 1. Full color intensity is reached in 15 to 25 minutes and remains constant for at least 2 weeks.

Note 2. Set the slit width at 1.0 mm. and use 1-cm. matched Corex cells when a Beckman spectrophotometer is employed.

Note 3. The derived equation is especially useful for determinations made in long intervals. It has been found that the slope α of the equation does not change with the aging of the reagents. On the other hand, there may be variations in the intercept β. To correct for this change, it is only necessary to analyze a known pure organophosphorus compound simultaneously with the unknown sample, determine the new β value from the known and use this value to calculate the phosphorus content of the unknown.

7. *Comments.* This experiment illustrates the application of spectrophotometry in organic analysis. Although the method described cannot discriminate organophosphorus functions in which phosphorus is bonded to carbon, it may be used to differentiate C–P and some C–O–P

linkages. Thus triphenylphosphate can be determined by alkali hydrolysis to the phosphate ion followed by the formation of the yellow heteropoly compound, whereas triphenylphosphine does not give the phosphate complex under the same conditions.

The stability of the vanadophosphomolybdate complex offers many advantages: A series of digestions may be carried out simultaneously, the color developed at a convenient time, and measurements performed when all solutions are ready.

13

Microdetermination of Functional Groups Using Special Apparatus

---

I. Introduction

The experimental methods described in this chapter are those in which some special apparatus (not considered as general equipment of the chemical laboratory) is needed in certain parts of the procedure. This necessitates the procurement of the special apparatus before the microdetermination can be performed. Sometimes there is more than one type of apparatus for the microdetermination of a particular functional group. Then a choice must be made to select an apparatus which is most suitable for the purpose. Some guiding principles for such a selection are presented, but it should be stressed that these do not apply in every case. Table 13.1 summarizes the procedures given in this chapter. Experiments recommended for a course in organic functional group analysis are listed in Appendix B.

II. Important Factors in the Selection of Special Apparatus

A. Cost.   Unless the apparatus will be in constant use and the microdetermination of the particular functional group becomes a routine operation, the cost of the special apparatus is usually the first consideration in its selection. Although it is logical to select an apparatus which costs the least, we should make sure that the apparatus meets certain standards so that frequent readjustments are not necessary to obtain satisfactory results.

B. Availability.   Numerous apparatus for the microdetermination of the various functional groups are described in the literature. However, the number of special functional group apparatus generally available is rather small. Some laboratory supply houses will manufacture special apparatus on order provided detailed drawings are furnished. In such

TABLE 13.1

Summary of Laboratory Procedures Requiring Special Apparatus

Experiment	Function	Method	Apparatus	Page
31	Alkoxyl	HI cleavage	Micro alkoxyl apparatus	558
32	Weak acid	Nonaqueous titration	Titration assembly	561
33	Carbonyl	NaBH₄ reduction	Ma-Scheinthal gasometric apparatus	564
34	Amino, amido	H₂SO₄ digestion	Micro-Kjeldahl apparatus	569
35	Nitro, nitroso	Reduction and H₂SO₄ digestion	Micro-Kjeldahl apparatus	573
36	Primary amino	Nitrosation	Modified Kainz apparatus	575
37	Nitro, nitroso	TiCl₃ reduction	TiCl₃ microtitration assembly	579
38	Azo, diazo	TiCl₃ reduction	TiCl₃ microtitration assembly	583
39	Hydrazino	Oxidation	Ma-Mattei gasometric apparatus	586
40	Active hydrogen	LiAlH₄ reduction	Ma-Scheinthal gasometric apparatus	588
41	Enol, keto	Grignard reaction	Soltys apparatus	590
42	Acyl	Hydrolysis	Kuhn-Roth apparatus	595
43	C-methyl	CrO₃ oxidation	Steam distillation apparatus	598
44	Carboxyl	Decarboxylation	Decarboxylation apparatus and gas chromatograph	600
45	Alkene	Catalytic hydrogenation	Ogg-Cooper apparatus	603
46	Alkene	Catalytic hydrogenation	Ma-Scheinthal gasometric apparatus	608
47	Amino acid	Enzymatic deamination	Steam distillation apparatus	609
48	Hydroxyl	Aquametry	Ma-Hensle aquametry apparatus	612
49	Quinone	TiCl₃ reduction	TiCl₃ microtitration assembly	615
50	Sulfhydryl	AgNO₃ titration	Amperometric titration assembly	617
51	Sulfoxide	Reduction and bromine oxidation	Micro Jones reductor	619
52	Alkimino	Quaternization and thermal decomposition	Ma-Schachter alkimino apparatus and gas chromatograph	622

cases an order for a single unit or a part of an assembly is expensive. It is advisable to choose a firm familiar with microchemical equipment and to furnish a copy of the original design. The names of firms which specialize in the construction of custom-designed apparatus is given in Appendix A.

C. Selection of Apparatus Which Is Versatile. When the selection of a special apparatus is considered for the determination of a particular functional group, some thought should be given to the possibility of determining other functional groups by the same or modified apparatus. Hence an assembly that can be employed for the determination of several functions is advantageous. The gasometric apparatus described in experiment 33 (see Figure 6.15, page 152), may be cited as an example; it can be used for the determination of aldehydes, ketones, carbohydrates, unsaturation and active hydrogen.

As was mentioned in Chapter 1, Section III, functional group analysis is usually based on mild reactions at moderate temperatures. The optimum temperature for quantitative yields sometimes varies, for the same function, with the structure and types of compound. Therefore it is advisable to select an apparatus that permits the determination to be carried out at different temperatures.

III. Modification of Special Apparatus

When the functional group apparatus is made to order, consideration should be given to modifications which would render it more convenient and useful. For example, the primary amino apparatus of Kainz (see Figure 8.8) has been modified to separate the components by means of ball and socket joints (Figure 8.9; experiment 36). Even though this change increases the cost of the apparatus, its utility is enhanced, since it becomes less fragile, easier to clean, and allows variation of the scrubbers.

IV. Cleaning and Storing of Special Apparatus

A special apparatus which is only occasionally used should be cleaned and dried immediately after use. All ground-glass joints should be separated by thin paper. It is not advisable to wrap the various parts and store them in drawers, since often a part will be missing when needed, and the whole setup becomes useless for immediate purposes. It is recommended to have the apparatus completely or partly assembled and the remaining components laid by the side. If the apparatus thus put away is placed in a tall cabinet with glass windows, the analyst will be immediately aware when some part is missing or broken and can replace it before the apparatus is brought out to be used again.

V. Functional Group Apparatus Which Is in Frequent Use

Functional group apparatus which is in frequent use, such as the micro-Kjeldahl and the gasometric assemblies, should be kept in good order all the time as a permanent setup in an appropriate place in the laboratory since they occupy little desk space. A convenient place is on the same bench with the standard $0.01N$ solutions which are kept in automatic-zero microburets.

VI. Experimental Procedures

Experiment 31. Microdetermination of Methoxyl and Ethoxyl Groups

1. Principle. The detailed discussion on the microdetermination of alkoxyl groups was given in Chapter 6, Section VI. Methoxyl and ethoxyl groups can be determined by cleavage with hydriodic acid. The equation for *p*-ethoxybenzoic acid is given in equation 1:

$$\text{HOOC}-\langle\bigcirc\rangle-\text{OC}_2\text{H}_5 + \text{HI} \rightarrow \text{C}_2\text{H}_5\text{I} + \text{HOOC}-\langle\bigcirc\rangle-\text{OH} \qquad (1)$$

The alkyl iodide is distilled and collected in a receiver, and its iodine content is then determined either gravimetrically or titrimetrically as shown in equations 2 to 6:

$$\text{C}_2\text{H}_5\text{I} + \text{AgNO}_3 \rightarrow \text{AgI} + \text{C}_2\text{H}_5\text{NO}_3 \qquad (2)$$

$$\text{C}_2\text{H}_5\text{I} + \text{Br}_2 \rightarrow \text{C}_2\text{H}_5\text{Br} + \text{IBr} \qquad (3)$$

$$\text{IBr} + 2\text{Br}_2 + 3\text{H}_2\text{O} \rightarrow \text{HIO}_3 + 5\text{HBr} \qquad (4)$$

$$\text{HIO}_3 + 5\text{HI} \rightarrow 3\text{I}_2 + 3\text{H}_2\text{O} \qquad (5)$$

$$3\text{I}_2 + 6\text{Na}_2\text{S}_2\text{O}_3 \rightarrow 6\text{NaI} + 3\text{Na}_2\text{S}_4\text{O}_6 \qquad (6)$$

2. Apparatus

A. MICRO ALKOXYL APPARATUS. Use either the micro alkoxyl apparatus of Elek (see Figure 6.10) or the ACS approved micro alkoxyl apparatus (see Figure 6.11) (Note 1). Both assemblies are commercially available.

B. FILTRATION DEVICE. For the gravimetric procedure, use the assembly shown in Figure 5.22.

C. MICROBURET. For the titrimetric procedure, use the buret as described in experiment 1.

D. IODINE FLASK. 125-ml. capacity, for the titrimetric procedure.

3. Reagents

A. HYDRIODIC ACID, SP. GR. 1.7. Available from Fisher Scientific Co., and other dealers. Specially prepared for micro alkoxyl analysis.

B. PHENOL. Reagent grade.

C. PROPIONIC ANHYDRIDE. (Note 2) Reagent grade.

D. Scrubbing Reagent Solutions.   (1) 5% $CdSO_4$ in water; (2) 5% $Na_2S_2O_3$ in water.

E. Nitrogen Gas.   Reagent quality; use the lecture bottle size cylinder.

F. Alcoholic Silver Nitrate Solution, Approx. 4%.   For the gravimetric procedure. Dissolve 4 g. of silver nitrate (reagent grade) in 100 ml. of 95% ethanol under reflux for 3 hours. Allow the solution to stand in a dark place for 2 days. Then decant it into a glass-stoppered amber bottle.

G. Standard Sodium Thiosulfate Solution, 0.05N ($= M/20$).   For the titrimetric procedure. See experiment 8 for preparation and experiment 19 for standardization.

H. Bromine.   Reagent grade, free from iodine. For the titrimetric procedure.

I. Formic Acid, 90%.   Reagent grade. For the titrimetric procedure.

J. Sodium Acetate in Acetic Acid, 10%.   Dissolve 10 g. of sodium acetate in 90 ml. of glacial acetic acid.

K. Potassium Iodide Solution, 10%.   Dissolve 10 g. of reagent grade potassium iodide in 90 ml. of distilled water.

L. Starch Indicator Solution, 1%.   See experiment 19.

M. Test Compounds.   Vanillin, m.p. 81°C; p-ethoxybenzoic acid, m.p. 198°C; anethole, b.p. 235°C.

4. Procedures

A. For Gravimetric Determination.

(1) *Assembling the apparatus.*   Assemble the apparatus as follows. Fill the scrubber bulb with a solution containing equal volumes of 5% cadmium sulfate and 5% sodium thiosulfate so that the gas inlet tube is about 15 mm. under the liquid (Note 3). Deliver 2.0 ml. of the alcoholic silver nitrate solution into the straight receiver tube (not the one with a siphon bent tube) and affix the receiver tube so that the delivery tube (without glass spiral) reaches about 5 mm. from the bottom.

(2) *Preparation of sample.*   Using the micro weighing tube (see Chapter 5, Section V; microboat or micro weighing bottle for liquid), weigh accurately about 0.1 meq. sample (Note 4) into the reaction flask.

Dissolve the sample in 0.2 ml. of propionic anhydride containing a crystal of phenol. Deliver 2.0 ml. (Note 1) of the hydriodic acid into the reaction flask and quickly connect the flask to the reflux condenser. Join the side arm of the reaction flask to the source of nitrogen (Note 5). Let the gas bubble through the solution at the rate of about 1 bubble per second.

(3) *Decomposition.*   Heat the contents of the reaction flask for 30 to 60 minutes. If a metal bath or heating stage (see Figure 5.19) is available, maintain the reaction temperature at 125°C.

(4) *Precipitation.* Silver iodide precipitates out in the course of analysis. After the heating period is completed, lower the receiver tube until the delivery tube is above the surface of the alcoholic silver nitrate solution. Disconnect the delivery tube from its rubber connection. Rinse the delivery tube with 0.5% nitric acid (1 volume of C.P. concentrated nitric acid to 200 volumes of water) and 95% ethanol alternately until all precipitate has fallen into the receiving tube. Add 0.5% nitric acid into the receiver tube until the volume is about four-fifths full. Then add 0.2 ml. of C.P. nitric acid.

Place the receiving tube in a beaker and fill the beaker with water at the same level as the alcoholic solution in the receiver tube. Heat the water in the beaker until the alcoholic solution begins to boil. Then remove the flame. Place the beaker containing the receiver tube in a dark place overnight.

(4) *Filtration.* Assemble the filtration device as directed in experiment 26 (see Figure 5.22). Quantitatively transfer the silver iodide precipitate into the previously weighed filter tube. Rinse alternately with 0.5% nitric acid and ethanol. Dry the filter tube and the precipitate at 110°C and reweigh.

B. FOR TITRIMETRIC DETERMINATION

(1) *Preparation of apparatus.* Fill the absorption tube (receiver tube with the siphon) with 5.0 ml. of the 10% sodium acetate in acetic acid. Add 6 drops of bromine (Caution!). Assemble the apparatus as shown in Figure 6.10 or Figure 6.11.

Fill the scrubber bulb with the scrubber reagent solution (see Procedure A above).

(2) *Preparation and decomposition of sample.* Weigh the sample as in Procedure A. Dissolve the sample, add hydriodic acid, connect to nitrogen source, and heat the reaction mixture as in Procedure A. After the heating period, lower the absorption tube. Disconnect the delivery tube and rinse it with a little distilled water.

(3) *Titration.* Now place an iodine flask containing 5 ml. of 10% sodium acetate solution under the absorption tube. Carefully remove the stopper of the siphon tube to transfer the contents of the absorption tube into the iodine flask. Rinse the absorption tube thoroughly with water and collect all rinsings in the iodine flask.

Swirl the contents of the flask and add formic acid dropwise to decolorize the bromine color. Close the flask and shake, if necessary. Avoid adding an excess of formic acid.

Add 2.0 ml. of 10% potassium iodide solution, and 3.0 ml. of 10% sulfuric acid. Stopper the flask at once. Shake the contents and allow to stand for 5 minutes. Then titrate the iodine by means of the standardized 0.5N sodium thiosulfate to the starch endpoint (see experiment 14).

(4) *Blank.* Run a blank determination on the reagents in the same manner without the use of the sample.

5. Calculations

A. FOR PER CENT ALKOXYL BY THE GRAVIMETRIC PROCEDURE

$$\% \text{ Alkoxyl} = \frac{[\text{wt. of precipitate (corrected)}](F)(100)}{\text{wt. of sample in mg.}}$$

where [wt. of precipitate (corrected)] = mg. of precipitate − 0.120 mg. (Note 6), and F = 0.1321 for % OCH_3; 0.1918 for % OC_2H_5.

B. FOR PER CENT ALKOXYL BY THE TITRIMETRIC METHOD

$$\% \text{ Alkoxyl} = \frac{(s - b)(\text{normality of Na}_2\text{S}_2\text{O}_3)(A)(100)}{(6)(\text{wt. of sample in mg.})}$$

where s = ml. of $Na_2S_2O_3$ for sample, b = ml. of $Na_2S_2O_3$ for blank, and A = 31.02 for % OCH_3; 45.04 for % OC_2H_5.

6. Notes

Note 1. Because the ACS approved reaction flask is larger, 8 ml. of hydriodic acid should be used instead of 2 ml. as in the Elek apparatus.

Note 2. Acetic anhydride may be used.

Note 3. The scrubbing device will not be effective if the gases do not come in contact with the solution for a sufficient length of time.

Note 4. One meq. is the molecular weight of the compound in mg. divided by the number of alkoxyl groups present.

Note 5. Use carbon dioxide if nitrogen is not available. Do not use a cylinder of gas without a reducing valve.

Note 6. This correction factor is empirical, although generally accepted.

7. Comments. The titrimetric method is the preferred procedure for micro alkoxyl determination. Owing to the favorable molar equivalence, standard 0.05N or 0.1N sodium thiosulfate can be used for microdeterminations on the 0.1 meq. scale.

Experiment 32: Microdetermination of Weak Acids by Non-aqueous Titration

1. Principle. The determination of acidic groups by titration with a standardized alkaline solution was extensively discussed in Chapter 3, Section II, and Chapter 11, Section II. It was shown in Chapter 3 that water cannot be used as solvent for the titration of weak organic acid because water itself is a weak acid. In addition, the nonaqueous titration of weak acids cannot be performed in an atmosphere that contains carbon dioxide or any other acidic oxide.

The titrimetric reactions between weak acids and a strong base are shown in equations 7 and 8 using phenol and sulfanilamide, respectively, as the acids and sodium methoxide as the titrant base:

$$C_6H_5OH + NaOCH_3 \rightarrow C_6H_5ONa + CH_3OH \qquad (7)$$

$$H_2NC_6H_4SO_2NH_2 + NaOCH_3 \rightarrow H_2NC_6H_4SO_2NHNa + CH_3OH \qquad (8)$$

2. Apparatus

A. ASSEMBLY FOR MICROTITRATION OF WEAK ACIDS. The assembly for microtitration of weak acids is shown in Figure 11.1. It is composed of the microburet (10-ml. capacity, graduated in 0.02 ml.), the microtitration vessel, and a magnetic stirrer.

The microtitration vessel is essentially a small Florence flask with a total capacity of approximately 50 ml. which has five necks, one in line with the vertical axis of the vessel, and the other four equally spaced, slightly oblique and lower. The vertical neck has a ground-glass joint that accommodates the tip of the microburet. Two diametrically opposed side openings are 10 mm. in diameter to allow insertion of electrodes. The other two openings permit continuous flushing with nitrogen gas. The nitrogen inlet tube ends about 5 mm. from the bottom of the microtitration vessel.

The automatic-zero microburet is gravity fed (Note 1). It has a ground-glass drip tip and a Teflon stopcock.

B. pH METER. Beckman pH meter, model H-2; reference standard calomel electrode, Beckman No. 270 with asbestos fiber junction; Beckman glass electrode, type E-2. Other standard pH meters such as Coleman model 31 may be used.

3. Reagents

A. STANDARD SODIUM METHOXIDE, $0.02N$ ($= M/50$). Prepare a stock solution of approximately $0.1N$ sodium methoxide as follows. Weigh about 3 g. (one piece) of metallic sodium (reagent grade) under kerosene or toluene. Quickly wipe off the hydrocarbon by wrapping and pressing with a filter paper and dip the piece of sodium (using forceps) in 25 ml. of absolute methanol for 15 seconds. Immediately transfer the sodium into a 1-liter volumetric flask containing 100 ml. of absolute methanol. (Caution! Use hood and keep away from flames.) After the sodium dissolves, stopper the flask and let the contents stand overnight and then fill to the mark.

Determine the concentration of this solution by titrating a 5.00-ml. aliquot against standardized $0.01N$ hydrochloric acid using phenolphthalein as indicator. Measure (preferably using the chamber with controlled atmosphere—see Figure 11.3) an aliquot which will make one liter of the standard $0.02N$ solution and transfer it into a 1-liter volumetric flask. Dilute the solution to the mark with a mixed solvent prepared by combining 1 liter of anhydrous benzene with 112 ml. of absolute methanol. Transfer this solution into the microburet and store it under nitrogen.

Standardization. Determine the exact strength of the $0.02N$ sodium methoxide by weighing 10 mg. (accurate to ± 0.01 mg.) of benzoic acid (acidimetric standard grade) into the microtitration vessel. Dissolve the benzoic acid and titrate it according to the direction given in the Procedure A.

B. INDICATOR SOLUTIONS

(1) *Thymol blue.* Dissolve 300 mg. of thymol blue in 100 ml. of absolute methanol.

(2) *Azo violet.* Dissolve 500 mg. of p-nitrobenzeneazoresorcinol in 100 ml. of benzene-methanol (1:2) mixture.

C. SOLVENTS. Dimethylformamide, pyridine, 3-methyl-2-butanone (reagent grade).

D. NITROGEN GAS. Use lecture bottle fitted with a needle valve.

E. TEST COMPOUNDS. Phenol, m.p. 42°C; sulfanilamide, m.p. 167°C; phenobarbital, m.p. 174°C; phthalimide, m.p. 233°C.

4. Procedures

A. FOR VISUAL TITRATION. With a transfer pipet, introduce 5.0 ml. of the solvent through the 10 mm. side neck of the microtitration vessel. Assemble the apparatus as shown in Figure 11.1. Adjust the flow of nitrogen so that individual bubbles can be seen. Set the magnetic stirring apparatus so that agitation is rapid, but spattering does not occur. Then add the indicator solution, two drops (0.03 ml.) of thymol blue or one drop (0.015 ml.) of azo violet by means of the capillary dropper, and neutralize the acid impurities in the solvent by adding standard sodium methoxide from the microburet to the appearance of the first permanent blue color, which is the basic color for both thymol blue and azo violet. Add about 0.1 meq. of the test sample (accurately weighed in a micro weighing tube) through the side neck and reweigh the micro weighing tube. After dissolution of the sample, titrate the contents of the titration flask to a definite blue. During the titration, bubble nitrogen gas through the vessel continuously and keep the two side necks allocated for electrodes closed.

B. FOR POTENTIOMETRIC TITRATION. Place 15 ml. of the solvent into the microtitration vessel. Adjust the flow of nitrogen and stirring as described in Procedure A. (For concurrent visual and potentiometric titration, introduce the indicator solution immediately after the sample.) Insert the electrodes in their appropriate locations, one facing the other so that they are at least 2 mm. below the surface of the liquid, and are separated by a distance of less than 5 mm. Keep the electrodes in place with a rubber tubing (inside diameter about 5 mm.) that fits snuggly into the 10 mm. openings. With the potentiometer properly connected and set, begin the titration with large increments of standard sodium methoxide solution and reduce the volume when approaching the equivalence point. Continue until the equivalence point is well passed. (For concurrent visual titration, read the volume in the microburet when the color changes.)

5. Calculations

A. FOR NEUTRALIZATION EQUIVALENT

$$\text{Neutralization equivalent} = \frac{(\text{mg. sample})}{(\text{ml. NaOCH}_3)(\text{normality of NaOCH}_3)}$$

B. FOR PER CENT COMPOUND

$$\% \text{ Compound} = \frac{(\text{ml. NaOCH}_3)(\text{normality of NaOCH}_3)(\text{meq. wt. cmpd. in mg.})(100)}{\text{wt. of sample in mg.}}$$

6. Note

Note 1. The pressure-fed type (Pregl type) automatic-zero microburet is not recommended for storing the standard solution owing to the high vapor pressure and temperature coefficient of methanol-benzene solvent mixture.

7. Comments. The same procedure can be used for standard lithium methoxide or quaternary ammonium hydroxides. Lithium wire should be used to prepare $0.02N$ lithium hydroxide solution. The lithium wire is first weighed without being wiped, then it is wiped off and the same procedure is followed as for sodium metal.

Experiment 33: Microdetermination of Carbonyl Groups by Gasometric Method

1. Principle. The methods for the determination of carbonyl compounds were fully discussed in Chapter 6, Section VII. The micro gasometric method presented in this experiment is for the purpose of introducing the gasometric technique. The method is based on the reduction of the carbonyl group to an alcohol group by means of sodium borohydride. For example, the reduction of benzaldehyde to benzyl alcohol is shown in equation 9:

$$4C_6H_5CHO + NaBH_4 + 2H_2O \rightarrow 4C_6H_5CH_2OH + NaBO_2 \qquad (9)$$

The unconsumed borohydride reagent is determined by the addition of dilute sulfuric acid to liberate hydrogen which is measured:

$$NaBH_4 + H_2SO_4 + 3H_2O \rightarrow 4H_2 + H_3BO_3 + NaHSO_4 \qquad (10)$$

Carbohydrates which have free aldehyde or ketonic groups can be determined in the same manner. Some compounds such as acid chlorides, which contain a carbonyl group, but cannot be determined by the usual methods employed for the estimation of carbonyl group functions, are also reduced by alkali borohydride (Note 1). However, the quantitative aspects of the reduction of acyl halides by borohydride still await investigation.

2. Apparatus

A. MICROGASOMETRIC APPARATUS. The assembly for microgasometric determination according to Ma and Scheinthal is shown in Figure 6.15. It consists of a lecture bottle size gas cylinder with a control valve A (Figure 13.1 shows a simple model), bubble counter B, three-way stopcock C, the reaction chamber DEFG, the gasburet HI, and leveling bulb J.

The reaction chamber DEFG is composed of the reaction flask F, which is fastened to the cap E by means of springs. The condenser G permits the reaction to be carried out at the boiling point of the solvent and is separated from the gasburet by a sintered glass disc H. One end of the three-way stopcock D is fitted with a rubber syringe cap M.

Fig. 13.1. Needle valve for lecture bottle size gas cylinder. Courtesy of Fisher Scientific Co.

B. HEATING AND STIRRING DEVICE. The controlled temperature bath suitable for the above assembly is shown in Figure 13.2. It has the shape of a large U-tube with a flat bottom. The two sides of the U-tube are connected by three channels allowing free circulation of the bath fluid. The heating unit QR (an aquarium heater) is immersed in one side, and the reaction flask F is placed in the other side. A magnetic stirring bar S is placed at the bottom so that the bath fluid may be stirred if necessary.

The simple magnetic stirrer ON is constructed from a toy motor O (Aristocraft Electric Motor, Newark, N.J., catalog No. 3b), which is attached to a magnet N, 19 mm. in diameter. The motor is run by a flashlight battery and controlled by a 6-volt D.C. variable portable rheostat (Note 2).

C. SYRINGE AND NEEDLE. 1-ml. syringe graduated in 0.01 ml. Needle of 20 gauge and 4 inches (about 100 mm.) long.

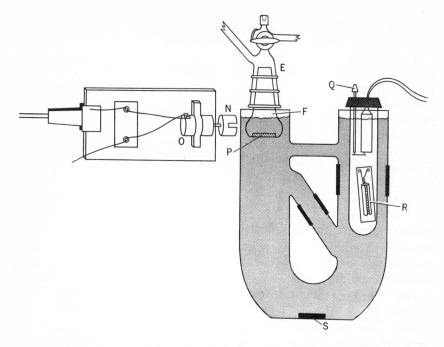

Fig. 13.2. Controlled temperature bath and simple magnetic stirrer.

D. MICROBEAKER. Cut a 10-mm. length of Tygon tubing of 4-mm. bore and plug one end with a piece of 5 mm. × 4 mm. glass rod.

3. Reagents

A. SODIUM BOROHYDRIDE. Crystals, high purity (available from Callery Co., Pittsburgh, Penn.).

B. SOLVENT. Diethyleneglycol dimethyl ether (Diglyme), or other high boiling glycol ether.

C. ISOPROPYL ALCOHOL. Reagent grade, free from aldehydes.

D. SULFURIC ACID, APPROXIMATELY 2M. Add 55.5 ml. of concentrated sulfuric acid to distilled water and dilute the solution to 1 liter.

E. SODIUM TETRABORATE. $Na_2B_4O_7 \cdot 10H_2O$ crystals.

F. HYDROGEN GAS. Use the lecture demonstration bottle or the regular gas cylinder fitted with a pressure regulator.

G. TEST COMPOUNDS. Vanillin, m.p. 81°C; p-dimethylaminobenzaldehyde, m.p. 74–75°C; p-bromoacetophenone, m.p. 52–53°C; D-glucose, dec. 147°C.

4. Procedure

A. PREPARATION OF THE STANDARD CURVE

(1) *Weighing the sodium borohydride.* Weigh to the microgram 2 to 6 mg. of sodium borohydride into the microbeaker (Note 3). Put in 4 to 5 micro stirring bars so that they fill the beaker. Lower the microbeaker into the reaction flask F (Figure 6.15). Add 1.0 ml. of Diglyme, 20 μl. of isopropyl alcohol, and 50 mg. of sodium tetraborate to the bottom of the reaction flask F.

(2) *Assembling the apparatus.* Lubricate the neck of the reaction flask F containing the materials mentioned earlier and affix the reaction flask to its cap E by the springs as shown in Figure 6.15.

(3) *Purging the system.* Lower the leveling bulb J to position K. Open the needle valve A of the hydrogen cylinder to start the hydrogen gas flowing through the system (after having set stopcocks C and D in their appropriate positions). The hydrogen gas passes through the system and escapes from the open end of the gasburet I into a hood (Note 4). Adjust the gas flow so that the gas bubbles pass through the bubble counter B at a moderate speed, and maintain a mercury seal in the gasburet I at level K.

After 5 minutes, connect the open end of the three-way stopcock C to the water aspirator. Raise the leveling bulb J to position L and turn the stopcock C momentarily to the vacuum line (the sintered-glass disc H should keep the mercury from backing up into the reaction vessel). After 15 to 20 seconds return the stopcock C again to the hydrogen line and the leveling bulb to position K.

Repeat this operation twice, place the leveling bulb J at position L, and allow hydrogen gas to push the mercury back so that the two columns of mercury in the gasburet HI are at the same level L. Now turn stopcock D (above the reaction flask cap E) so that no more hydrogen gas enters the reaction flask, and turn the three-way stopcock C to let hydrogen escape to the atmosphere. Then shut off the needle valve A of the gas cylinder.

Level up the two mercury columns in the gasburet so that the pressure inside is the same as atmospheric. Read the volume (i.e., the level of mercury in the gasburet), temperature, and atmospheric pressure.

(4) *Mixing the contents.* Place the stirrer (ON in Figure 13.2) under the reaction flask F and start the motor. The microbeaker will tilt over and the stirring bars come out of the microbeaker. Then move the stirrer ON and clamp the board holding it in a position shown in Figure 13.2. Place the controlled temperature bath under the reaction flask (see Figure 13.2) containing the material and micro stirring bars. Start the motor so that

the micro stirring bars will revolve to agitate the contents of the reaction flask. Maintain the controlled temperature bath at $50 \pm 0.5°C$ for 30 minutes to allow the sodium borohydride to dissolve. Then remove the bath to cool the solution to room temperature.

(5) *Liberation of hydrogen.* Now turn the stopcock D (above the reaction flask cap E) to allow 0.40 ml. of $2M$ sulfuric acid to enter the reaction flask by means of the syringe. Withdraw the syringe needle and return the stopcock D to the former position.

Continue stirring the contents of the flask. Lower the leveling bulb J as the mercury level of the gasburet lowers due to the liberation of hydrogen. After 20 minutes (or until no more changes in volume are observed), level up the mercury columns and again read the volume, temperature, and pressure.

(6) *Plotting the standard curve.* From the volume of hydrogen liberated from a measured amount of sodium borohydride, calculate (by the perfect gas law) the number of millimoles of hydrogen produced. Perform several runs of the same batch of sodium borohydride using from 2 to 5 mg. samples and plot the quantity of hydrogen (in millimoles) *vs.* the weight (in milligrams) of sodium borohydride. If the various points fall on a straight line, the sodium borohydride is of uniform quality and can be used by weighing the solid reagent for the determination of carbonyl groups.

B. DETERMINATION OF THE CARBONYL COMPOUND

(1) *Preparation of the sample.* Weigh accurately a sample containing about 0.1 meq. of carbonyl function into the bottom of the reaction flask F. Add 1 ml. of Diglyme, 20 μl. of isopropyl alcohol, and 50 mg. of sodium tetraborate.

(2) *Weighing the sodium borohydride.* Weigh accurately into the micro-beaker a quantity of sodium borohydride sufficient to react with the sample. Lower the microbeaker and sodium borohydride into the reaction flask F.

(3) *Assembling the apparatus.* See direction under A(2).

(4) *Purging the system.* See direction under A(3).

(5) *The reduction reaction.* Follow the direction under A(4) to mix the sample and the sodium borohydride.

(6) *Determining the unconsumed sodium borohydride.* Follow the direction under A(5).

5. Calculations

A. FOR HYDROGEN EQUIVALENT. (1) Calculate from Procedure B(6) the amount of hydrogen (a, in millimoles) produced by the unconsumed sodium borohydride. (2) Determine from the standard curve the amount of hydrogen (b, in millimoles) which would have been produced by the sodium borohydride with the sample absent.

$b - a$ = the hydrogen equivalent of the sample.

B. FOR PER CENT CARBONYL GROUP

$$\% \; C{=}O = \frac{(\text{Hydrogen equivalent of sample})(28.01)(100)}{\text{wt. of sample in mg.}}$$

6. *Notes*

Note 1.   Generally acid chlorides are reduced by sodium borohydride in nonaqueous systems as shown in equation 11:

$$2RC{-}Cl + NaBH_4 \rightarrow (RCH_2O)_2NaBCl_2 \tag{11}$$
$$\underset{O}{\overset{\|}{}}$$

The primary alcohol is produced upon treatment with water (eq. 12):

$$(RCH_2O)_2NaBCl_2 + 2H_2O \rightarrow 2RCH_2OH + NaCl + BCl(OH)_2 \tag{12}$$

Note 2.   A flashlight bulb may be used as resistor, but then the stirring speed cannot be varied at will.

Note 3.   Alternately, an exactly measured volume of a prepared solution of sodium borohydride may be used. Sodium borohydride is less stable in solution, however, than in solid form.

Note 4.   There should not be any flame in the vicinity of the hydrogen outlet and the hood should be well ventilated.

7. *Comments.*   This experiment demonstrates the operation of a versatile gasometric apparatus. It can be used to measure the volume of gas consumed or liberated in the reaction. The assembly permits the analysis to be performed at a controlled temperature up to the boiling point of the reaction mixture.

Experiment 34: Microdetermination of Amino Groups by the Regular Kjeldahl Method

1. *Principle.*   The regular Kjeldahl method (see Chapter 8, Section III-F-4) is concerned with the conversion of the amino group to ammonium ion by (1) heating the sample with concentrated sulfuric acid in the presence of catalysts, and (2) neutralization of the resulting mixture with sodium hydroxide. Using aniline as an example, the reactions may be expressed by equations 13 and 14:

$$C_6H_5NH_2 + H_2SO_4 + 14[O] \rightarrow (NH_4)HSO_4 + 6CO_2 + 2H_2O \tag{13}$$
$$(NH_4)HSO_4 + NaOH \rightarrow NH_3 + NaHSO_4 + H_2O \tag{14}$$

In this experiment, the ammonia is separated from the solution by steam distillation, collected in 2% boric acid solution, and determined by titration with standard 0.01N acid using as indicator a mixture of methyl red and bromocresol green.

$$NH_3 + HCl \rightarrow NH_4Cl \tag{15}$$

Amides, ureas, and barbiturates that can be hydrolyzed to amine or ammonia can be determined by this method without modification.

2. Apparatus

A. DIGESTION FLASK. Use the commercial 15-ml. or 20-ml. micro-Kjeldahl digestion flasks, or prepare the flask from ordinary 15-cm. (6-inch) Pyrex test tubes by blowing out the bottom to form a bulb of about 25-mm. diameter and 6-ml. capacity.

B. DISTILLATION APPARATUS. The micro-Kjeldahl distillation assembly shown in Figure 8.10 is composed of two compact units joined glass to glass with the short rubber tubing B. This renders the apparatus less rigid, and reduces the danger of breakage due to bumping when water boils in the steam generator A. The assembly is conveniently clamped onto an iron stand and occupies a desk space of 30 × 40 cm. The steam generator A is made from a 1-liter round-bottomed flask to which a side arm is attached for refilling. When it is two-thirds filled with water before distillation is begun, enough steam will be generated for 8 to 12 determinations (Note 1).

C. MICRO-KJELDAHL DIGESTION STAND. Any model.

D. MICROBURET. Pregl type, 10-ml. capacity graduated in 0.02 or 0.05 ml.

3. Reagents

A. STANDARD HYDROCHLORIC ACID, 0.01N ($= M/100$). See experiment 1 (Note 2).

B. SULFURIC ACID, SP. GR. 1.84. C.P.

C. CATALYSTS. Powdered selenium, free from nitrogen; pulverized mixture of potassium sulfate (1 part) and copper sulfate pentahydrate (3 parts).

D. SODIUM HYDROXIDE, APPROXIMATELY 30%. Dissolve 150 g. of sodium hydroxide pellets (reagent grade) in 350 ml. of distilled water. Store the solution in a polyethylene bottle.

E. BORIC ACID, 2%. Dissolve 10 g. of boric acid (crystals) in 500 ml. of boiling distilled water. After cooling, transfer the solution into a glass-stoppered bottle.

F. MIXED INDICATOR SOLUTION. Prepare 0.1% bromocresol green and 0.1% methyl red solutions in 95% ethanol separately. Mix 10 ml. (Note 3) of the bromocresol green with 2 ml. of the methyl red in an amber bottle provided with a dropper drawn out to a fine capillary that delivers approximately 0.05 ml. per 4 drops.

G. TEST COMPOUNDS. Acetanilide, m.p. 114°C; glycine, m.p. 228°C; aniline, b.p. 183°C; urea, m.p. 133°C; uric acid, dec. 400°C.

4. Procedure

A. DIGESTION. Accurately weigh out a sample (5 to 10 mg.) containing about 0.05 meq. of the amino function and transfer it into the bottom of the digestion flask. Use a long-handled micro weighing tube (Figure 5.6) for solid samples. For semi-solids and heavy oils, use a porcelain microboat (Figure 5.5, Coors size 5-zero) which is slid into the digestion flask with the sample. Add 5 mg. of powdered selenium and 25 mg. of copper sulfate-potassium sulfate mixture. Then introduce 1.0 ml. of concentrated sulfuric acid to cover the sample and catalysts. (Caution! When sucking the acid up the pipet by mouth!) Heat the digestion mixture on the micro-Kjeldahl digestion stand and boil the solution for 10 minutes. The reaction mixture turns brown and then clarifies (Note 4). After the mixture has been cooled, add 2 ml. of distilled water, mix by swirling the digestion flask, and cool the solution again.

B. DISTILLATION AND TITRATION. Place a beaker under the condenser F (Figure 8.10). Heat the distilled water in the steam generator A to boiling by means of a flame (about 10 cm. high) with the ground-glass or Teflon plug on the funnel E and the pinch clamp D closed. With cold water running in the condenser, adjust the rate of steam distillation so that about 5 ml. of distillate is collected per minute. Now remove the burner, whereupon the condensate in the distilling flask G is sucked back into the steam trap C. Fill funnel E with distilled water and lift the plug momentarily to drain the water into the distilling flask G. Replace the burner under the steam generator A for about 20 seconds and remove it again. Meanwhile, introduce 5 ml. (need not be accurately measured) of 2% boric acid and 0.05 ml. of the mixed indicator into a clean 50-ml. Erlenmeyer flask. Fill the microburet with standardized 0.01N hydrochloric acid to the zero mark. By this time the distilling flask G is empty.

Replace burner under the steam generator A and open pinch clamp D to remove liquid from the steam trap C. Leave the pinch clamp on the glass tube through which the steam escapes. Replace the beaker under the condenser with the Erlenmeyer flask containing boric acid and support the flask in an oblique position, so that the tip of the condenser is completely immersed in the liquid.

Smear a trace of vaseline on the lip of the digestion flask to prevent the liquid from dripping down the outside. Remove the plug on the funnel E, pour the contents of the digestion flask into the distilling flask G. Rinse the digestion flask twice with about 2 ml. of distilled water, and pour the rinsings into the funnel E. Then introduce 8 ml. of 30% sodium hydroxide and replace the plug. Add about 5 ml. of distilled water to the funnel E to serve as liquid seal above the plug. Replace the pinch clamp D on the rubber tubing, whereupon steam enters the distilling flask G, stirs up the digestion mixture and sodium hydroxide, and liberates ammonia which escapes with steam through the condenser into the boric acid solution.

The boric acid solution changes from bluish purple to bluish green as soon as it comes in contact with ammonia. (The change, which is very sharp, takes place 20 to 60 seconds after the pinch clamp is closed and usually coincides with the time when the first drop of condensate reaches the Erlenmeyer flask.) One minute after the boric acid has changed color, lower the Erlenmeyer flask so that the condenser tip is about 1 cm. above the liquid. Wash the end of the condenser with a little distilled water. Continue distillation for another minute; then remove the burner. Bring the Erlenmeyer flask containing the distillate to the titration stand and titrate until the blue color disappears. (Note 5.) By this time the distilling flask G is again empty. Now wash the funnel as described previously and repeat the operation for the next sample.

5. Calculations. The results of micro-Kjeldahl determination are usually expressed as the nitrogen content of the sample.

$$\% \ N = \frac{(\text{ml. HCl})(\text{normality of HCl})(14.008)(100)}{\text{mg. sample}}$$

6. Notes

Note 1. Other types of micro-Kjeldahl apparatus may be employed with only slight modification of the procedure.

Note 2. If standard 0.01N hydrochloric acid is not readily available, a 0.01000N acid titrant may be conveniently prepared by dissolving exactly 3.8994 g. of C.P. potassium biniodate ($KIO_3 \cdot HIO_3$) in a 1-liter volumetric flask and making up to the mark.

Note 3. Since the purity of the solid indicators obtained from dealers may vary, it is advisable to adjust the mixture so that the color change corresponds to that described in the procedure. It is not feasible to prepare a large amount of the mixed indicator solution, because the indicators deteriorate at different rates. One bottle (12 ml.) of the mixed indicator solution serves for 200 determinations and keeps for about 6 months.

Note 4. If the reaction mixture remains brown after boiling for 10 minutes, it shows the incomplete destruction of the organic material. One drop

(0.04 ml.) of 72% perchloric acid may be added to the *cold* reaction mixture (Caution!) and the flask heated again. This process may be repeated until the brown color is discharged, but not more than 1 drop of perchloric acid should be added each time. The appearance of blue color of cupric ions and red selenium dioxide does not interfere with the determination.

Note 5. If preferred, the titration may be continued until a faint pink tinge appears; 0.02 ml. is then subtracted from the buret reading. There is no danger of missing the endpoint, because after the pink tinge appears the intensity of the pink color increases tremendously with a trace more of $0.01N$ hydrochloric acid. The titration may be done in daylight or artificial light.

7. Comments. This experiment demonstrates a rapid routine microanalytical procedure. A number of samples can be digested on the same stand. By distilling the batch consecutively, an operator can easily run eight to ten distillations and titrations in an hour.

Since the organic compound is totally destroyed in the analysis, and since the titration can be performed with precision of ± 0.02 ml. of $0.01N$ acid, it is advisable to use a 0.05 meq. sample to save the material to be analyzed and to avoid the need of refilling the 10-ml. microburet during titration.

Cyano groups may be determined by this procedure, provided that there is no loss of hydrogen cyanide upon heating the compound with sulfuric acid (see Chapter 8, Section V-D-1).

Heterocyclic nitrogen compounds that contain one nitrogen in the ring can be quantitatively converted to ammonia by using mercuric oxide in place of selenium as the catalyst. Because mercury forms a stable complex with ammonia, the sodium hydroxide solution should be mixed with 5% of sodium thiosulfate to precipitate mercuric sulfide at the distillation step.

Experiment 35: Microdetermination of Aromatic Nitro and Nitroso Groups by the Modified Kjeldahl Method

1. Principle. The aromatic nitro and nitroso functions (Chapter 8, Section XI) can be quantitatively reduced to the amino function. By performing the reduction in an acidic medium, the amino compound is retained in solution as a salt. For example, nitrobenzene is converted to aniline hydrochloride as shown in equation 16:

$$C_6H_5NO_2 + 3Zn + 7HCl \rightarrow C_6H_5NH_3^+Cl^- + 3ZnCl_2 + 2H_2O \qquad (16)$$

The amino group then can be determined by the regular micro-Kjeldahl method (see experiment 34).

2. Apparatus

A. DIGESTION FLASK. Use the commercial 30-ml. micro-Kjeldahl flask.

B. MICRO-KJELDAHL DISTILLATION ASSEMBLY. See experiment 34.

C. MICRO-KJELDAHL DIGESTION STAND. See experiment 34.

D. MICROBURET. Pregl type, 10-ml. capacity, graduated in 0.02 or 0.05 ml.

3. Reagents

A. STANDARD HYDROCHLORIC ACID, 0.01N. See experiment 1.

B. ACETIC ACID, GLACIAL. C.P.

C. METHANOL. C.P.

D. ZINC METAL. Powder or granular, 40 mesh, C.P.

E. HYDROCHLORIC ACID. Concentrated, C.P.

F. SULFURIC ACID, SP.GR. 1.84. C.P.

G. POTASSIUM SULFATE. Anhydrous, reagent grade.

H. SELENIUM METAL. Powder, free from nitrogen.

I. BORIC ACID SOLUTION, 2%. See experiment 34.

J. SODIUM HYDROXIDE SOLUTION, 30%. See experiment 34.

K. MIXED INDICATOR SOLUTION. See experiment 34.

L. TEST COMPOUNDS. Nitrobenzene, b.p. 211°C; picric acid, m.p. 122°C; p-nitrobenzoic acid, m.p., 241°C.

4. Procedure

A. REDUCTION. Accurately weigh 5 to 10 mg. of the compound to be analyzed, corresponding to about 0.7 mg. nitrogen, into the bottom of the 30-ml. of micro-Kjeldahl digestion flask. Introduce 1 ml. of glacial acetic acid to dissolve the sample, and warm the flask, if necessary, to effect solution. Upon cooling, add 100 mg. of zinc and 1.5 ml. of methanol. Then add 2 drops (0.1 ml.) of concentrated hydrochloric acid to start the reduction. When the evolution of gas slows down, add more hydrochloric acid, two drops at a time. Heat the flask over a small flame toward the end, to keep the evolution of hydrogen proceeding smoothly. (About 0.4 ml. of concentrated hydrochloric acid is needed to react with the zinc in the flask.)

B. DIGESTION. Now add two drops of concentrated sulfuric acid to the reaction mixture. Gently boil the reaction mixture to remove the volatile solvents, but avoid evaporating the contents of the flask to dryness. Allow the flask to cool, add 1.5 ml. of concentrated sulfuric acid, and again heat the flask until the solution darkens. After the flask has cooled, introduce 700 mg. of anhydrous potassium sulfate, 25 mg. of selenium, and 0.5 ml. of concentrated sulfuric acid. Boil the contents of the digestion flask for 1 hour after the solution clarifies.

c. DISTILLATION AND TITRATION. Allow the flask to cool, and before its contents solidify carefully introduce 3 ml. of distilled water along the walls of the vessel (Note 1). Transfer the solution containing the ammonium sulfate to the micro-Kjeldahl distillation apparatus and perform the distillation and titration according to Procedure B of experiment 34.

5. *Calculations.* The result is generally reported as nitrogen content of the sample.

$$\% \; N = \frac{\text{(ml. HCl)(normality of HCl)(14.008)(100)}}{\text{mg. sample}}$$

6. *Notes*
Note 1. The contents of the digestion flask should not be permitted to solidify to a hard mass at this stage; otherwise it is difficult to bring the solid into solution.

7. *Comments.* Aromatic compounds possessing the N–N linkage (e.g., azo, diazo, hydrazones, and hydrazino compounds) also can be determined by the procedure described in this experiment. It should be ascertained, however, either from the literature or with a pure sample of the compound, that no molecular nitrogen gas escapes prior to the reduction step.

Experiment 36: Microdetermination of the Primary Amino Function by Gasometric Method

1. *Principle.* Primary amino groups react with nitrous acid liberating one mole of nitrogen per equivalent (see Chapter 8, Section III-C). Aliphatic compounds react rapidly and directly—without the intermediate diazonium salt formation—as shown in equation 17 for an amino acid:

$$CH_3CH(NH_2)COOH + HNO_2 \rightarrow N_2 + CH_3CH(OH)COOH + H_2O \tag{17}$$

Aromatic compounds at low temperatures (0°C) form diazonium salts that, when heated, decompose to yield nitrogen and predominantly phenolic compounds:

$$C_6H_5NH_3^+Cl^- + HNO_2 \rightarrow [C_6H_5N_2]^+Cl^- + 2H_2O \tag{18a}$$

$$[C_6H_5N_2]^+Cl^- + H_2O \xrightarrow{\text{Heat}} N_2 + C_6H_5OH + HCl \tag{18b}$$

The volume of nitrogen gas produced is therefore a measure of the quantity of the primary amino function present in the sample. Since nitrous acid is unstable, it is prepared *in situ* by the reaction of a sodium nitrite solution with acetic acid:

$$NaNO_2 + HAc \rightarrow HNO_2 + NaAc \tag{19}$$

Potassium bromide and cupric chloride are added to the reaction mixture as catalysts and to suppress the decomposition of nitrous acid. Nevertheless, the latter reaction always occurs to some extent, as shown by the equation:

$$3HNO_2 \rightarrow 2NO + HNO_3 + H_2O \tag{20}$$

The nitric oxide interferes with the determination since it is not absorbed by potassium hydroxide in the micro azotometer. In the present experiment, nitric oxide is removed by liquid reagents (Note 1) stored in two scrubber tubes. The following reactions probably occur:

$$HBrO_3 + 3NO \rightarrow 3NO_2 + HBr \tag{21}$$

$$HBrO_3 + 5HBr \rightarrow 3Br_2 + 3H_2O \tag{22}$$

$$Br_2 + 2Na_2S_2O_3 \rightarrow 2NaBr + Na_2S_4O_6 \tag{23}$$

2. Apparatus

A. THE PRIMARY AMINO GROUP ASSEMBLY. Use the apparatus of Ma, Maurmeyer, and Monaco shown in Figure 8.9. The assembly consists of the carbon dioxide generator L, reaction tube J, two scrubber tubes F and E, and semimicro azotometer (5-ml. capacity, graduated in 0.02 ml.).

3. Reagents

A. SODIUM NITRITE STOCK SOLUTION, 1%. Dissolve 1 g. of sodium nitrite (reagent grade) in 99 ml. of distilled water. Before use, dilute 1 part of this solution with 2 parts of water.

B. ACETIC ACID-SODIUM ACETATE MIXTURE. Dissolve 10 g. of sodium acetate trihydrate in 250 ml. of distilled water. Add 250 ml. of 50% (v/v) acetic acid and mix the solution.

C. POTASSIUM BROMIDE SOLUTION, 10%. Dissolve 50 g. of potassium bromide (reagent grade) in 450 ml. of distilled water.

D. CUPRIC CHLORIDE SOLUTION, 4M. Dissolve 268 g. of cupric chloride in 500 ml. of distilled water.

E. POTASSIUM BROMATE SOLUTION (APPROXIMATELY 0.12M). Dissolve 5 g. of potassium bromate (reagent grade) in 75 ml. of water. Add to this solution 150 ml. of dilute (1:1) sulfuric acid.

F. SODIUM THIOSULFATE SOLUTION, 40%. Dissolve 40 g. of sodium thiosulfate in 60 ml. of distilled water.

G. POTASSIUM HYDROXIDE SOLUTION, 50%. Carefully dissolve 200 g. of potassium hydroxide pellets in 200 ml. of distilled water.

H. MERCURY. For the azotometer.

I. SOLID CARBON DIOXIDE. Use "dry ice" of high purity, free from air.

J. TEST COMPOUNDS. Alanine, dec. 293–5°C; valine, dec. 298°C; glycine, dec. 228°C; aniline, b.p. 183–4°C; p-aminobenzoic acid, m.p. 186°C.

4. Procedure

A. PREPARATION OF THE APPARATUS.   Assemble the apparatus as shown in Figure 8.9. Clamp all ball joints which should be lubricated with a trace of stopcock grease.

Fill the thermos bottle L with crushed "dry ice." Open stopcock K to let carbon dioxide escape into the atmosphere until the carbon dioxide generator is completely free of trapped air.

Fill the azotometer B with mercury and 50% potassium hydroxide solution. Add a pinch of mercuric oxide and a $\frac{1}{2}$-inch brad (nail without head) on top of the mercury (Note 2).

Fill scrubber tube F three-quarters full of the potassium bromate reagent solution, and the scrubber E with the sodium thiosulfate solution. Lubricate the necks and affix the tubes with the springs.

B. PREPARATION OF THE SAMPLE.   Accurately weigh a sample containing about 0.1 meq. of amino group into the reaction tube J. Introduce by means of a pipet 10 ml. of the acetic acid-sodium acetate mixture and swirl the tube until the sample dissolves. Add 1 ml. of the potassium bromide and 1.5 ml. of the cupric chloride solutions. Lubricate the neck of the reaction tube and attach it to the train. Place 2.0 ml. of the diluted sodium nitrite solution in the funnel H.

C. PURGING THE SYSTEM.   Lower the leveling bulb A of the azotometer to keep the level of the potassium hydroxide at the wide part of the azotometer. Purge the system free of air in the following manner. Close stopcocks C and D. Open stopcocks G, I, and K so that carbon dioxide escapes through G. After 2 minutes, close G and open D. After 2 more minutes, close D and open C slowly to let the carbon dioxide escape through the azotometer. The bubbles forming at the bottom of the azotometer should practically disappear before reaching the surface of the potassium hydroxide if the system is free of air. Now close stopcock C, raise the leveling bulb A to fill the azotometer B with potassium hydroxide solution. Close the stopcock on top of the azotometer and lower the leveling bulb half way. Carefully open the stopcock C (Note 3) so that not more than three to four bubbles will stay in the whole length of the azotometer at the same time. Observe if there is any gas collected in the azotometer after 2 minutes. If not, the reaction is ready to start. Otherwise, repeat the purging process until the system is completely air-free.

D. REACTION AT ROOM TEMPERATURE.   Now turn the stopcock K of the carbon dioxide generator so that no gas escapes into the reaction tube J or into the atmosphere. Turn the stopcock I above the reaction tube J to allow 1.0 ml. of the diluted sodium nitrite solution to run into the reaction tube. The reaction mixture will generate gases. Lower the leveling bulb more, if necessary, so that the gas enters the azotometer smoothly. When no more gas is evolved, introduce 0.2 ml. of the diluted sodium nitrite solution to the reaction tube J to check if there was sufficient nitrite to react with all the amino group.

E. MEASUREMENT OF THE VOLUME OF NITROGEN. Close the stopcock C and turn stopcock K to let carbon dioxide pass into the reaction tube J. Carefully open stopcock C again and control the speed of gas flow so that not more than four bubbles stay in the azotometer at one time. Close C when all gas bubbles are absorbed on rising along the azotometer. Adjust the leveling bulb A so that the pressure inside the azotometer is the same as the atmosphere. Measure the volume and record the temperature and barometer readings.

F. REACTION AT ELEVATED TEMPERATURE. Repeat the operation just described. Place a heating stage (Figure 5.19) or water bath (kept below 80°C) under the reaction tube J. Bubbles will be formed in the reaction tube if more nitrogen is liberated. Otherwise, the passage of gas into the azotometer B only means the expansion of gas volume in the system due to increase of temperature.

5. *Calculations*

A. FOR PER CENT AMINO GROUP

$$\% \text{ NH}_2 = \frac{(\text{millimol. N}_2)(16.02)(100)}{\text{wt. of sample in mg.}}$$

The number of millimoles of nitrogen produced is found by the following formula:

$$\text{Millimol. N}_2 = \frac{(V_s - 0.01V_s - V_b) \times F}{28.016}$$

where V_s = observed volume, $0.01V_s$ = correction due to vapor pressure of KOH and drainage, V_b = blank correction, and F = wt. in mg. per ml. of nitrogen at the particular temperature and pressure. Look up F from the nitrogen reduction tables or calculate it by perfect gas law.

B. FOR PER CENT COMPOUND

$$\% \text{ Compound} = \frac{(\text{millimol. N}_2)(\text{meq. wt. of compound in mg.})(100)}{\text{wt. of sample in mg.}}$$

6. *Notes*

Note 1. Use of solid scrubber would be advantageous. This problem is being investigated.

Note 2.   The mercuric oxide helps to break up the bubbles at the surface of mercury. The nail can be conducted by a magnet to go up the azotometer to break up foams.

Note 3.   Stopcock C has a cut groove for easy control of gas flow.

7. Comments.   This experiment demonstrates a gasometric method in which the gas evolved is collected and measured. A mixture of gases is generated in the reaction vessel. All gaseous products, except nitrogen and carbon dioxide, should be completely removed before the gas stream passes into the azotometer.

Experiment 37: Microdetermination of Nitro and Nitroso Groups by Titanous Chloride Reduction

1. Principle.   The nitro and nitroso (Chapter 8, Section XI-B) functions, respectively, are reducible by titanous chloride in acidic media. The reactions are illustrated by equations 24 and 25:

$$C_6H_5NO_2 + 6TiCl_3 + 6HCl \rightarrow C_6H_5NH_2 + 6TiCl_4 + 2H_2O \qquad (24)$$

$$C_6H_5NO + 4TiCl_3 + 4HCl \rightarrow C_6H_5NH_2 + 4TiCl_4 + H_2O \qquad (25)$$

The nitro or nitroso compound is treated with a measured amount of standard titanous chloride solution. After the reduction is completed, the excess of titanous chloride is determined by titration with standardized ferric ammonium sulfate using ammonium thiocyanate as the indicator.

The reduction of nitroso groups takes place at a pH different from that for nitro groups. Therefore, when nitroso and nitro compounds are present in a mixture, it is possible to find conditions so that only the nitroso groups are reduced, leaving the nitro groups unaffected.

2. Apparatus

A. ASSEMBLY FOR TITANOUS CHLORIDE MICROTITRATION.   The apparatus for microtitration using titanous chloride is shown in Figure 8.12. It consists of the reaction flask D, microburet E, and the nitrogen purification train ABC.

The reaction flask D is constructed from a 50-ml. Erlenmeyer flask. It has a ground-glass neck and two side arms, each 25 mm. long. One side arm has an inner diameter of 9 mm. Into this side arm is inserted a glass tube of 4 mm. I.D., which is bent so that its tip of 1-mm. bore remains 30 mm. above the bottom of the flask. The other side arm, which serves as outlet for the stream of nitrogen and for adding the reagents, has an inner diameter of 11 mm.

The microburet E, of the gravity-fed Machlett type, has 10-ml. capacity and is graduated in 0.05 ml. It is fitted with a ground-glass joint having a drip tip 20 mm. long. The 1-liter reservoir should be covered with aluminum foil to protect the titanous chloride solution from sunlight.

The nitrogen purification train consists of two 125-ml. Erlenmeyer flasks connected with the source of nitrogen. Flask A contains $1N$ chromous chloride solution kept over amalgamated zinc; flask B contains distilled water previously boiled to remove absorbed oxygen. Each flask carries a two-hole rubber stopper with glass tubings. The tube leading into the chromous chloride solution is drawn out to a fine capillary tip. The Erlenmeyer flask C contains water and is connected with rubber tubing to the side arm of the reservoir of the microburet E.

B. MICROBURET. Koch type, 5-ml. capacity, graduated in 0.02 ml., for dispensing the standardized ferric ammonium sulfate solution.

3. Reagents

A. STANDARD TITANOUS CHLORIDE SOLUTION, $0.04N$ ($= M/25$). Boil 1 liter of distilled water in an Erlenmeyer flask for 15 minutes and cool it to room temperature while a slow stream of nitrogen is conducted through the flask. Place 100 ml. of concentrated hydrochloric acid in a 1-liter volumetric flask, add 20 ml. of 20% titanous chloride (from Fisher Scientific Co., New York, N.Y.). Swirl to mix and then fill the flask to the mark with distilled water. After mixing, transfer the solution through a funnel containing glass wool into the reservoir of the microburet E (Figure 8.12), the delivery tube of which should be protected by a glass wool plug. Add 200 g. of zinc amalgam (see later) into the reservoir. Allow the titanous chloride solution to stand in the reservoir overnight before standardization.

Standardization. Introduce into the reaction flask D 10 ml. of $1.8M$ sulfuric acid and exactly 5.00 ml. of the standard $0.06N$ potassium dichromate solution. Attach the flask to the Machlett microburet and connect the Erlenmeyer flask B to one of the side arms (see Figure 8.12). Pass nitrogen through the apparatus for 5 minutes at the rate of fifteen bubbles per 10 seconds (20 ml. per minute) while stirring the solution continuously with the magnetic stirrer F. Add the $0.04N$ titanous chloride from the Machlett microburet until the pale yellow color of the solution almost disappears. Now add 2 drops (0.03 ml.) of diphenylamine indicator. Continue the titration until the deep purple color changes to a very pale grayish blue, lasting for 1 minute.

B. STANDARD FERRIC ALUM SOLUTION, $0.035N$ ($= 0.035M$). Dissolve 6.75 g. of ferric ammonium sulfate decahydrate in 70 ml. of distilled water. Add 10 ml. of concentrated sulfuric acid slowly with stirring, and then dilute the solution to 400 ml. Determine the titer of the solution as follows.

Flush the reaction flask D, which is attached to the Machlett microburet, for 5 minutes with nitrogen at the rate of 20 ml. per minute. Deliver into the flask 3.50 ml. of the standard titanous chloride solution. Add 4 ml. of $12M$ hydrochloric acid through the side arm. Disconnect the reaction flask from the Machlett microburet and attach it to the 5-ml. microburet containing the ferric alum solution. Titrate the contents of the reaction flask D with the ferric alum solution until the pale blue color almost disappears. Then introduce 2 ml. of $2.5M$ ammonium thiocyanate indicator solution and continue the titration until a pink coloration, lasting for 1 minute, is obtained.

c. STANDARD POTASSIUM DICHROMATE SOLUTION, $0.06N$ ($= M/50$). Recrystallize reagent grade potassium dichromate from water. Dry at 150°C for 6 hours. Dissolve 1.4710 g. of this reagent in a 500-ml. volumetric flask and dilute the solution to the mark.

d. AMALGAMATED ZINC. Place 100 g. of mossy zinc in a 400-ml. beaker. Introduce a solution containing 10 g. of mercuric chloride, 5 ml. of $12M$ hydrochloric acid and 150 ml. of distilled water. Stir for 5 minutes, decant the supernatant liquid, and wash the amalgam several times with distilled water.

e. CHROMOUS CHLORIDE, APPROXIMATELY $1N$. Dissolve 26.7 g. of chromous chloride hexahydrate in 80 ml. of distilled water and add 20 ml. of $12M$ hydrochloric acid. Transfer the solution into the 125-ml. Erlenmeyer flask A (Figure 8.12), which is attached to the nitrogen train, and allow it to stand overnight before use.

f. DIPHENYLAMINE INDICATOR SOLUTION, 0.5%. Dissolve 0.5 g. of diphenylamine in 100 ml. of concentrated sulfuric acid.

g. AMMONIUM THIOCYANATE INDICATOR SOLUTION, $2.5M$. Dissolve 101 g. of the solid in distilled water and make up to 500 ml.

h. SODIUM ACETATE SOLUTION, $2.5M$. Dissolve 102 g. of CH_3COONa in distilled water and make up to 500 ml.

i. DILUTE SULFURIC ACID, $1.8M$. Dilute 50 ml. of concentrated sulfuric acid to 500 ml.

j. TEST COMPOUNDS. 2,4-Dinitrobenzene, m.p. 173°C; p-nitroaniline, m.p. 147°C; p-nitrosophenol, m.p. 125°C; 1-nitroso-2-naphthol, m.p. 109°C.

4. Procedures

a. DETERMINATION OF NITRO GROUPS. Weigh accurately 3 to 8 mg. of the compound [containing about 0.05 meq. (Note 1) of the nitro function] to be analyzed into the reaction flask D. Add 4 ml. of 95% ethanol and stir magnetically until dissolution is complete. Assemble the apparatus as shown in Figure 8.12. Add 7 ml. of 2.5M sodium acetate solution and flush the reaction flask D with nitrogen for 5 minutes at the rate of 20 ml. per minute. Titrate with the standardized 0.04N titanous chloride until the color turns deep violet. Wait 3 minutes and then add 4 ml. of concentrated hydrochloric acid. Now transfer the reaction flask to the 5 ml. microburet and titrate with the standardized 0.035N ferric alum until the pale blue color of titanous chloride almost disappears. Add 2 ml. of 2.5M ammonium thiocyanate indicator solution and continue the titration until a pink coloration, lasting for 1 minute, is obtained.

Perform a blank with the same procedure and reagents as used in the titration of the sample.

B. DETERMINATION OF THE NITROSO GROUPS. Accurately weigh 5 to 10 mg. (containing about 0.05 meq. of nitroso group) of the nitroso compound into the reaction flask D and dissolve the sample in 5 to 10 ml. of distilled water or 95% ethanol. Add 2.5 ml. of 2.5M sodium acetate, attach the flask to the Machlett microburet, and flush with nitrogen for 5 minutes, at the rate of 20 ml. per minute. Add the standardized 0.04N titanous chloride until the solution turns deep violet (Note 2). Wait 3 minutes and then add 4 ml. of 12M hydrochloric acid. Now attach the reaction flask D to the 5-ml. microburet and titrate with standardized 0.035N ferric alum until the pale blue color almost disappears. Add 2 ml. of 2.5M ammonium thiocyanate indicator solution and continue the titration until a pink coloration which lasts at least 1 minute is obtained.

Perform a blank determination in the same manner.

C. DETERMINATION OF NITROSO GROUPS IN PRESENCE OF NITRO GROUPS. Place the accurately weighed sample (containing about 0.05 meq. of the nitroso function) in the reaction flask D, and dissolve it in 5 to 10 ml. of distilled water or 95% ethanol. Add 4 ml. of 12M hydrochloric acid and pass nitrogen through the apparatus for 5 minutes. Now add 6.00 ml. of the standardized 0.04N titanous chloride. After waiting for 3 minutes, attach the reaction flask to the 5-ml. microburet and titrate with the standardized ferric alum using 2 ml. of 2.5M ammonium thiocyanate as indicator. Perform a blank with the same procedure and reagents.

5. Calculations

A. FOR PER CENT NITRO GROUPS

$$\% \ NO_2 = \frac{(ml. \ TiCl_3 \ consumed)(normality \ of \ TiCl_3)(46.01)(100)}{(6)(wt. \ of \ sample \ in \ mg.)}$$

B. FOR PER CENT NITROSO GROUPS

$$\% \text{ NO} = \frac{(\text{ml. TiCl}_3 \text{ consumed})(\text{normality of TiCl}_3)(30.01)(100)}{(4)(\text{wt. of sample in mg.})}$$

6. Notes

Note 1. One milliequivalent of nitro function is the milligram molecular weight of the compound divided by the number of nitro groups in the molecule.

Note 2. N-nitroso compounds should be treated with an excess of 50 to 150% of titanous chloride, and the reduction allowed to proceed for 10 minutes before the hydrochloric acid is added.

7. Comments. A standard solution of $0.04N$ titanous chloride is employed in this experiment because of the favorable molar equivalence for nitro and nitroso groups (see equations 24 and 25). A $0.01N$ solution of titanous chloride deteriorates too easily to be useful as standard solution.

Experiment 38: Microdetermination of N–N Linkages in Aromatic Compounds by Titanous Chloride Reduction

1. Principle. Titanous chloride can be used as a reagent for quantitative reduction of several types of aromatic compounds which have N–N linkages. Thus the reaction of azo compounds (Chapter 8, Section VI-B) is shown in equation 26, using *p*-amino-azobenzene as an example:

$$\text{C}_6\text{H}_5\text{N}{=}\text{NC}_6\text{H}_4\text{NH}_2 + 4\text{TiCl}_3 + 4\text{HCl} \rightarrow \text{H}_2\text{NC}_6\text{H}_4\text{NH}_2 + \text{C}_6\text{H}_5\text{NH}_2 + 4\text{TiCl}_4 \quad (26)$$

The reaction of diazonium salts (Chapter 8, Section VI-D) is shown in equation 27, using benzenediazonium chloride as an example:

$$2\text{C}_6\text{H}_5\text{N}{=}\text{NCl} + 4\text{TiCl}_3 + 2\text{HCl} \rightarrow \text{C}_6\text{H}_5\text{N}{=}\text{N(NH}_2)\text{NC}_6\text{H}_5 + 4\text{TiCl}_4 \quad (27)$$

Arylhydrazines (Chapter 8, Section IX) are reduced by titanous chloride, provided there is also a nitro group on the benzene nucleus (Note 1). For instance, *p*-nitrophenylhydrazine consumes 8 molar equivalents of titanous chloride, as shown in equation 28:

$$(\text{NO}_2)\text{C}_6\text{H}_4\text{NHNH}_2 + 8\text{TiCl}_3 + 8\text{HCl} \rightarrow \text{H}_2\text{NC}_6\text{H}_4\text{NH}_2 + 8\text{TiCl}_4 + \text{NH}_3 + 2\text{H}_2\text{O} \quad (28)$$

Procedures are given in this experiment for the microdetermination of azo and diazonium compounds and of nitro-arylhydrazines, and also for the determination of an azo function in the presence of a nitro function, and of a nitro-arylhydrazine in the presence of nonreducible arylhydrazines.

2. Apparatus. See experiment 37.

3. Reagents. See experiment 37.

A. TEST COMPOUNDS. Azobenzene, m.p. 67–8°C; Congo red dye; methyl orange; *p*-diazodimethylaniline zinc chloride; *p*-nitrophenylhydrazine, m.p. 156–157°C.

4. Procedures

A. DETERMINATION OF AZO GROUP. Weigh accurately a 5 to 10 mg. sample (containing about 0.05 meq. of azo function) into the reaction flask D (Figure 8.12) which contains 5 to 10 ml. of distilled water or 95% ethanol. Assemble the apparatus as shown in Figure 8.12 and dissolve the sample by stirring with a magnetic stirrer. Add 5 ml. of 2.5M sodium acetate solution (Note 2) and flush the apparatus with nitrogen for 5 minutes at the rate of 20 ml. per minute. Introduce the standardized 0.04N titanous chloride from the Machlett microburet until the solution turns deep purple (1 to 2 ml. excess). Wait 3 minutes and then add 4 ml. of 12M hydrochloric acid to the reaction mixture. Detach the reaction flask D from the Machlett microburet and connect the former to the 5-ml. Koch microburet containing the standardized 0.035N ferric alum. Titrate with the ferric alum solution until the blue color of the titanous chloride nearly disappears. Then add 2 ml. of 2.5M ammonium thiocyanate indicator solution and continue titration until a pink color, lasting for 1 minute, is observed.

Perform a blank with the reagents and 3.00 ml. of the titanous chloride solution.

B. DETERMINATION OF AZO COMPOUNDS IN THE PRESENCE OF NITRO COMPOUNDS. Accurately weigh the sample into the reaction flask D and dissolve it in 5 to 10 ml. of distilled water or 95% ethanol, as described previously. Then introduce 4 ml. of 12M hydrochloric acid. After flushing with nitrogen for 5 minutes, add a measured volume (about 6 ml.) of the standardized 0.04N titanous chloride which is equivalent to at least a 100% excess for the azo group. When the reduction is complete (after about 3 minutes), back-titrate with the standardized 0.035N ferric alum and 2 ml. of 2.5M ammonium thiocyanate indicator solution to a pink endpoint lasting for 1 minute. Perform blanks with the same procedure and reagents.

C. DETERMINATION OF DIAZONIUM GROUPS. Weigh accurately 10 to 15 mg. sample (containing 0.05 to 0.10 meq. of the diazonium function) into the reaction flask D and dissolve it in 5 ml. of distilled water. Add 5 ml. of 2.5M sodium acetate and pass nitrogen through the apparatus for 15 minutes. Add about 100% excess of the standardized titanous chloride, and continue stirring the reaction mixture for 10 minutes before adding 4 ml. of $12M$ hydrochloric acid. Detach the reaction flask D from the Machlett microburet and titrate the contents of the reaction flask with the standardized ferric alum solution. Add 2 ml. of $2.5M$ ammonium thiocyanate near the equivalence point. The endpoint is reached when the red color persists for 1 minute. Perform a blank determination.

D. DETERMINATION OF NITRO-ARYLHYDRAZINES. Follow the direction given in Procedure A, using about 5 mg. sample and 5 to 10 ml. of 95% ethanol as solvent.

E. DETERMINATION OF NITRO-ARYLHYDRAZINE IN THE PRESENCE OF NON-REDUCIBLE ARYLHYDRAZINE. Accurately weigh into the reaction flask D a sample containing not more than 3 mg. of the nitro-arylhydrazine. Dissolve the sample in 10 ml. of 95% ethanol. Proceed according to the directions given in Procedure A.

5. Calculations

A. FOR PER CENT N—N LINKAGE IN AZO COMPOUNDS (Note 3)

$$\% \text{ N--N} = \frac{(\text{ml. TiCl}_3 \text{ consumed})(\text{normality of TiCl}_3)(28.02)(100)}{(4)(\text{wt. of sample in mg.})}$$

B. FOR PER CENT N—N LINKAGE IN DIAZONIUM SALTS

$$\% \text{ N--N} = \frac{(\text{ml. TiCl}_3 \text{ consumed})(\text{normality of TiCl}_3)(28.02)(100)}{(2)(\text{wt. of sample in mg.})}$$

C. FOR PER CENT NITROGEN IN NITRO-ARYLHYDRAZINE

$$\% \text{ N} = \frac{(\text{ml. TiCl}_3 \text{ consumed})(\text{normality of TiCl}_3)(14.01)(100)}{(6x + 2)(\text{wt. of sample in mg.})}$$

where x = number of nitro groups on the benzene nucleus.

6. Notes

Note 1.   Phenylhydrazine and halogen substituted phenylhydrazines are not reducible by titanous chloride.

Note 2.   To determine methyl orange, the buffer solution should be added after the standardized titanous chloride solution has been introduced; otherwise the compound will precipitate out.

Note 3.   When azobenzene is determined, the number in the denominator should be 2 instead of 4, because the product of reduction is benzidine as shown in Chapter 8, Section VI-B, equation 57.

7. Comments.   This experiment illustrates the general applicability of titanous chloride in functional group analysis, and the methods for selective determination of certain nitrogen functions.

Experiment 39:   Microdetermination of the Hydrazino Function by Gasometric Method

1. Principle.   The hydrazino function upon complete oxidation yields one mole of nitrogen gas (see Chapter 8, Section IX). In many cases, the oxidation can be accomplished by a mild oxidizing agent such as cupric ions. Thus *p*-nitrophenylhydrazine undergoes the reaction shown in equation 26:

$$O_2NC_6H_4NHNH_2 + 4CuSO_4 + H_2O \rightarrow N_2 + O_2NC_6H_4OH + 2Cu_2SO_4 + 2H_2SO_4 \quad (26)$$

The determination involves the measurement of the quantity of nitrogen gas liberated from a known weight of the sample. Heating is usually required to bring the oxidation to completion.

Potassium iodate and ferric chloride are also employed as oxidants for some hydrazino compounds.

2. Apparatus

A. The Micro Hydrazino Apparatus.   The complete assembly for the microdetermination of the hydrazino function is shown in Figure 8.11. It consists of the carbon dioxide generator KL, reaction flask A, reflux condenser E, and semimicro azotometer FG. The side arm B of the reaction flask is fitted with a sleeve-type rubber stopper D. The plug of the stopper is hollow to within a short distance from the top. The sleeve can be folded down over the neck of the side arm, and it thus holds the stopper securely in position during handling and prevents leakage. The diaphragm can be punctured readily with a syringe needle. The puncture seals automatically after the needle is withdrawn.

B. Syringe and Needle.   The syringe should have 5.0-ml. capacity and glass tip; the needle is 26-gauge and 1-inch (25 mm.) long.

C. Heating Stage.   See Figure 5.19.

3. Reagents

A. Cupric Sulfate Solution, Saturated.   Add 25 to 30 g. of pure copper sulfate to 100 ml. of distilled water. Shake well and allow to stand for several days.

B. Ferric Chloride Solution, 2M.   Dissolve 54 g. of $FeCl_3 \cdot 6H_2O$ in distilled water in a 100-ml. volumetric flask and dilute to the mark.

C. Potassium Iodate Solution, Approximately 0.3M.   Dissolve 6.5 g. of potassium iodate in distilled water and dilute to 100 ml.

D. Test Compounds.   *p*-Nitrophenylhydrazine, m.p. 156–7°C; benzhydrazide, m.p. 114–5°C; isonicotinic hydrazide, m.p. 170–3°C.

4. Procedure

A. PREPARATION OF THE APPARATUS. Assemble the apparatus as shown in Figure 8.11. See experiment 36 for the operation of the azotometer. The carbon dioxide generator KL holds a solution of potassium bicarbonate on the upper part and dilute sulfuric acid at the bottom [E. Poth, *Ind. Eng. Chem., Anal. Ed.*, **3,** 202 (1931)]. Do not recharge the azotometer and carbon dioxide generator until they are spent. Place the heating stage H on a support that can be removed so that the former can be lowered to disengage the reaction flask A without disturbing the rest of the assembly.

B. DETERMINATION OF THE HYDRAZINO GROUP. Remove the rubber stopper D from the reaction flask and introduce through the side arm B an accurately weighed sample containing about 0.1 meq. of the hydrazino function. Add 2 ml. of water, and dilute sulfuric acid or glacial acetic acid to dissolve the sample. Turn the stopcock of the carbon dioxide generator to purge the reaction flask A free from air. Then replace the rubber stopper D and let the carbon dioxide expel all air from the remaining part of the apparatus (see experiment 36 about checking the system). Now fill the azotometer and turn off the stopcock J of the carbon dioxide generator.

Introduce 4.0 ml. of the cupric sulfate solution (or other oxidizing reagent solution) by means of the syringe (Note 1) through the rubber diaphragm. Gradually raise the temperature of the heating stage while controlling the speed of the gas going into the azotometer with the stopcock on the delivery tube leading to the azotometer. If the gas stops, turn the stopcock J of the carbon dioxide generator carefully to maintain a continuous flow.

Turn off the heater switch when the contents of the reaction flask begin to boil, but maintain the temperature of the heater for 10 minutes. When all nitrogen gas has been driven into the azotometer, read the volume, temperature, and atmospheric pressure.

Repeat the heating and allow the contents of the reaction flask to boil for 5 minutes while a slow current of carbon dioxide passes through. Observe if any more nitrogen is produced.

C. THE BLANK. Perform an experiment using a sample which does not contain nitrogen.

5. Calculations

A. FOR PER CENT COMPOUND

$$\% \text{ Compound} = \frac{(\text{millimoles N}_2 - \text{blank})(\text{meq. wt. of compound in mg.})(100)}{\text{wt. of sample in mg.}}$$

B. FOR PER CENT HYDRAZINO NITROGEN

$$\% \ N = \frac{(\text{millimoles } N_2 - \text{blank})(28.02)(100)}{\text{wt. of sample in mg.}}$$

6. Note

Note 1. Cupric sulfate attacks the metal of the needle; hence, rinse it out immediately.

7. Comments. This experiment describes the technique of generating and collecting nitrogen gas while the reaction mixture is under reflex. The operation is not as easy as the other gasometric methods presented in this chapter because of the relatively large free space of, and the temperature variations inside, the apparatus.

Experiment 40: Microdetermination of Active Hydrogen by Lithium Aluminum Hydride

1. Principle. Lithium aluminum hydride reacts with an active hydrogen function (see Chapter 11, Section III-C) to liberate one molar equivalent of hydrogen. Thus isopropyl alcohol reacts to give hydrogen according to equation 27:

$$4(CH_3)_2CHOH + LiAlH_4 \rightarrow 4H_2 + LiOCH(CH_3)_2 + [(CH_3)_2CHO]_3Al \qquad (27)$$

The quantity of hydrogen produced by the sample is measured in the gasometric apparatus.

2. Apparatus

A. GASOMETRIC APPARATUS. Use the gasometric apparatus of Ma and Scheinthal shown in Figure 6.15. See experiment 33 for description.

B. SYRINGE AND NEEDLE. See experiment 33.

3. Reagents

A. LITHIUM ALUMINUM HYDRIDE REAGENT SOLUTION, APPROXIMATELY 0.25M. Dissolve 0.5 g. of lithium aluminum hydride in 50 ml. of Diglyme or other high-boiling ether (Note 1).

B. SOLVENT. Anhydrous Diglyme.

C. HYDROGEN GAS. See experiment 33.

D. TEST COMPOUNDS. Isopropyl alcohol, b.p. 82°C; *p*-bromophenol, m.p. 64°C.

4. Procedure

A. PREPARATION OF THE SAMPLE. Accurately weigh a solid sample containing approximately 0.1 meq. of active hydrogen into the reaction flask F. Dissolve the solid in 2 ml. of Diglyme. If the sample is liquid, introduce 0.1 meq. by means of the syringe, after the apparatus has been purged.

B. ASSEMBLING THE APPARATUS.   Add 2 or 3 dry micro stirring bars into the reaction flask F. Assemble the apparatus as shown in Figure 6.15.

C. PURGING THE SYSTEM.   Now purge the system free from air according to the direction given in experiment 33, Procedure A(3), page 567. Be sure to replace all air in the three-way stopcock D above the reaction chamber with hydrogen before affixing the rubber cap M for the syringe.

D. INTRODUCTION OF THE LITHIUM ALUMINUM HYDRIDE SOLUTION. Place the leveling bulb J at position L. Close the system by means of the stopcocks. Adjust the mercury in the two columns of the gasburet to be at the same level (i.e., the pressure inside the system being identical to the atmospheric pressure). Read the volume (mercury level in the gasburet), temperature, and barometric pressure (Note 2). Then lower the leveling bulb J slightly so that the pressure inside the gasburet is about 30 mm. below the atmospheric pressure. Inject through the rubber cap M exactly 1.00 ml. of the lithium aluminum hydride solution (or a volume sufficient to react with the active hydrogen in the sample) into the reaction flask F (Note 3). Turn stopcock D to close flask F after withdrawing the syringe needle. Place the magnetic stirrer (Figure 13.2) under the reaction flask F and start stirring. Watch the mercury level as the hydrogen is liberated by the reaction, and lower the leveling bulb J accordingly.

E. MEASURING THE FINAL VOLUME.   When there is no more change in the mercury level, stop the stirrer. Adjust the leveling bulb J so that the pressure inside the gasburet is again identical to atmospheric pressure and record the volume, temperature, and pressure.

F. BLANK DETERMINATION.   Perform an experiment using exactly the same quantities of reagents, but without the sample.

5. *Calculations*

A. FOR PER CENT ACTIVE HYDROGEN

$$\% \text{ Active H} = \frac{(\text{ml. H}_2 \text{ at STP for sample} - \text{ml. at STP for blank})(1.008)(100)}{(22.4)(\text{wt. of sample in mg.})}$$

6. *Notes*

Note 1.   Care must be taken in weighing and handling lithium aluminum hydride. About 0.5 g. of the hydride is rapidly transferred from the vessel supplied by the manufacturer to an aluminum foil placed on the balance pan and immediately introduced into a 250-ml. Pyrex bottle containing 50 ml. of the dry solvent. The bottle is immediately stoppered with a cork covered with aluminum foil and provided with a calcium chloride tube which is charged with calcium chloride and sodium hydroxide pellets so that neither moisture nor carbon dioxide enters into the dispersion. The bottle is shaken from time to time and warmed over a hot plate until complete solution is obtained in about 15 minutes.

Note 2. If the reaction is to be performed at a temperature different from room temperature, place the reaction flask inside the controlled temperature bath as shown in Figure 13.2.

Note 3. Be sure that all air is expelled from the syringe needle. The needle should pass through the stopcock channel before the plunger is pushed to deliver the reagent into the reaction flask.

7. Comments. The same procedure can be used when the Grignard reagent (see Chapter 11, Section III-B) is employed. The latter reagent is recommended for samples which contain reducible groups.

Experiment 41: Simultaneous Microdetermination of Enol and Keto Functions by Grignard Reagent

1. Principle. Methyl magnesium iodide reacts with the enol function to liberate a molar equivalent of methane (see Chapter 11, Section III-B). The same reagent also reacts mole per mole with the keto function, but no methane is liberated (see Chapter 6, Section VII-B-2-B). Therefore the Grignard reagent can be used for the simultaneous determination of keto and enol forms in a tautomeric mixture. For instance, a sample of acetylacetone contains both tautomers:

$$CH_3-\underset{\underset{O}{\|}}{C}-CH_2-\underset{\underset{O}{\|}}{C}-CH_3 \rightleftharpoons CH_3-\underset{\underset{OH}{|}}{C}=CH-\underset{\underset{O}{\|}}{C}-CH_3 \qquad (28)$$

On treatment with a measured amount of methyl magnesium iodide the enol form reacts according to equation 29, liberating an equivalent of methane:

$$CH_3-\underset{\underset{OH}{|}}{C}=CH-\underset{\underset{O}{\|}}{C}-CH_3 + 2CH_3MgI \rightarrow CH_4 + CH_3-\underset{\underset{OMgI}{|}}{C}=\overset{\overset{H}{|}}{C}-\overset{\overset{OMgI}{|}}{\underset{\underset{CH_3}{|}}{C}}-CH_3 \qquad (29)$$

whereas the keto form reacts without liberation of methane:

$$CH_3-\underset{\underset{O}{\|}}{C}-CH_2-\underset{\underset{O}{\|}}{C}-CH_3 + 2CH_3MgI \rightarrow CH_3-\overset{\overset{CH_3}{|}}{\underset{\underset{OMgI}{|}}{C}}-CH_2-\overset{\overset{OMgI}{|}}{\underset{\underset{CH_3}{|}}{C}}-CH_3 \qquad (30)$$

Hence the quantities of the enolic and ketonic groups present in a sample can be determined by the amount of methane gas produced according to equation 29 and the amount of methyl magnesium iodide consumed according to equations 29 and 30.

2. Apparatus

A. MICRO ACTIVE HYDROGEN APPARATUS OF SOLTYS. The assembly for active hydrogen determination according to Soltys is shown in Figure 11.8. Detailed description is given in Figure 13.3. The apparatus is designed so that a measured volume of the Grignard reagent can be introduced in a closed system (Note 1), and consists of a methane generator and a methanometer.

Methane Generator. The apparatus consists of the removable reaction flask (a), the two burets (b_1 and b_2), the Grignard reagent stock flask or reagent vessel (c), the two three-way stopcocks, one of which is on the bottom (S-a) and the other on the top (S-b). The Grignard reagent stock flask has a capacity of 50 ml. and is provided with a ground-glass stopper and two outlets. The outlet on the top leads to stopcock S-b. The outlet on the side is a capillary tubing, with one arm that extends to the bottom of the Grignard reagent vessel and another that leads to buret b_2, where it forms an automatic zero-point adjustment. The reaction flask a, which has a capacity of 8 ml., is attached by means of a ground-glass joint to a hollow stopper, or head. The capillary inlet tube d, which may be connected with either buret b_1 or b_2, depending on the position of stopcock S-a, is sealed to S-a and extends through the hollow stopper into the reaction flask. Another capillary tubing leads from the hollow stopper to the right side arm of stopcock S-b. Buret b_2 is graduated to 0.02 ml. and has a capacity of 2 ml.; it serves for the measurement and the introduction of the Grignard reagent. Buret b_1 is also graduated to 0.02 ml. but has a capacity of 1 ml. and is used for the introduction of the aniline. An automatic shaking device is connected to the apparatus by means of a wire attached to the capillary inlet tube.

The Methanometer. This consists of two parallel gasburets (b_3 and b_4), each having a capacity of 7 ml.; both are graduated to 0.02 ml. The methane buret b_4 carries two three-way stopcocks at its upper end, which facilitate the admittance of methane or dry nitrogen, respectively. Buret b_3 is open on the top to permit establishment of equilibrium with the atmospheric pressure. Its curved bottom is sealed to buret b_4 and is provided with an outlet that connects both burets by means of a rubber tubing to the mercury leveling bulb, which is suspended from a rack having a pinion adjustment.

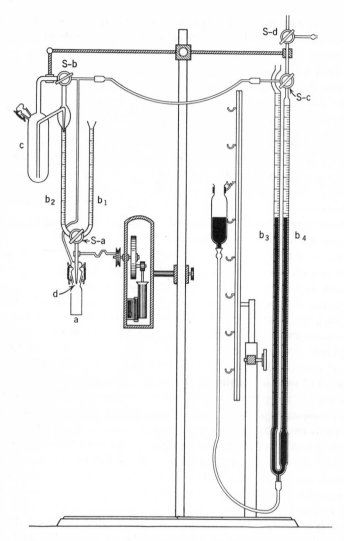

Fig. 13.3. The methane generator and methanometer. Reprinted from J. B. Niederl and V. Niederl, *Organic Quantitative
Microanalysis*, 2nd ed., John Wiley and Sons, New York, 1942.

B. APPARATUS FOR SEMIMICRO PREPARATION OF GRIGNARD REAGENT.
Figure 11.10 shows the apparatus for the preparation of small quantities
of pure Grignard reagent. Part A consists of a flask provided with stopcocks
for the inlet and outlet of pure dry nitrogen. The microcondenser fits into

a ⊺ joint through which the charge is also introduced. The lower part of the flask is provided with a fritted glass disc for filtration of the reagent. The stopcock ends in a stem B, which fits into flask C, which serves as a mixing flask for preparative work or for storage until the reagent is transferred into the stock vessel of the methane generator. Flask C is provided with gas inlet and outlet tubes and with a wide stoppered opening for cleaning and the introduction of other reagents in preparative work. For analytical purposes, after the reagent is prepared and filtered into vessel C it is transferred without contact of air by connecting stopcock G to the opening of the storage vessel of the methane generator and then closing stopcock B and applying slight nitrogen pressure through stopcock D.

3. Reagents

A. GRIGNARD REAGENT SOLUTION, APPROXIMATELY $1M$. Use the apparatus described in the preceding section. Dry thoroughly parts A and C and then open the lower stopcock of part A. Dry nitrogen is admitted through stopcock D, while stopcock E is opened and stopcocks F and G are closed. It takes about 2 to 3 minutes to flush the apparatus and then all stopcocks (including B) are closed. The inlet of nitrogen is transferred to stopcock F, and a gentle flow is maintained, stopcock E being open. The microcondenser is then removed and 25 ml. of freshly distilled amyl ether (dried over calcium hydride or sodium) is introduced followed by 0.6 g. of magnesium and 2.5 ml. of methyl iodide (dried over calcium hydride). The microcondenser is replaced, and the reaction is initiated by warming the flask A with a small electric bulb or micro hot plate.

If the apparatus and reagents are perfectly dry the reaction is complete within 10 to 15 minutes. Then both stopcocks F and E are closed and flask C is flushed with nitrogen introduced through stopcock D, while stopcock G is partially opened. Stopcock B is then opened, and a slight pressure of nitrogen is applied at F, while G is partially closed. The solution of the organometallic reagent is forced into flask C while any unreacted magnesium is retained by the fritted glass filter. When the filtration is complete, stopcock B is closed, G is connected to the opening of the storage vessel in the methane generator, and a slight nitrogen pressure is applied at D while flask C is tilted slightly so as to have most of the reagent solution near the opening of stopcock G. As a precaution, stopper H is securely attached to the flask C by means of a wire or rubber band. About 8 ml. of the reagent is retained in flask C to determine its strength. Stopper H is opened and 5 ml. of the reagent is rapidly transferred into an excess of $0.1N$ hydrochloric acid and titrated back with $0.1N$ sodium hydroxide. The concentration of the reagent should be about 1 molar.

B. SOLVENTS.   Anethole, amyl ether or Diglyme. Dry the solvent over calcium hydride.

C. ANILINE.   Freshly redistilled.

D. NITROGEN.   Prepurified quality (available from a dealer) in lecture demonstration cylinders.

E. TEST COMPOUNDS.   Acetylacetone, b.p. 139°C; ethyl acetoacetate, b.p. 181°C (Note 2).

4. Procedure

A. PREPARATION OF THE APPARATUS.   Assemble the Soltys apparatus as shown in Figure 11.8. All parts should be absolutely dry. Connect the apparatus to the nitrogen cylinder and pass a stream of nitrogen through the apparatus. Place the Grignard reagent and aniline in the respective reservoirs.

B. PREPARATION OF THE SAMPLE.   While nitrogen gas is passing through, disconnect the reaction flask F, and accurately weigh into the flask a sample that will liberate 1 to 2 ml. of methane and will not consume more than 1.5 ml. of the Grignard reagent. Add 0.5 ml. of the solvent into the flask and reconnect it to the assembly. Shake the flask with the air-driven wheel C to dissolve the sample and equilibrate the temperature.

C. ADDITION OF THE REAGENT.   After 10 minutes, raise the mercury in the gasburet to the zero mark. Then charge the Grignard reagent buret with the reagent. Close the system and let the nitrogen gas run directly into the atmosphere (or turn off the cylinder).

Lower the leveling bulb of the gasburet about 10 cm. Deliver an exact amount of the Grignard reagent into the reaction flask (Note 3). Shake the reaction flask for 5 minutes.

D. MEASUREMENT OF THE VOLUME OF METHANE PRODUCED BY THE ENOL FUNCTION.   Stop the shaker. Adjust the leveling bulb of the gas-buret so that mercury in the two graduated tubes is at exactly the same level. Measure the volume and also observe and record the temperature and atmospheric pressure.

If necessary, place the reaction flask in the heating bath K and shake the flask for 5 minutes. Remove the heating bath. Continue shaking until the temperature is again equilibrated. Measure the volume once more.

E. MEASUREMENT OF THE TOTAL VOLUME OF METHANE.   Introduce an exact volume (0.5 to 1.0 ml.) of aniline into the reaction flask by lowering the leveling bulb of the gasburet and turning the stopcock. Shake the reaction flask for 5 minutes. Then measure the volume of methane as described in Procedure D. Again record the temperature and barometer readings.

F. DETERMINATION OF THE STRENGTH OF THE GRIGNARD REAGENT. Run a blank in the same manner, with all reagents but without the sample. It is desirable to use the exact same amounts of the Grignard reagent as in the determination of the sample. Remember, however, that the gasburet has a total capacity of 7.0 ml.

5. *Calculations*

A. FOR PER CENT ENOL FUNCTION

$$\% \text{ OH} = \frac{(\text{millimoles of CH}_4 \text{ in step D})(17.01)(100)}{\text{mg. sample}}$$

B. FOR PER CENT KETO FUNCTION

$$\% \text{ CO} = \frac{(b - \text{millimoles of CH}_4 \text{ in step E})(28.01)(100)}{\text{mg. sample}}$$

where $$b = \frac{(\text{ml. of Grignard in step A})(\text{millimoles of CH}_4 \text{ in step F})}{\text{ml. of Grignard in step F}}$$

6. *Notes*

Note 1. The gasometric apparatus of Ma and Scheinthal (Figure 6.15) also can be used. The exact volumes of Grignard reagent and aniline introduced are then measured with calibrated syringes.

Note 2. Acetoacetic ester will react with the Grignard reagent because of (1) the enol, (2) the keto, and (3) the ester functions.

Note 3. The amount of Grignard reagent added should not generate more than a total of 6 ml. of methane in the determination.

7. *Comments.* It is difficult to obtain good precision in this experiment. If the temperature and atmospheric pressure fluctuate during each step, it will be necessary to apply corrections according to the gas law.

Since methane might be slightly soluble in the solvent employed, it is desirable to use methane in place of nitrogen in the system. However, a cylinder of methane which is entirely free from moisture, oxygen, and carbon dioxide is difficult to obtain. If the amounts of impurities are not large, a blank correction may serve the purpose.

Experiment 42: Microdetermination of Acyl Groups by the Kuhn-Roth Method

1. *Principle.* Acyl groups (see Chapter 6, Section V) are determined by hydrolysis. For example, acetanilide is hydrolyzed by heating with dilute sulfuric acid as shown in equation 31:

$$CH_3CONHC_6H_5 + H_2SO_4 + H_2O \rightarrow CH_3COOH + C_6H_5NH_3HSO_4 \qquad (31)$$

Ethyl benzoate when heated with aqueous sodium hydroxide forms sodium benzoate, which upon acidification yields the free acid:

$$C_6H_5COOC_2H_5 + NaOH \rightarrow C_6H_5COONa + C_2H_5OH \qquad (32)$$

$$C_6H_5COONa + H_2SO_4 \rightarrow C_6H_5COOH + NaHSO_4 \qquad (33)$$

In the Kuhn-Roth method, the free carboxylic acid is distilled off, collected, and determined by titration with $0.01N$ alkali.

2. Apparatus

A. KUHN-ROTH MICRO ACETYL APPARATUS. The apparatus, shown in Figure 6.1, consists of a three-necked flask; one neck for the gas inlet tube, the center neck containing a filling tube with a ground-in plunger-type glass stopper, and the third neck fitted with a reversible condenser. The condenser, made of quartz, is bent at different angles at each end, allowing in one angle for reflux, and in the other, distillation.

3. Reagents

A. HYDROLYZING REAGENTS.

(1) *Sodium hydroxide in methanol-water mixture, 4%.* Dissolve 4 g. of sodium hydroxide pellets in 50 ml. of distilled water. Mix with 50 ml. of methanol.

(2) *Aqueous sodium hydroxide, 5N.* Dissolve 20 g. of sodium hydroxide pellets in 100 ml. of distilled water.

(3) *Dilute sulfuric acid 1:2.* Carefully add 100 ml. of concentrated sulfuric acid to 200 ml. of distilled water.

(4) *p-Toluenesulfonic acid, approximately 20%.* Dissolve 25 g. of p-toluenesulfonic acid in 100 ml. of distilled water.

B. STANDARD SODIUM HYDROXIDE SOLUTION, $0.01N$ ($= 0.01M$). See experiment 1.

C. BARIUM CHLORIDE. Reagent grade.

D. PYRIDINE. Reagent grade.

E. PHENOLPHTHALEIN INDICATOR SOLUTION, 1%. See experiment 1.

F. NITROGEN GAS. Use a lecture bottle size cylinder with a needle valve.

G. TEST COMPOUNDS. Acetanilide, m.p. 114°C; acetylsalicylic acid, m.p. 135°C; ethyl benzoate, b.p., 213°C.

4. Procedure

A. HYDROLYSIS. Test the sample for its solubility in each of the four hydrolyzing reagents. If the sample is insoluble in all four, dissolve it in pyridine and use the alcoholic sodium hydroxide.

Accurately weigh about 0.1 meq. sample into the micro acetyl apparatus through the center neck. Lubricate all joints with water or metaphosphoric acid. Add the proper hydrolyzing reagent (4 ml., if methanolic sodium hydroxide is used; 1 ml. for the others) and add 1 ml. of water to the filling tube as a seal.

Connect the gas inlet tube to the nitrogen cylinder and adjust the gas flow to 4 bubbles per second. Heat the reaction mixture in a boiling water bath (Note 1) and reflux for 0.5 hour (Note 2). Remove the water bath and cool.

B. DISTILLATION AND TITRATION.   Break the water seal of the filling tube. Rinse the inside of the condenser with 5 ml. of distilled water so that the rinsings go into the flask. Remove the condenser and rinse thoroughly. Reconnect the condenser for distillation. At this point, if any pyridine or methanol was used, distill using a small flame and collect 5 to 6 ml. of distillate which is discarded. Add to the filling tube 1 ml. of $5N$ sodium hydroxide, if sulfuric acid was used; add 0.5 ml. of $5N$ sodium hydroxide, if p-toluenesulfonic acid was used; add 1 ml. of the 1:2 dilute sulfuric acid, if alcoholic or aqueous sodium hydroxide was used. Lift the plunger sufficiently to allow the reagent to flow into the flask. Then add 2 ml. of distilled water. Finally, fill the filling tube with 7 ml. of water. With a current of nitrogen passing through the contents of the flask, distill over a small flame, collecting the distillate in a 25-ml. graduated cylinder with a 45-degree funnel to guide the liquid flow.

When the contents of the flask have been reduced to about 4 ml., add 5 ml. of distilled water by carefully raising the plunger of the filling tube without interrupting the distillation. Refill the filling tube and repeat the operation until the distillation is complete. Collect four separate portions of 20, 15, 10, and 5 ml., respectively, in 50-ml. Erlenmeyer flasks.

Test for the presence of sulfate by adding a crystal of barium chloride to each Erlenmeyer flask. There should be no turbidity. Then titrate the contents of each flask with standardized $0.01N$ sodium hydroxide to the phenolphthalein endpoint (see experiment 1).

5. Calculations

A. FOR PER CENT ACETYL GROUP

$$\% \ CH_3CO = \frac{\text{(total ml. NaOH)(normality of NaOH)(43.04)(100)}}{\text{mg. sample}}$$

B. FOR PER CENT BENZOYL GROUP

$$\% \ C_6H_5CO = \frac{\text{(total ml. NaOH)(normality of NaOH)(105.11)(100)}}{\text{mg. sample}}$$

6. Notes

Note 1. The flask and the two side arms should be immersed in water.

Note 2. 0.5-Hour heating time is an average. N-acyl compounds may require heating as long as 3 hours.

7. Comments. This method is useful for acetyl, benzoyl, and a few other acyl groups whose parent acids are sufficiently volatile when heated at the boiling point of the aqueous solution employed in the experiment.

Experiment 43: Microdetermination of Methyl Side Chains by Chromic Acid Oxidation

1. Principle. A methyl side chain of the type $R—CH(CH_3)—CH_2—R'$ (see Chapter 11, Section V-C) may be oxidized by chromic acid in sulfuric acid to yield acetic acid. For example, the oxidation of α-methylbutyric acid may be expressed in the following manner:

$$3CH_3CH_2CH(CH_3)COOH + 10CrO_3 + 15H_2SO_4 \rightarrow 6CH_3COOH + 3CO_2 \\ + 5Cr_2(SO_4)_3 + 18H_2O \quad (34)$$

The acetic acid formed can be separated by steam distillation and determined by titration with standard sodium hydroxide solution:

$$6CH_3COOH + 6NaOH \rightarrow 6CH_3COONa + 6H_2O \quad (35)$$

Similarly, acetone may be oxidized as shown in equation 36:

$$3CH_3(CO)CH_3 + 8CrO_3 + 12H_2SO_4 \rightarrow 3CH_3COOH + 3CO_2 \\ + 4Cr_2(SO_4)_3 + 15H_2O \quad (36)$$

The discussion on the interpretation of the results of the oxidation of C-methyl groups given in Chapter 11, Section V-C should be reviewed. It should be noted that acetone yields one mole-equivalent of acetic acid and α-methyl butyric acid two mole-equivalents of acetic acid only under ideal conditions.

2. Apparatus

A. HEATING DEVICE. Use a rocking sand bath or the furnace of Tashinian, Baker and Koch (Figure 11.13).

B. STEAM DISTILLATION APPARATUS. Use the apparatus shown in Figure 6.6, which consists of the steam generator A, trap B, distilling flask D, and condenser E.

C. REACTION TUBES. See experiment 5.

3. Reagents

A. CHROMIC ACID SOLUTION, 5N (= 5/3M). Dissolve 166.77 g. of chromic anhydride (reagent grade) in 1 liter of distilled water.

B. SULFURIC ACID, SPECIFIC GRAVITY 1.84. Reagent grade.

C. STANDARD SODIUM HYDROXIDE SOLUTION, 0.01N (= M/100). See experiment 1.

D. PHENOLPHTHALEIN INDICATOR SOLUTION, 1%. See experiment 1.

E. TEST COMPOUNDS. α-Methylbutyric acid, b.p. 69–70°/7 mm.; acetone, b.p. 56°C; bixin, dec. 217°C; vitamin A acetate, m.p. 57–58°C.

4. Procedure

A. PREPARATION OF THE SAMPLE. Weigh accurately into the reaction tube a sample containing about 0.1 meq. of methyl group. Use the long micro weighing tube (Figure 5.6) for solids and the micro weighing pipet (Figure 5.11) for low-boiling liquids. [In the latter case add the sulfuric–chromic acid mixture (4:1) to the reaction tube, first. Then break the tip and air chamber of the micro weighing pipet containing the liquid sample. Drop all parts into the reaction tube. If necessary, use a glass rod to break the liquid chamber under the acid solution. Cut the portion of the glass rod that was dipped into the acid solution and drop it into the reaction tube.] Dissolve the sample with 1.0 to 2.0 ml. of concentrated sulfuric acid. Cool the solution in the ice bath and carefully deliver into the reaction tube 4.0 ml. of the 5N chromic acid (Note 1). Seal the reaction tube (see experiment 13 and Figure 5.20).

B. THE OXIDATION. Place the reaction tube in the heating bath or furnace. Gradually raise the temperature to 110°C. Heat the reaction mixture for 1 to 2 hours.

C. DISTILLATION AND TITRATION. Cool the reaction tube to room temperature. Heat the tip with a flame to open a hole and relieve the pressure. Then open the tube as described in experiment 13.

Transfer the contents of the reaction tube to the distilling flask D (Figure 6.6). Rinse the reaction tube with distilled water. Assemble the steam distillation apparatus. Place a 250-ml. Erlenmeyer flask under the condenser E and start distillation. Collect 100 ml. of distillate.

Add 0.10 ml. of phenolphthalein indicator solution to the distillate. Titrate with the standardized 0.01N sodium hydroxide until a pink color persists for 30 seconds.

5. Calculations

A. FOR PER CENT METHYL GROUP

$$\% \ CH_3 = \frac{(ml. \ NaOH)(normality \ of \ NaOH)(15.03)(100)}{mg. \ sample}$$

6. Notes

Note 1. Alternately, the chromic acid–sulfuric acid mixture may be previously prepared by adding 1 volume of concentrated sulfuric acid to 4 volumes of the 5N chromic acid solution. This mixture is then added to the reaction tube containing the solid sample. It is better, however, to dissolve the solid sample before adding the chromic acid solution to disperse the sample into the oxidizing mixture.

7. Comments.   This experiment demonstrates a sealed-tube reaction in which considerable pressure is produced. Hence the sealed tube requires more care in preparation.

Experiment 44:   Microdetermination of the Carboxyl Group by Decarboxylation

1. Principle.   Compounds containing the carboxyl group (Chapter 7, Section I-C-2), when heated in an inert atmosphere, liberate carbon dioxide. For example, the reaction for *p*-hydroxybenzoic acid is illustrated in equation 37:

$$HOC_6H_4COOH \rightarrow HOC_6H_5 + CO_2 \tag{37}$$

This reaction is catalyzed by quinoline and cupric carbonate. The carbon

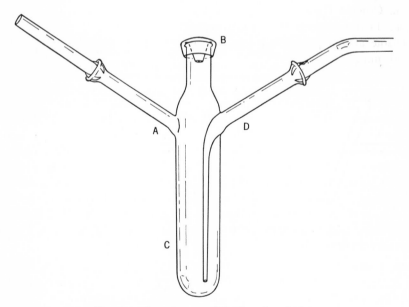

Fig. 13.4. Reaction vessel for decarboxylation.

dioxide liberated can be conducted into the gas chromatograph, scanned, and determined by the recording device.

2. Apparatus

A. REACTION VESSEL.   The reaction vessel for decarboxylation is shown in Figure 13.4. It has two side arms with ball-and-socket joints. The side arm D has a delivery tube reaching to about 5 mm. from the bottom of the reaction vessel and serves as the inlet of the inert gas (helium). The side arm A is connected to the gas chromatographic column. The neck of the reaction vessel is fitted with a syringe cap B (rubber stopper of the sleeve type, see experiment 39). The reaction vessel can be closed by the syringe cap B, and two stopcocks (see Figure 13.5) connected to the side arms. Multiple determinations may be performed by joining several reaction vessels to a manifold (shown in Figure 13.5), the terminals of which are connected to the gas chromatograph.

B. HEATING DEVICE.   Use a heating stage, preferably with electronic control (see Figure 5.19).

C. GAS CHROMATOGRAPH.   Consult a textbook on theory and practice of gas chromatography.

3. Reagents

A. QUINOLINE.   Reagent grade.

B. COPPER CARBONATE.   Reagent grade.

C. TEST COMPOUNDS. p-Hydroxybenzoic acid, m.p. 215°C; o-chloro-benzoic acid, m.p. 142°C; 2,4-dinitrobenzoic acid, m.p. 183°C; malonic acid, m.p. 135°C.

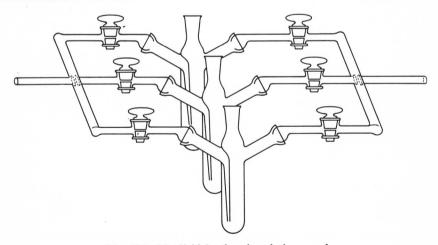

Fig. 13.5. Manifold for decarboxylation vessels.

4. Procedure

A. DETERMINATION OF THE SAMPLE

(1) *Preparation of the sample.* Accurately weigh about 0.1 meq. of the solid sample into the reaction vessel C (Figure 13.4) by means of the micro weighing tube. (Introduce liquid samples through the cap B with a syringe after the apparatus has been purged free of air.) Add 10 mg. of cupric carbonate, insert the syringe cap B, and connect the reaction vessel to the helium source and gas chromatograph through the manifold (Figure 13.5). With the other reaction vessels shut off, open the stopcocks connected to the side arms and allow helium to flush the apparatus for 5 minutes. Switch on the recorder to check if the system is free from air and carbon dioxide. Continue purging the apparatus until no air or carbon dioxide can be detected on the chromatogram.

(2) *Decarboxylation.* Now inject by means of a syringe with 4-inch needle, 10 μl. of quinoline into the reaction chamber C (Note 1). Close both stopcocks on the side arms. Place the reaction chamber C in the heating stage. Gradually raise the temperature of the heating stage and then maintain it at 220°C for 30 to 60 minutes. If quinoline vaporizes to the upper part of the reaction vessel, cool that part with a wet cloth and tap the reaction vessel so that the liquid quinoline runs down to the bottom of the vessel.

(3) *Measuring the carbon dioxide.* After the predetermined heating period, reset the heating stage to 100°C (Note 2). Wait 5 minutes to equilibrate the temperature of the contents of the reaction chamber C; then set the recorder and, with the other reaction vessels shut off, open the stopcocks on both side arms to send the gases into the gas chromatographic column. The response should appear on the recorder within 5 seconds.

B. PREPARATION OF THE CALIBRATION CURVE.

Prepare the calibration curve by weighing out 0.05, 0.10, and 0.15 meq., respectively, of the pure compound and perform the determination in the same manner as for the sample to be analyzed. Plot the height of response *vs.* quantity of the compound. A straight line should be obtained.

5. Calculations

A. FOR PER CENT COMPOUND

$$\% \text{ Compound} = \frac{(\text{meq. cmpd. found})(\text{meq. wt. of cmpd. in mg.})(100)}{\text{wt. of sample in mg.}}$$

6. Notes

Note 1. Make sure that all air has been expelled from the syringe needle.

Note 2. Alternately, the heating stage may be removed and a beaker containing boiling water heated by an electric immersion heater placed under the reaction chamber C. The heating stage then can be used to heat the other reaction tubes in the manifold.

7. Comments. This experiment demonstrates the use of gas chromatography in functional group analysis. It has advantages over other methods because gas chromatographic determination is discriminative. Thus, if other acidic oxides are also produced in the decarboxylation of the sample, they are not recorded as carbon dioxide, as they would be if the resulting gases were determined by absorption with a measured amount of an alkaline solution and back-titration with standard acid.

Experiment 45: Microdetermination of the Alkene Function by Catalytic Hydrogenation: Method I

1. Principle. The methods for the determination of the alkene function have been extensively discussed in Chapter 10, Section II. Catalytic hydrogenation is often used in the study of pure samples. The equation for the catalytic hydrogenation of cinnamic acid is given below:

$$C_6H_5CH{=}CHCOOH + H_2 \xrightarrow[\text{catalyst}]{} C_6H_5CH_2CH_2COOH \qquad (38)$$

The method involves the measurement of the volume of hydrogen gas consumed by a known amount of the compound to be analyzed.

2. Apparatus

A. MICROHYDROGENATION APPARATUS. The apparatus of Ogg and Cooper is shown in Figure 10.1. Modify the assembly in the following manner. Replace the reaction flask MK with one having two side arms as shown in Figure 10.3. Omit the hydrogen purification train ABDE (Note 1). However, since it may be desirable if hydrogen of high purity is not available, it is described below.

The purification train consists of a standard micro electric combustion furnace A heated to approximately 750°C so that the platinum star contact catalysts in the 8-mm. inside diameter quartz combustion tube B will effectively remove the oxygen from the hydrogen gas. The water so formed is absorbed by indicating Drierite in the inner tube of the absorption tube D. If the hydrogen gas is wet, it is advisable to place a drying tube before the combustion tube to remove the moisture and thus prolong the life of the absorbent in D.

Tubes E and F are used to saturate hydrogen with the solvent to be used in the reaction vessel. One inch (2.5 cm.) of the solvent is placed in E, and the inner tube of F is filled with glass wool to prevent mechanical carry-over of the solvent.

All the 7/15 standard-taper ground joints in the hydrogen train are sealed with de Khotinsky cement. The purification train is attached to stopcock 1 of the apparatus by a glass tubing with a Tygon tubing connector. Buret G and manometer H have parallel and coinciding graduations, with 0.02-ml. intervals from 0 to 7 ml. Mercury is leveled in G and H by raising or lowering leveling bulb I with a rack and pinion device shown in Figure 10.1. The reaction unit is connected to the buret by the 12/2 ball joint J, held in place by a suitable clamp. The 20-ml. reaction flask K is connected by a 14/20 ground-glass joint L and held in place by two steel springs. The side arm and stopper M are made from 10/12 ground joints. The stopper, which extends into the neck of the flask, has a groove near the tip and perpendicular to its long axis. The sample cup N is hung on the stopper and dropped by turning M. Cup N is made by drilling an aluminum rod about 6 mm. in diameter and 8 mm. long so that its volume is about 0.1 ml. The Nichrome wire handle is attached through two holes drilled on opposite sides of the cup. The stirring bar O is made by sealing fine iron filings in a glass tube about 3 mm. in outside diameter and about 15 mm. long. The cup attached to stopcock 2 facilitates cleaning the tube leading to the reaction vessel. Stopper M and joint L are greased carefully before each analysis, and stopcocks and ball joint are lubricated frequently to prevent loss of hydrogen.

3. Reagents

A. CATALYSTS (Note 2). Several types of catalysts are described below. The platinum carbon is slightly more active than the palladium carbon. The palladium carbon has been used for a variety of compounds and in conjunction with the mixed catalyst may be used for the reduction of ketones.

(1) *Platinum carbon 5%.* About 2 g. of purified Norit charcoal in an evaporating dish is stirred with 2.5 ml. of a 10% solution of chloroplatinic acid and 6 ml. of water. (The charcoal is purified by boiling 10 g. of it with 100 ml. of 6N hydrochloric acid for 10 minutes, filtering, and washing with distilled water until the pH of the filtrate is between 5 and 6.) The evaporating dish is placed on a steam bath and the mass is stirred until it is homogeneous. Heating is continued with occasional stirring until the mass is sufficiently dry to be pulverized with a glass rod. The dish containing the powder is placed in an oven heated to 100 to 120°C for 30 minutes, and is then cooled to room temperature; the powder is transferred to a small Erlenmeyer flask with 10 ml. of 1% hydrazine hydrate solution. The flask is immersed in an ice-salt bath and cooled to about −5°C, and about

10 ml. of $1N$ sodium hydroxide solution previously cooled to about 0°C is added all at once. After standing at -5 to 0°C for 2 hours, the mixture is filtered through a suction filter, water being used to transfer the mass adhering to the sides of the flask. (The catalyst should not be left uncovered by water for any length of time.) Washing with 20 ml. portions of water is continued four to five times. The catalyst is then washed once with 10 ml. of alcohol, and before all the alcohol has passed through the charcoal 5 ml. of ether is added, followed by another 10-ml. portion. The funnel is removed from suction as soon as all the ether has drained off. The catalyst is spread on a piece of glazed paper, dried in nitrogen for 10 to 15 minutes, and then transferred to a small screw-cap bottle. If the alcohol is allowed to drain through the charcoal and the cake becomes exposed to air, oxidation of the adhering alcohol will set the charcoal on fire. For the preparation of 10% platinum charcoal the amount of chloroplatinic acid given previously is doubled.

(2) *Palladium carbon 5%.* The method described for the preparation of 5% platinum carbon is used, except that a palladium chloride solution is substituted for the chloroplatinic acid; a sufficient quantity of palladium chloride is added to 2 g. of charcoal so that on reduction 100 mg. of palladium metal will be formed. Commercially available 5 or 10% palladium carbon has slightly less activity than the palladium catalysts prepared by this method.

(3) *Mixed catalysts.* In an evaporating dish are placed 4 g. of nickel nitrate $(NiNO_3 \cdot 6H_2O)$, 1 g. of ferrous chloride, 0.1 g. of manganese chloride $(MnCl_2 \cdot 4H_2O)$, and 0.3 ml. of 10% chloroplatinic acid; 50 ml. of water are added, and the mass is stirred until the salts are dissolved. Ten grams of purified Norit charcoal is added with stirring and the mixture is heated over a water bath with occasional stirring until dry. The mixture is heated at 120 to 130°C for 15 minutes, as in the preparation of the platinum catalyst, and is then cooled to room temperature and treated with 2 ml. of 1% hydrazine hydrate and 50 ml. of $1N$ sodium hydroxide solution. The mass is allowed to stand for one-half hour and is then filtered. The catalyst is washed twice with 100 ml. of water, once with 100 ml. of water containing 0.5 ml. of dilute acetic acid, and then twice with distilled water; it is dried by carefully heating at 120 to 130°C with stirring. The dried charcoal mass is placed in an 8-inch test tube with a side arm connected to an exhaust system. The tube is provided with a rubber stopper and a glass tube reaching nearly to the bottom for the inlet of hydrogen. The 8-inch tube is clamped to a stand in a nearly horizontal position and a thermometer is wired to its side. The inlet tube is connected to a hydrogen tank provided with a bubble counter. Hydrogen is passed through for

10 minutes; then a small flame is placed at such a distance from the tube containing the charcoal that the temperature rises slowly to 180 to 200°C. The hydrogen is passed through slowly for 30 minutes after this temperature has been reached; heating then is discontinued and the mass is allowed to cool while a stream of hydrogen passes through the tube. The hydrogen inlet is removed and replaced with a solid rubber stopper covered with tin foil. The catalyst prepared by this method is pyrophoric, and care should be exercised in weighing it. It is used in conjunction with palladium carbon for the reduction of ketones.

B. HYDROGEN. Highest purity, preferably a lecture bottle size cylinder fitted with a needle valve.

C. SOLVENTS. Glacial acetic acid; dioxane.

D. TEST COMPOUNDS. Cinnamic acid, m.p. 133°C; β-carotene, m.p. 183°C; crotonic acid, m.p. 72°C.

4. Procedure

A. PREPARATION OF THE APPARATUS. Assemble the apparatus as directed previously. Place the stirring bar in the reaction flask. Connect the source of hydrogen to the top stopcock 1 of the gasburet and pass hydrogen gas through the apparatus (Note 3), the stopper carrying the metal cup being disengaged.

B. PREPARATION OF THE SAMPLE. With a current of hydrogen going through the apparatus, bring the stopper carrying the metal cup to the microbalance. Place the metal cup in the cavity of the aluminum stand (Figure 5.8b). Accurately weigh a sample that contains about 0.1 meq. of the alkene function in the metal cup.

Disengage the other stopper of the reaction flask (Figure 10.3). Lubricate the stopper carrying the metal cup and sample with stopcock grease. Carefully insert the metal cup and place the stopper in position. Add the catalyst (300 to 800 mg.) and solvent (3 to 5 ml.) into the reaction flask through the other side arm. Start the magnetic stirrer and turn the stopcock 2 above the long tube R connecting the reaction flask so that hydrogen gas also escapes through the short bent tube. Lubricate the other stopper (Note 4) and close the reaction flask.

Adjust the leveling bulb of the gasburet to keep the mercury level at 6.00 ml. Now turn the stopcocks to close the hydrogenation system.

C. HYDROGENATION. Observe the level of mercury in the gas buret after 5 minutes. If there is no change, raise the leveling bulb 50 mm. for 5 minutes and return the bulb to the first position. If the mercury level resumes to 6.00 ml., the system is ready for hydrogenation. Record the temperature and barometer readings.

Now carefully turn the stopper carrying the metal cup containing the sample and drop the cup into the solvent and catalyst. Raise the leveling bulb of the gasburet so that there is a slight pressure (about 30 mm. Hg) applied to the system. Observe the movement of the mercury level in the gasburet. Stop the stirrer when the mercury ceases to rise. Level up the mercury columns in the gasburet. Read the volume, temperature, and atmospheric pressure.

Then raise the leveling bulb and start the magnetic stirrer again. Check the volume, temperature, and pressure after 10 minutes. Repeat this process until the volume in the system becomes constant.

Run a blank using the exact same amounts of reagents.

5. Calculations

A. As Number of Moles of Hydrogen Consumed per Mole of Compound.

$$H_2/mol. = \left(\frac{V}{22.4}\right)\left(\frac{Pc}{760}\right)\left(\frac{273}{t+273}\right)\left(\frac{mol. \ wt. \ in \ mg.}{sample \ wt. \ in \ mg.}\right)$$

where V = vol. of H_2 used = (initial buret reading − final buret reading) − blank (Note 5). Pc = barometer reading in mm. − 3 mm. for brass scale correction.

B. For Per Cent Alkene Function

$$\% \ C{=}C = \frac{(millimoles \ H_2 \ used)(24.02)(100)}{wt. \ of \ sample \ in \ mg.}$$

C. For Per Cent Purity (Compound)

$$\% \ Purity = \frac{(millimoles \ H_2 \ used)(meq. \ wt. \ of \ compound \ in \ mg.)(100)}{wt. \ of \ sample \ in \ mg.}$$

6. Notes

Note 1. The hydrogen purification train is necessary if highest purity grade hydrogen is not available.

Note 2. Use the same catalyst as in the synthetic work of the sample to be analyzed.

Note 3. Keep flames away from the surrounding area.

Note 4. The second stopper also may be one with a hook. Then it can carry a second metal cup containing an extra catalyst or a duplicate sample. After the first hydrogenation (see Procedure c) the second metal cup is dropped and the operation is repeated.

Note 5. All three volumes should be expressed under the same temperature and pressure.

7. Comments. The product of reaction in this experiment can be easily recovered. Analysis of the product will indicate whether other functional groups besides the C=C have been affected.

Experiment 46: Microdetermination of the Alkene Function by Catalytic Hydrogenation: Method II

1. Principle. See experiment 45.

2. Apparatus. Use all apparatus described in experiment 33.

3. Reagents. Use the same reagents given in experiment 45.

4. Procedure

A. PREPARATION OF THE SAMPLE. Place 300 to 500 mg. of the catalyst and 3 ml. of solvent in the reaction flask F (Figure 6.15). Accurately weigh a sample containing about 0.1 meq. of the alkene function into a microbeaker made of Tygon tubing and glass rod (Note 1). Put 3 or 4 micro stirring bars into the microbeaker above the sample. Carefully lower the microbeaker containing the sample and micro stirring bars into the bottom of the reaction flask F. Lubricate the neck of the reaction flask and affix it to the cap E by the springs as shown in Figure 6.15.

B. PURGING THE SYSTEM. Purge the gasometric apparatus free from air according to the directions given in experiment 33, Procedure A(3), page 567.

C. HYDROGENATION. Using the syringe and a 4-inch needle, introduce more solvent into the reaction flask F, if necessary, so that the solvent level reaches about two-thirds of the microbeaker. Turn the stopcocks to close the gasometric apparatus. Adjust the leveling bulb J so that the two columns of mercury in the gasburet HI are at the exact same level. Record the volume, temperature, and barometric pressure.

Now raise the leveling bulb J to apply a pressure of about 30 mm. on the gasburet. Switch on the magnetic stirrer. The microbeaker will tilt over and the hydrogenation starts. Follow the rise of the mercury column in the gasburet by raising the leveling bulb J, maintaining a pressure of about 30 mm.

D. MEASURING THE FINAL VOLUME. When there is no change in the volume of the gas in the buret HI for 5 minutes, stop the magnetic stirrer. Adjust the leveling bulb J to equilibrate the pressure on both sides of the gasburet. Read the volume, temperature, and barometer.

5. Calculations. See experiment 45.

6. Note

Note 1. Alternately, an accurately weighed sample can be dissolved in the solvent in a 10-ml. volumetric flask, and an aliquot of this solution is delivered into the reaction flask F after the system has been purged. The micro stirring bars should be placed at the bottom of the reaction flask F.

7. Comments. This experiment demonstrates: (1) the versatility of a simple gasometric apparatus, and (2) another procedure of microhydrogenation.

Experiment 47: Microdetermination of the Primary Amino Group in Amino Acids by Enzymatic Method

1. Principle. In the presence of pyrophosphate buffered to pH 8.3, D-amino acid oxidase is capable of oxidatively deaminating a large number of α-amino acids of the D-configuration. The action of the enzyme has been shown to involve the transfer of one hydrogen atom from the amino acid to the isoalloxazine ring of the coenzyme. Using alanine as example, the reaction is shown in equation 39:

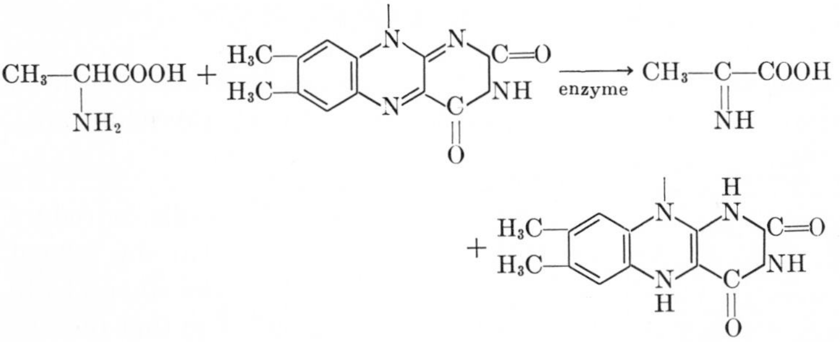

$$CH_3—CHCOOH + \underset{NH_2}{} \text{(isoalloxazine)} \xrightarrow{\text{enzyme}} CH_3—C—COOH$$

(39)

The imino acid produced in this reaction is then hydrolyzed nonenzymatically with the formation of the α-keto acid and the liberation of ammonia,

$$CH_3C(NH)COOH + H_2O \rightarrow NH_3 + CH_3COCOOH \tag{40}$$

whereas the reduced coenzyme is oxidized by molecular oxygen with the formation of hydrogen peroxide:

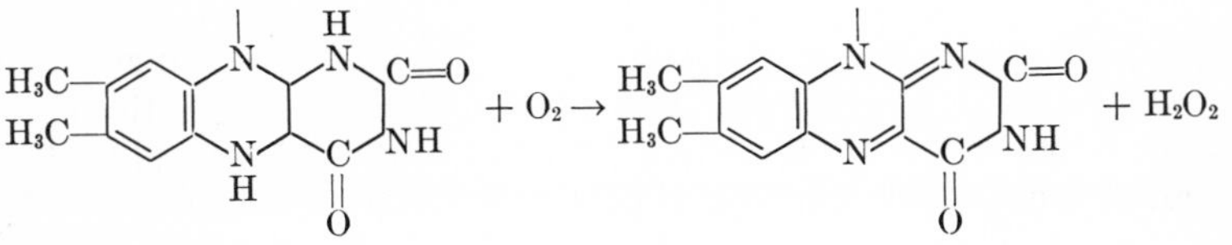

$$+ O_2 \rightarrow + H_2O_2 \tag{41}$$

For enzymatic deamination to take place, the amino acid being attacked must possess a hydrogen atom and an amino group on the α-carbon atom. To drive the reaction to completion, it is necessary to use a large excess of the enzyme and add enough catalase to destroy the hydrogen peroxide produced. After these reactions are complete, a base is added which is stronger than ammonia, but does not hydrolyze any amino compound which may be present, and the ammonia is quantitatively steam-distilled into a 2% boric acid solution. The distillate is then titrated with standardized 0.01N hydrochloric acid to the endpoint of methyl red–bromocresol green mixed indicator.

2. Apparatus

A. REACTION VESSEL FOR DEAMINATION. Use the commercial 30-ml. micro-Kjeldahl digestion flask.

B. ASSEMBLY FOR DISTILLING OF AMMONIA. Use the steam distillation apparatus shown in Figure 6.6.

C. MICROBURET. 10-ml. capacity, graduated in 0.02 or 0.05 ml.

3. Reagents

A. STANDARD HYDROCHLORIC ACID, 0.01N ($= M/100$). See experiment 1.

B. METHYL RED–BROMOCRESOL GREEN MIXED INDICATOR SOLUTION. See experiment 34.

C. D-AMINO ACID OXIDASE. Available from Nutritional Biochemical Corp., Cleveland, Ohio (Note 1).

D. CATALASE. Available from Biochemical Division, Armour Co., Kankakee, Ill. (Note 1).

E. PYROPHOSPHATE BUFFER SOLUTION. Mix 8 ml. of 1N hydrochloric acid with 100 ml. of 2M sodium pyrophosphate. The pH of the resulting solution should be 8.3.

F. BORAX-CARBONATE SOLUTION. Dissolve 10 g. of potassium carbonate and 50 g. of borax in a 1-liter volumetric flask and make up to the mark.

G. BORIC ACID, 2%. See experiment 34.

H. TEST COMPOUNDS. D-Alanine, dec. 297°C; α-aminobutyric acid, dec. 304°C; DL-methionine, dec. 281°C.

4. Procedure

A. DEAMINATION. With the long micro weighing tube (Figure 5.6) accurately weigh 5 to 10 mg. of the amino acid, corresponding to about 0.05 meq. of the primary amino group, into the bottom of a 30-ml. micro-Kjeldahl digestion flask. Add into the digestion flask about 10 times the sample weight of D-Amino acid oxidase, 5 ml. of the pyrophosphate buffer, and 0.5 ml. of catalase. Cover the digestion flask with aluminum foil. Incubate the reaction mixture in a drying oven maintained at 35 to 37.5°C. Shake the digestion flask gently during the incubation over 10-minute intervals until the contents of the flask are homogeneous. Allow the digestion flask to stand in the oven from 60 to 90 minutes.

B. DISTILLATION OF AMMONIA.   Assemble the steam distillation apparatus as shown in Figure 6.6. Lower the receiver F, move the pinch clamp C to the rubber tubing, and boil the water in flask A to pass steam through the system to clean it out. Then remove the burner, return the clamp C to the glass tubing, and detach the distilling flask D. Allow to cool. Meanwhile introduce 5 ml. of 2% boric acid into a clean 50-ml. Erlenmeyer flask, add 3 drops (0.08 ml.) of the mixed indicator and place the flask under the condenser E as shown in Figure 6.6.

Smear a trace of vacuum grease on the lip of the micro-Kjeldahl digestion flask containing the reaction mixture. Pour the contents of the flask into the distilling flask, followed by three washings with 4-ml. portions of the cold borax-carbonate solution. Add 1 drop (approximately 0.6 ml.) of Dow-Z antifoam A to prevent foaming. Affix the distilling flask to the assembly by means of the springs as shown in Figure 6.6. Use vacuum grease to insure air-tight connection between glass joints. Now replace the burner under the steam generator A. Move pinch clamp C down to the rubber tubing to force the steam into the distilling flask D. Keep the distillation rate at about 2 ml. per minute. The contents of the 50-ml. Erlenmeyer flask turn blue as soon as ammonia comes over. After 15 ml. of distillate has been collected, lower the 50-ml. Erlenmeyer flask and allow the distillation to continue for 2 more minutes. Wash the tip of the condenser with distilled water.

C. TITRATION.   Titrate the distillate in the 50-ml. Erlenmeyer flask with the standardized 0.01N hydrochloric acid. The endpoint is a neutral grayish color.

Perform a blank determination with the same reagents and procedure, without the sample.

5. *Calculations*

A. FOR PER CENT COMPOUND

$$\% \text{ Compound} = \frac{(\text{ml. of HCl})(\text{normality of HCl})(\text{meq. wt. of amino acid in mg.})(100)}{\text{wt. of sample in mg.}}$$

6. *Note*

Note 1.   The D-amino acid oxidase and catalase should be stored in the refrigerator.

7. Comments. This experiment demonstrates the specificity of the enzymatic method and its application to functional group analysis. Thus, if DL-alanine is analyzed, only one-half molar equivalent of ammonia will be liberated.

Experiment 48: Microdetermination of Aliphatic Hydroxyl Groups by Aquametry

1. Principle. The hydroxyl function (see Chapter 7, Section IV) reacts with carboxylic acid in the presence of a catalyst to produce an ester and one molar equivalent of water. Thus tertiary butyl alcohol forms *t*-butyl acetate and water as in equation 42:

$$(CH_3)_3COH + CH_3COOH \rightarrow H_2O + CH_3COOC(CH_3)_3 \qquad (42)$$

This reaction reaches equilibrium when only a part of the alcohol has reacted and, hence, cannot be used for quantitative analysis. However, complete conversion of the alcohol can be accomplished by using boron trifluoride in acetic acid as a catalyst. This permits the quantitative determination of the water formed by titration with the Karl Fischer reagent (see Chapter 11, Section XIII and Chapter 3, Section IV):

$$H_2O + C_5H_5N \cdot I_2 + C_5H_5N \cdot SO_2 + C_5H_5N \rightarrow 2C_5H_5N \cdot HI + C_5H_5NO(SO_2) \quad (43)$$

The endpoint is determined electrometrically by the "dead stop" method which is dependent on the depolarization of the electrodes when a trace amount of free iodine appears in the solution.

2. Apparatus

A. ASSEMBLY FOR MICRO AQUAMETRY. The assembly for the microdetermination of water by the Karl Fischer reagent is shown in Figure 7.1. The reaction flask A has three side arms C, D, and E. Arms D and E are for the insertion of the electrodes and the tube with stopcock, respectively, as shown in the figure. When these two accessories are not needed (such as for visual determination of the endpoint and/or the direct determination of water in organic samples), the two openings can be closed with ground-glass stoppers. The side arm C is parallel to the base of the flask and carries a Teflon plunger, 60 mm. long. The end of the plunger is cut out so that a microboat B can be placed in it loosely.

The Wiberley microburet IGH has a drip tip F which is connected to the neck of the reaction flask A by a ground-glass joint.

B. "DEAD STOP" INDICATOR. Available from Metro Scientific, Inc., Carle Place, L.I., New York.

C. MAGNETIC STIRRER

D. HEATING STAGE. See Figure 5.19.

3. Reagents

A. The Karl Fischer Reagent (water equivalent approximately 2 mg. per ml.).   Prepare a stock solution of the Karl Fischer reagent with water equivalent of approximately 6 mg. per milliliter as follows. Dissolve 133 g. of iodine (reagent grade) in 425 ml. of anhydrous pyridine in a 1-liter volumetric flask. Add 425 ml. of anhydrous methyl cellosolve. Stopper the flask and cool the contents in an ice bath. Meanwhile collect 70 ml. of anhydrous liquid sulfur dioxide from a tank of pure sulfur dioxide, using a large test tube immersed in acetone–dry ice bath as the receiver. Add the liquid sulfur dioxide to the volumetric flask in small portions with constant swirling.

Before placing the Karl Fischer reagent into the reservoir of the Wiberley microburet (Figure 7.1), transfer an aliquot into a simple buret. Protect the buret from moisture with a calcium chloride tube. Quickly determine the approximate strength of the Karl Fischer reagent by titrating it against sodium tartrate dihydrate (see Procedure A). Then dilute a suitable portion of the stock solution with anhydrous methyl cellosolve to obtain the required strength of Karl Fischer reagent for microdeterminations, and transfer the latter into the reservoir H of the Wiberley microburet. Close the funnel I with a drying tube.

B. The Boron Trifluoride Catalyst Solution (3 g. BF_3/25 ml.). Place 15 ml. of glacial acetic acid in a 25-ml. volumetric flask. Weigh the flask and its contents. Then place the flask in an ice bath and pass a stream of boron trifluoride from a tank of pure boron trifluoride into the acetic acid in the volumetric flask for 5 minutes. Stopper the volumetric flask, wipe it dry, and reweigh. Bubble more boron trifluoride until 3 g. of the gas has been introduced. Then fill the volumetric flask to the mark with glacial acetic acid and thoroughly mix the solution.

C. Solvents.   Pyridine, methyl cellosolve, glacial acetic acid, all anhydrous.

D. Sodium Tartrate Dihydrate.   Highest purity grade.

E. Test Compounds.   Methanol, b.p. 64°C; t-butyl alcohol, b.p. 82°C; DL-tartaric acid, m.p. 204°C.

4. Procedure

A. Standardization of the Karl Fischer Reagent (Note 1).   Accurately weigh about 5 mg. of sodium tartrate dihydrate into the platinum microboat. Place the microboat and contents in the trough of the plunger and insert the latter into the side arm C of the reaction flask A (see Figure 7.1). Remove the tube E and place the magnetic stirring bar in the flask A. Introduce 2.0 ml. of anhydrous methanol to the reaction flask. Replace the tube E and connect it to a small drying tube. Connect the electrodes to the "dead stop" indicator. Start the magnetic stirrer. Fill the microburet to the zero mark. Add the Karl Fischer Reagent into the solvent until the endpoint is shown by the "dead stop" indicator. Take the reading of the microburet. (This is the blank which should not be more than 0.10 ml.) Now stop the stirring and push in the plunger and turn it to drop the platinum microboat and contents into the solvent. Withdraw the plunger and start stirring. Deliver the Karl Fischer reagent into the solution slowly until the endpoint of titration is indicated.

B. DETERMINATION OF WATER IN THE SOLVENTS (NOTE 2). Use the directions given above, except that the side arm C is closed with the plunger without the microboat, the liquid sample to be analyzed is introduced through the opening of side arm E, and no methanol is added.

C. DETERMINATION OF HYDROXYL GROUPS

(1) *Preparation of the sample.* Assemble the apparatus as shown in Figure 7.1. Connect electrode D to the "dead stop" indicator and attach a drying tube to the side tube E. Place a magnetic stirring bar in the reaction flask A. Weigh accurately a solid sample containing about 0.1 meq. of the hydroxyl function into the microboat and place it in the trough of the plunger. (For liquids, use a micro weighing bottle and drop it into the flask through the side arm E after the acetic acid is added.) Momentarily remove the side tube E and introduce 2.0 ml. of glacial acetic acid by means of a pipet or a syringe, followed by 1.0 ml. of the catalyst solution. Fasten the springs (not shown in the figure) to keep the joints in position.

(2) *Esterification.* Place the heating stage under the reaction flask A. Open the stopcock of the side arm E to equilibrate the pressure on warming. When the heating stage reaches 60°C, close stopcock E and maintain the temperature at 60°C for 0.5 hour. If much vapor reaches the microburet tip F, wrap a piece of aluminum foil around the neck of the reaction flask A to form a funnel and place a piece of "dry ice" on the foil to cool the area.

(3) *Titration.* After the heating period is over, remove the heating stage and cool the flask A to room temperature. Open stopcock E. Momentarily remove the side arm and introduce 1.0 ml. of anhydrous pyridine. Place the magnetic stirrer under the reaction flask A. Add the Karl Fischer reagent slowly until the endpoint is shown by the "dead stop" indicator.

(4) *Blank Determinations.* Perform blank determinations on the reagents, solvents, and also the sample to be analyzed, since the latter may contain water as impurity.

5. Calculations

A. FOR NORMALITY OF KARL FISCHER REAGENT

$$N = \frac{(\text{mg. sodium tartrate dihydrate})(156.6)}{\text{ml. Karl Fischer reagent}}$$

B. FOR PER CENT HYDROXYL GROUP

$$\% \text{ OH} = \frac{(\text{ml. Karl Fischer reagent} - \text{blank})(\text{normality})(0.944)(100)}{\text{wt. of sample in mg.}}$$

6. Notes

Note 1. This is also the micro procedure for the determination of water in solid organic samples.

Note 2. This is also the micro procedure for the determination of water in organic solutions and liquids.

7. Comments.
The procedure described in this experiment may be used for the determination of aliphatic carboxyl groups by replacing acetic acid with methanol and dissolving the boron trifluoride in methyl cellosolve.

Experiment 49: Microdetermination of Quinones by Titanous Chloride Reduction

1. Principle. Many quinones (Chapter 7, Section VII) are quantitatively reduced by titanous chloride to the dihydroxy compounds. For example, 1,4-benzoquinone reacts as shown in equation 44:

$$+ 2\text{TiCl}_3 + 2\text{HCl} \rightarrow \quad + 2\text{TiCl}_4 \tag{44}$$

The stoichiometry just shown necessitates the preparation of more dilute standard titanous chloride solution than that employed for the microdetermination of nitro and nitroso compounds (see experiment 37).

2. Apparatus

A. ASSEMBLY FOR TITANOUS CHLORIDE MICROTITRATION. See experiment 37.

B. MICROBURET. Koch type, 5-ml. capacity, graduated in 0.02 or 0.05 ml.

3. Reagents

A. STANDARD TITANOUS CHLORIDE, $0.02N$ ($= M/50$). Place 900 ml. of distilled water, 100 ml. of concentrated hydrochloric acid, 10 ml. of 20%

titanous chloride (available from Fisher Scientific Co., New York, N.Y.), and 20 g. of zinc amalgam in a round-bottomed flask. Boil the mixture under a reflux condenser until the colloid of titanous hydroxide disappears, as shown by the absence of a Tyndall effect. (Reflux time required ranges from 15 to 60 minutes.) Cool the flask in the ice bath. Then transfer the titanous chloride solution into the reservoir of the Machlett microburet (see Figure 8.12) through a funnel containing glass wool. Wrap the residual zinc amalgam in glass wool and place it in the reservoir. Standardize the solution against potassium dichromate (see experiment 37).

B. STANDARD FERRIC ALUM SOLUTION, $0.02N$ ($= 0.02M$). See experiment 37.

C. NEUTRAL RED INDICATOR SOLUTION, 1%. Commercial.

D. OTHER REAGENTS. See experiment 37.

E. TEST COMPOUNDS. p-Benzoquinone, m.p. 115–116°C; 1,4-naphthoquinone, m.p. 121–124°C; 2-aminoanthraquinone, m.p. 248–250°C.

4. Procedure. Using the micro weighing tube (Figure 5.6) accurately weigh 5 to 15 mg. of the sample into the reaction flask D. Add a magnetic stirring bar and 5 ml. of acetone and dissolve the sample over the magnetic stirrer. Connect the reaction flask to the assembly as shown in Figure 8.12. Introduce 7 ml. of $2.5M$ sodium acetate solution through the side arm and again stir the solution. Pass nitrogen through the flask for 5 minutes at the rate of 15 bubbles per 10 seconds. Deliver the standardized titanous chloride solution into the reaction mixture until an excess of 1 to 2 ml. is present, as is indicated by a darkening of the solution. After stirring for 5 minutes (Note 1), introduce 4 ml. of concentrated hydrochloric acid. Then detach the reaction flask D from the Machlett microburet and connect the flask to the Koch buret containing the standardized ferric alum solution. Deliver the ferric alum solution into the reaction flask D until the color of the solution lightens. Now add 2 ml. of $2.5M$ ammonium thiocyanate indicator solution and 1 drop (0.04 ml.) of the neutral red indicator. Continue the titration until the color of the reaction mixture turns blue-violet.

Perform a blank using the same reagents and procedure without the sample.

5. Calculations

A. FOR PER CENT QUINONE FUNCTION

$\% (C{=}O)_2$

$$= \frac{[(\text{ml. TiCl}_3 - \text{blank})(\text{normality TiCl}_3) - (\text{ml. Fe}^{3+})(\text{norm. Fe}^{3+})](56.02)(100)}{(2)(\text{wt. of sample in mg.})}$$

B. For Per Cent Compound

$$\% \text{ Compound } = \frac{(\text{ml. TiCl}_3 \text{ consumed})(\text{norm.})(\text{meq. wt. of cmpd. in mg.})(100)}{(2)(\text{wt. of sample in mg.})}$$

6. *Note*

Note 1. For quinones not reducible at room temperature, detach the Machlett buret from the reaction flask D at this point and join a reflux condenser to the neck of the flask. Close the side arm, replace the magnetic stirrer with a heating stage, and reflux the solution under nitrogen for 10 minutes. Then cool the solution to room temperature before introducing 4 ml. of concentrated hydrochloric acid.

7. *Comments.* This experiment demonstrates the use of titanous chloride for the determination of a functional group that does not contain nitrogen.

Experiment 50: Microdetermination of the Sulfhydryl Function by Amperometric Titration

1. Principle. The sulfhydryl function reacts with silver ions to form the silver salt (see Chapter 9, Section II-B) which is insoluble in water or alcohol. Therefore the sulfhydryl function can be determined by titration with a standard solution of silver nitrate. Using *o*-mercaptobenzoic acid as example, the reaction is represented in equation 45:

$$\text{HOOC}(C_6H_4)\text{SH} + \text{AgNO}_3 \rightarrow \text{HOOC}(C_6H_4)\text{SAg} + \text{HNO}_3 \tag{45}$$

The endpoint is determined amperometrically, which involves the measurement of the diffusion current when all the sulfhydryl compound has reacted and when a slight excess of silver ion is present in the solution.

2. Apparatus

A. Amperometric Titration Assembly. This is shown in Figure 9.1. The various components are identified as follows:

A = Microburet   B = Calomel cell-glass electrode
C = 100-ml. beaker   D = Magnetic stirrer
E = Magnetic stirring bar   F = Dropping mercury electrode
G = Nitrogen inlet tube   H = Connecting tube to nitrogen tank
I = Cardboard   J = Neoprene tubing
K = Mercury   L = Leveling bulb
M = Capillary tube   N (and B) = Leads to polarograph
      connection

B. Polarograph. Consult I. M. Kolthoff and J. Lingane, *Polarography*, 2nd. ed., Vol. II, Interscience, New York, N.Y., 1952, pp. 887–913, on the use of the polarograph and amperometric titration.

3. Reagents

A. STANDARD SILVER NITRATE SOLUTION, $0.05N$ ($= M/20$).   Weigh 8.5 g. of silver nitrate (reagent grade) into a 1-liter volumetric flask and make up to the mark (Note 1). Standardize against sodium chloride in the following manner. Accurately weigh about 50 mg. of pure sodium chloride (primary standard grade) into a 125-ml. iodine flask. Add 20 ml. of distilled water to dissolve the solid. Then add 100 mg. of dextrin and 0.3 ml. of dichlorofluorescein indicator solution. Titrate the contents of the flask with the $0.05N$ silver nitrate solution. Shake the flask vigorously. The endpoint is shown by a pink tinge. Store the solution in an amber bottle.

B. AMMONIUM NITRATE ($0.25M$)-AMMONIUM HYDROXIDE ($1M$) BUFFER. Weigh 20.01 g. of ammonium nitrate into a 1-liter volumetric flask. Add 50 ml. of distilled water. Stopper and shake the flask until the solid dissolves. Introduce 500 ml. of 95% ethanol. Add 8.0 ml. of concentrated ammonium hydroxide and shake again. Then dilute the solution to the mark with 95% ethanol. Transfer to an amber bottle for storage.

C. ETHANOLIC GELATIN SOLUTION, 0.01%.   Dissolve 10 mg. of gelatin in 100 ml. of 95% ethanol.

D. TEST COMPOUNDS.   o-Mercaptobenzoic acid, m.p. 164°C; iso-octyl-thioglycollate, b.p. 125°C/17 mm.; cysteine hydrochloride, m.p. 175°C.

4. Procedure.   Accurately weigh about 0.1 meq. of the sample into a clean 100-ml. beaker. Dissolve the sample in 5 ml. of 95% ethanol (Note 2). Add 25.0 ml. of the ammonium nitrate–ammonium hydroxide buffer and 1.0 ml. of the 0.01% ethanol gelatin solution. Add the stirring bar into the beaker. Assemble the apparatus as shown in Figure 9.1. Pass a current of nitrogen through the solution to expel the absorbed oxygen. Start the magnetic stirrer. Lower the dropping mercury electrode and make sure that a steady flow of mercury (drop by drop) occurs inside the solution at all times. Then immerse the calomel cell-glass electrode into the solution. Connect the leads to the polarograph. Slowly deliver the standardized $0.05N$ silver nitrate from the micro buret. Record the reading of the polarograph after each increment of the titrant. Continue titration until significant increases in the current are observed.

5. Calculations.   Plot the current *vs.* volume of titrant to get the equivalence point. Calculate the result as follows.

A. FOR PER CENT SULFHYDRYL GROUP

$$\% -SH = \frac{(\text{ml. AgNO}_3)(\text{normality of AgNO}_3)(33.07)(100)}{\text{wt. of sample in mg.}}$$

B. FOR PER CENT COMPOUND

$$\% \text{ Compound} = \frac{(\text{ml. AgNO}_3)(\text{normality of AgNO}_3)(\text{meq. wt. of cmpd. in mg.})(100)}{\text{wt. of sample in mg.}}$$

6. Notes

Note 1. 0.02N Silver nitrate solution may be used for better precision. However, since the strength of 0.02N silver nitrate is more difficult to maintain, it requires frequent standardization.

Note 2. Use water to dissolve cysteine hydrochloride. Also use an aqueous solution of ammonium nitrate–ammonium hydroxide buffer.

7. Comments. This experiment demonstrates the application of amperometric titrimetry in the microdetermination of organic functional groups.

Experiment 51: Microdetermination of the Sulfoxide Function Using the Micro Jones Reductor

1. Principle. The sulfoxide function (see Chapter 9, Section VI-C) can be quantitatively reduced by nascent hydrogen to the sulfide, as illustrated in equation 46 using benzyl sulfoxide as an example:

$$(C_6H_5CH_2)_2SO + Zn + 2HCl \rightarrow (C_6H_5CH_2)_2S + H_2O + ZnCl_2 \tag{46}$$

With the micro Jones reductor, the sulfide is separated from the mixture and then determined by bromine oxidation (see experiment 23).

$$(C_6H_5CH_2)_2S + Br_2 + H_2O \rightarrow (C_6H_5CH_2)_2SO + 2HBr \tag{47}$$

2. Apparatus

A. MICRO JONES REDUCTOR. The micro Jones reductor (see Figure 9.2) is composed of two U-tubes connected by ground-glass joints. One U-tube contains the funnel A and the reducing column E which holds the zinc amalgam, and the other U-tube FG acts like a spigot.

B. MICROBURET. 5-ml. capacity, graduated in 0.01 ml.

C. TITRATION FLASK. Use a 125-ml. iodine flask.

3. Reagents

A. ZINC METAL. 20-mesh, reagent grade (Note 1).

B. MERCURIC CHLORIDE. Reagent grade.

C. STANDARD POTASSIUM BROMATE SOLUTION, 0.1N ($= M/60$). For aromatic sulfoxides. See experiment 23 for preparation and standardization of potassium bromate solution.

D. STANDARD POTASSIUM BROMATE SOLUTION, 0.07N ($= 7/600M$). For aliphatic sulfoxides.

E. POTASSIUM BROMIDE. Reagent grade.

F. POTASSIUM IODIDE SOLUTION, 15%. See experiment 23.

G. STARCH INDICATOR SOLUTION, 1%. See experiment 19.

H. ETHANOLIC HYDROCHLORIC ACID, 5%. Mix 5 ml. of concentrated hydrochloric acid with 95 ml. of 95% ethanol.

I. TEST COMPOUNDS. Benzyl sulfoxide, m.p. 134°C; phenyl sulfoxide, m.p. 69–70°C.

4. Procedure

A. PREPARATION OF THE MICRO JONES REDUCTOR. Place 100 g. of the 20 mesh zinc metal in a 250-ml. beaker. Add 100 ml. of $2N$ hydrochloric acid and stir for 1 minute to etch the surface of zinc. Prepare a solution containing 400 mg. of mercuric chloride in 50 ml. of $1N$ hydrochloric acid and immediately add it to the zinc in the beaker. Stir the mixture for 5 minutes. Decant off the supernatant liquid. Wash the zinc amalgam several times by decantation.

Insert a wad of glass wool D into the lower arm E (reducing column) of the U-tube. Transfer the zinc amalgam into the column. Pack the column loosely by gently tapping the U-tube. Place a layer of glass wool on top of the zinc amalgam. Run distilled water through the funnel A to wash the column several times. Then wash the column once with a 10% solution of acetic acid. Finally, just before the micro Jones reductor is used for reduction, wash the column twice with the 5% solution of hydrochloric acid in 95% ethanol.

B. REDUCTION OF SULFOXIDE. Accurately weigh a sample containing about 0.1 meq. of the sulfoxide function into a 10-ml. micro-Kjeldahl digestion flask (Note 2). Smear a trace of vaseline on one side of the lip of the digestion flask (Note 3). Add 5 ml. of the 5% ethanolic hydrochloric acid into the micro digestion flask to dissolve the sample. With the stopcock B of the micro Jones reductor closed and the water bath kept at 50°C, transfer the sample solution into the funnel A. Then turn the stopcock to let the solution move through the U-tube at such a speed that the liquid front travels through the entire length of the reducing column E in 10 minutes. Collect the effluent in a 125-ml. iodine flask. Rinse the digestion flask with 5 ml. of the 5% ethanolic hydrochloric acid solution and transfer the rinsings into the funnel A. Then run 40 ml. of glacial acetic acid through the micro Jones reductor.

C. DETERMINATION OF THE SULFIDE. The procedure for the determination of the sulfide in the effluent depends on the nature of the compound (see experiment 23).

(1) *For aliphatic compounds.* Add 1.5 ml. of concentrated hydrochloric acid into the iodine flask containing the effluent, followed by a

solution of 500 mg. potassium bromide in 2 ml. of water. Swirl to mix the contents. Then titrate with the standardized $0.07N$ potassium bromate. The endpoint is the appearance of bromine color which persists for 30 seconds.

(2) *For aromatic compounds.* Add 2.0 ml. of concentrated hydrochloric acid into the iodine flask containing the sulfide. Deliver exactly 5.00 ml. of the standardized $0.1N$ potassium bromate into the flask. Swirl to mix the contents. Add 500 mg. of potassium bromide. Stopper and shake the flask for 1 minute. Place the flask in a water bath at 60°C for 2 minutes, then cool it to room temperature. Add 2 ml. of 15% potassium iodide solution. Stopper and shake the flask for 1 minute, then titrate with the standardized $0.1N$ sodium thiosulfate to the starch endpoint.

Run a blank determination using the identical amounts of reagents.

5. *Calculations*

A. FOR ALIPHATIC SULFOXIDES

$$\% -SO = \frac{(\text{ml. KBrO}_3)(\text{normality of KBrO}_3)(48.06)(100)}{(2)(\text{wt. of sample in mg.})}$$

$$\% \text{ Compound} = \frac{(\text{ml. KBrO}_3)(\text{normality of KBrO}_3)(\text{meq. wt. of cmpd. in mg.})(100)}{(2)(\text{wt. of sample in mg.})}$$

B. FOR AROMATIC SULFOXIDES

$$\% -SO = \frac{(b-s)(\text{normality of Na}_2\text{S}_2\text{O}_3)(48.06)(100)}{(2)(\text{wt. of sample in mg.})}$$

where b = ml. of $\text{Na}_2\text{S}_2\text{O}_3$ for blank, and s = ml. of $\text{Na}_2\text{S}_2\text{O}_3$ for sample.

$$\% \text{ Compound} = \frac{(b-s)(\text{normality of Na}_2\text{S}_2\text{O}_3)(\text{meq. of compound in mg.})(100)}{(2)(\text{wt. of sample in mg.})}$$

6. *Notes*

Note 1. Amalgamated zinc (8 to 30 mesh) is available commercially (Fisher Scientific Co., New York, N.Y.).

Note 2. If a 10-ml. micro-Kjeldahl digestion flask is not available, use a 6-inch test tube without a flange.

Note 3. This is a simple way to prevent the solution from running onto the outer wall of the lip.

7. *Comments.* This experiment demonstrates the operation of the micro Jones reductor.

A relatively concentrated standard potassium bromate solution is used in the experiment because of the large volume in the titration flask.

It will be found that aliphatic sulfoxides give higher precision and accuracy than the aromatic compounds.

Experiment 52: Differential Microdetermination of Alkimino Groups by Gas Chromatography

1. Principle. The alkimino function (see Chapter 8, Section II) is usually determined by quaternization with hydriodic acid, followed by thermal decomposition of the quaternary ammonium iodide to yield the alkyl iodide. Using methyldiphenylamine as an example, the reactions are shown in equations 48 and 49:

$$(C_6H_5)_2NCH_3 + HI \rightarrow (C_6H_5)_2(CH_3)NH^+I^- \tag{48}$$

$$(C_6H_5)_2(CH_3)NH^+I^- \xrightarrow{300°} (C_6H_5)_2NH + CH_3I \tag{49}$$

The alkyl iodide is separated from the reaction mixture by volatilization. A mixture of alkyl iodides will be produced if the sample contains more than one kind of alkimino groups. In the latter case, the combined alkyl iodides can be collected and then differentially determined by means of gas chromatography.

2. Apparatus

A. THE MICRO ALKIMINO APPARATUS. The micro alkimino apparatus of Ma and Schachter is shown in Figure 8.6. It consists of the reaction flask C, siphon compartment B, condenser D (Note 1), scrubber tube E, delivery tube F, and receiver tube G. (When used in this experiment, F is connected to the chromatographic column M as shown in Figure 13.6.)

B. THE ASSEMBLY FOR COLLECTION, SEPARATION, AND SENSING. Figure 13.6 shows parts of the apparatus used for the gas chromatographic separation and determination of alkyl iodides. The collector IJK has a small bulb at the bottom and a specially designed glass key J. The drying tube F_1 is connected to the long arm I by a ground-glass joint. IJK can fit inside the beaker P or a Dewar flask (not shown).

The gas chromatographic column M consists of a glass coil packed with glass rings and tricresyl phosphate. One end of the column M is connected to the collector IJK through the arm L; the other end is connected by means of a ball-and-socket joint to the delivery tube F (Figure 8.6) of the alkimino apparatus (Note 2). The sensor N is inserted in the middle of the column M, which is placed in a large beaker, O.

The other sensor N_1 is inserted in the simulator Q. When the gas chromatographic separation is in operation, one arm of the U-tube is connected to the Y-tube R. The other side of R is then connected to long arm I of the collector IJK by means of a rubber tubing carrying a ground-glass inner joint. The center limb of R is connected to the cylinder of nitrogen gas.

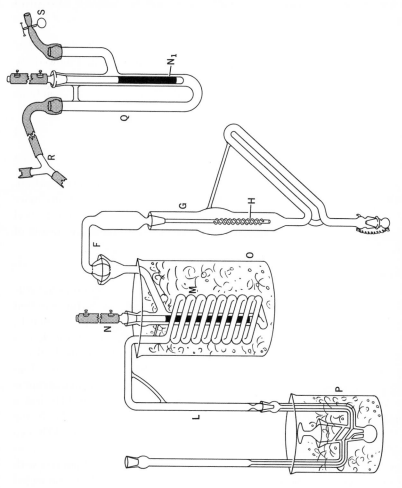

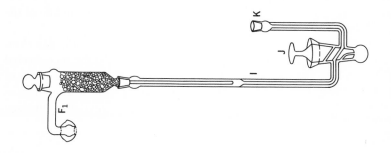

Fig. 13.6. Assembly for gas chromatographic separation of alkyl iodides.

c. Gas Chromatograph and Recorder. See C. Phillips, *Gas Chromatography*, Academic Press, New York, 1956, for the construction and operation of the gas chromatograph.

3. Reagents

a. Hydriodic Acid, sp. gr. 1.7. See experiment 31.

b. Ammonium Iodide. Reagent grade.

c. Cation Exchange Resin. Amberlite IR-120 (H form) or other sulfonic acid resin of equal quality.

d. Sodium Carbonate Solution. Approximately $0.1M$.

e. Tricresyl Phosphate. Reagent grade.

f. Nitrogen Gas. Use lecture bottle size cylinder with a needle valve.

g. Test Compounds. Theobromine, m.p. 337°C; theophylline, m.p. 264°C; methyldiphenylamine, b.p. 296°C; N-ethylacetanilide, m.p. 55°C; tri-*n*-butylamine, b.p. 211°C.

4. Procedure

a. Preparation of the Apparatus. Fill the scrubber tube E (Figure 8.6) with the cation exchange resin. Using the large spherical ground-glass joint as a funnel, pass 500 ml. of $0.1M$ sodium carbonate through the tube E by connecting the narrow end of E to the suction line (Note 3). Keep the resin moist.

Connect the narrow end of the scrubber tube containing the prepared resin to the reaction flask C through the siphon compartment B and condenser D, as shown in Figure 8.6. (For all joints in this apparatus use tricresyl phosphate as a lubricant.) Connect the wide end of the scrubber tube E to the drying tube F_1 (Figure 13.6) which is packed with indicator treated silica gel (Note 4).

Connect the drying tube F_1 to the long arm of the collector IJK. Set the glass key J in the collecting position so that the alkyl iodides condense at the small bulb. Place the collector IJK in the Dewar flask (not shown) and surround the collector with crushed "dry ice."

b. Preparation of the Sample and Decomposition. Connect the dropping funnel A to the siphon compartment B. Connect the side tube of reaction flask C to the nitrogen source and pass a current of nitrogen through the system to displace the air. Use a bubble counter to observe the rate of nitrogen gas. Keep the rate at 1 bubble per second for 10 minutes.

Remove the dropping funnel and introduce into the pocket of the siphon compartment B an accurately weighed sample containing 0.1 to 0.4 millimoles of total alkyl iodides. Use the weighing tube (Figure 5.6) for solid samples and the glass cup or syringe for liquids. Add 100 mg. of ammonium iodide by means of a weighing tube to cover the sample and replace the dropping funnel.

Place 2.5 ml. of hydriodic acid (sp. gr. 1.7) in the dropping funnel. Deliver 0.25 ml. of the acid into the pocket of the siphon compartment B (Note 5).

Immerse about 10 mm. of the reaction flask C in a metal bath (Wood's metal) at 75°C. Gently warm the walls of the siphon compartment B with a small flame until condensing vapors in the siphon tube initiate siphoning of the hydriodic acid. Then raise the temperature of the metal bath until the boiling acid produces sufficient vapor to maintain an almost continuing siphoning of dissolved ingredients into the reaction flask C, thus emptying the siphon chamber. (This will take place within 3 or 4 minutes.)

Readjust the rate of nitrogen gas to 1 bubble per 10 seconds. Heat the metal bath to 360°C or until the reaction flask C dries out.

Now remove the metal bath and let the assembly cool down to 130°C. Introduce a second batch (0.25 ml.) of the hydriodic acid to the siphon compartment B. Repeat the operation described until all hydriodic acid in the dropping funnel A has been exhausted.

c. GAS CHROMATOGRAPHY.   Now close off the small bulb at the bottom of the collector IJK (Figure 13.6) by turning the glass key J 180°. Remove the Dewar flask. Disengage the drying tube F_1 from the arm I and connect I to the Y-tube R by means of a ground-glass joint (not shown) and rubber tubing. Connect the center tube of the Y-tube R to the nitrogen cylinder. Open the pinch clamp S of the simulator Q for 1 minute to remove all air in the simulator.

Connect the ground-glass joint K of collector IJK to the limb L of the chromatographic column M and drive out the air in the column with nitrogen.

Set the sensors N and N_1 in their respective ground-glass joints in column M and simulator Q. Connect the electrical leading wires to the terminals and circuit of the panel on the gas chromatograph. Plug in the male receptical to the direct current source to heat the sensors.

Using the tap key on the control, carefully adjust the bridge variable resistor (rheostat) until the meter reading is zero.

Turn the variable resistor to the least sensitive position and connect the output to the pen of the recorder. Slowly increase the sensitivity adjustment until there is a slight response on the recorder, while the balanced bridge still shows zero on the microammeter when the tap key is tapped for a second or two.

Place the beakers under the collector IJK and column M in position and fill them three-fourths full of water. Heat both water baths to boiling. Then turn the glass key J 180° to drive the alkyl iodides into the column M. (The flow rate of nitrogen is maintained at 1 bubble per 10 seconds.) Turn on the recorder and record for 25 minutes.

5. Calculations. Evaluate the peaks of the individual alkyl iodides by comparison with the calibration curves. Express the results in mg. of alkyl iodide found.

A. FOR PER CENT ALKIMINO GROUP

$$\% \text{ NR} = \frac{(\text{mg. RI})(\text{sum of atom wt. of NR})(100)}{(\text{mg. sample})(\text{mol. wt. of RI})}$$

6. Notes

Note 1. The water condenser is replaced by an electrically heated tube for higher alkimino groups.

Note 2. When the delivery tube F and receiver G are attached to the gas chromatographic column M as shown in Figure 13.6, the total amount of alkyl iodides can be determined (see experiment 31) and checked against the sum of individual iodides found on the recorder.

Note 3. The reactions for the absorption of hydrogen iodide and iodine in the cation exchange column may be represented by equations 50 to 52:

$$\text{HI} + \text{R–SO}_3\text{Na} \rightarrow \text{NaI} + \text{R–SO}_3\text{H} \tag{50}$$

$$\text{I}_2 + \text{NaI} \rightarrow \text{NaI}_3 \tag{51}$$

$$\text{I}_2 + \text{Na}_2\text{CO}_3 \rightarrow \text{NaI} + \text{NaOI} + \text{CO}_2 \tag{52}$$

Note 4. It is not advisable to use Anhydrone as the drying agent in this experiment. If the ion exchanging resin is overloaded, some hydrogen iodide will pass into the drying tube to produce the explosive perchloric acid.

Note 5. Use more hydriodic acid if necessary, so that the sample is completely covered.

7. Comments. This is an elaborate experiment. However, it offers training in the application of gas chromatography to quantitative organic microanalysis and also experience in complicated procedures.

Appendix A

Supply Houses for Equipment and Apparatus

Name of Firm	Address	Equipment and Apparatus
Fisher Scientific Co.	717 Forbes Ave., Pittsburgh 19, Pa.	General
Greiner Scientific Corp.	22 N. Moore St., New York 13, N. Y.	General
Metro Scientific, Inc.	141 Old Country Rd., Carle Place, L.I., N. Y.	Micro aquametry equipment
Microchemical Specialties	1823 Eastshore Highway, Berkeley 10, Calif.	Ultramicro apparatus
Micro-Ware, Inc.	572 Broadlawn Terrace, Vineland, N. J.	Has in stock most of the apparatus described in the text; will accept orders of special design.
E. H. Sargent & Co.	4647 W. Foster Ave., Chicago 30, Ill.	General
A. H. Thomas Co.	Vine St. at Third, Philadelphia 5, Pa.	General

Appendix B

Laboratory Assignments for a One-Semester Course in Organic Functional Group Analysis

Period	Assignment	Procedure Given in Experiment No.
	Part I: Experiments that do not require special apparatus. The student is asked to perform all these assignments to acquaint himself with the general techniques of quantitative organic analysis. Each experiment requires about five hours of laboratory work.	
1	Determination of acidic functions by aqueous titration.	1
2	Determination of basic functions by nonaqueous titration.	3
3	Determination of hydroxyl groups by acetylation.	5
4	Determination of carbohydrates by periodate oxidation.	11
5	Determination of carbonyl groups by oximation.	6
6	Determination of carbonyl compounds by hydrazone formation.	7
7	Determination of acyl groups by saponification and ion-exchange.	13
8	Determination of quaternary ammonium salts by titrimetric method.	27
9 to end of the term	*Part II:* Experiments which require special apparatus. Each student is assigned two to three experiments. He is expected to assemble the apparatus, perform the analysis, and demonstrate the operation to his classmates who are not given the particular experiment. The individual experiment requires from five to ten hours of laboratory work.	
	Determination of alkoxyl groups.	31
	Determination of amino groups by micro-Kjeldahl procedure.	34
	Determination of the nitro group by titanous chloride reduction.	37
	Determination of the aliphatic hydroxyl group by aquametry.	48
	Determination of active hydrogen by lithium aluminum hydride.	40
	Determination of unsaturation by catalytic hydrogenation.	45
	Determination of the sulfhydryl group by amperometirc titration.	50

Appendix C

List of Figures

Author Index

Subject Index

(**Abbreviations:** app. = apparatus, dtmn. = determination, procedure = experimental procedure given in the text.)

Acetal function, 107
  alkoxyl group in, 107
  by aquametry, 107
  by hydrolysis, 107
  cyclic, 108
  in wine, 109
  Raman spectra of, 107
Acetaldehyde, dtmn. of, 150, 156
  sodium bisulfite addition product, as test compound, 550
Acetanilide, as test compound, 514, 571, 596
Acetates, dtmn. of, 220
Acetic acid, in alkalimetry, 425, 427, 429, 433, 434, 435
  in water dtmn., 472
  participation in reactions, 426
Acetic acid—sodium acetate, reagent solution, 576
Acetic anhydride, as test compound, 533
  for amino dtmn., 231
  for hydroxyl dtmn., 186
  for water dtmn., 475
  in alkalimetry, 426, 428, 433, 434, 435
Acetoacetanilide, as test compound, 503
Acetone, as test compound, 599
  dtmn. of, 156
  in acidimetry, 400, 401
  in alkalimetry, 427, 430
  oxidation in C-methyl dtmn., 442
Acetonitrile, in acidimetry, 400
  in alkalimetry, 428, 434, 435, 437
Acetonylglycerate, dtmn. of, 390
Acetous perchloric acid (*see also* Perchloric acid)
  0.01N standard solution, 487

Acetylacetone, active hydrogen in, 419
  as test compound, 594
Acetylating reagent, preparation of, 494
Acetyl chloride, for amino dtmn., 231
  for hydroxyl dtmn., 187
Acetylenic compounds, procedure for, 527
Acetylenic group, 382 (*see also* Alkyne function)
Acetylenic hydrogen, dtmn. of, 385
Acetyl group, 123 (*see also* Acyl function)
Acetylide, in alkyne dtmn., 385
Acetylsalicylic acid, as test compound, 596
Acetyl value, 184
Acid amide, 13 (*see* Carbonamide function)
Acid anhydride function, anilide formation, 109
  by acid-base titrimetry, 110
  colorimetric methods, 112
  hydrolysis, 109
  infrared absorption, 109
  procedure for, 532, 534
  with aromatic amine, 112
  with hydroxylamine, 112
  with morpholine, 110
  with oxalic acid, 112
  with substituted anilines, 111
Acid anhydrides, procedure (anilide formation) for, 532
  procedure (indirect bromination) for, 534
  reaction with substituted aniline, 42
Acid-base, concepts, 32
  table, 36
  titrimetry, 35, 396, 424
Acid chlorides, dtmn. of, 459
  procedure for, 534
  reduction by borohydride, 565